THE FOUNDERS OF
NEUROLOGY

Discipulus est prioris posterior dies.

PUBLILIUS SYRUS
(*Sententiae,* 1st century B.C.)

La science n'est pas, elle devient.

JULES SOURY
(*Le système nerveux central,* 1899)

The FOUNDERS of NEUROLOGY

One Hundred and Forty-Six Biographical Sketches

By Eighty-Eight Authors

Compiled and Edited by

WEBB HAYMAKER

*Senior Scientist
National Aeronautics and
Space Administration
Ames Research Center
Moffett Field, California*

FRANCIS SCHILLER

*Associate Clinical Professor of Neurology
Lecturer in History of Health Sciences
University of California Medical Center
San Francisco, California*

SECOND EDITION

CHARLES C THOMAS · PUBLISHER

Springfield · Illinois · U.S.A.

Published and Distributed Throughout the World by
CHARLES C THOMAS • PUBLISHER
BANNERSTONE HOUSE
301-327 East Lawrence Avenue, Springfield, Illinois, U.S.A
NATCHEZ PLANTATION HOUSE
735 North Atlantic Boulevard, Fort Lauderdale, Florida, U.S.A.

First Edition, 1953
Second Edition, 1970

With **THOMAS BOOKS** *careful attention is given to all details of manufacturing and design. It is the Publisher's desire to present books that are satisfactory as to their physical qualities and artistic possibilities and appropriate for their particular use.* **THOMAS BOOKS** *will be true to those laws of quality that assure a good name and good will.*

Printed in the United States of America

B-7

PREFACE

*T*HE writer of a note to Charles C Thomas recommending a new printing of *The Founders,* or a revision, tempered his suggestion by adding: "The type of material presented is not of such a nature that it ever gets out of date." Or does it? What seems firmly established *die priori,* will it necessarily appear so *die posteriori?* A review of the 1953 edition made it evident that a considerable number of the biographies needed, here and there, a different orientation, a new slant. More important, some who obviously were "founders" had to be added. Hence a mere reprinting would not do.

Who, then, we continued to ask ourselves, was a Founder, and not merely a Refiner? And what, in fact, is Neurology? For Neurology was not all founded by neurologists. Physicians long past, treating epilepsy or paralysis, had never heard its name—like Molière's Monsieur Jourdain, learning one day that all his life he had been speaking prose. *Neurologia* first occurred to Thomas Willis as an analogy to *myologia* and *osteologia.* Willis also was the first to focus on the subject as we understand it, hence we must go back to him. Why not go further back? Did Galen or the Hippocratic writers not know and teach a lot about the nervous system? True, but it was not their major concern. The early founders of neurology were its emancipators. Subsequent founders in the eighteenth century made inroad after inroad until Neurology took on facets not even dreamed of in the earlier days. A greater number of the men who transformed Neurology in these transitional years, including neurochemists, have been added to the assemblage that made up the 1953 edition.

On the other hand, not every neurologist who may be considered "great" is included here. To approximate the 1953 format we have, reluctantly, eliminated a sizable number of previous names, for reasons of economy, and on the grounds—history being a fickle mistress—that some contributions seemed less resilient to the inroads of time. Our selection and our compromises will no doubt

v

be subject to criticism on many counts, as selections must be. Some
men, some discoverers, may loom larger on San Francisco Bay than
they do, say, on the banks of the Moskva, the Thames, the Seine,
or the Danube, and vice versa.

Sporadic criticism has been raised against the 1953 edition with
its somewhat anecdotal treatment of the historical figures. The reason for that is in itself partly historical. For what essentially makes
up *The Founders* started back in June, 1948, during a meeting of
neurologists and neuropathologists in Atlantic City when, late one
night around a table on the Boardwalk, some members began relating anecdotes about their teachers. Not to let the accounts of
the more personal traits of bygone neurologists fall into oblivion,
that small group of story tellers set about the task which took
shape in the first edition. It was a collaborative venture: an author's manuscript was passed to others who, in turn, would add
what they knew. (The first edition was intended as a *vade mecum*
sent by the Armed Forces Institute of Pathology and the Army
Medical Library to the Fourth International Neurological Congress in Paris in 1949.) In the present sketches the historical setting has received greater emphasis than before. Some will still ac-
cuse us of hero worship, others of dwelling on foibles. As to the
latter reproach, we'd like to quote Johannes Müller: "A man's
greatness may be such that to tell of his faults is to praise him."
The present edition is again not designed as a history of neurology, but, instead, a gathering of short biographies to satisfy readers
who want their historical information modest, accurate and lively.

After a good deal of deliberation about the sequence we decided
to persist with that used in the first edition: alphabetical within
sub-specialties, with a chronological break in the mid-nineteenth
century for the anatomists. A more cogent categorization, alas, did
not occur to us. We shrank from straight alphabetization in dictionary fashion, as much as from the straight chronology of the birth
register. But we concede that several placings are open to question.

A final word of explanation on the editing of the biographies
prepared by the authors now past and defenseless. We thought it
our business to check, add, and eliminate a statement here and
there, to dim, brighten, or transform some passage or other, to
quibble over spellings and the like. We hope to be forgiven if, for

better or for worse, we assume our fair share of responsibility for the outcome.

For collaborating on that first edition, we continue to feel indebted to General J. H. McNinch, then Director of the Army Medical Library, and his staff, in particular Mr. Karl A. Baer, biographer to the Library. To those who loaned portraits for reproduction we also remain grateful. To Prof. Dr. Kolle we owe permission to reproduce the signatures of a dozen or so of the Founders.

For secretarial work, which seemed unending, we are indebted to Mrs. Virginia A. Hughes, Ames Research Center, and for the vast amount of library research, we wish to express especial appreciation to Mrs. Betty Sherwood and her staff—Mrs. Olga Kallos, Mrs. Barbara Peshel and Mrs. Marilyn Kanemura—also of Ames. All authors join in expressing deep appreciation to Mr. Payne Thomas for having made available this series of 112 reworked previous biographies and 34 new ones.

THE EDITORS

THE MEANING OF SOME OF THE ACADEMIC
TERMS USED IN THE BIOGRAPHIES

S INCE the reader may not be entirely familiar with such terms as *agrégé, habilitation, venia legendi, Professor Extraordinarius* and *Bachelor of Medicine,* frequently used in this volume to denote an individual's position in the academic hierarchy, a few words of explanation seem in order.

France. The word *faculty* (from *facultas*—meaning facility) carries with it a different connotation in France than in some other countries. Thus, in English universities the word faculty refers to the teaching personnel of a university, whereas in countries of the European continent the word signifies a division or a department of the university. Thus, *Faculté de Médecine* means the School of Medicine of a French university. In medieval times, universities were municipal civic organs and, so, preeminently democratic institutions of learning. With the end of the feudal period and with the increasing assertion of centralized monarchical statism of the 17th and 18th centuries, they became "royal" universities, and since then have remained state-governed agencies of higher education, usually under the budgetary and political dominion of the state ministry of public education. In France, as in most other countries of continental Europe, there are no private or corporate universities or schools of medicine as they are known in the countries of Anglo-Saxon lineage.

The degree of Bachelor of Arts from a *lycée* (college) has for centuries been a prerequisite of matriculation at the Faculty of Medicine of a French university. In the early 1900's another requirement was introduced, namely, a certificate of premedical study in physics, chemistry, and natural history. Once matriculated, the student embarks on five years (until recently, at any rate) of formal instruction.

A distinctive feature of the French system is that clinical training begins in the first year of medicine. The other peculiarity, since the time of Napoleon, is the *concours.* On completing the

ix

first year the student is eligible for a competitive examination in anatomy, medicine and surgery, a *concours* for an appointment as *externe des hôpitaux*—a part-time, nonresident hospital position. The successful candidates are placed in any one of the municipal hospitals in the Assistance Publique, the Public Welfare Administration of the City of Paris (or the respective *département,* in the provinces). Those who do not seek or do not receive the appointment of externe (about one-half of the applicants fail to pass the examination for this appointment) are required, nevertheless, to complete the "stages" of clinical training in medicine, surgery, obstetrics, and certain major specialties in various municipal hospitals affiliated with the university. Completion of these "stages" during the third to fifth year is necessary before a student is eligible for graduation.

Faculté de Médecine, an academic institution run by the central government, and Assistance Publique, the hospital administrations run by the local authority, collaborate as best they can, which is not always a matter of complete harmony. The externeship marks the beginning of the formal medical *training* of the student at the hospital services and is quite distinct from his medical *education* at the Faculty of Medicine. The maximum duration of the externeship has varied—and so has the minimum period required before the medical student is eligible for competitive examination for an appointment as interne at one of the municipal hospitals (*interne des hôpitaux*).

The examination for internship is highly competitive in Paris, for usually there are more externes seeking interneship appointments than there are vacancies available. The functions and status of the *interne des hôpitaux* are equivalent to those of the full-time resident house officer in an American hospital, except for one difference: the *interne des hôpitaux,* even though he may have completed the five-year curriculum of the medical school and two years of externat, does not yet have the degree of Doctor of Medicine. He is a physician "de facto" but not yet "de jure," so to speak. The duration of internship is from one to four years. Many of the distinguished physicians of France made their first important contributions while they were still internes, i.e., mere apprentices of clinical medicine and surgery.

All students who have completed the curriculum of five years at the Faculty of Medicine and have fulfilled the required two-year minimum of the "stage" clinical experience (and regardless of whether or not they have been externes or internes) are eligible for the *examens d'état* (final examinations) in which a final sifting of the students takes place. Those who pass are permitted to present a doctoral thesis before a commission of professors appointed by the Dean. After the thesis is successfully "defended"— seldom is the defense unsuccessful—and after it is published at the candidate's expense, a diploma of Doctor of the University of Paris (or elsewhere) is granted.

Such is the traditional pattern of what may be called the professional education and training of the French physician.

The system of higher competitive examination for hospital training and appointments has been much criticized and is in the process of being abolished. It tended to stifle the youthful energies by the cut and dried formalities of dogmatic medicine. But it has had, at least in the past, its incontestable merit. The French system of hospital interneship has provided an incomparable clinical experience. It is this system, later adopted in other countries, which has reared the outstanding clinicians for which France is so legitimately renowned. Someone has rightly stated: "There is nothing in clinical medicine that some French clinician hasn't already seen and described."

The professional and academic medical career in France is rooted in the clinical experience of interneship. An interne who shows the inclination and has the ability to advance in the academic field of medicine has the opportunity of becoming *chef de clinique* of the hospital service of a faculty professor in charge of the service. This, as far as we know, is not a competitive appointment, but is made on the basis of personal qualities and scientific work done during interneship. Only former internes who have received their doctorate are eligible for the appointment. A *chef de clinique* has the privilege of seeing private patients outside the university. His official duties are thus part-time, and consist of supervision of the service and teaching of internes, externes and medical students of the service. The status of a *chef de clinique* is very similar to that of an assistant professor in an American university hospital. The title indicates, therefore, not only a university rank but also a municipal hospital position. The duration of the appointment is unlimited.

The position of chef de clinique usually affords the opportunity of following an academic career at the university. Competitive examination and presentation of a *thèse d'agrégation* lead to the next university rank—that of *professeur agrégé* (associate professor). Only a few ever become full professors.

Different titles are employed in the non-clinical fields. Thus, the equivalent of instructor in such academic pursuits as histology, anatomy, physiology, pathology, etc., is called a *préparateur;* the equivalent to the rank of assistant professor in these fields in the School of Medicine of a University is referred to as *chef des travaux à la faculté* and *chef de laboratoire à la faculté.* These three positions are filled by appointment.

The crowning achievement in the clinical career of the French physician was that of being appointed *médecin* (or *chirurgien*) *des hôpitaux* by the Assistance Publique, through a concours. Not only must written and oral examinations in clinical and academic fields be passed, but the candidate, to be successful, must have achieved a high measure of personal and academic distinction.

A *médecin* (or *chirurgien*) des hôpitaux is a physician-in-chief (a reputed practitioner by definition) of a service in a municipal hospital. The appointment carries no university rank or status. Many a renowned *médecin* (or *chirurgien*) des Hôpitaux de Paris had no university status beyond that of former chef de clinique, although his prestige was equal to or even greater than that of a professor. Babinski, for instance, was *chef de clinique* of Charcot at the Salpêtrière but never received the rank of *professeur agrégé* or *médecin des hôpitaux.*

A distinguished few are elected to the Académie de Médecine. Exceedingly few, usually when they have reached a venerable age and are deemed "immortal", receive the highest academic honor by election to the Académie des Sciences, one of the four academies of the Institut de France (not to be confused with the Collège de France, a research and teaching institute).

It should be pointed out that while the pattern of the professional and academic career in neurology was the same as that in other fields of medicine, the educational system in psychiatry took a slightly different turn in the early 19th century. This is of some importance because contributions to neurology were derived from the field of psychiatry almost as much as from the basic sciences and internal medicine. The mental hospitals, or *asiles d'aliénés,* as the French with straightforward honesty and Gallic logic call them, are both under the Ministry of the Interior and administered like other hospitals by the regional *départements* (e.g., in Paris the Département de la Seine). In these asylums competitive examinations are held for the position of *interne des asiles d'aliénés de la Seine* (a training appointment in psychiatry), *assistant des asiles d'aliénés* (equivalent to senior physician in most American state hospitals), and *médecin des asiles* (equivalent to *médecin des hôpitaux,* i.e., psychiatrist-in-chief). As a rule the head of the psychiatric services is also a professor at the Faculté de Médicine.

PAUL I. YAKOVLEV

Germany. After obtaining his M.D. and his medical license— when he is granted *Ärztliche Approbation*—the young physician who aspired to university life usually began as *Assistent* in a university clinic or institute. After several years of scientific work documented by a number of original publications, his professor then sponsored him for nomination as *Privatdozent.* After he had been elected he obtained *venia legendi* (*venia,* permission; *legendi,* of lecturing), that is he became entitled to give courses of lectures in his particular field. This made him officially a junior member of the faculty. The complex procedure through which the candidate had to make his way in order to earn his venia legendi was known as *Habilitation.* A prerequisite was the submission of an original major research work known as the *Habilitationsschrift.* The candidate was also required to give a lecture before the faculty, after which each faculty member could engage him in discussion. If he passed this test he was then entitled to give an official public lecture known as the *Antrittsvorlesung,* to which the faculty members, the student body, and the public were invited. After the completion of this requirement the *venia legendi* was granted. This did not carry any official salary but entitled the Privatdozent to collect lecture fees from his students. In order to make a living, he usually continued in his position as Assistent. Some, however, went into private practice and relinquished their assistantship.

After several years of successful activity, the *Privatdozent,* upon recommendation of the faculty, received the title of (*nichtbeamteter, ausserplanmässiger*) *ausserordentlicher Professor,* or *Extraordinarius.* This means that he was given the title of professor without salary. There were, however, a few positions such as (*beamteter, planmässiger*) *ausserordentlicher Professor,* or *planmässiger Extraordinarius,* which carried a salary.

The climax of the academic career was the appointment as *ordentlicher öffentlicher Professor,* or *Ordinarius,* in charge of an established chair, usually combined with the directorship of a clinic or institute. The appointment was made by the government upon recommendation by the faculty.

If a chair was vacant, not only could an Extraordinarius of that university qualify as a candidate for the position, but also an Ordinarius, Extraordinarius or even Privatdozent of any other university.

After a number of years of successful work, the imperial governments usually conferred on the Professor the honorary title of *Geheimrat* (privy councillor) in Germany, or *Hofrat* (court councillor) in Austria. A still higher title was *Wirklicher Geheimer Rat* or *Wirklicher Geheimer Hofrat* (actual privy councillor, etc.) which often carried also the title *Exzellenz* (your excellency).

In Germany, a full professor was never retired but was merely relieved of his official duties (*von den amtlichen Pflichten entbunden*) and of his directorship; he continued to receive his full salary. This, however, was only part of the earnings of a professor, who derived most of his income from lecture fees and, in the case of clinicians, from private practice. Much the same applied in Austria except that the professor was retired on reaching a certain age.

We should remember that until not long ago neurology in central Europe, and neurohistology in particular, was a branch of psychiatry. Neurohistology was in many instances a noble hobby, almost, of men usually holding academic appointments as psychiatrists; this gave them the time and the inspiration for scrutinizing the organ of the mind and its pathology.

HARTWIG KUHLENBECK
E. A. SPIEGEL

Great Britain. In Great Britain neurological medicine was first fostered and established as a special interest of general physicians whose practice covered the whole range of internal medicine. In the 1920's appointments as neurologist, or physician-in-charge of the department for nervous diseases, began to be made at Guy's and some other London hospitals. Only since 1962 have universities begun to give academic titles in neurology, with professors in the Universities of London, Oxford and Glasgow. The highest status of a practising neurologist is *honorary physician* to one of the great hospitals where he has charge of a full service in internal medicine. In London the neurologist is, in addition, usually a physician to a special neurological hospital (the National Hospital for the Paralyzed and Epileptic [now the National Hospital for Nervous Diseases] or the Maida Vale Hospital for Nervous Diseases, or the West End Hospital). The first staff appointment to any of these hospitals is as assistant physician, then by a laborious promotion by seniority to *physician-to-outpatients,* and finally *full visiting physician.* All these appointments are purely honorary. The first full time appointment in neurology in Britain was that of director of the research unit at the National Hospital in 1932. Gowers was physician to University College Hospital and to the National Hospital, and Jackson to the London Hospital and to the National Hospital. Head was physician to the London Hospital alone. Ferrier was physician to King's College Hospital and physician to the National Hospital, with an honorary title of Professor of Neuropathology in King's College of the University of London.

A high civil distinction given to neurologists is the royal bestowal of one of the classes of the various orders of knighthood. These could be, respectively, member, officer, commander, or knight. Conferral of the last of these honours entitled the recipient to the prefix "Sir" before his first name. He is then no longer addressed as "Dr." It is customary to place initials of these decorations after the name: O.B.E. for example, indicates an officer of the Order of the British Empire, C.B. a Commander of the Order of the Bath. Gowers became Sir William Gowers in 1897. Ferrier was knighted in 1911. The Order of Merit, instituted in 1902, is given for outstanding achievement. Sherrington and Adrian have been the only neurological recipients and, more recently, Penfield. The next distinction higher than knighthood is that of a Barony, which is the lowest order of peerage and entitles the recipient to be called "Lord." The late Lord Brain was the first neurologist to be raised to the peerage and Lord Adrian was the first physiologist to be so honoured. The most coveted scientific honour is election to Fellowship of the Royal Society (F.R.S.).

In Britain, licence to practice medicine is granted to those who graduate from a university as *Bachelor of Medicine* and *Bachelor of Surgery,* and also to licentiates of the Royal Colleges of Physicians. The Royal Colleges are professional corporations entirely separate from the Universities. The consultant physician is expected to have obtained the M.D. by further examination and thesis, and also to have passed the membership examination of one of the Royal Colleges of Physicians (which entitles him to the qualification M.R.C.P.). Elevation to Fellowship of a Royal College of Physicians (F.R.C.P.) is by election, after an interval of at least five years from obtaining the membership.

The first neurosurgeons in Britain also practised general surgery, and held appointments as honorary surgeon to general hospitals, as well as honorary visiting surgeon to special hospitals. Fellowship of the Royal College of Surgeons of London, Edinburgh or Ireland (F.R.C.S.) is gained by special examination, and is essential for a surgical consultant. By tradition all surgeons are called "Mr." instead of "Dr." The universities confer the degree of Bachelor of Surgery, together with the M.B., on graduation. Some aspiring to consultant practice in surgery now take the advanced degree of Master of Surgery by special examination. The same civil and scientific awards may be made to surgeons as to physicians.

D. Denny-Brown

CONTENTS

Biographical Sketches

SECTION I

NEUROANATOMISTS OF EARLIER TIMES
(Born before 1850)

SECTION IV

INVESTIGATORS OF NEURAL TRANSMISSION
AND NEUROCHEMISTRY

SECTION V

NEUROPATHOLOGISTS

SECTION VI
CLINICAL NEUROLOGISTS

SECTION VII

NEUROSURGEONS

SECTION VIII

A NEUROHISTORIAN

SECTION IX

OTHER SOURCES FOR THE HISTORY
OF NEUROLOGY 579

THE FOUNDERS OF
NEUROLOGY

I

NEUROANATOMISTS OF EARLIER TIMES
(Born before 1850)

FRANÇOIS BAILLARGER (1809–1890)

*F*RANÇOIS BAILLARGER was born of a middle-class family, in Montbazan, Indre-et-Loire, France. His education was entrusted to an old priest who was, however, a better apiarist than scholar. Baillarger studied medicine at Paris under Esquirol and devoted his professional career to the management of the mentally ill, first at Charenton and later at Ivry. He was also physician to the Salpêtrière (from 1840), where he worked for some twenty years. To him Trélat and Magnan owed their deliverance from cholera, for it was he who personally nursed them back to health.

An energetic, sociable person, noted as a teacher and given to philanthropy, he founded with Longet and Cerise in 1843 the *Annales médico-psychologiques* in which he published many of his papers, and later he was the moving spirit in establishing the *Société médico-psychologique* and the *Association mutuelle des médecins aliénistes*. He was vitally interested in hospital administration, the care of prisoners, deficiency disorders and cretinism, and made the usual run of mental hospital observations. In 1865, according to André Ombredane,[1] Baillarger pointed out that patients with aphasia had lost the power of voluntary speech but nevertheless retained certain automatic expressions that were not always employed correctly. This contribution was recognized by Hughlings Jackson, who called it "Baillarger's principle."

Baillarger's interests were mainly clinical, and his descriptions of behavior in various types of mania, melancholia and general paralysis were true to form but not really enlightening. He described the manic-depressive cycle and the stupor of melancholia, and he noted the unequal pupils in dementia paralytica and their occasional association with locomotor ataxia. From his description of these disorders, however, it must be concluded that as a clinician he was working in etiological darkness.

Outstanding among his works on psychiatry was that on hallucinations—which brought him the Prix de l'Académie (1842). According to Zilboorg and Henry,[2] Baillarger "was the first to sense

5

Jules Gabriel François Baillarger

that hallucinations are what we would call today spontaneous results of a psychological reaction; he called them 'involuntary.' He
also studied the role of the state which is intermediary between
that of being asleep and that of being awake, at which time nor-

Portrait, courtesy of the Library of the New York Academy of Medicine.

mal people have hallucinatory experiences, now called 'hypnagogic.' "

Baillarger's name endures as an eponym like those of Vicq d'Azyr and Gratiolet because of a minor incident in his career when, at the age of thirty, while still engaged in clinicopathologic correlations, he presented in 1840 a paper before the Académie Royale de Médecine on the structure of the gray matter of the cortex.[3] Gennari, Vicq d'Azyr and Soemmerring had noted white lines in the cortex with the naked eye by gross dissection; Baillarger, on the other hand, made his advance by cutting thin slices of fresh cortex, placing them between two pieces of glass, and observing them with the aid of a light held behind them. By this means he divided the cortex into six layers of alternate white and gray laminae. He was able to satisfy himself that the white lines seen by Gennari in the occipital area could be traced in all parts of the cortex, although they were far less conspicuous anteriorly than posteriorly. This continuation of Gennari's line has therefore come to be known as the "external line or white stripe of Baillarger" (Fulton).[4] Baillarger's stripes attracted much attention and as late as 1907, Elliot Smith—who at that time was in Cairo—examined freshly cut slices of brain with a hand lens, and taking the stripes as landmarks, was able to distinguish some forty sharply delimited cortical areas.[5]

Not only was Baillarger the first to demonstrate that the cortex is made up of layers ("resembling a gray ribbon with three white bands in it"), but he was also the first to show that fibers connected the cortex with the internal white matter. "At the summit of the convolutions," he wrote, "the white matter is entirely united to the gray matter by many fibers. A simple juxtaposition of these two components is thus inadmissible."[3]

After 1840, Baillarger was drawn more fully to the clinic, from which he made one more sally into the field of anatomical research. This netted him in 1845 the credit of having first shown that the surface of the human brain, in comparison to its volume, is less than that in smaller animals and that as a compensatory measure larger brains undergo greater fissuration than smaller ones—in short that the difference in external form of lissencephalic and gyrencephalic brains is explicable on the basis of the geometric law of volumes, namely, that the volume increases as the cube of the diameter while the surface increases as the square.[6,7] This observation has stood the test of time.

SAN FRANCISCO, CALIFORNIA   WALTER FREEMAN

References

[1]*Etudes de psychologie médicale.* I. *Perception et langage.* Rio de Janeiro, Atlantica, 1944.   [2]*A history of medical psychology.* New York, Norton, 1941, p. 396.   [3]Mém. Acad. Roy. Méd. Paris, 1840, *8:*149–183.   [4]Bull. Inst. Hist. M., Balt., 1937, *5:*895–913.   [5]J. Anat. Physiol., 1907, *41:*237–254.   [6]Gaz. hôp., 1945, *18:*179.   [7]Bull. Acad. méd., Paris, 1845, *10:*558.

References to Biography and Works: 1) France méd., 1902, *49:*473–475 *et seq.* (Magnan).   2) Ann. méd.-psychol., Paris, 1892, 7. sér., *16:*5–58 (contains bibliography; Ritti, Dureau).   3) *External morphology of the primate brain.* Springfield, Thomas, 1950 (Connolly).   4) *The comparative anatomy of the nervous system of vertebrates, including man.* 2 vol. New York, Macmillan, 1936 (Kappers, Huber and Crosby).

CHARLES BELL (1774–1842)

*T*HE impetus given to the growth of physiology by the work of William Harvey in the seventeenth century was slow in reaching the study of neurology. Charles Bell wrote in 1811, shortly before he published his first work on the nervous system, that ". . . there was a singular indifference to the study of the nerves; and an opinion very generally prevailed that as the notion of the ancients had descended to us uncontroverted and unimproved, the subject was entirely exhausted. The hypothesis that a nervous fluid was derived from the brain, and transmitted by nervous tubes, was deemed consistent with anatomical demonstration, and there was no hope of improvement." Bell rose to this challenge and made numerous contributions to the knowledge of the nervous system, some of which are of prime importance.

Charles Bell was one of the large group of Scottish surgeon-anatomists who left Edinburgh during the eighteenth century and en-

Charles Bell

riched the medical and scientific life of London. Charles owed much of his training to his oldest brother, John Bell, a brilliant and successful Edinburgh surgeon; but he also suffered as the innocent bystander to a feud between John and members of the medical faculty of the University of Edinburgh. As a result of

Portrait, courtesy of the National Library of Medicine, Bethesda, Maryland.

these differences, both brothers were denied further positions at the University and the Royal Infirmary, and Charles felt constrained to migrate to London.

The personality and career of Charles Bell largely reflect the influence of his mother. Widowed when her youngest son was but four years old, she very ably assumed the responsibilities of rearing and educating her four sons. She was a remarkable woman, intelligent and artistic, who instilled in her sons high ideals, ambition, cultural interests, and a devotion that bordered on reverence. It is not surprising then that Charles was a sensitive and esthetic person and an accomplished artist.

His arrival in London at the age of thirty found him lonely, frustrated, and discouraged. In contrast to a brilliant beginning on a surgical career in Edinburgh, he found himself totally unknown and disregarded in London. He was, however, sustained by certain triumphs and appreciations. Shortly after his arrival, he published *Essays on the anatomy of expression in painting*,[1] for the instruction of artists, which was based on his anatomical knowledge. This beautiful work won him great recognition in art circles, if not in surgery, and gave him an entree to the artistic and social life of London.

To further his surgical career as well as to provide earnings while it was developing, Bell opened a private school of anatomy, and subsequently purchased the Old Windmill Street School of Anatomy originally started by William Hunter.

The neurological studies of Charles Bell began while he was still a student in Edinburgh when he wrote the section on the nervous system for his brother John's *Anatomy of the human body*. As so frequently happens, the early interest became the lasting preoccupation of his life to which he returned time after time. His contributions in this field cover a wide range. He established the fact that the nerves of the special senses could be traced from specific areas of the brain to their end organs. Above all he demonstrated that the spinal nerves carry both sensory and motor functions and that sensory fibers traverse the posterior roots whereas the motor fibers run through the anterior roots (Bell's Law).[2-4] There resulted a bitter and futile dispute as to priority between

Bell and the French physiologist, François Magendie, who more definitively established the separate functions of the nerve roots by animal experimentation.

Bell also described muscle sense or proprioceptive sensation. He demonstrated that the fifth cranial nerve was sensory to the face and motor to mastication, whereas the seventh controlled the muscles of expression.[3,4] The eponyms of the respiratory nerve of Bell and Bell's palsy[5,6] have made his name familiar to all subsequent generations of medical students. The facial palsy described by him was of varied etiology: gunshot wounds, syphilis, and even goring by an ox.[6]

From its full beginnings, the career of Charles Bell evolved into one of fame and brilliance. He was instrumental in founding the Middlesex Hospital and Medical School. As surgeon to this institution, he attended the wounded after Corunna and Waterloo. There was a captivating twinkle behind his eyeglasses, and he was genial and unaffected. Renowned physicians from all over came to visit him in London, and his travels abroad became triumphant processions. He received many honors including knighthood, conferred by the enthusiastic Lord Brougham. His achievements in the field of neurology have established him as one of the great surgical scientists of history.

CHICAGO, ILLINOIS   LEO M. ZIMMERMAN

References

[1]*Essays on the anatomy of expression in painting*. London, Longman, Reese, Hurst & Orme, 1806.   [2]*Idea of a new anatomy of the brain* etc. (1811). In *Sir Charles Bell: His life and times*. Edinburgh, Livingstone, 1958 (Gordon Taylor and Walls).   [3]Philos. Trans. Roy. Soc. London, 1821, *111*:398 *et seq.*; 1822, *112*:284 *et seq.*   [4]*An exposition of the natural system of the nerves* etc. London, Spottiswode, 1824. [5]Philos. Trans. Roy. Soc. London, 1829, *119*:317–330.   [6]*The nervous system of the human body*, 3rd ed. London, Spottiswode, 1844.

References to Biography: 1) *The life and labours of Sir Charles Bell*. London, Bentley, 1860 (Pichot).   2) *Great ideas in the history of surgery*. Baltimore, Williams & Wilkins, 1961 (Zimmerman and Veith).

PAUL BROCA (1824–1880)

*P*IERRE PAUL BROCA was born at little Sainte-Foy-la Grande, between Bordeaux and Bergerac, close also to the most famous remains of man's neolithic past. He came from combative Gascon and Huguenot stock. His father, a country doctor and former Napoleonic surgeon, was noted for "unflinching probity, courage and grave irony," his mother for "great intelligence" and "a prodigious memory." Paul's plenitude of gifts—as an investigator, innovator and rebel, yet also as a moderator and organiser —was already apparent when he was a student leader. Professor of surgery eventually, he started his career in Paris at seventeen, and was the youngest prosector and Secretary of the Société Anatomique ever. There he described muscular dystrophy as a primary affection of muscle before Duchenne[1]; rickets as a nutritional disorder before Virchow[2]; and the venous spread of cancer independently of Rokitansky.[3] Among his 500-odd publications—"he never wrote anything mediocre," a contemporary said—is a classic 900-page monograph on aneurysms,[4] as well as the first experiments on the continent using hypnotism for surgical anesthesia.[5] Much resisted by the medical establishment in France, the introduction of the microscope into the diagnosis of cancer was partly due to his youthful efforts. So was, a little later, and throughout his life, his foundation of Anthropology as the science we know today. Among the plethora of novel subjects he treated was Cro-Magnon man[6] and neolithic trephination.[7] In 1858 and 1859 his heretic denial of the immutability of race and species[8]—the offensive central idea also of Darwin's more famous work that year—compelled Broca to establish a platform of his own: the world's first Anthropological Society, followed by his School and Institute of Anthropology.

On this background—aided by an early association with François Leuret (1797–1851) and Pierre Gratiolet (1815–1865), the comparative anatomists, and with Jean Baptiste Bouillaud (1796–1881), the intrepid developer of the ideas of Gall—Broca contributed to neurology the concept of functional localization by cerebral convolution. This, in the 1860's, opened the way for Hitzig, Ferrier, Munk, Wernicke, etc., on the one hand; to mid-twentieth

Pierre Paul Broca

century ideas about the inferomesial aspect of the hemisphere—the "great limbic lobe" or "limbic system"—on the other, in 1878 and 1879.[9]

It was a memorable day when Broca demonstrated before the *Société d'Anthropologie* in Paris—with his old father looking on in silent admiration—the brain lesion of his first patient who had suffered from *aphémie*[10] (renamed aphasia by Trousseau). From

Portrait, courtesy of Dr. Maurice Genty, Académie de Médecine, Paris, France.

this and subsequent observations he concluded that the integrity of the posterior part of the left third frontal convolution was indispensable to articulate speech, and he therefore termed this region the *circonvolution du langage*. (Later Ferrier referred to it as "Broca's convolution.")

On March 24, 1863, Broca's cautious view about the unheard-of dominance for speech by the left cerebral hemisphere was received by the Académie de Médicine.[11] On the same date and on the same page it is recorded that Gustave Dax (1815–1893) deposited a hitherto unpublished memoir by his deceased father Marc, written in 1836.[12] In a series of forty-odd patients Marc Dax (1771–1837) had correlated loss of speech with right hemiplegia, due in some cases to known left hemisphere trauma. Much heat was generated over these interpretations: first in the series of weekly meetings of the Académie de Médicine in 1865; three years later at the session of the British Association for the Advancement of Science in Norwich, where both Broca[13] and Jackson expressed their latest views; unfortunately their discussion, if any, is not on record.[14] Posthumously Broca was again challenged by Pierre Marie, his former interne. In 1906 Marie sought out the very brain described by Broca: it had a parieto-temporal lesion in addition to the frontal one insisted on by Broca.[15]

Broca's and Wernicke's ideas about circumscribed localization in the cerebral cortex are giving way to Jackson's approach; but this does not reduce the importance of his discovery, nor will it be forgotten that it was Broca, the meticulous observer, who established in principle the functional significance of the various areas in the cortex.

Broca was strongly built, with an expansive forehead and lustrous brown eyes. Fiery, righteous, but benevolent, and an excellent raconteur, he was adored by his associates, and it is said that those who were once his friends were his friends for life. While still in his thirties he furthered Brown-Séquard's difficult career. Standing for many years at one corner of the Faculté de Médecine, until carted off on orders by the German Army in the Second World War, was Broca's statue, with that of Vulpian not far off. Here he could still survey Paris much as it was in 1871 during the Commune when, as vice-president of the Council of Public

Assistance, Broca risked his life to spirit seventy-five million francs from that institution's treasury to the government in Versailles. To do this he devised the bold scheme of hiding the assets, stuffed into travelling bags, on an old wagon loaded with potatoes; the cart was safely driven past the Communard-manned gate of Paris. He received not so much as a vote of thanks from the conservative Government.

Broca was married to the wealthy daughter of Dr. J. G. A. Lugol (1786–1851), of iodine fame. Both his sons distinguished themselves: Auguste as professor of pediatric surgery, André as professor of medical physics. Politically active, rather far left of center, and a towering public figure, Broca was elected in 1880 as a lifetime member of the Senate, to represent "France et Science"— only for six months, however. At fifty-six, still at the height of his restless powers, he suddenly died, presumably from coronary occlusion.

KURT GOLDSTEIN

References

[1]Bull. Soc. anat. Paris, 851, *26*:50–64   [2]*Ibid.*, 1852, 27:141 *et seq.*, and 542 *et seq.*   [3]*Ibid.*, 1850, 25:45 *et seq.*, and Mém. Acad. méd., Paris, 1852, *16*:453–820 (sic).   [4]*Des anévrysmes et de leur traitement.* Paris, Labé & Asselin, 1856.   [5]Bull. Soc. chir. Paris, 1859, *10*:247–270. [6]Bull. Soc. d'Anthrop., 1868, *3*:350–392, 454–510.   [7]*Ibid.*, 1874, *9*:542–555; 1876, *11*:236–251, 431–440.   [8]J. de physiol., 1858, 2.sér., *1*:385–498.   *Ibid.*, 1879, 2:385–455.   [10]Bull. Soc. anthrop. Paris, 1861, 2:235–238; Bull. Soc. anat. Paris, 1861, *36*:330–357. Also in *The cerebral cortex.* Springfield, Thomas, 1960 (Bonin).   [11]*Exposition des titres et travaux* and Bull. Acad. Méd., 1863, *28*:497.   [12]Gaz. hebd. Paris, 2.sér., 1865, *2*:259–269 (Dax). Neurology, 1964, *14*:851–854 (Joynt and Benton).   [13]Trib. méd., Paris, 1869, 254–256, 266–269. [14]Lancet, London, 1868, p. 386.   [15]Sem. méd., Paris, 1906, *26*:241–247. Broca's papers on the brain, also in *Mémoires d'Anthropologie de Paul Broca.* Vol. 5. Paris, Reinwald, 1888.

References to Biography: 1) *Paul Broca, correspondence,* 1841–1857. 2 vol. Paris, Schmidt, 1886.   2) Rev. anthrop., Paris, 2.sér., 1880, *3*:577–608 (contains bibliography; Pozzi).   3) Rev. mens. méd. chir.,

Paris, 1880, *4*:745–764 (Reclus).   4) Rev. Hist. Sci., Paris, 1966, *14*:47–86 (Huard).   5) *Miscellaneous papers, 1882–1913*, Washington, D.C. (Fletcher).   6) Bull. Hist. Med., 1947, *21*:322–334 (Riese).

LOCKHART CLARKE (1817–1880)

*T*HIS English neurologist was born in London. While he was still a small boy, his father died; and his mother, who had been left with adequate financial means, took her family of seven to France for their education. As a student in France, Clarke is said to have shown no unusual ability and to have been regarded by his family as rather indolent. But after returning to England in 1830, he displayed more interest in intellectual pursuits and later chose a career in medicine, a profession which had already claimed his grandfather and one of his elder brothers. After receiving his medical training at Guy's and St. Thomas' Hospitals, he was licensed by the Apothecaries Society and went to live with his mother at Pimlico where he entered into the general practice of medicine.

It was during the period of his life from 1851 to 1868, while engaged in general practice, that Clarke carried on those detailed investigations which have given his name to posterity. In addition to fundamental investigations on the anatomy and histology of the central nervous system, he published a number of papers on various clinical subjects, stressing the view that much could be learned of the function of the nervous system in man by carefully correlating the clinical and pathological data.

Clarke's investigations, carried out with great skill and characterized by extreme thoroughness, were illustrated with excellent drawings from his own hand. He is best known for his researches on the spinal cord, which he fixed in spirits of wine, then terpentine. He established the presence of the nucleus dorsalis, called by him the "posterior vesicular column" ("column of Clarke"), and described the nucleus intermediolateralis.[1-3] He was the first to distinguish the lateral from the medial cuneate nucleus (he called the lateral nucleus the "outer restiform nucleus"),[4] though today the lateral cuneate nucleus is named after von Monakow because

Jacob Augustus Lockhart Clarke

it was he who traced its fibers to the cerebellum.[5] Another contribution was the introduction of the method of mounting cleared
sections in balsam,[1] a major advance in histological technique. Several of his most important publications on anatomy (e.g.,
"Clarke's column") are to be found in the *Philosophical Transactions of the Royal Society of London* from 1851 to 1868. As a close
rival of Stilling, he was found wanting with regard to the nerve
fiber. Stilling had described the herring bone-patterned lines in
the myelin of nerve fibers in 1855, and illustrated them in 1856;

Portrait, courtesy of the National Library of Medicine, Bethesda, Maryland.

Clarke, in 1860, argued that they were mechanical artefacts in the form of folds. That they were true incisures was established some years later (in 1874) by H. D. Schmidt, then in New Orleans, and by A. J. Lanterman, of Cleveland (then in Germany).

In 1868[6] Clarke described syringomyelia more or less as it is known today, being preceded in this respect only by Gull.[7] A further understanding of this disorder was soon to appear in the contributions of Hallopeau,[8] Charcot and Joffroy,[9] and that by Th. Simon,[10] who distinguished it from hydromyelia. In the late 1880's the clinical descriptions by Fr. Schultze,[11] Kahler,[12] and Bäumler[13] brought more light to the subject and the turn of the twentieth century saw the great monograph of Hermann Schlesinger (1866–1934), of Bohemia (Austria), who became professor of medicine at the Allgemeines Krankenhaus in Vienna. In this monograph Schlesinger discussed 260 cases of the disorder.[14] The masterpiece on syringobulbia by Jonesco-Sisesti appeared in 1932.[15]

Although little appreciated by his own clinically oriented profession, Clarke's research was given recognition by the Royal Society, which elected him Fellow in 1854, and ten years later awarded him its Gold Medal for his scientific achievements. He was also made an Honorary Fellow of the King and Queen's College of Physicians of Ireland in 1867. Only after obtaining an additional medical degree from St. Andrews in 1869, he became Member of the Royal College of Physicians of London, but now left general practice, limiting himself to consultations in diseases of the nervous system. Two years later he was appointed physician to the Hospital for Epilepsy and Paralysis at Regent's Park, a position held by him until his death from tuberculosis at the age of sixty-three.

Clarke's contemporaries have described him as a man of the highest character, "with a singleness of purpose, of noble independence, honest and just, conscientious and intellectually keen," but with a singularly retiring and reserved disposition. He never acquired a large practice and is reputed not to have been well off financially. The major satisfaction which he received in life came from his research accomplishments, which brought him world-wide recognition. It is these achievements which give his name a permanent place in neurology.

WILBUR K. SMITH

References

[1]Philos. Trans. Roy. Soc. London, 1851, *141*:607–621.   [2]*Ibid.*, 1859, *149*:437–467.   [3]Arch. Neur. Psychiat., Chicago, 1933, *30*:1025–1045 (subsequent account of Clarke's nucleus, by Pass).   [4]Philos. Trans. Roy. Soc. London, 1868, *158*:263–331.   [5]Neur. Zbl., 1885, *4*:265–268. Arch. Psychiat., Berlin, 1891, *22*:1–26.   [6]Med.-Chir. Trans., London, 1868, *51*:249–262 (with Johnson).   [7]Guy's Hosp. Rep., London, 1862, *8*:244–258.   [8]Gaz. méd., Paris, 1870, 3.sér., *25*:183.   [9]Arch. Physiol., Paris, 1869, *2*:354–367 *et seq.*   [10]Arch. Psychiat., Berlin, 1875,*5*:108–163.   [11]Zschr. klin. Med., 1888, *13*:523–557.   [12]Prag. med. Wschr., 1888, *13*:45–47 *et seq.*   [13]Deut. Arch. klin. Med., 1887, *40*:443–543. [14]*Die Syringomyelie.* Leipzig u. Wien, Deuticke, 1895.   [15]*La syringo-bulbie. Contribution à la physiopathologie du tronc cérébral.* Paris, Masson, 1932.

References to Biography: 1) *Dictionary of national biography.* London, Smith, Elder & Co., 1885, *10*:428 (Bettany).   2) Brit. Med. J., 1880, *1*:170–171 (anon.).

DOMENICO COTUGNO (1736–1822)

*L*IQUOR COTUNNII is the cerebrospinal fluid, but none of this author's publications betrays that fact by its title. You will find it in *De ischiade nervosa commentarius* (1764), an elegant hundred page monograph for the first time featuring the *nervous* origin of sciatica, as opposed to the belief, then current, that the mischief is always in the *ischium,* bone or joint. In this unexpected context, is the cerebrospinal fluid just a special bonus for the attentive reader, offered by an economic writer? Not quite, for Cotugno has his freshly discovered fluid play, as Hydrops, the role of chief villain in the drama of *malum Cotunnii,* or sciatica.

Voltaire's *Candide* (1758), Rousseau's *Émile* (1762): the en-

Domenico Cotugno

lightened seventeen fifties and sixties also saw the publication of Morgagni's *Seats and causes of disease investigated by the means of anatomy* (1761) and Auenbrugger's *New invention to detect the hidden diseases of the chest by way of percussion* (also 1761). As to the foundations of neurology, a ghost had to be laid at rest, a myth buried: the "animal spirit" had to be exorcized from heads attempting to become factual in their thinking. What, after all, it boiled down to was at first perhaps only the raising of a boiling point: that exquisite volatile substance—or nonsubstance—transformed into a liquid, distillation discarded. Cotugno's fluid, how-

Portrait, courtesy of the New York Academy of Medicine.

ever, was real and bore little resemblance to the *succus nerveus* flowing down tubular nerves, in which he too may have believed. Introduced already in 1680 by Borelli, the nerve juice, replaced the Galenic *pneuma psychikon* or animal spirit, and was next substituted by Prochaska's, and Haller's, *vis insita* or *nervosa,* to yield, in turn, to animal electricity (with Fontana) and membrane depolarization.[1]

Cotugno's birthplace lay in Italy's dry heel: Ruvo di Puglia (Apulia), a small town near Bari. Born under the sign of Aquarius he was to spot real water, identical with that which he had seen before in the aqueous labyrinth of the ear, similar also to pericardial and pleural moisture. Vieussens some eighty years earlier had made fairly strong and provocative statements about a clear ventricular fluid—as opposed to the classical vagueness of humor and phlegm—present during life and in health.[2] Swedenborg, the Obscure, had published some well-observed facts about the fluid some twenty-five years earlier; but Cotugno was hardly aware of that wayward opus.[3] And it was through Magendie,[4] belatedly informed of his important forerunner, that Cotugno's contribution joined the mainstream of medical knowledge. In a few paragraphs he showed, simply and clearly, that the fluid always surrounds the brain, that it fills all the pia-arachnoid interstices, as well as the ventricles, and makes its way down easily and regularly through the aqueduct of Sylvius—or Aranzio—down further the "perpendicular" fourth ventricle, to surround the spinal cord in a space "also always filled with it." Cotugno's is an open system—Magendie supplied his own controversial opening in 1825/28, Luschka adding his in 1855. To prove the point of a free circulation, Cotugno decapitates cadavers stood up on their feet—short of doing the *in vivo* lumbar punctures which Quincke introduced in 1891. On some ten small pages he manages to accommodate the pathology of communicating hydrocephalus *ex vacuo* in cerebral atrophy, and the incoagulability of cerebrospinal fluid in health, like urine which, as he too had discovered, gets cloudy through boiling only in disease. The cerebrospinal water is in *perenni statu renovationis,* through "exudation" by minimal arteries and reabsorption by minimal veins. It penetrates into the dural sleeve of the nerve root; hence it is apt to accumulate in the sheaths of the

sciatic nerve and so give pain along its course. Such pain, weakness, and limping may be cured; if necessary by vesicants and caus-
tics to draw out the hydrops.[5] Many such patients, en route to the
island of Ischia, out in the Gulf of Naples, since antiquity a haven
for all manner of "sciatica," must have passed through his hands.

Cotugno was a graduate of Salerno, the world's oldest medical
school, situated on the neighboring gulf. In his fifties, he saw the
school closed down by Murat, a general made King of Naples by
Napoleon. For most of his life, however, Cotugno studied and
practiced medicine in Naples itself. There he also held the chair of
anatomy, after his main work, done before his thirties, had
brought him recognition at home and abroad. Two diaries of his
travels are extant: one through Italy, the other, later, to Vienna
and Western Germany. Wherever he went he indulged a passion
for libraries (the work of Celsus, on whom he wrote, in particular), the visual arts, and music. The glorious Roman past wherever he looked, the century's craze for waterworks, and the Har-
veyan revolution of the century before: we may see them reflected
in Cotugno's preoccupation with circulation and aqueducts. For in
an earlier important discovery about the inner ear[6] he had also
struck water, instead of the traditional Aristotelian *aer ingenitus*.
Valsalva had been his forerunner here (1704); even earlier Duver-
ney, with the assistance of his physicist friend, Mariotte (1683);
Scarpa (1772) finally perfected the anatomy of the membranous
labyrinth with its afferent two nerves. "The cochlea is our harpsi-
chord," Cotugno wrote, its nervous filaments so arranged that the
longest reach the apex, and so he anticipated Helmholtz's work of
one hundred years later.

A poor man's son, Cotugno made the *Incurabili* his heirs as he
left 100,000 ducats to the hospital for the chronically ill of that
name. Here he had worked practically all his life, lonely but serene to all appearances, dignified by scholarly restraint and sweet
reasonableness. A mind remarkable but unhurried, he wrote in
moderation, on the rest treatment of consumption, the skin lesions
of smallpox (a dermatological classic),[7] the physiology of sneezing,
the intracranial venous circulation, the "spirit of medicine," and
on "meditation" which makes "the cerebral fibers reverberate"—
the best preparation for the academic gentleman. His tranquilizers

in those turbulent days were the bucolics of Virgil, the odes of
Horace, the epistles of Seneca, lightened, maybe, with sips of the
Falernian or the stronger Apulian, occasionally, perhaps, taken
from that 2000 years old black and red terracotta vessel, its foot a
horse's head, the Greek *rhyton* he had found as a boy digging for
antiques in the sunbaked Apulian soil.

SAN FRANCISCO, CALIFORNIA   FRANCIS SCHILLER

References

[1]*Handbook of physiology*. Washington, D.C., Amer. Physiol. Soc., 1959,
sect. 1, vol. 1, p. 1–58 (Brazier).   [2]*Neurographia universalis*. Leyden,
Certe, 1685 (Vieussens).   [3]*Three transactions on the cerebrum*. Philadelphia, Swedenborg Sci. Assoc., 1938, vol. 1, p. 624 *et seq.;* vol. 2, p. 134
(Swedenborg).   [4]J. de Physiol. exper. et pathol., *5:*27, 1825; *7:*1, 66,
1827; *8:*211, 1828.   [5]*De ischiade nervosa commentarius*. Naples, Si-
moni, 1764, p. 9–14.   [6]*De aquaeductibus auris humanae internae
dissertatio*. Naples, St. Thomas Aquinae Typogr., 1760.   [7]*De sedibus
variolorum syntagma*. Naples, 1775.

References to Biography: 1) *Essays on the history of Italian neurology*.
Milan, Ist. d. storia d. medicina, 1953, 51–66 (Belloni); 67–74
(Schullian).   2) Bull. Inst. Hist. Med., Balt., 1935, *3:*701–738 (Viets).
3) Amer. Med. Hist., 1935, *8:*1–9 (Levinson).   4) Med. Hist., 1957,
*1:*91–114 (Woollam, on c.s.f.).

PAUL FLECHSIG (1847–1929)

*P*AUL EMIL FLECHSIG was the son of a Protestant cler-
gyman, in Zwickau, Saxony, and was educated in that city.
In 1865 he began the study of medicine in Leipzig, where he came
under the influence of the brothers Ernst and Eduard Weber in
anatomy, Schweigger-Seidel in histology, and Carl Ludwig in physiology. In 1870, when he was only twenty-three, he received the
M.D., his inaugural dissertation being *Bemerkungen über Meningitis luetica* . . . (Leipzig, Fr. Andrae's Nachfolger, 1870); and
with the outbreak of the Franco-Prussian War he was pressed into
service as surgeon. On demobilization two years later, he returned

to Leipzig, where he was appointed assistant at the Institute of Pathology and at the Medical Polyclinic.

Impressed by Meynert's contribution on the structure of the mammalian brain which had just appeared in Stricker's[1] *Handbuch* (1872), Flechsig prepared a set of brain sections from the human newborn, and was struck by the presence of white streaks formed by early myelinating tracts. Here was Flechsig's cue; and by following it he was to show that "we may learn as much of the course of fibers by studying them in their birth as in their death—in their development as in their decay" (Gowers). Already in 1872 a re-

Portrait, courtesy of the National Library of Medicine, Bethesda, Maryland. Signature, courtesy of Dr. Hartwig Kuhlenbeck, Philadelphia, Pennsylvania.

port of his preliminary findings[1] at a national meeting in Leipzig brought him encouragement from von Helmholtz and Ludwig. He concentrated at first on myelogenesis of the spinal cord, both in man and experimental animals, amplifying the work of Türck and Bouchard, which had been based on secondary degeneration. The emphasis was on the course of the dorsal spinocerebellar tract,[2] which became known as "Flechsig's tract," and on the pyramidal tract, which he traced from the precentral and postcentral parts of the cortex.[2] Flechsig came to the conclusion that complete function of a tract is assumed only when its fibers have become myelinated, a view still considered correct.

In 1873 he was made chief of the histological section in the Institute of Physiology under Carl Ludwig, and in 1875 became Privatdozent. During the next few years he studied primary systemic disorders of the spinal cord, the course of the medial lemniscus, and the myelogenesis of the internal capsule, which he subdivided into anterior limb, posterior limb, and knee.[3-5] In 1877 he was promoted to Extraordinarius and soon thereafter became Ordinarius of psychiatry. Having, however, rather scanty knowledge of psychiatry, he obtained several years' leave of absence so that he could study at the most progressive institutions in Germany and abroad. On these travels he spent some time in Paris, visiting Charcot at the Salpêtrière.

In 1882 Flechsig opened his new Irrenklinik and soon visitors and students from all corners of the earth gathered around him— Beevor, Bekhterev, Darkschewitsch, Schütz, Tschirch, Yakowenko, Popov, Blumenau, Klimov, Donaldson, O. Vogt, Martinotti and Held. Flechsig was at first preoccupied with the therapy of epilepsy and general paralysis and the pathology of tabes dorsalis. Bekhterev and Held collaborated with him on myelogenetic studies. Flechsig's assistant, H. Schütz, wrote, in 1891, a memorable treatise on the dorsal longitudinal fasciculus.[6] Another pupil was Richard Arwed Pfeifer, whose work on cerebral vascularization was technically perfect—there are no finer plates on capillary distribution in the brain than in his *Die Angioarchitektonik der Grosshirnrinde* (Berlin, Springer, 1928)—but he refused to publish his method. "Work with me six months in my laboratory," he used to say, "and then you will know all about it."

In 1893 Flechsig embarked on the study of myelogenesis in the hemispheres. He discovered the auditory radiation and on the basis of myeloarchitecture distinguished thirty-six cortical areas. During the ensuing years he developed, step by step, his theory of projection and association centers.[7] The cortex was divided by him into 1) primary and secondary projection areas—motor and sensory—and 2) association, or cognition, areas. His view that the parietal lobe is a primary sensory area which transmits the impulses it receives to a parietal association area for elaboration was long-lived, but fell by the wayside when others recognized that thalamic fibers reach all parts of the parietal lobe and that the "association area" is also a projection area.

In Flechsig's opinion the region of the brain most important for mental life was the parietotemporo-occipital association "zone" bounded inferiorly by the hippocampal gyrus. Lesions in this region, he felt, led to the development of dementia, whereas lesions in the frontal associative zone had no such effect. These views were epitomized in the address which he delivered at his inauguration as rector of the University of Leipzig for the year 1894–95, an address published in 1896 under the title, *Gehirn und Seele* (Leipzig, Veit) and subsequently reprinted several times. Bianchi, in 1903[8] acknowledged that while Flechsig's myelogenetic method had furnished "une grande impulsion" to the knowledge of the anatomy and development of the brain, his conclusions in regard to the functional significance of the frontal lobe were erroneous: "La zone frontale est siège de la synthèse intellective et émotive de la personnalité. Voilà la seule conclusion légitime." Flechsig's myelogenetic method was also submitted to a searching analysis by C. and O. Vogt,[9,10] who disagreed with Flechsig on some points, particularly in regard to the time of myelination of certain projection systems.

In 1901 Flechsig became one of the founders of the International Brain Commission, and in 1904 received an honorary D.Sc. from Oxford University.

A typical Voigtländer, Flechsig was a big, broad, bulky individual with a tendency to be abrupt and dogmatic. He frequently declared that it is the duty of a Professor to think "other than others." His students did not consider him their friend, but conceded that he was extraordinarily erudite. In a case of severe vertigo,

Flechsig once found at autopsy a parasitic cyst in the IVth ventricle; ever after he laid such emphasis on the importance of parasitic cysts as a cause of vertigo that his dissertations on the subject became part of the Flechsig lore, which the students made a point to keep alive. He tended to have a poor memory for the discoveries of others: Oscar Vogt tells the story that back in 1894 he showed a newly found group of fibers (in the corpus callosum) to Flechsig and that three weeks later Flechsig demonstrated them to him as his (Flechsig's) discovery. According to Folke Henschen, Flechsig had an aversion to socialism, so much so that on one occasion, on peering at the brain of a well-known socialist which had just been removed by him at autopsy, he remarked: "My! what dysharmonic convolutions!" At the age of seventy-four, Flechsig retired from his official duties at the University of Leipzig where he had spent more than fifty years. Oskar Vogt relates that he had grown so accustomed to his cottage in the garden behind the clinic, forgetting that it belonged to the University, that he refused to budge from it and had to be evicted. Nonetheless he continued to work as "ein Forscher aus Leidenschaft," stimulating those around him to the very end.

MOFFETT FIELD, CALIFORNIA   WEBB HAYMAKER

References

[1]Tagebl. 45.Versamml. Deut. Naturforsch. u. Aerzte. Leipzig, Reusche, 1872, p. 75. [2]*Die Leitungsbahnen im Gehirn und Rückenmark des Menschen.* Leipzig, Engelmann, 1876. [3]Arch. Heilk., Leipzig, 1877, *18*:101–141 *et seq.* [4]Arch. Anat. Entw., 1881, p. 12–75. [5]*Plan des menschlichen Gehirns.* Leipzig, Veit, 1883. [6]Arch. Psychiat., Berlin, 1891, *22*:527–587. [7]*Anatomie des menschlichen Gehirns und Rückenmarks auf myelogenetischer Grundlage.* Leipzig, Thieme, 1920. [8]C. rend. XIVᵉ Congr. Internat. de Méd., Madrid, 1903. Vol. 5. Sect. Neuropath. Madrid, Sastre, 1904, p. 468–485. [9]Allg. Zschr. Psychiat., 1901, *58*:707–709. [10]J. Psychol. Neur., Leipzig, 1903, *2*:160–180.

References to Biography: 1) *Meine myelogenetische Hirnlehre. Mit biographischer Einleitung.* Berlin, Springer, 1927 (Flechsig). 2) Arch. Psychiat., Berlin, 1930, *91*:1–8 (Schröder).

AUGUSTE FOREL (1848–1931)

*A*UGUSTE HENRI FOREL was born on a country estate near Morges, Switzerland, on the shore of Lake Geneva. At the early age of seven he found interest in observing insects, especially ants, and at eleven years Huber's famous work on the behavior of ants literally became his bible. When fourteen he was sent to Lausanne to pursue secondary studies at the Collège Cantonal and later he attended that city's Academy. In 1866 he began to study medicine in Zürich, at the same time continuing his investigations on ants, publishing papers and becoming a member of the Swiss Entomological Society. His teacher, von Gudden, made such a deep impression on him that he resolved to become a psychiatrist.

After completing courses in Zürich in 1871, he took the cantonal medical examination in Lausanne but, because of local medical politics, failed to pass. For the next few months he traveled through Switzerland, working on a monograph dealing with the ants indigenous to that country. The winter of 1871–72 was spent in Vienna, studying neuroanatomy under Meynert and preparing his doctoral dissertation on the thalamus opticus of mammals.[1] Although in disagreement with many of Meynert's fundamental teachings, Meynert nevertheless accepted the thesis and had it published in the Proceedings of the Vienna Academy of Sciences. Forel passed the cantonal medical examination in Lausanne in 1872, but did not succeed in obtaining the position in a psychiatric institution of his native canton for which he had applied. In 1873 he went to the Ludwig-Maximilians-Universität in Munich as one of von Gudden's assistants, becoming Privatdozent in 1877 after completing his important paper on the tegmental region in which he described the tegmental fields, the zona incerta, and various other hitherto unknown structures.[2] He also had a significant part in devising the first usable brain microtome.

Forel started on a myrmecological expedition to Colombia in 1878, but had to abandon it at St. Thomas in the Virgin Islands because of the sudden death of his companion and friend, Steinheil. The following year he was appointed director of the

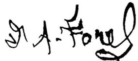

Burghölzli Asylum and professor of psychiatry at the University of Zürich. His predecessor was Hitzig and he was succeeded, in turn, by Bleuler, Maier and Bleuler, Jr. In 1882 Forel married Emma Steinheil, the young daughter of his deceased friend.

Forel's fundamental paper, in which the neuron theory was unequivocally stated, was published in 1887.[3] This work, based on pathological and functional evidence, appeared about two months

Portrait, courtesy of Dr. Hartwig Kuhlenbeck, Philadelphia. Signature from letter dated September 24, 1927.

after that of W. His, in which similar conclusions had been reached on the basis of histogenetic studies. Thus, His and Forel must be credited with the independent formulation of the concept of cellular and functional units for which some years later Cajal furnished the strongest support and for which Waldeyer coined in 1891[4,5] the term "neuron." In addition to his research in brain anatomy, recorded in his collected neuroanatomic papers,[6] Forel studied the therapeutic value of hypnotism and worked on many other problems of psychiatry. He was particularly interested in the difficult problems of memory and of brain-mind relationship. Oskar Vogt became a worker in his laboratory in the summer of 1894, and in 1902 they collaborated in founding the *Journal für Psychologie und Neurologie,* which some years ago (1954) was re-named the *Journal für Hirnforschung.*

In 1898 Forel retired from his duties as director and professor to return to his native Canton de Vaud, spending the rest of his life in travel, doing research on ants, writing on philosophy, studying sexual problems,[7] and enthusiastically crusading for alcoholic abstinence, monism, pacifism, and later, socialism. He had always been known as a fearless crusader and indefatigable worker of great intellectual honesty and strong convictions. In 1912 he suffered a cerebral vascular accident resulting in right hemiplegia. Courageously he overcame this condition and at sixty-four years of age learned to write with his left hand. He remained active in his fields of interest until his death at the age of eighty-three.

PHILADELPHIA, PENNSYLVANIA   HARTWIG KUHLENBECK

References

[1]Sitzber. Akad. Wiss. Wien, Physiol. Abt., 1872, *66:*25–58.   [2]Arch. Psychiat., Berlin, 1877, *7:*393–495.   [3]*Ibid.,* 1887, *18:*162–198. [4]Deut. med. Wschr., 1891, *17:*1213–1218 *et seq.*   [5]Berlin klin. Wschr., 1891, *28:*691.   [6]*Gesammelte hirnanatomische Abhandlungen mit einem Aufsatz über die Aufgaben der Neurobiologie.* München, Reinhardt, 1907.   [7]*Die sexuelle Frage.* München, Reinhardt, 1905. (Engl. trans. by Marshall: *The sexual question.* New York, Repman, 1909). (Review by Collins in J. Nerv. Ment. Dist., 1909, *36:*255–256.)

References to Biography: 1) *Rückblick auf mein Leben. Mit einem Nachwort von O. L. Forel.* Zürich, Europa, 1935 (Forel). (Review by Maier in Schweiz. Arch. Neur. Psychiat., 1935, *35*:383.) (Engl. trans.: *Out of my life and work.* New York, Norton, 1937. French trans.: *Auguste Forel mémoires.* Neuchatel, Baconnière, 1941).   2) Deut. Zschr. Nervenh., 1931, *122*:117–118 (Veraguth).   3) Schweiz. med. Wschr., 1948, *78*:838–839 (O. L. Forel).   4) Schweiz. Arch. Neur. Psychiat., 1950, *65*:421–425 (Steck).   5) Med. Welt, 1928, *2*:1–5 (O. Vogt).   6) Arch. Neur. Psychiat., Chicago, 1931, *26*:1303–1305 (Adolf Meyer).   7) J. Comp. Neur., 1893, *3*:1–6 *et seq.* (Adolf Meyer).

FRANZ GALL (1758–1828)

*F*RANZ JOSEPH GALL, the scholar and neuroanatomist, is buried under Gall, the showman and phrenologist—a term, by the way, he neither invented nor approved of. It was coined by Johann Christoph Spurzheim (1776–1832) after this assistant, collaborator and coauthor had parted ways with his master. Nevertheless, phrenology made Gall the most influential scientist of his day, ranking in the eyes of the philosopher Auguste Comte with Galileo, Newton and Lavoisier, much as we might cast Freud with Marx, Darwin and Einstein in a similar quartet for our century.

As to the anatomist, even Flourens who posthumously demolished him had to admit: "I shall never forget the feeling I experienced the first time I saw Gall dissect a brain. It seemed to me that I had never seen this organ before."

Gall, made to sound in an English context like the synonym of bile, was actually descended from the Italian Gallo, and Franz did resemble that brightly plumed male bird somewhat, being proud and independent, outgoing and overfond of "chicks," also forgetful and sloppy. "Neither sin nor friends will ever leave me," he once declared. Born in the Grand-Duchy of Baden (Tiefenbronn), he studied medicine in Strasbourg without acquiring an accent in keeping with his French education. He was already married when, at the age of twenty-three, he moved to Vienna where he graduated only four years later. That he was a gay blade with provocative ideas did anything but discourage his clientele; both in Aus-

GALL

tria and later in Paris he had a large and lucrative practice which
included the *haut monde* of politics and letters. This allowed him
to live in style, keep a menagerie, indulge in gardening, women,
and the brain.

In 1791 he published *Medico-philosophical investigations of nature and art in health and disease,*[1] in which he scorned metaphysi-
cians and vitalists in science, and drew some unflattering parallels

Portrait, from Collection de la Bibliothétique de l'Académie Nationale de Médecine, cliché Assistance Publique, Paris, vol. 5, p. 30.172.

between man and beast. He also blasted the notion of a "senso-rium commune" as "the seat of the soul," and postulated different places in the brain for representing the various mental faculties. This heady stuff was not quite phrenology yet, and certainly never anything like evolution, not to speak of materialism. Yet the Em-peror considered it to be just that and in conflict with morals and religion. Consequently, as of Christmas Eve 1801, Gall lost his *venia legendi* and the permission to publish his "doctrine about heads," lest, the witty Emperor wrote, "some lose their heads over it." Gall tolerated the bigoted atmosphere of the Hapsburg capital for over three more years. He was forty-seven when he left with Spurzheim on a sensational lecture tour, with demonstrations from the audience, leading the pair through the Protestant parts of Eu-rope, acclaimed, contradicted, but at least not interdicted. Goethe, whose Olympian mask Gall took, was impressed. So was Paris, where after two years of traveling, Gall settled and stayed for the remainder of his life, from 1807 to 1828. Although the foreigner's controversial ideas were not particularly palatable to either Napo-leon or the restored Bourbon Kings, they left him alone to teach or practice as he pleased.

If we disregard the sensational aspects of Gall's psychological no-menclature, the ludicrous detail, and what we must consider his betrayal of the very principle he professed—strict observation—and instead concentrate on the essentials, we cannot but agree with those contemporaries who saw in him the inaugurator of an en-tirely new and immensely fruitful concept. It was, in fact, the con-cept of the multiple functions of the brain. Not only the anatomi-cal structure but the site of an organ, and of its parts, determined their function. He had learned from Johann Peter Frank (famous for having conceived the idea of Public Health, and also an even-tual refugee from Vienna) that the spinal cord itself was a chain of ganglia[2]; from Pourfour du Petit that the pyramids had a crossed arrangement[3]; from Willis, that the cortex was a store-house of impressions.[4] These and other notions he rearranged and filled with a novel emphasis. Willis' corpora striata became the ce-rebral ganglia, i.e. relays in the path indicated by the pyramids, while the convolutions were the very origin of what we would call behavior. The fiber strands which he dissected, including the cra-nial nerves, all took their "nourishment" from gray matter. He showed that the cranial nerves issued from the oblongata, not from the cerebral hemispheres, and that the pyramids were too narrow to contain the whole of the cerebral outflow or inflow.[5]

It is to Gall's credit that he was after "phenomena . . . conditions . . . not causes," that he shunned the large psychological entities of the philosophers: Will, judgment, memory, etc. These were, and are to this day, regarded as "elementary" and perhaps localisable, instead of being, as he suggested, mere abstracts and attributes. Gall's attempt, however, at being realistic and specific with his "amativeness," "philoprogenetiveness," "comparative sagacity," "wit," etc., was doomed to failure, until these chimeras were replaced by the motor and sensory regions for face, arm, leg, and so on. Gall also had an inkling of levels and is thus the most important tie in the chain between Thomas Willis and Hughlings Jackson, Broca, Hitzig, Ferrier and all the others who exploited his idea of cortical parcellation and localization. Given that period when "physical signs," like those of percussion and auscultation, were sought to uncover hidden diseases, we can understand his haste to base a diagnosis of personality on cranial "bumps," molded, he thought, by the underlying convolutions. His organology, that dared to make an inventory of the mind and to find a pigeonhole for each item, was no doubt eighteenth century quixotic, yet it casts a long shadow on twentieth century cybernetics. It initiated the organic trend in psychology and psychiatry, the classification of psychotics and criminals; it cut across the artificial barriers between races and nations. Gall established the belief that character traits, talents, and mental aberrations are organic, inborn, God-given, like the sleep-walking he had suffered from as a child, or that "purest most innocent instinct" of his, that "blind impulse to force their secrets from nature, animals and men." To such forces, he said, and not to any ambitious planning on his part he owed his achievements.

SAN FRANCISCO, CALIFORNIA   FRANCIS SCHILLER

References

[1]*Philosophisch-medizinische Untersuchungen über Natur und Kunst im kranken und gesunden Zustände des Menschen.*   Leipzig, Baumgärtner, 1800. [2]*Kleine Schriften praktischen Inhalts*, etc. Wien,

1797, p. 284 (Frank).   ³*Handbook of physiology.* Washington, D.C., Amer. Physiol. Soc., 1959, sect. 1, vol. 1, p. 1–58 (Brazier).   ⁴*Cerebri anatome,* etc., 1664 (Willis). In *Opera omnia.* Amsterdam, Wetstenius, 1682, p. 34.   ⁵*Recherches sur le système nerveux en général et sur celui du cerveau en particulier.* Paris, Schoell, 1809.

References to Biography: 1) *Wisconsin studies in medical history.* 1956, no. 1 (Ackerknecht and Valois).   2) Bull. Hist. Med., 1947, 21:275–321 (Temkin).

CAMILLO GOLGI (1843–1926)

*T*HIS persevering, headstrong, reserved man was born in Corteno (Lombardy), a small and lonely town in the midst of the mighty Alps. Today the town is called Corteno Golgi. His parents named him Camillino, but later on the young Golgi considered the name too fancy. His father, Alessandro, a graduate of the University of Pavia, practiced medicine in the area.

Camillo obtained his medical degree in Pavia in 1865, when he was twenty-two. From 1865 to 1872 he was resident in the Ospedale di San Matteo in Pavia, frequently working in the Instituto di Patologia Generale, directed by Giulio Bizzozero. Here, under the direction of Cesare Lombroso, Golgi carried out studies on pellagra (resulting in his first publication, in 1868), also on the pathology in forty-five cases of smallpox (Golgi's was the first important publication on pathology of the bone marrow). It was the influence of his great friend Bizzozero and his reading of Virchow's *Cellularpathologie* that led Golgi to turn to the study of the structure of the nervous system—this despite his father's advice that he should now turn his thoughts to making a livelihood. Golgi's work on psammomas (which he considered to be "dural endotheliomas") appeared in 1869, his initial studies on the neuroglia of the cerebral gray and white matter in 1870 and 1871.

Financial needs compelled him to accept a position as chief resident physician in the Ospizio-Cronici in Abbiategrasso. In this small town, away from all academic activity, with a laboratory consisting only of a microscope and a few instruments set up in the kitchen of his home, Golgi, working mostly at night by candlelight, discovered a chromate of silver method, *la reazione nera,* for

staining the nervous tissue, with which he was to revolutionize the
concept of the histological structure of the nervous system. A well-
stained preparation is a mine, he would say. He described this
method in 1873[1] and again in 1875[2] in connection with a study of

Portrait, courtesy of Dr. J. R. M. Innes, Falls Church, Virginia.

cerebral gliomas. In 1874 he made the first clinico-pathological application of his method, selecting a case of chorea for the purpose.

He was called in 1875 to the University of Pavia as Extraordinarius in histology. He was then thirty-two. Here he spent virtually the remainder of his academic life (until 1918), at first
under conditions which would have discouraged less determined
men. Pupils and scholars, many of them from abroad, soon flocked
to his laboratory, among them Marchi, Monti, Sala, Negri,
Fridtjof Nansen, and Perroncito, his nephew, adopted son, and
successor. But even so, up to 1887 little reference was made to Golgi's work in the foreign literature. All this changed, however, after
von Kölliker's visit with him in the spring of that year.

Golgi's classic on the histology of nervous centers appeared in
1883–84,[3] his no less monumental *Studi sulla fina anatomia degli
organi centrali del sistema nervoso* (Milano, Hoepli) in 1886.
Found in both, but particularly in his *Studi*, is his description of
type I and type II nerve cells of the cerebral cortex: the former,
motor in function, send their axons down through the white matter to subcortical centers; the latter (some short, some long), sensory, ply their way entirely within the cortex. *Opera omnia* (Milano, Hoepli), the three volumes which illustrate the formal elegance of his drawings, were published in 1903. Descriptions of the
musculo-tendinous end organ and of peripheral and central nerve
fibers[4] were made in 1880. The cytoplasmic reticular substance of
nerve and other cells has been called the Golgi apparatus since his
clear portrayal of it in 1898.[5,6] Von La Valette Saint George had
described the apparatus in the sexual cells of snails in 1867.[7]

Golgi's interest in the nervous system was on the wane during
the 1890's. He turned to other subjects and made particularly outstanding contributions to the field of malarial research. In 1886 he
related the fever curve to the stages of development of the malarial
parasite in the blood, and in 1892 demonstrated that whereas in
the pernicious type of malaria the parasite develops in the organs,
in typical intermittent malaria it passes through its life cycle while
in the blood. But he was still working under primitive conditions.
He took heart when von Kölliker notified him in 1893 that the
Medical Faculty at Würzburg had awarded him a prize of one
thousand silver marks in recognition of his work. Still, the jeal-

ousy rampant in Pavia made his life difficult. Finally he received a new "Institute"—some rooms without gas, light, heat or running water; all that hard winter he worked at the bench in his overcoat.

Although Golgi showed the way to the neuron by his stain, his observations were such as to make him postulate that nerve fibers within the central nervous system, both efferent and afferent, lose their individuality, break up into many secondary branches, and so form networks ("retia nervosa diffusa"). As Clarke and O'Malley (1968) comment, none of Golgi's publications picture the network, and in his *Studi* . . . it is described, vaguely, as composed of the branching axis cylinders of type II cells (sensory) and all the side extensions of the cells of type I (motor). Dorsal root fibers, too, he contended, become part of a diffuse nerve network as they terminate in the gray matter of the cord; sensory impulses reach the axons of motor fibers, i.e., the axonal side fibrils, through the mediation of the network. In so saying, Golgi excluded dendrites and cell bodies from the reflex arc, their only function—according to him—being nutritive for the axon. In forming a rete nervosum diffusum, nerve cells would not act in isolation; hence no strict localization of cerebral functions would be possible. Erroneous though his nerve-net theory might be, Golgi's views do support the idea that the nervous system acts as a whole, a concept which, as Clarke and O'Malley put it, would be received with sympathy today.

Cajal was as appreciative of the contributions of Golgi as any other, and he once described their relationship as that of "two Siamese brothers attached at the back." Their furious polemic on the interrelation of nerve cells seems never to have died down, judging from Golgi's bitter denunciation of his rival at Stockholm when they received, jointly, the Nobel Prize in 1906.

In his advancing years Golgi was elected rector of the University of Pavia twice and for a few years member of the Royal Senate. At eighty-three he knew the end was near and, surrounded by the family, he fell into eternal sleep. *Gloria, gloria a te, o immune della morte* . . . , was the benediction pronounced by Ottorino Rossi at the sepulchre.

HIALEAH, FLORIDA   ARMANDO FERRARO

References

[1]Gazz. med. Ital. lombarda, 1873, *6*:244–246.   [2]Riv. sper. freniat., 1875, *1*:66–78.   [3]Arch. Ital. biol., 1883, *3*:285–317; 1884, *4*:92–123. [4]Arch. acad. med., Tor., 1880, *4*:221–246.   [5]Arch. Ital. biol., 1898, *30*:60–71.   [6]Rev. sudamer. morf., B. Air., 1948, *6*:115–133 (history of Golgi apparatus; Sosa). [7]J. R. Micr. Soc., London, 1935, *55*:28–31 (Douglas).

References to Biography: 1) J. Path. Bact., London, 1926, *29*:500–514 (Da Fano).   2) Arch. Neur. Psychiat., Chicago, 1926, *15*:623–627 (Viets).   3) Penfield (Ed.), *Neurological biographies and addresses.* London, Oxford U. P., 1936 (Chorobski), p. 121–127.   4) *The nervous system and its constituent neurones.* New York, Stechert, 1909 (Barker).   5) *The human brain and spinal cord.* Berkeley, U. of Calif., 1968 (Clarke and O'Malley).   6) *Cajal y su labor histológica.* Madrid, Tipografía Artística, 1935 (Tello).   7) Kolle (Ed.): *Grosse Nervenärzte.* Vol. 2. Stuttgart, Thieme, 1959, p. 3–12 (Pilleri).

PIERRE GRATIOLET (1815–1865)

n OT FAR from Cyrano's gasconnading and wine-growing Bergerac lies square-built little Sainte-Foy-la-Grande, where Louis Pierre Gratiolet was born. Today, Boulevard Gratiolet duly opens into Place Broca. This topographical item also symbolizes a neurohistorical fact: without Gratiolet, Broca would not have been in a position to identify the anatomical landmark for localizing expressive aphasia. As a co-founder of Broca's Société d'Anthropologie, Gratiolet is in every way linked to that story, yet his merit vastly transcends his role in it. To no one more than to him do we owe our whole manner of looking at the morphology of the cerebral convexity. Some of us may remember his name, attached as it rightly is to the optic radiation[1]; but he is a neglected Founder.

"Neglect" . . . "irritating" . . . "unjust" were some of the charges Broca made against the Establishment at the open grave of his fellow neuroanatomist. Gratiolet, he said, was allowed to "vegetate" in Paris until the last two years of his life, doing most of his writ-

Pierre Gratiolet

ing in a study barely seating two, leaving a wife and three children unprovided for, in a miserable apartment. Broca gave the address: Rue Guy de la Brosse. It was one of the shortest, narrowest and dingiest in Paris, dignified only by the name of the court physician who, under Louis XIII, had spent a fortune and a lifetime to see

Portrait from Mém. Soc. d'Anthropol., 1865; courtesy of Dr. Mary A. B. Brazier, Los Angeles, California.

the first botanical garden established in France, the Jardin des Plantes. Here, a few steps away, was the place where Gratiolet had spent most of his existence. With its Muséum de l'Histoire Naturelle, and the men who had worked there (Buffon, Daubenton, Cuvier, Jussieu, Geoffrey Saint-Hilaire, Quatrefages), it gave France her leading name in biology—and to the surrounding streets theirs.

Though born in the same little town, Paul Broca and Pierre Gratiolet had not known each other as boys. Dr. Gratiolet senior, Catholic, Royalist, and married into the local aristocracy, had fared ill in Protestant Sainte-Foy-la-Grande, and not much better in Bordeaux either, where he moved with his ten-year-old son when Broca was still an infant. Gratiolet Jr. went to study in Paris where he soon had to support his widowed mother. Blainville (1777–1850), the successor of Cuvier, discovered him at the Salpêtrière—again only across the road—and attached him to his anatomical laboratory. Impressed by this brilliant *aide-naturaliste,* Blainville considered him for his successor; as a lecturer Gratiolet was a resounding success. But after Blainville's death he lacked support; he was named professor only toward the end of his short, hard life, though famous in international learned circles.

Around 1840 Gratiolet began to collaborate with François Leuret (1897–1851) on the comparative anatomy of the nervous system. *Orang-outang, sive Homo sylvestris, or, the anatomy of a pygmie compared with that of a monkey, an ape, and a man,* by Edward Tyson (1699), had led the procession of primates coming under scientific scrutiny. Comparative anatomy, fascinating to eighteenth century savants, became the basis for evolutionary speculation before and after Darwin. (The animal dissections up to the Vesalian revolt were substitutive, not comparative in character.) Only after Vicq d'Azyr had introduced fixation in alcohol[2] could brains of any sort be worked at with the required leisure and accuracy.

The issue of the cerebral convolutions, so spectacularly raised by Gall, forced even his opponents to pay it close attention. First Rolando, then Leuret and Gratiolet, noticed the pattern of increasing complexity in the ascending series of mammalian brains, discovered some order in the chaotic mass of appendages covering the laboriously dissected "leaves" of white matter. Leuret, better known for the *traitement moral* of his psychiatric patients, died after the first volume of *Anatomie comparée du système nerveux considéré dans ses rapports avec l'intelligence*[3] was published. The primate part was left to Gratiolet. Soon he published a magnificent atlas and mémoire on the cerebral folds of man and primates[4]—truer to life than Tiedemann's,[5] Foville's,[6] or Huschke's[7] similar renditions. In painstaking detail he established those astonishing similarities, and the differences, between man, ape and monkey. Here for the first time we find nearly all the convolutions as we know them, enumerated, and classified by lobes; those that are major and on the surface, as well as the minor and buried ones, the connecting *plis de passage*. The important contributions of Friedrich Tiedemann (1781–1861)[8] in this field, which appeared as early as 1816,[9] dealt with embryonic and fetal human brains. Phylogenetic development of the basal cortex and its shiftings came to be analyzed, first by Broca,[10] and in our own time by Spatz.[11] Reichert (1811–1884), too, comes into the story, for he described the time of appearance of pallial infoldings and the extent to which they involved the brain wall, calling those that indented the ventricular surface, primary fissures.

Gratiolet's attempts here and elsewhere at describing the developmental features of skull and brain, in order to distinguish between "inferior" and "superior" races, we must call rather unsuccessful. White superiority was to him an axiom, but white inhumanity deplorable. (Eleven years later Hans Karl Leopold Barkow [1798–1873][12] in Breslau confirmed Tiedemann's[13] assertion that the Negro's brain was indistinguishable from that of the white man.)

Gratiolet also fought an inspired, elegant, but losing battle against cerebral localization.[14] He remained an exponent of the old order, yet he found much that was fundamentally new, a specialist, penetrating and skilled in his field, saintly in his life.

SAN FRANCISCO, CALIFORNIA   FRANCIS SCHILLER

References

[1]Compt. rend. Acad. Sci., Paris, 1854, *39*:274. [2]*Traité d' anatomie et de physiologie*. Vol. 1. Paris, Didot, 1785. [3]*Anatomie comparée*

du système nerveux considéré dans ses rapports avec l'intelligence.
Paris, Bailliére, vol. 1, 1839; vol. 2, 1857.   [4]*Mémoire sur les plis cérébraux de l'homme et des primatès.* Paris, Bertrand, 1854.
[5]*Icones cerebri simiarum.* Heidelberg, Mohr u. Wintel, 1821.
[6]*Traité complet de l'anatomie ... du système nerveux,* etc. Paris, Fortin, Masson, 1844.   [7]*Schädel, Hirn und Seele des Menschen und der Thiere, nach Alter, Geschlecht und Race.* Jena, Mauke, 1854.
[8]Arch. Psychiat., Berlin, 1936, *105*:250–290 (biography of Tiedemann, by Idelberger). *Ludwig Edinger 1855–1918.* Wiesbaden, Steiner, 1959, p. 48–50 (works of Tiedemann, by Spatz).   [9]*Anatomie und Bildungsgeschichte des Gehirns im Foetus des Menschen.* Nürnberg, Stein, 1816. For contributions of Tiedemann, see *The human brain and spinal cord. A historical study.* Berkeley, U. of Calif., 1968, p. 395–397 (Clarke and O'Malley).   [10]Rev. anthrop., Paris, 1872, 2.sér., *1*:358–498; 1879, 2:385–455.   [11]*Evolution of the forebrain; phylogenesis and ontogenesis of the forebrain.* Stuttgart, Thieme, 1966, p. 135–152 (Hassler and Stephan, Eds.).   [12]*Comparative Morphologie des Menschen und der menschenähnlichen Thiere.* Vol. 3. Breslau, Hirt, 1865, p. 121.   [13]*Hirn des Negers, verglichen mit dem des Europäers.* Heidelberg, Winter, 1836.   [14]Bull. Soc. anthrop. Paris, 1861, 2:66, 238, 421.

Reference to Biography: Mém. Soc. anthrop. Paris, 1865, 2:112 (Broca).

BERNARD von GUDDEN (1824–1886)

*B*ERNARD ALOYS von GUDDEN was born in Kleve, Germany, near the Dutch frontier. He studied in Bonn, Berlin, and then in Halle, where he received the M.D. in 1848. His career was marked by successive appointments to positions of eminence in psychiatry: he became director of the Unterfränkische Landes-Irrenanstalt in Werneck in 1855, was associated with mental institutions at Siegburg, Illenau and Würzburg, was appointed professor of psychiatry at Zürich in 1869, and then at the University of Munich, in 1872, where he was also director of the Kreis-Irrenanstalt. For many years he was editor of the *Archiv für Psychiatrie und Nervenkrankheiten.*

Von Gudden appeared on the scene at a time when a considerable number of highly useful technical tools and methods had

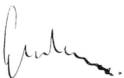

been made available. Alcohol as a tissue fixative had been used by Vicq d'Azyr in 1786[1] and by Reil in 1809[2] (the same year that he described the insular cortex named after him); chromic acid and its salts by Hannover in 1840[3]; formaldehyde fixation came much later: it was first employed by Blum in 1893[4]; a method for serial sectioning of the brain by hand had been devised by Stilling in 1842[5]; paraffin embedding had been introduced by Edwin Klebs in

Portrait, courtesy of Prof. Dr. W. Krücke, Frankfurt-am-Main, Germany.

1869[6]; and carmine as a staining agent for nerve cells had been popularized by Gerlach in 1858.[7] Carmine as a cell stain, dependent
on fixation in potassium bichromate, continued in use for a considerable time, even after Nissl had introduced his methylene blue
method in 1885. Thus, Forel[8] used it for the cellular changes in
retrograde phenomena, von Monakow[9] for similar purposes, and
even as late as 1914, Winkler and Potter[10] preferred the Gerlach
method because it gave such an excellent contrast to the structure
of the gray matter as compared to that of the white.

Taking full advantage of the crude methods available at the
time, von Gudden embarked on a series of epochal experiments.
He is perhaps best known for his studies on the partial decussation
of the optic paths,[11-13] a subject which occupied him for some thirty
years. His method of producing secondary atrophy of central structures following removal of sense organs or cranial nerves in young
animals ushered in a fresh advance in experimental neurology. In
full grown animals from which eyes had been removed when they
were young, he demonstrated not only crossed and uncrossed optic
fibers, but also a supraoptic commissure and the transverse peduncular tract,[11-13] both of which now bear his name. He also was the
first to describe the interpeduncular nucleus. Not only that but
also the tegmental nuclei, known of all who work on the midbrain
today as the dorsal and ventral tegmental nuclei of Gudden. The
observation that lesions of the cerebral cortex do not cause atrophy of peripheral nerves came to be known as Gudden's Law. But
one of von Gudden's greatest contributions was his observation in
1870[11] that destruction of certain areas of the cerebral cortex leads
to atrophy of specific thalamic nuclei. Here, again, very young animals were used and they were allowed to live as long as ten
months before the effects of decortication on the thalamus were
determined. Nowadays the study of the thalamocortical projections is generally carried out on adult animals which are sacrificed
within one or two months after the cortical extirpations. This is
the retrograde cell degeneration method of Nissl, which should be
distinguished from the atrophy method of von Gudden: in the one
the nerve cells undergo degenerative changes, while in the other
the cells completely disappear. This pioneer work of von Gudden
initiated the modern study of the thalamus. Von Monakow, of

Zürich, learned this technique from von Gudden, and was thus enabled to make important contributions to experimental neurology from 1882 onward, beginning in that year with his work on thalamocortical connections.[14]

In 1875 von Gudden devised a microtome for sectioning the whole human brain. His student, Forel, relates that this enabled him to make the first complete serial sections.[15] When collodion for embedding was introduced by Duval in 1879,[16] von Gudden immediately took advantage of the method. He later tried his hand at defining certain areas of the cortex by Golgi's chromate of silver method. His many papers, including posthumous ones, were brought together by his friend, H. Grashey in 1889.[17] His slide collection is still to be found in the Deutsche Forschungsanstalt für Psychiatrie in Munich, an institution undamaged in World War II.

Von Gudden enjoyed great prestige and made a powerful impression on the scientific world of his day. His laboratory was the mecca for anatomists and psychiatrists, among them Forel, who came to von Gudden in 1874. In his autobiography,[17] Forel relates that von Gudden was an unpredictable genius. "If one could make an ensemble of all the contrasts and the contradictions possible," he wrote, "one would obtain a Gudden." Now and again von Gudden showed no regard for anyone or anything, defects of which he was conscious, for he often said in a vexed tone: "Every one of my errors revenges itself bitterly." He was free from all pedantry and in discussions permitted his assistants the greatest liberty: he was interested in their scientific growth, but was completely unconcerned for their future. Although his conversation was punctuated by flashes of brilliance, he would drop the most artless remarks, for instance, that he disbelieved that somnambulism existed, for he (von Gudden) always slept well without dreaming. "I learned enormously while with Gudden," wrote Forel, "but above all how not to direct an asylum, for," as he added, "his tendency to let everything drift resulted in indescribable disorder."

In 1875 Gudden was made a noble and was appointed physician-in-charge of the mad king, Ludwig II of Bavaria, who was confined to one of his castles on Starnbergersee. At intervals, von Gudden's young pupil, Franz Nissl, attended the king. On a fateful Sunday afternoon in June, 1886, von Gudden took the king for a walk in one of the parks on the castle grounds. The two of them set out alone. The subsequent events, as reconstructed by Grashey, were as follows: Near the shore of the lake the king dashed away and jumped into the water with suicidal intent. Von Gudden rushed after him and managed to seize him, but the king slipped loose. In the ensuing struggle the king, a large, powerful man, stunned von Gudden with a blow to the head, and held him under the water until he was drowned. The king then walked deeper into the lake and drowned himself. Why, people asked, had von Gudden walked into the park alone with a man he knew to be insane and suicidal? Purposely, in order to win the king's' confidence, as Kraepelin suggested? It was a misunderstanding, Grashey and Spatz maintained: "No attendant shall go with us," Gudden had instructed—implying perhaps that an attendant should *follow* behind?

JAMES W. PAPEZ

References

[1]*Oeuvres de Vicq d'Azyr.* Vol. 6. Paris, Duprat-Duverger, 1805, p. 24. [2]Arch. Physiol., Halle a.S., 1809, *9*:136–208.   [3]Arch. Anat., Physiol., wissensch. Med., 1840, p. 549–558.   [4]Zschr. wissensch. Mikr., 1893, *10*:314–315.   [5]*Untersuchungen über die Functionen des Rückenmarks und der Nerven.* Leipzig, Wigand, 1842.   [6]Arch. micr. Anat., 1869, *5*:164–166.   [7]*Mikroskopische Studien aus dem Gebiete der menschlichen Morphologie.* Erlangen, Enke, 1858.   [8]Arch. Path., Berlin, 1887, *18*:162–198.   [9]*Ibid.,* 1898, *31*:1–73 et seq.   [10]*An anatomical guide to experimental researches on the rabbit's brain.* Amsterdam, Versluys, 1914.   [11]Arch. Psychiat., Berlin, 1870, *2*:693–723.   [12]Arch. Ophth., Berlin, 1874, 2.Abth., *20*:249–268.   [13]*Ibid.,* 1879, 1.Abth., *25*:1–56.   [14]Arch. Psychiat., Berlin, 1882, *12*:141–156.   [15]*Auguste Forel mémoires.* Neuchatel, Baconnière, 1941. [16]J. de l'anat., physiol., 1879, *15*:185–188.   [17]*Bernhard von Gudden's gesammelte und hinterlassene Abhandlungen.* Wiesbaden, Bergmann, 1889 (Grashey, Ed.)

References to Biography and Works: 1) Münch. med. Wschr., 1886, *33*:577–580 et seq. (Kraepelin).   2) Wien. med. Bl., 1886, *9*:729–731 (Meynert).   3) Arch. Psychiat., Berlin, 1925, *76*:21–46 (Wallenberg). 4) *The primate thalamus.* Chicago, U. of Chicago, 1938 (Walker).   5) Münch. med. Wschr., 1962, *104*:870–871 (Spatz).

WILHELM HIS (1831–1904)

*H*IS came of an old patrician Swiss family whose wealth enabled him to finish at the best schools of Europe the medical studies which he had begun at Basle (1849) and Bern (1850). In Berlin, the venerable Johannes Müller instilled in him the inquiring attitude, and Remak's lectures (1850–52) on the theory of the germ layers had a determining influence on his later work. At Würzburg (1852–53), Virchow gave him the right start in research, and although he had no formal instruction from von Kölliker, he owed much to this great microscopist. After passing his examination in medicine *summa cum laude* (Basle, 1854), he journeyed to Paris where he worked in the laboratories of Brown-Séquard and Claude Bernard.

He returned to Basle as Privatdozent under Meissner (1856) whom he soon succeeded, becoming Ordinarius (1857); and after fifteen fruitful years there, he accepted the chair of anatomy at the University of Leipzig (1872) vacated by the retirement of Ernst Weber. He remained at Leipzig for the rest of his life. Keibel and Mall were among his most distinguished students.

Rather early in his career, His announced a new classification of tissues based on histogenesis,[1] and with this as a guide formulated an extensive research program in developmental anatomy, centering largely on the nervous system. Although one of the greatest students of histogenesis, he never lost sight of the embryo as a whole, as evidenced by an epochal three-volume work on the subject.[2] In 1887 he established that axons are outgrowths from primitive nerve cells,[3] and by 1889 demonstrated the individuality of nerve cells. Dendrite, neurite, neuropil, neuroblast and spongioblast are familiar neurological terms which he introduced. Moreover, he established proof of Hensen's hypothesis that the neural parts of the nervous system originate in the ectoderm, while the blood vessels arise in the mesoderm. After His's lucid explanations, the ectodermal origin of Virchow's neuroglia was no longer contested. The very end of his life saw him still actively engaged in this major field of his interest, his last work being *Die Entwickelung des menschlichen Gehirns während der ersten Mo-*

nate (Leipzig, Hirzel, 1904). Many of His's embryologic findings were disputed by Hochstetter, of Vienna, but the fact remains that though his embryologic material was of poor quality he was able to make fundamental discoveries, whereas others with perfect material could not match it with ideas.

Portrait, courtesy of the National Library of Medicine, Bethesda, Maryland.

His was one of the founders of the *Anatomische Gesellschaft* (1886), and by drafting the final report of the international commission on anatomic nomenclature he was largely responsible for the B.N.A.[4] He founded the *Zeitschrift für Anatomie und Entwickelungsgeschichte* (1876) and helped to found the *Archiv für Anthropologie* (1876). He was the guiding spirit (from 1886) in the organization of the Brain Commission which established the Central Institute for Brain Research at Amsterdam (1908), with Ariëns Kappers as director.

Science is also indebted to him for new or improved methods. He devised the best microtome of the time (1866). The embryograph, a device for the drawing of sections on wax plates and then setting the plates in juxtaposition, was invented by him, and the His-Steger models (F. J. Steger was his assistant) are to be found in anatomical museums the world over.

His's interests were exceedingly broad: he took his stand—one of reasoned scepticism—on the much disputed question of Darwinism; Rütimeyer and he made an important contribution to anthropology through their *Crania Helvetica* (Basle, Georg, 1864); he wrote a detailed review (1870) of *Microcosmos,* by Lotze, with whose realistic idealism he concurred heartily; and he sharply attacked Haeckel's *biogenetisches Grundgesetz.* An interesting sidelight is that he identified the remains of Johann Sebastian Bach, unearthed from the yard of the Johanneskirche in Leipzig after lying buried there for almost a century and a half; his account of this investigation appeared in 1895.

His way of life was Spartan in its simplicity and in its serious devotion to duty. Abhorring trite and conventional expression, he became a master of the art of terseness in speaking and in writing. Almost every vacation found him at Basle, for his Swiss homeland was close to his heart. A sociable person, he opened his home in Leipzig to colleagues and at all times to students from Switzerland. Much of His's microscopic work was done in his home, where for years he also experimented with daguerrotypes. His son, Wilhelm His, Jr., became the distinguished anatomist whose name is linked with the cardiac atrioventricular bundle he first described (1893).

A. T. RASMUSSEN

References

[1]*Die Häute und Höhlen des Körpers.* Basle, Schweighauser, 1865 (reprinted 1903). [2]*Anatomie menschlicher Embryonen.* 3 vol. Leipzig, Vogel, 1880–85. [3]Abr. Math.-Phys. Cl. k. Sächs. Gesellsch. Wissensch., 1887, *13*:477–514. [4]*Die anatomische Nomenclatur. Nomina anatomica.* Leipzig, Veit, 1895.

References to Biography: 1) *Lebenserinnerungen.* Leipzig, als Manuskript gedruckt, 1904 (His). 2) Deut. med. Wschr., 1904, *30*:1438–1441 *et seq.* (Waldeyer). 3) Amer. J. Anat., 1905, *4*:139–161 (Mall). 4) Anat. Anz., 1904, *25*:161–208 (contains bibliography; Fick). 5) *Wilhelm His der Anatom. Ein Lebensbild.* Berlin u. Wien, Urban & Schwarzenberg, 1931 (contains selected bibliography; W. His, Jr.). 6) Q. Phi Beta Pi M., 1942, *39*:19–38 (contains bibliography; Bast).

RUDOLF ALBERT von KÖLLIKER (1817–1905)

*V*ON KÖLLIKER was born in Zürich, Switzerland, and spent most of his early life there. His medical training was begun in his native city and continued in Bonn and then Berlin (1839–41), where Johannes Müller and Jakob Henle exerted a particularly strong influence on him. Summer vacations were spent on Helgoland and Föhr, in work on zoological problems which culminated in a paper on sexual physiology of invertebrates,[1] for which the University of Zürich awarded him the Ph.D. in 1842. After receiving the M.D. at Heidelberg (1843) he returned to Zürich.

As Prosector under Henle, he soon became Privatdozent, then Extraordinarius of physiology and comparative anatomy (1844). In 1847 he accepted the chair of comparative anatomy at Würzburg and two years later also became Ordinarius in human anatomy. In 1864 he relinquished the chair of physiology, continuing as head of the Institute of Anatomy and the Institute of Comparative Anatomy, Microscopy and Embryology. He retired from the former post in 1897, from the latter in 1902, at the age eighty-five years! His mental acumen was such that he published twenty

papers in the last eight years of his life. Von Kölliker's most outstanding pupil was Gegenbaur.

One of the leading biologists of the nineteenth century, he devoted prodigious effort to the study of the finer structure of the
nervous system. The second volume of his *Handbuch der Gewebe-
lehre des Menschen,* 6th edition (Leipzig, Engelmann, 1889–96),
is as much a classic as any of Cajal's great works. In that volume
appeared the results of his study of Golgi preparations, undertaken after he had seen Cajal's sections in 1889. Also to be found
there is his key observation that fibers from the dorsal and ventral
tegmental nuclei of Gudden run forward into the hypothalamus,
a system on which the concept of a midbrain-hypothalamic-pitui-
tary activating system has recently been framed.[2]

In a paper published in 1845 von Kölliker anticipated by almost

Portrait, courtesy of Prof. Dr. W. Krücke, Frankfurt-am-Main, Germany.

fifty years Waldeyer's formulation of the neuron theory by stating, more cautiously than Remak or Helmholtz, that nerve fibers are secondary to nerve cells, and at least some of them are processes of nerve cells, and later he provided proof that nerve fibers are continuous with nerve cells. In the concluding chapter of his *Handbuch* (6th ed. vol. 2, p. 810) appeared an epitome of his belief, which may be translated as follows: "All nerve cells must have essentially the same function and their functional dignity depends solely upon the different extraneous stimuli which might impinge upon them or upon the many possibilities of answers to a stimulus." From his pen came the first work on comparative embryology,[3] in which are included his important observations on the relation of the vertebrate notochord to the adult spine and skull. His three-volume *Mikroskopische Anatomie* (Leipzig, Engelmann, 1850–54) and his contributions to the developmental anatomy of the eye and ear[4] are also celebrated works.

Von Kölliker had the astuteness to recognize immediately the genius of Cajal. As a stranger from Spain and scientifically almost unknown even in his own country, Cajal came, in 1889, to a meeting of the German Anatomical Society at the University of Berlin, of which von Kölliker was chairman, and demonstrated his preparations to a group he knew well to be a little arrogant and very critical. But Cajal won the esteem of the members of the Society not only by the beauty of his preparations but also through the energetic support given him by von Kölliker. Subsequently Cajal wrote: "A noble exception among great investigators, Kölliker united a great talent for observation . . . with enchanting modesty and exceptional rectitude and calmness of judgment."

Von Kölliker "was a dignified figure, a veteran of pure science" (Garrison). His geniality brought him many friends. His lifelong passion for hunting and mountain climbing was exercised to the full. He was a yodeler of rare ability. Widely traveled, he was most fascinated by England, where he acquired the enduring friendship of William Sharpey. He received many honors, among them the order *Pour le mérite*—the highest ranking in Germany, which made him *Seine Excellenz*—but they never spoiled his personal charm.

SAN FRANCISCO, CALIFORNIA   GERHARDT von BONIN

References

[1]*Beiträge zur Kenntnis der Geschlechtsverhältnisse und der Samen-flüssigkeit wirbelloser Thiere*. . . . Berlin, Logier, 1841. [2]Nalbandov (Ed.), *Advances in Neuroendocrinology*. Urbana, U. of Ill., 1963 (Nauta), p. 5–28. [3]*Entwicklungsgeschichte des Menschen und der höheren Thiere*. Leipzig, Engelmann, 1861. [4]Verhandl. d. phys.-med. Gesellsch. in Würzb., n.F., 1833, p. 2–16.

References to Biography: 1) *Erinnerungen aus meinem Leben*. Leipzig, Engelmann, 1899 (Koelliker). 2) Anat. Anz., 1906, *28*:539–552 (contains selected bibliography, Waldeyer). 3) Zschr. wiss. Zool., 1906, *84*:I–XXVI (contains bibliography; Ehlers).

BERNARD LUYS (1828–1897)

*P*ARISIAN by birth, Jules Bernard Luys spent most of his life in his native city or its environs. His doctorate in medicine in 1857 was obtained on the basis of a thesis on the microscopic pathology of tuberculosis. In 1862 he became médecin des hôpitaux and chef de service at the Salpêtrière and the Charité, and two years later succeeded Marcé as director of the Maison de Santé Esquirol at Ivry-sur-Seine.

Luys soon found his metier in the problems of the structure and connections of the brain. He was the first to portray the internal nuclei and tracts of the brain in three-dimensional visualizations. He was an excellent draughtsman and photographer, and his reconstructions were founded on carefully made drawings, as well as photographs, of sections through all parts of the brain. These were all portrayed in his first and most important book, completed when he was thirty-seven: *Recherches sur le système nerveux cérébro-spinal: sa structure, ses fonctions, et ses maladies* (Paris, Baillière, 1865). Here were depicted the two structures which bear his name: the subthalamic nucleus and the centre médian of the thalamus. He referred to the subthalamic nucleus as the "bande-lette accessoire de l'olive supérieure" and recognized its spatial relation to the red nucleus, which he called the "olive supérieure." Meynert, in 1872,[1] considered it to be a subdivision of the substan-

Jules Bernard Luys

tia nigra, and in 1884[2] called it the "discus lentiformis." Forel, in 1877,[3] provided the term "corpus Luysii." More of the story of this nucleus is to be found in a paper by Denkhaus.[4] Many years were to pass before the clinical import of Luy's subthalamic nucleus was to be determined: in 1927 Martin,[5] and in 1934 Martin and Alcock,[6] presented convincing evidence that lesions affecting this nucleus result in hemiballismus (a term coined by Kussmaul,[7] though some have given the credit to von Economo).[8] As to the centre médian nucleus, its functional significance is still unknown.

Portrait from *Prog. méd., Par.,* 3.sér., 6:141, 1897.

Before 1865 there was some inkling in the writings of Türck (1859) and Hughlings Jackson (1864) that the thalamus is concerned with sensibility, but the publication of Luy's book in that year marks the beginning of knowledge of thalamic function. He recognized four centers, each mediating one of the senses. They were the anterior or olfactory center, the middle or optic center, the median or somesthetic center, and the posterior or acoustic center. He was intensely interested in the arrangements of the fibers within the white matter and depicted them with spirit. He came, however, to the mistaken conclusion that all cortical connections are interrupted in the basal ganglia and hence divided the long tracts into superior and inferior groups of converging fibers, recognizing, however, that some afferent fibers were reflex and that they did not reach the thalamus. The thalamus, then, was the *sensorium commune,* while the corpus striatum was the subcortical motor center.

In his physiological studies he attempted to show that destruction within the thalamus leads to specific sensory loss, while damage to the corpus striatum produces alterations of motility. The cerebral cortex was considered the organic substratum of motor and sensory functions, its gradual destruction leading to paralysis and finally to dementia. In 1874 his book on reflex cerebral activity appeared,[9] and soon thereafter his *Le cerveau et ses fonctions* (Paris; Baillière) (2nd ed., 1876), which was translated into English.[10] In them, as in his first book, he attempted to integrate neuroanatomy, neuropathology and physiologic psychology. Among his accomplishments was the effective use of photography in the illustration of brain anatomy; a large volume[11] testifies to his pre-eminence in this field in which he was a pioneer.

The major part of Luy's career was spent in clinical work, especially in the study of insanity, hysteria and hypnotism. He wrote many articles and two books on hypnotism, and he was one of the founders of the Société d'Hypnologie et de Psychologie. Little came from his work in this field for he allowed himself to be deluded by his patients; for instance, he was responsible for perpetuating the folly that patients may profit therapeutically from drugs placed at a distance from them. In his latter days the quality of his scientific work sharply declined as he shifted his emphasis more and more from the objective to the subjective.

Luys was a vigorous, active and industrious man. Of ingratiating personality, he was revered by his colleagues. His later years were marred by increasing deafness. He continued to attend the meetings of the Académie de Médecine and the Société de Biologie when he could no longer hear the proceedings, smiling recognition to his many friends. He had just retired to the country when, at the age of 69, he was fatally stricken.

CHICAGO, ILLINOIS   WENDELL J. S. KRIEG

References

[1]In Stricker, S., *Handbuch der Lehre von den Geweben.* Vol. 2. Leipzig, Engelmann, 1872.   [2]*Psychiatry. A clinical treatise on diseases of the forebrain.* London, Putnam's Sons, 1885 (trans. by B. Sachs). [3]Arch. Psychiat., Berlin, 1877, *7*:393–495.   [4]*Ibid.,* 1942, *115*:61–81. [5]Brain, London, 1927, *50*:637–650.   [6]*Ibid.,* 1934, *57*:504–516. [7]Neur. Cbl., 1898, *17*:603–604.   [8]Wien. klin. Wschr., 1910, *23*:429– 431.   [9]*Etudes de physiologie et de pathologie cérébrales. Des actions réflexes du cerveau dans les conditions normales et morbides de leurs manifestations.* Paris, Baillière, 1874.   [10]*The brain and its functions.* New York, Appleton, 1882.   [11]*Iconographie photographique des centres nerveux.* 2 vol. in 1. Paris, Ballière, 1873.

References to Biography and Works: 1) Rev. hypnot., Paris, 1898, *12*:185–186 (Dumont-Pallier).   2) Ann. méd. psychol., Paris, 1897, 8. sér., *6*:321–323 (Ritti).   3) Chron. méd., Paris, 1897, *3*:589–591 (not signed).   4) Rev. hypnot., Paris, 1898, *12*:91–93 (not signed). 5) Progr. méd., Paris, 1897, 3. sér., *6*:141–142 (M.B.). 6) *The primate thalamus.* Chicago, U. of Chicago, 1938 (Walker).

THEODOR MEYNERT (1833–1892)
"Erst seit Meynert ist das Gehirn beseelt"

*I*N THE HISTORY of neurology and psychiatry, Theodor Meynert stands out as a prophet of things to come. He inspired the work of Flechsig, Wernicke and Forel, and he left his mark on Freud's thought. Thanks to Meynert the Vienna School came to rival the Salpêtrière and Queen Square; to him we owe some of the current dynamic concepts in neurology and psychiatry.

Meynert was born in Dresden, the child of a writer and an opera singer. The artistic background and certain Bohemian characteristics never left him. The family moved to Vienna when he was eight. Here he spent long and rather wild student years, finally receiving the M.D. in 1861. Sobering down, and driven by an intense desire to emulate his teacher, Rokitansky, he became Dozent in 1865, Prosector of the Wiener Landesirrenanstalt in 1866, Director of the psychiatric clinic in 1870, and Ordentlicher

Portrait, courtesy of the National Library of Medicine, Bethesda, Maryland.

Professor of nervous diseases in 1873. Meynert's successor to the chair of psychiatry was Krafft-Ebing; subsequent holders of the chair, which came to include that new specialty, neurology, were Leidesdorf, Wagner-Jauregg and Poetzl.

Meynert began his studies of the nervous system early in his medical career. At that time precise microtomes were not yet known. Employing the methods of Benedict Stilling, he acquired an excellent command of histological technique which enabled him to cut serial sections. From these he obtained a masterful grasp of the structural plan of the central nervous system. It was in 1867 that Meynert first called attention to regional differences in the cerebral cortex,[1] and in the following year appeared his masterpiece: *Der Bau der Grosshirnrinde und seine örtlichen Verschiedenheiten, nebst einem pathologisch-anatomischen Corollarium* (Leipzig, Engelmann). He set out avowedly to prove or refute certain theories about the brain. "The main function of the central organ," he stated, "is to transmit the fact of existence to an ego gradually shaping itself in the stream of the brain . . . If we look upon the cortex as an organ functioning as a whole then the information that it subserves the processes of the mind is all that can be said . . . To think further about the cortex is impossible and unnecessary . . . But our hope to understand eventually the function of the hemispheres is raised again by the opposite assumption which leads us straight to an organology of the central surface . . . Between these two theoretical possibilities the facts have to decide" (translation by Gerhardt von Bonin). Meynert then gave a detailed account of the structure of the cerebral cortex, of the differences in what is now known as the visual area— where he described the solitary cells which still bear his name— and analyzed minutely the hippocampal formation, the olfactory lobe, and the septum pellucidum. In concluding, Meynert distinguished between cortex with white surface (allocortex) and cortex with gray surface (neocortex). These two types of cortex were subsequently referred to as "heterogenetic" and "homogenetic" by Brodmann,[2] and as the "allocortex" and "isocortex" by O. Vogt.[3]

Meynert's formulation of the problem of brain structure was of historic importance. He coined the term, "organology of the cortex." His anatomical studies led him to new ideas concerning the mode of function of the brain as an organ. He considered the cerebral cortex as a retentive recording tissue surmounting the radial bundles, on which the sensory and other impulses were projected by afferent paths, each registered image being the product of a special group (pattern) of simultaneously perceived sensations. He was the first to show that central integration was dependent on this association process.[4,5] His views on the projection of motor paths from the cerebral cortex downward were also dynamic concepts. He did not realize the importance of the short cortical connections to the thalamus in internalized cerebral activity, but he was the first to elaborate the sensory feedbacks from muscular movement to the cortex as the sense of innervation. Like Hughlings Jackson, he anticipated Fritsch and Hitzig by dividing the convexity of the brain into an anterior motor and a posterior sensory quarter. On phylogenetic grounds he launched the idea of a functional antagonism between cortex and basal ganglia (including the substantia nigra), giving rise under disease conditions to extrapyramidal disorders. Forgotten until a few years back was his observation that fibers descending from certain areas of the cortex (such as the cingulate cortex) give off collaterals which cross into the opposite hemisphere via the corpus callosum. His brilliantly written book on psychiatry, translated into English by Bernard Sachs,[6] was the epitome of his fundamental concepts. Edinger remarked to Sachs in 1888: "You have managed to translate Meynert into English; it is difficult for us to understand his German." Meynert's *Klinische Vorlesungen über Psychiatrie auf wissenschaftlichen Grundlagen* (Wien; Braumüller) appeared in 1890.

In offering a classification of mental diseases on a purely anatomical basis, Meynert went too far—he even objected to the use of the term "psychiatry"—and although his views on mental diseases have been referred to as "brain mythology" (by Gruhle), time has decided in favor of many of them. The supraoptic commissure which now bears his name was described by him in 1872.[7]

Meynert's novel point of view made a deep impression on his contemporaries. His ideas drew many visitors to Vienna even though he had the reputation of being a poor teacher. August Forel, who spent seven months (1871–72) with Meynert at the old insane asylum on Lazarettgasse, had to hold back his great dis-

appointment in Meynert's lectures and laboratory. His department, Forel relates, was disorderly and filthy, not unlike the Ori-
ental Quarter of Vienna, and through it all romped Meynert's two
children. In peering at crudely-cut brain sections together, Forel
could seldom follow Meynert—"his imagination played around me
ten times more than my own"—and thus Forel—who was then only
twenty-three—came to discount more and more the value of
Meynert's anatomical schemes and his conception of the plexus
of communication between different parts of the brain. Bernard
Sachs, as a novice attempting to learn neuroanatomy in Meynert's
laboratory some years later (1882), found it disconcerting that he
had to struggle alone with a series of brain sections for a month
before the Master would show the least interest in him. "A very
stormy day," said Sachs to Meynert on greeting him one morning.
"I have not yet had time to think about it," was the reply; and
Sachs remarked to himself, "That settled that." Meynert tried to
be amiable to his assistants but was seldom cordial. Urbanity was
a luxury in which his brilliant mind would not allow him to indulge.

This man with a massive head surmounting a short body, a
sprawling bushy beard, and mane-like hair which had the habit of
falling down into his eyes, had an expression mirroring melancholy;
his wife had died early, and now death had robbed him of his sev-
enteen-year-old son. Despite his troubles, or perhaps because of
them, there was robustness in his poetry, regarded highly by the
critics of that day. The same may be said of his drawings of the
brain, to be found at the Neurological Institute of Vienna to this
day.

JAMES W. PAPEZ

References

[1]Vjschr. Psychiat., 1867, 1:77–93 et seq.   [2]Vergleichende Lokalisationslehre der Grosshirnrinde in ihren Principien, dargestellt auf
Grund des Zellbaues. Leipzig, Barth, 1909 (reprinted 1925).   [3]Con-
grès 20e des médecins alién. et neurol. de France; 8 août 1910. Brussels, 1911; p. 3–11.   [4]Sitzber. Akad. Wiss. Wien, 1870, 60, Abth.
2:547–566. [5]Leidesdorf, M., Lehrbuch der psychischen Krankheiten.
Erlangen, Enke, 1865, p. 45–73.   [6]Psychiatry. A clinical treatise on

diseases of the forebrain. London, Putnam's Sons, 1885.   [7]Stricker, S., *Handbuch der Lehre von den Geweben des Menschen und der Thiere.* Leipzig, Engelmann, 1872, *2*:694–808.

References to Biography: 1) J. Psychol. Neur., Lpz., 1930, *40*:256–281 (contains bibliography; Anton).   2) Jahrb. Psychiat., Lpz. u. Wien, 1892, *11*:3–11 (Fritsch).   3) *Barney Sachs, 1858–1944. An autobiography.* New York, privately printed, 1949 (with biographic notes by Nathan Straus and Foster Kennedy).   4) Zschr. ges. Neur. Psychiat., 1939, *165*:17–38 (de Crinis).   5) *Auguste Forel mémoires.* Neuchatel, Baconnière, 1941.   6) Kolle (Ed.), *Grosse Nervenärzte.* Vol. 2. Stuttgart, Thieme, 1959, p. 98–105 (von Stockert).

CHRISTIAN REIL (1759–1813)

*R*EIL worked as a neuroanatomist only late in middle-age and shortly before he died; dissecting the brain is an occupation rather on the sedate side, and spending most of one's years in Halle, a smallish Prussian university town, does altogether not suggest much excitement. But take an enthusiast, place him among the unprecedented explosions in sentiments, ideas, and real gunfire that filled the air around the end of the eighteenth century, and you begin to understand why hardly a dull moment slowed the life of Reil. His temperament, his intellectual development, made him move from avant-garde to avant-garde, from rationalism to romanticism, from humanitarianism to nationalism. He does not fit the present-day notion of the man of science which is a product of the late nineteenth century: the specialist, cool and uninvolved, smoking his English pipe in an ivory tower. Yet we do expect the intellectual, artist or scientist, born after say, 1750, to have "revolutionized" his field: in this sense the spirit of the Enlightenment, of tradition overthrown, of "breakthroughs," is still with us. All of Reil's undertakings, in physiology or mental health, were revolutionary; and he was a skilled innovator in anatomy (early description of the lens, its ciliary ligament, and the macula lutea), before he finally tackled the organ of the mind. This he did in a manner so fundamental as only one or two others had done since Thomas Willis.

Johann Christian Reil

Johann Christian Reil was born in the same year as Danton and Schiller and only four years after Pinel. In Germany medical thought allied itself heavily to the new trends in philosophy, the social and the national surges, and medical writing came close to poetry. At the same time it began to influence, as public health, practical administrative decisions. It is the mixture of lofty feeling, abstract reasoning, and down-to-earth social welfare, of airy rhetoric and solid industry, which Reil's work reflects.

The piety of the parsonage in Rhaude—the village in northernmost Germany where he was born—may have lingered in the man even though he crowned his high school years with a rhymed speech "In praise of medicine." This, and not the paternally in-

J. C. Reil as Knight of the Order of the Red Eagle. Portrait, courtesy of the New York Academy of Medicine.

tended theology, he took up, first in Göttingen—too pedantic—then Halle, to return as a graduated practitioner to the rural north. Five years later, and for the next twenty-three, he was back in Halle, soon a full professor and health director of the town.

Now Halle had been the fountainhead of one of the most powerful streams in medical thought: Stahl's *animism* (1737). It made the "soul" the prime mover of biological processes, substituted later, in *vitalism,* by the "life-force." Under this title, in the first book to establish his fame, Reil fought vitalism.[1] For organic matter was only a more complex form of the inorganic—and Reil founded the first journal solely devoted to physiology.[2] Only ideas were immaterial: as a follower of Kant he saw mere interaction in the relationship between mind and body—and he founded the first journal devoted to psychiatry.[3]

Simultaneously with William Tuke in York and Philippe Pinel in Paris, Christian Reil in Halle was shocked by the traditional punishment meted out to those who must be regarded as insane by those who regard themselves as normal. He sought to undo the millennial alienation between the two groups, to replace condemnation by therapy. One of his main works is entitled *Rhapsodies on the use of a psychic method to cure mental derangement.*[4] The rhapsodic manner was of course not absent from any of his writings, whether they dealt with his sweeping new metabolic view of fever as opposed to the "essential fevers" of old,[5] or with the anatomy of the brain. Nor was this organ—"mysterious bridal bed where body and soul celebrate their nuptial orgies"—absent from any of his medical writings. In conjunction with such wayward daydreaming, Reil soberly perfected Willis' method of blunt dissection and Vicq d'Azyr's technique of hardening the brain in alcohol by adding alkali. Above all he introduced the most fundamental concept of the *nucleus,* together with such factual details as the "lentil" surrounded by an "external" and an "internal capsule"; a "corona radiata" that projected vital energy emanating from the "lenticular" nucleus; and, of course, the "island" that carries his name. A host of new neuroanatomical facts are contained in the series of papers[6] that he was relieved to produce, thanks to a prolonged indignant vacation from teaching, when Napoleon closed down the rebellious university. Reopened by Jerome Bonaparte, now king of a greater Westphalia, Halle was never the same, and Reil accepted a call to the medical school recently established in Berlin. Soon after Napoleon's defeat near Leipzig, Reil, an eager participant in the national war of liberation, fatally contracted typhoid on an inspection tour through overcrowded military hospitals. The shortage of doctors had made this incurable reformer suggest a second type of medical training besides the regular one: "nurseries" (*pépinières*) for "routine" physicians (*routiniers*). The dreamer was also eminently practical: almost a one-man chamber of commerce, and as the city's director of health (Stadt-Physicus), he organized and financed a prosperous resort in Halle.

As a physician and surgeon—he fought that separation—Reil was circumspection, competence, humility, and kindness all in one, as Goethe, a onetime patient of his, glowingly testified. And according to another writer (Börne): "Whom he did not cure did lose his life; his hope, never."

In all his writings Reil oscillated between elation and depression, certainty and doubt. With Faust, with the fashionable German *Naturphilosophie,* he was after the unifying formula, the great deep analogy thought to pervade everything in the universe. "I believe I have disentangled the major part of the brain's structure," he wrote, "which is a kernel and convolutions"; elsewhere he called it " a nucleus and organs surrounding the nucleus on all sides"—only to utter despondency in a third passage about the brain as a whole: "Here as in the case of the cerebellum I am left in the dark about the link between convolutions and nucleus. The ganglionic chain coming up the spinal cord and continuing from the most posterior to the most anterior cerebral ventricle, the axis connecting floor of fourth ventricle, corpora quadrigemina, optic thalamus, and corpus striatum—to unravel that I almost despaired."[5] So close, yet so far away—posterity, although it has found that link, shares that feeling.

SAN FRANCISCO, CALIFORNIA   FRANCIS SCHILLER

References

[1]*Von der Lebenskraft.* Barth, Leipzig, 1910 (Sudhoff, Ed.).   [2]Arch. f. d. Physiol., 1795–1815.   [3]Mag. f. d. psych. Heilk., 1805–6.

[4]*Rhapsodien über die Anwendungen der psychischen Curmethode auf Geisteszerrüttungen.* Halle, Curt, 1803.   [5]*Über die Erkenntnis und Cur der Fieber. Besondere Fieberlehre.* Vol. 4. *Nervenkrankheiten.* Halle, Curt, 1805.   [6]Arch. f. d. Physiol., 1807/8, *8:*3; 24 (1–58, 273–304, 385–425). *Ibid.,* 1809, *9:*136 (nucleus), 196 (insula), 202 (int. caps.), 206 ("sun of the hemisphere"), 125–135, 136–208, 485–524. *Ibid.,* 1812, *11:*89–116, 345–376 (illustr.).

References to Biography: 1) Verh. Ges. deut. Naturforsch., 1913, p. 85–115 (Neuburger).   2) *History and philosophy of knowledge of the brain and its functions.* Springfield, Thomas, 1958, p. 154 *et seq.* (Lewis).   3) J. Nerv. Ment. Dis., 1916, *43:*1–22 (White).   4) Nova Acta Leopoldina. Leipzig, Barth, 1960, *22:*1–159 (Zaunick, Ed.).

ROBERT REMAK (1815–1865)

*R*EMAK was born in a ghetto in Poznan, a Polish city which had just been incorporated into Prussia following Napoleon's defeat. Remak's father ran a cigar store and sold lottery tickets. Robert's graduation from the Gymnasium at the age of eighteen, with honors, entitled him to attend any school of higher learning in Germany. He chose the University of Berlin. There he studied medicine under Johann Schönlein and Johannes Müller, and after graduating, became Müller's assistant at the Charité. The position brought no stipend, which made it necessary for Remak to spend most of his time in general practice. From 1843 to 1847 he was clinical assistant to Schönlein, but occupied himself mostly with pathological and especially embryological investigations.

Among the early neurocytologists, Remak was foremost. Most of his publications were epoch making. His works were in three fields: microscopic anatomy of nervous tissues, embryology, and electrotherapy. As early as 1836, when a compound microscope came into his possession, he published treatises on the histological structure of the nervous system.[1,2] In his doctoral thesis of 1838 he recognized that the sympathetic fibers were gray because they were nonmyelinated ("Remak's fibers") and, most important, that axons of nerves were continuous with cells in the spinal cord

Robert Remak

Portrait, courtesy of the National Library of Medicine, Bethesda, Maryland.

("Remak's band," christened "axis cylinder" by Purkyně); also that the sympathetic ganglion is the real center of the organic [autonomic] nervous system.[3] His name became linked with the intrinsic ganglia of the heart, which he was the first to describe.[4] It was he who first mentioned the myelin sheath, which soon thereafter (1838) was described by Schwann. (Another year was to pass before Schwann published his observations of the neurolemmal sheath.) After Baillarger's demonstration of the white bands in the cortex of the gross brain, Remak was the first to recognize histologically the six cortical cell layers.[4]

In the early 1850's, Remak's attention was turned to embryology of the nervous system. He defined for the first time the three germ layers and their significance for the development of the main tissue systems of the human body, and was a pioneer in the study of the formation of the neural tube.[5,6] Indeed he shared with von Baer (1792–1876) the credit for founding the science of the germ layers. Among those who attended Remak's lectures on embryology was Wilhelm His, who later was to become the master in the field. Another student, von Kölliker, also owed much to the novel ideas Remak imparted.

Remak's substitution of the induced for the galvanic current in the treatment of nervous diseases, culminating in a book on the subject,[7] provoked much professional jealousy, but was later acknowledged by such an authority as His as "epoch making." In this field he ranks with Addison and Duchenne de Boulogne. Among his works in clinical neurology, the most outstanding was that on ascending neuritis (1861). Other contributions are indicated in Garrison's invaluable check-list of texts illustrating the history of medicine[8] and in Soury's incomparable *Le système nerveux central* . . . (2 vol., Paris, Naud, 1899).

While still at the height of his power, and apparently in the best of health, he took a trip from Berlin to Kissingen. Here he suddenly died. The obituary notes were peculiarly reticent concerning his personal characteristics. For Remak had been not only unusually gifted and indefatigable, but also impulsive in word and deed, riding roughshod over some traditions held sacred by his contemporaries. His sensitive but aggressive temperament and his refusal to abandon the Jewish faith made life difficult for him, bitter, and often tempestuous. In his whole career he had to depend on the intercession of those few who recognized his worth; and it was only through Alexander von Humboldt that the cabinet of Friedrich Wilhelm IV eventually (in 1847) granted him permission to join the faculty of Berlin—as a Privatdozent. Later (in 1859) he was made Extraordinarius.

JAMES W. PAPEZ

References

[1]Arch. Anat. Physiol., Lpz., 1836; p. 145–161.   [2]Froriep's Notizen, 1837; No. 47, 54, 58.   [3]*Observationes anatomicae et microscopicae de systematis nervosi structura.* Berolini, Reimerianis, 1838.   [4]Arch. Anat. Physiol., Lpz., 1844, p. 463–472.   [5]*Untersuchungen über die Entwickelung des Wirbelthieres.* Berlin, Reimer, 1851.   [6]Arch. Anat. Physiol., Lpz., 1862; p. 230–241.   [7]*Galvanotherapie der Nerven- und Muskelkrankheiten.* Berlin, Hirschwald, 1858.   [8]Bull. Inst. Hist. M., Balt., 1933, *53*:333–434.

References to Biography: 1) Berl. klin. Wschr., 1865, *2*:372 (not signed).   2) Deut. Klinik, 1865, *17*:413–414 (not signed).   3) Wien. med. Presse, 1865, *6*:915–917 (Benedikt).   4)Berl. klin. Wschr., 1865, *2*:372 (His.).   5) *Forgotten leaders in modern medicine.* Philadelphia, Amer. Philosoph. Soc., 1954 (Kisch).   6) J.A.M.A., 1967, *200*:550–551.

GUSTAF RETZIUS (1842–1919)

(O)NE of the leaders during the classical period of neuroanatomy was Gustaf Magnus Retzius, a man of amazing industry and versatility. His studies of nerve cells and their processes in a wide variety of invertebrates and vertebrates helped establish the foundation upon which the neuron doctrine was based. Studies of a large series of subprimate, simian and human brains, fetal and adult, clarified many of the more difficult problems of brain morphology.[1,2] He made outstanding contributions to the knowledge of the sensory organs, nerve terminations, and the supporting tissues and ependyma of the central nervous system. His investiga-

Portrait, courtesy of Prof. Folke Henschen, Stockholm, Sweden.

tions in prehistoric craniology over some thirty years were among the major contributions to physical anthropology.[3] No wonder that in 1901 he should examine the skull, allegedly of the Swedish novelist Carl Almquist—solemnly exhumed in Bremen, to be buried with full honors in native soil near Stockholm—and demonstrate that it was not Almquist's or, for that matter, apparently not even a male's skull.[4]

Anders Retzius, professor of anatomy in Stockholm and famous for devising the cranial index, was his father. Born in Stockholm, Gustaf entered the University of Upsala in 1860. In 1864, he edited and published the fundamental researches in anthropology of his father who had just died, and began his own comprehensive studies on prehistoric crania. After receiving his medical degree in 1871, Retzius became Docent in anatomy at the Caroline Institute (Karolinska mediko-kirurgiska Institutet), where, with Axel Key, in 1869, he had begun researches on the membranes and cavities of the nervous system. In 1875–76 appeared their monumental work in this field, in which they affirmed through injection experiments and dissections the existence of the foramina of Magendie (discovered in 1825) and Luschka (1859), and presented the view that the cerebrospinal fluid escapes from the subarachnoid space through the Pacchionian bodies into the subdural space, then into the venous sinuses, and that some of it reached the cervical lymphatics.[5] Many years were to pass before Weed (1914) advanced the opinion, now generally accepted, that most of the fluid is absorbed by the arachnoidal villi.

Retzius' studies on the labyrinth were equally impressive.[6] His many papers of this period were published as annual volumes.[7]

In recognition of his attainments, Retzius was made *personligt* professor of anatomy at the Caroline Institute in 1877. From 1884 to 1887 he served as chief editor of the *Aftonbladet,* a leading Stockholm newspaper owned by his wife's father, but in 1888 he returned to the Institute as professor of anatomy, resigning the following year. Commanding ample means he thenceforth devoted himself to research.

Nineteen folio volumes of *Biologische Untersuchungen,* printed on the press of the *Aftonbladet,* including only his own work, with hundreds of figures from his own hand, appeared from 1890 to 1920.[8] Among a wide range of subjects the finer anatomy and the comparative morphology of the nervous system were predominant. Appearing in another volume, published in 1896,[9] was his account of the laminae of the cerebral cortex, in which he confirmed many of Cajal's observations. He was thus one in the long line of investigators of the layering of the cortex—starting with Baillarger, Remak, Rudolf Berlin, and Meynert; proceeding through the Russian histologist, Vladimir Aleksandrovich Betz (1834–1894), who discovered in the fifth lamina of the human precentral cortex the giant pyramidal cells that bear his name (1874,[10] 1881[11]); and on through the British psychiatrist William Bevan Lewis (1847–1929[12]) who, in 1878, established the existence, generally, of pyramidal cells in Meynert's fifth layer and divided the cortex into six layers; then followed the studies of Oskar Vogt, Brodmann, Campbell, and others.

To Retzius' 333 scientific titles,[13] numerous sketches of scientists and several volumes of poems must be added, and he wrote several cantatas.

Naturally Retzius inspired assistance from others and received widespread recognition. In 1908 he delivered the Croonian Lecture before the Royal Society of London, choosing as his subject, *The principles of the minute structure of the nervous system,*[14] and in the following year he gave the Huxley Lecture on *The so-called North European race of mankind* before the Royal Anthropological Institute.[15] He was not only one of "De Aderton" of the Swedish Academy, the group of eighteen men who decided on the bestowal of the Nobel Prize for Literature, etc., but also a member of the Swedish Academy of Science, which chooses Nobel laureates in physiology and medicine.

Both he and his wife belonged to a club bequeathing their brains to scientific research. Removed by Folke Henschen, Retzius' brain is now in the collection of élite brains in the Museum of Pathology of the Caroline Institute.

O. LARSELL

References

[1]*Das Menschenhirn.* 2 vol. Stockholm, Norstedt, 1896.   [2]*Cerebra simiarum illustrata. Das Affenhirn in bildlicher Darstellung.* Jena,

Fischer, 1906. ³*Crania suecica antiqua.* Stockholm, Aftonbladets-druckerei, 1900. ⁴*The human skull. A cultural history.* London, Thames and Hudson, 1965, p. 126–127 (Henschen). ⁵*Studien in der Anatomie des Nervensystems und des Bindegewebes* (with Key). 2 parts. Stockholm, Samson & Wallin, 1875–76. ⁶*Das Gehörorgan der Wirbelthiere.* 2 vol. Stockholm, Samson & Wallin, 1881–84. ⁷*Biol. Untersuch.* Stockh., vol. 1–2, 1881–82. ⁸*Ibid.*, N.F., vol. 1–19, 1890–1920. ⁹*Das Menschenhirn. Studien in der makroskopischen Morphologie.* Stockholm, Norstedt, 1896. ¹⁰Zbl. med. Wiss., 1874, *12:*578–580 *et seq.* ¹¹*Ibid.*, 1881, *19:*193–195 *et seq.* ¹²Brain, 1878, *1:*79–96 ¹³*Ibid.*, 1920, *19:*81–100. ¹⁴Proc. R. Soc., London, 1908, ser.B, *80:*414–443. ¹⁵J. R. Anthrop. Inst., Gr. Britain, 1909, *39:*277–313.

References to Biography and Works: 1) Man, London, 1919, *19:*149–150 (Keith). 2) Sc. Month., 1920, *10:*559–569 (Larsell). 3) *Biografiska anteckningar och minnen* (autobiographic notes and recollections). 2 vol. Upsala, 1933, 1948 (Retzius). 4) *Observations on the pathology of hydrocephalus.* Medical Research Council Special Report Series No. 265. London, His Majesty's Stationery Office, 1949 (Russell). 5) *The human brain and spinal cord. A historical study illustrated by writings from antiquity to the twentieth century.* Berkeley, Univ. of Calif., 1968 (Clarke and O'Malley). 6) *Garrison's history of neurology.* Springfield, Thomas, 1969 (McHenry).

LUIGI ROLANDO (1773–1831)

*T*HE two pairs of brains we carry inside our heads had intrigued observers for a long time. Two sets: one tall, above, and to the front; the other small, behind, and in the basement, so to speak—what were they for? Physiology was forever asking the animated question, anatomy supposedly giving the sedate answer. Around the turn of the eighteenth century the matter was less settled than ever. There was another matter to disturb Luigi Rolando, the brilliant personal physician to the King of Savoy, in Turin. Bonaparte had moved in over the Alpine passes, forcing the ancient house of Piedmont and Savoy to take refuge in their scrubby mountain island of Sardinia, and be cut off for twelve

Luigi Rolando

years from the civilized world. Rolando, now in his thirties, was
made professor of "theoricopractical medicine" at Sassari, the island's second little university. His laboratory facilities, if we may
use the anachronistic term, were practically nil. But was Flourens in
Paris so much better equipped? After all, Rolando had everything
he knew how to use: experimental animals (the island abounded in
goats, rabbits, guinea pigs, turtles, and all manner of birds), a tre-
phine, a small sharp knife, a tiny spoon for making ablations inside the posterior fossa. Almost certainly he had also taken into
exile Varolio's four little anatomy volumes of 1591, and Mala-

carne's *Encefalotomia Nuova Universale,* published in 1780 in
Turin, Rolando's home town. Back on the mainland he would add
electrical stimulation, cathode to brain, anode to muscle.

Theories on the function of the cerebellum had moved as in a
game of musical chairs. Broadly, the observations made on its position and its injuries suggested two roles: one, a backroom assignment as the organ of memory; the other, a low caste position for
doing the vital but menial tasks in subservience to the big fellow
on top. Rolando belonged to the second school. To him, moreover, the cerebellar lamellation suggested the arrangement and the
capacity of the Voltaic pile, as it did to Reil in Germany, independently, it seems, but in keeping with the universal scientific climate humming with electricity. This hypothesis of an electromo-
tor in the basement Rolando set out to prove.[1] *Incertezza*—stagger-
ing—he found, was caused by "minor" damage, whereas complete
destruction of the cerebellum led to "locomotor paralysis." He
thus effectively refuted many a predecessor's claim for sensory, intellectual, or vital functions. But to the end of his life—back in
Turin, with access to Magendie's criticism and Flouren's independent experiments—he refused to believe that cerebellar lesions
abolished only the "regulation," not the strength of movements.
Yet one must, with John Fulton, give Rolando credit for having
been the "most colorful figure in the story of the cerebellum."[2]

His later work on the gyri of the forebrain—Malacarne's *processi
enteroidei*—deserves our greatest respect.[3] In nonprimate animals,
he admitted, Cuvier and Meckel had noticed the constancy of the
cerebral folds. But he could show that the human convolutions,
too, come in a regular pattern, that at least two of them run verti-
cally, and that the one on the mesial side of the hemisphere surrounds what Broca was to call the "limbus." True, Vicq d'Azyr,
the main authority in these matters, or rather his draughtsman,
had depicted the central vertical fissure of the hemisphere as early
as 1786, but had been silent about it. Not so Rolando, who also
did all his remarkable engravings himself; the fissure was rightly
given Rolando's name, by Leuret.[4]

Like most of his contemporaries, Rolando lacked understanding
for Gall's visionary fusion of gray and white matter; he believed in
their polarity. Then as now, the applied physics of the day pro-

vided the model for understanding the nervous system. Three types of nerve fibers existed, Rolando thought. One of these conductors, we note with interest, served muscle tone or "mobility"; it was "unipolar, positive," in contrast to the "bipolar," serving phasic "movement"[5]: a gamma and an alpha system, so to speak. (The third, "negative," was sensory.) Much greater things might still be done for science, he urged, endearingly in 1830, if only more money were made available for the purpose.[3]

The substantia gelatinosa is proof that he also had a sharp eye for grey matter when he spoke of its "diversity" in the (unstained) spinal cord. To his surprise that no one had mentioned it, he said, "a particular gray matter" exists in the posterior third of the posterior horn. "This new substance is more *gelatinous* . . . of a different color, generally less reddish, and darker."[5]

"Simplicité, bonhomie, modestie et douceur," were Rolando's virtues (according to one of his assistants). Also, with great originality and discernment, not a little stubbornness, we might add.

SAN FRANCISCO, CALIFORNIA   FRANCIS SCHILLER

References

[1]*Saggio sopra la vera struttura del cervello dell'uomo e degl'animali e sopra le funzioni del sistema nervoso.* Sassari, Stampa Privileg., 1809.   [2]*Functional localization in the frontal lobes and cerebellum.* Oxford, U. P., 1949, p. 107.   [3]*Della struttura degli emisferi cerebrali.* Mem. R. Accad. Sci. Torino, 1831, *35:*103–145.   [4]*Anatomie comparée du système nerveux considéré dans ses rapports avec l'intelligence.* Paris, Didot, 1839–1857.   [5]*Saggio sopra la vera struttura del cervello,* etc. Turin, 1828, vol. 1, p. 253, 285.

References to Biography: 1) Arch. gén. Med., 1831, *26:*283 (Coster). 2) Belloni (Ed.), *Essays on the history of Italian neurology.* Milan, Ist. di Storia della Medicine, 1963, p. 204 (Fadiga).   3) Canad. Med. Ass. J., 1932, *26:*220 (Rawson).   4) *Handbook of physiology.* Washington, D.C., Amer. Physiol. Soc., 1954, sect. 1, vol. 1, p. 1–58 (Brazier).

THEODOR SCHWANN (1810–1882)

*A*S A founder of neurohistology, Schwann is perhaps not sufficiently appreciated. That part of his work tends to be overshadowed by the two massive and fundamental contributions to biological advance in general which have made him famous: the cellular basis of living organisms, and fermentation. In importance and extent these are much greater than his contribution to neurology as such, represented by the description of the particular cell and sheath that take his name.

Theodor Schwann was born a book seller's son at Neuss near Düsseldorf; he had his schooling in the Jesuit College at Cologne and entered the University of Bonn in 1829. All his critical discoveries were made in the few years that followed, before he was thirty. After postgraduate studies at Würzburg and Berlin, and failing in 1839 to obtain a suitable academic position in his homeland, he accepted an appointment to the Chair of Anatomy in the Catholic University of Louvain. In 1848 he moved to the neighbouring Liège to hold the Chair of Anatomy in that University until his retirement in 1880. He never married, and he died while visiting his brother in Cologne in 1882.

A spare man with a fine head and lively eye, Schwann is said to have lived very simply, to have avoided deliberately the strife of scientific controversy, and to have risen above all petty jealousies. Throughout his life, which in large part was that of an expatriate in Belgium, he remained a quietly ardent German patriot, deeply religious, an active member of the Roman Catholic Church, modest, friendly, and on the whole fairly content. Only once, very much against his aversion to publicity, he saw himself forced to defend, in a pamphlet, his convictions as an objective scientist, when they were seemingly brought into conflict with his creed. He had been unfairly quoted in the Catholic press of having acknowledged as genuine the antics of a young woman pretending to be inspired by the Holy Ghost.

The first major subject Schwann revolutionized was fermentation, by showing that it is associated with *living* organisms.[1] The endorsement of this observation was very slow because it involved

a reorientation of accepted thinking. Fermentation continued to be associated with putrefaction and death until the time of Pasteur, who wrote to Schwann in 1878: "For twenty years I have been travelling along some of the paths opened up by you."

In 1839 the epoch-making monograph by Schwann was published, with his bishop's approval, on the "accordance in the structure and growth of animals and plants"; it was translated into English by Henry Smith for the Sydenham Society in 1847.[2] After that date Schwann made little original contribution to science.

Portrait, courtesy of Dr. Gilbert Causey.

This against the enormous productivity of the ten years—1829 to 1839—underlines the early brilliance of so many distinguished scientists. But it is worthwhile noting that during the years at Bonn, Würzburg and Berlin, and then at Louvain, Schwann was in contact with that remarkable teacher, Johannes Müller, and such fellow students as Henle, Bischoff, Remak and Schleiden. In 1839 Schleiden was Professor of Botany at Louvain, Schwann the Professor of Anatomy. Increasingly he may have fallen victim to his relative isolation as a foreigner, in a scientifically rather sterile milieu, and succumbed to his own tendency of turning inward for philosophical abstraction. Honorary membership in many learned societies did not reverse this trend.

Historians have not failed to show that Schwann had his fore-runners—especially in France: Dutrochet, Raspail—also Purkyně. But his capital share in establishing the cell theory throughout the scientific world remains hardly diminished—in biological litera-ture perhaps only the "Origin of species" had a greater impact.

In the text on the microscopical structure of plants and animals the cell of Schwann is illustrated by elegant drawings. It should be borne in mind that Schwann was using his descriptions of this cell to support the basic thesis of the cell nucleus and its protoplasm forming a universal unit of structure. The development of a nerve presented considerable difficulty in this generalization, as did also the muscle fibre. Schwann, in his text, discusses muscle first and builds up a case for the multinucleate muscle fibre formed by the fusion of a number of "primary" muscle cells; the result is a syncy-tium with multiple nuclei: this he called a "secondary" muscle cell. He goes on to discuss nerves and nerve fibres, and it is likely that, by following the muscle analogy too closely, he was led into designating as a "primary nerve cell" in peripheral nerve the cell which, from his descriptions, would correspond to what is now called a Schwann cell. A number of these "primary" nerve cells he believed fused together to form a syncytium—the Schwann sheath of later days. The axon, in his way of thinking, constitutes a clear central strand forming within the syncytium. For a myelinated fiber the white myelin is deposited between the central core and the cell membrane. An attractive sequence when viewed in the light of the histology of his day, but untenable today. The first major advances were due to Remak,[3] to Deiters,[4] then to Ranvier.[5] In pathology, Schwann lives on unhappily through the term "Schwannoma,"[6] for it suggests that ectoplasmic bits of his ghost act as the parent tissue of the neoplasm. José Verocay (1876–1927) (Uruguayan working chiefly in Prague[7]) had called it neur-in-oma—*inos* meaning "fiber,"[8] thus leading the line of believers in the ectodermal origin of this tumor, i.e., its derivation from the Schwann cell and sheath.

Theodor Schwann was not only a keen observer but also had a keen appreciation of the importance of generalizations following observations. The recognition of the immense contribution that these generalizations have made to biological and neurological understanding cannot be overstated, and the fact that his descriptions and deductions have had to be modified in an age of biochemistry and biophysics in no way detracts from their fundamental importance.

LONDON, ENGLAND   GILBERT CAUSEY

References

[1]Poggendorffs Ann. 1837, XLI.   [2]*Mikroskopische Untersuchungen über die Übereinstimmung in der Struktur und dem Wachsthum der Thiere und Pflanzen*. Berlin, Reimer, 1839. *Microscopic researches into the accordance in the structure and growth of animals and plants.* Transl. by H. Smith, London, Sydenham Soc., 1847, p. 142–153. [3]*Observationes anatomicae et microscopicae de systematis nervosi structura*. Berlin, Reimer, 1838, p. 9 *et seq.*   [4]*Untersuchungen über Gehirn und Rückenmark* etc. Edit. by M. Schultze. Braunschweig, Vieweg, 1965, p. 55 *et seq.*   [5]*Leçons sur l'histologie du système nerveux*. Paris, Savy, 1878.   [6]Amer. J. Path., 1932, *8:*367–415 (Masson).   [7]Verh. Deut. path. Ges., 1928, *23:*546 (biography of Verocay, by Ghon). Discurso pronunciado en el Acto de Conmemoración del Cincuentenario de la Fundación del Hospital Militar, Montevideo (biography of Verocay, by Mautone).   [8]Beitr. path. Anat., 1910, *48:*1–68 (Verocay).

References to Biography: 1) *The cell of Schwann.* Edinburgh, Livingstone, 1960 (Causey).   2) Münch. med. Wschr., 1910, *57:*2703–2705 (Sudhoff).

BENEDICT STILLING (1810–1879)

"EVERYBODY has seen them," the *Dictionnaire encyclopé-dique de médecine et de chirurgie* of 1883 says, "those magnificent enormous volumes, with their excellent plates. They will be consulted for many years to come as the imperishable monument of anatomy they are." "We have great reason to thank this author for his work on the medulla oblongata and pons. . . ." says Kölliker in his *Manual of histology* (1852), "for the first accurate observation regarding the fiber course [of the cranial nerves] . . . all probably becoming connected . . . with well-defined parts of the gray substance, which Stilling not inappropriately calls nerve nuclei."

Stilling? Derived from "stillness," it was the pen name, first, of *Heinrich Jung*-Stilling (1740–1817), a pietistic writer and friend of Goethe. Admiration, no doubt, for this immensely popular, somewhat philosemitic novelist, made *Benedict* Stilling's father, a Jewish wool merchant of Kirchhain in Hesse-Cassel, adopt that name (as was the custom), when he became emancipated to citizenship under Jerome Bonaparte (1808). The original Heinrich Jung-Stilling, also a doctor, had performed cataract extractions, written his most famous allegorical novel *Nostalgia* (1794), and taught economics at nearby Marburg. It was to the medical school at Marburg that young Benedict Stilling came four decades later from his native Kirchhain. Here he won fame not only as a student but also as surgical assistant. In 1832 he homografted the cornea of a rabbit.[1] In the next year he published the first thorough microscopic study on intravascular clotting,[2] and introduced a new method of hemostasis; he turned and implanted the cut end back into a lateral slit of the artery.[3] And before another renowned hemostatist and ovariotomist—Sir Thomas Spencer-Wells (1818–1897)—Stilling created his—safer—extraperitoneal method of ovariotomy (1837).

An eminent surgeon, then, but one who could sign his publications only as "General practitioner and operateur in Cassel." Several offers for academic positions, all tied to conversion and baptism, must be declined, he felt—regretfully, no doubt. Soon after

Benedict Stilling

graduation, at the age of twenty-three, he had been heard of in the capital, and was lured away from Marburg. Pressed by his co-religionists, Stilling became the first Jewish civil servant in the principality by accepting the position of "Landgerichts-Wundarzt" (surgeon to the electoral law courts). Some thought the honor excessive; his transfer from the capital to Eiterfeld (literally "Pusfield"), a mean burgh, made him resign and for the rest of his life devote himself to his ever-growing private practice.

Portrait from Münch. med. Wschr., 1910, 57:699.

Not entirely, though. Aside from visiting famous colleagues in Germany, London, Edinburgh or Paris, "I let no day pass," wrote Stilling, "without bestowing a good part of my leisure on the study of the nervous system and its structure."[4] He entered neuroanatomy through the back door of what we now would call a fashionable psychosomatic fad: "Spinal irritation."* But in writing about it, he was already in 1840 postulating sympathetic *vasomotor* nerves,[5] before Claude Bernard. Two years later, in collaboration with Joseph Wallach (1813–1878), he published the first of those gorgeous volumes that could be measured in feet rather than inches, one of them in Latin and German, read side by side on the vast page. They were on the spinal cord,[4] medulla oblongata,[6] pons,[7] and cerebellum,[8] of animals and man. The giant size was deemed necessary for the realistic if fabulous rendering of the ten- or fifteen-fold magnification of the sections, cut with a razor dipped in alcohol, in three endless series: transverse, longitudinal and oblique. If he—after Rolando (1824) and contemporary with Valentin and Hannover (1840)—was not the sole originator of the method, Stilling, self-taught, was the most devoted and thorough explorer of serial sectioning and reconstructing, doing here the first detailed work "in an endeavor almost without parallel," according to Deiters[9] (1834–1863). This effort, without benefit of staining, revealed to him and the world that basic concept of neurology, the *nerve nuclei*. Stilling described the nuclei of nearly all the cranial nerves, and the intramedullary ("central") course of their roots. He also had a good idea of the unbelievable interconnectedness of cells and fibers, of the implied presence of fasciculi proprii, of the fact that a large part (he actually thought the majority) of fiber systems do not originate in the cerebral hemispheres; and he accepted against much opposition Remak's observation (1837) of fiber origin from nerve cell.

Stilling's nerve nuclei in the oblongata and midbrain which opened an epoch in neurological thought, should not be confused with "Stilling's nucleus," a cell aggregate in the spinal cord situated approximately in the same position as "Clarke's nucleus," but at different levels.

Married to the daughter of a banker, he had three sons, one of

---

* No doubt the origin of osteopathy and chiropractic.

whom became a prominent ophthalmologist (J. Stilling, 1842–1915). While he received several prizes from the French Academy and the King of Belgium, his fatherland, in the person of the king of Prussia, rewarded him only with the title of Geheimer Sanitätsrat (privy Health councillor), when Cassel was annexed to Prussia in 1866.

The story of Stilling's unswerving life, full and yet frustrated, we owe to the great Kussmaul who called him "immortal"; and we have his photograph which well reflects a friendly yet iron determination: after all, he had made up his mind to be a surgeon at the age of six. The last works of the ailing man, unable to tackle his vast project of investigating the cerebral hemispheres, were a monograph on urethral strictures, and a commemorative essay on Jules Papin (1647–1712), of pressure cooker and steam engine fame: Papin, you see, as a Huguenot émigré, *had* been professor at Marburg University.

SAN FRANCISCO, CALIFORNIA   FRANCIS SCHILLER

References

[1]*Die künstliche Pupillenbildung in der Sclerotica. Nebst einem Anhange über die Verpflanzung der Hornhaut Keratoplastik.* Marburg, Elwert, 1833.   [2]*Die Bildung und Metamorphose des Blutpfropfs oder Thrombus* etc. Eisenach, Baerecke, 1834.   [3]*Die Gefässdurchschlingung* etc. Marburg, Elwert, 1834.   [4]*Neue Untersuchungen über den Bau des Rückenmarks.* Kassel, Hotop, 1859.   [5]*Physiologische* etc. *Untersuchungen über die Spinal-Irritation.* Leipzig, Wigand, 1840.   [6]*Über Textur und Functionen der Medulla oblongata.* Erlangen, Enke, 1843.   [7]*Über den Bau des Hirnknotens* etc. Jena, Mauke, 1846.   [8]*Untersuchungen über den Bau des Kleinen Gehirns des Menschen.* 3 vol. Kassel, Krieger (Fischer), 1864–1868.   [9]*Untersuchungen über Gehirn* etc. Braunschweig, Vieweg, 1865, p. 149 (Deiters).

References to Biography: 1) Tagebl. d. Versamml. deutsch. Naturf. u. Aerzte, Baden-Baden, 1879, *52*:34 *et seq.*, 53 *et seq.* (Kussmaul). 2) Münch. med. Wschr., 1910, *57*:699–700 (Strauss).   3) Bull. Hist. Med., 1969, *43*:67–84 (Schiller).

LUDWIG TÜRCK (1810–1868)

$\mathcal{J}$ ÜRCK, a native of Vienna, attended the University there and obtained his degree in medicine in 1837. Three years later, he was appointed physician in the Allgemeines Kranken- haus. Soon afterward a subdepartment of neurology was created in Internal Medicine, of which he was put in charge (1847). Partly because of his modest and retiring disposition—"Herr Türck was always a bit too late," Czermak, his successful rival, quipped—he did not receive recognition for a long time and was given aca- demic rank only toward the end of his life.

Türck's interest in neurology manifested itself soon after his graduation, when he published several articles on cerebral apo- plexy. During this period, neurology in Vienna was largely of a speculative character, and dominated by the theories of Benedict Stilling, of Cassel, on "spinal irritation," originally an English idea. This also attracted Türck who, in 1843, published a book on the subject, but even at that time his independent and scientific approach was evident. In 1844 he went to Paris, where he was in- fluenced mostly by Ricord, whose lectures on syphilis he translated into German. There followed a relatively quite period of five years devoted largely to clinical observation. The neuroanatomical dark- ness of the time and the critical attitude of the Viennese are re- flected by the remark the distinguished Josef Hyrtl (1810–1894) made in his well-known *Lehrbuch* (1846): "Die Anatomie des in- neren Baues des Gehirns ist und bleibt wahrscheinlich für immer ein mit sieben Siegeln verschlossenes und überdies noch in Hiero- glyphen geschriebenes Buch." ("The internal anatomical struc- ture of the brain is now, and probably always will remain, a book sealed with seven seals, and written, moreover, in hieroglyphics.")

From 1849 onward, Türck made his chief contributions to neu- rology. His most important original investigations were concerned with secondary degeneration in the central nervous system.[1-3] In this work he was influenced by the studies of Sir Charles Bell (1774–1842) on the physiology of nerve conduction, and by the observation made by his close friend and associate, C. Wedl, that

compound granular corpuscles develop in the region of injury of
the central nervous system. Based on neuropathological observations in cases of hemiplegia and compression of the spinal cord,[1]
and confirmed by experimental investigations, Türck established

Portrait, courtesy of Library of College of Physicians of Philadelphia, Pennsylvania. (Photographer: Schultz, Vienna.)

the principle that the direction of tract degeneration corresponds to the direction of conduction. Thus, focal capsular lesions in the brain produce degeneration of the corticospinal tract, and transverse lesions of the spinal cord result in degeneration of the centripetal tracts above the level injured, and of the centrifugal tracts below. In this way, he was able to outline six tracts in the spinal cord, one of which, the anterior corticospinal tract, bears his name.[4] He did not recognize this tract as such—he called it the "Hülsen-Vorderstrangbahn" after Burdach—but he knew that it emanated from the region of the pyramidal decussation. In regard to the lateral corticospinal tract, it was he who discovered a century ago that it passed through the internal capsule and the middle third of the basis pedunculi in its course downward.[2,3] He felt that the secondary degeneration was due probably to an interruption of conduction.

Türck was an originator of the concept of system disease of the spinal cord, and he described the syndrome of hemisection of the cord[5] "a little too late" to share the distinction with Brown-Séquard. His work on spinal tract degeneration, although it proved to be one of the major medical discoveries of the nineteenth century, was ignored by the scientific world for more than a decade. In 1866 Bouchard, an assistant of Charcot, took up the subject where Türck had left off, and some ten years later Türck's studies served as the foundation for the study of myelogenesis by Flechsig.

Türck made many other contributions to neurology. Highly significant were his neuro-ophthalmologic investigations in cases of Bright's disease and brain tumor. He was one of the first to describe the mechanism of choked disc. His studies on the cutaneous distribution of individual spinal nerve roots (1856–68) are classics. He was, in fact, the first to detect a segmental arrangement in the cutaneous area supplied by the sensory roots (1856). He was also a pioneer in the study of sensory localization in the cerebral cortex, the course of the optic pathways, trigeminal neuralgia, tabes dorsalis,[6] and multiple sclerosis.

In the last ten years of his life, Türck abandoned the field of neurology and became interested in laryngology. It is still disputed whether he or Czermak first invented the laryngoscope. His contribution to this field[7] received at that time much greater attention than his previous studies, so much so that in the Memorial Address by Sigmund at the unveiling of his bust in the Allgemeines Krankenhaus following his sudden death from typhus in 1868, Türck's researches in neurology were scarcely mentioned.

SAN FRANCISCO, CALIFORNIA   N. MALAMUD

References

[1]Zschr. k. k. Gesellsch. Ärzte zu Wien (Med. Jahrb.), 1849, *1*:173–176. [2]*Ibid.*, 1852, 2:511–534.   [3]*Ibid.*, 1853, 2:289–317.   [4]Sitzber. math. naturw. Klasse Akad. Wiss., Wien, 1853, *11*:93.   [5]Rev. thérap. méd.-chir., Paris, 1857, p. 309–316.   [6]Zschr. k. k. Gesellsch. Ärzte zu Wien (Med. Jahrb.), 1855, *16*:517–532.   [7]*Praktische Anleitung zur Laryngoskopie.* Wien, Braumüller, 1860. (Review by Semeleder in Med. Jahrb., 1861, *17*:1–8.)

References to Biography: 1) Jahrb. Psychiat. Neur., Wien, 1910, *31:* 1–21 (contains collected works, p. 23–194; Neuburger).   2) Wien. Klinik, 1889, *15*:165–192 (Heitler).   3) *Die Wiener medizinische Schule im 19. Jahrhundert.* Graz, Bohlau, 1965, p. 186–194 (Lesky).

AUGUSTUS VOLNEY WALLER (1816–1870)

W) ALLER was born on a farm in Kent, England. His childhood was spent in the south of France, but he returned to school in his native country at the age of fourteen. Later, when a student in Paris, he became interested in the histologic structure of the tongue of the frog, and his first and most notable observations were made on such preparations. After graduating in Paris (1840), he practiced medicine in Kensington in London for ten years (1842–1851), but whenever he could spare time from seeing patients he would not tire in going back to his microscopic degenerations. In this period two of his papers were published in the *Philosophical Transactions of the Royal Society.* The first of these was an account of diapedesis of the white cells of the blood, already noted by Addison. The second dealt with the effects of transection of the glossopharyngeal and hypoglossal nerves of the frog,[1] a study in which Waller established the nature of degeneration of the peripheral part of the nerve.

Augustus Volney Waller

In 1851 Waller decided to give up medical practice and devote himself entirely to physiologic studies. He went to Bonn, where, with the ophthalmologist Julius Ludwig Budge (1811–84), he began experiments on the pathway of the pupillary dilator fibers.[2] Together, they noted that when the vagosympathetic trunk of the dog was severed the degeneration of the peripheral end of the nerve was incomplete. The remaining intact fibers were identified with the sympathetic trunk and were traced to the 1st and 2nd thoracic segments of the spinal cord. When, in the intact animal, this

Portrait, courtesy of Dr. D. Denny-Brown, Southborough, Massachusetts.

region was stimulated, the pupils enlarged, but when the cervical part of the sympathetic trunk was sectioned unilaterally the electrical stimulation no longer caused pupillary dilatation on that side. They named these segments the "ciliospinal center." For this work, Budge and Waller were awarded the Monthyon Prize of the Académie des Sciences for 1852. In 1852[3] and 1853[4] Budge and Waller described the vasoconstrictor action of the cervical sympathetic, which was in confirmation of the discoveries of Claude Bernard in 1851 and Brown-Séquard in 1852. Not long afterward the vasoconstrictor action of the sympathetic supply to the upper limbs was described by Claude Bernard (1862), Schiff (1862)[5] and Cyon (1868),[6] and that to the lower limbs by Claude Bernard (1854) and Ostroumoff (1876).[7] This period was the dawn of knowledge of the function of the autonomic system.[8]

Waller is best known for his study of trophic degeneration of nerve fibers as a method of investigating the anatomy of the nervous system. This was described in a series of memoirs communicated to the Académie des Sciences, the most important of which was his first, which appeared in 1851: *Nouvelle méthode pour l'etude du système nerveux applicable à l'investigation de la distribution anatomique des cordons nerveux.*[9] His approach gained immediate recognition as the "Wallerian method," and in 1856 he was awarded the Monthyon Prize for the second time.

Waller moved from Bonn to Paris in 1856, but almost immediately became seriously ill with what appears to have been rheumatic fever. During the next two years he recuperated in England, and had just taken up a new appointment as professor of physiology in Birmingham when further illness forced him to retire to Bruges, then to the Pays de Vaud, in search of health. By 1868 he was well enough to begin a quiet medical practice in Geneva, where he again briefly renewed his physiologic studies. He was, however, greatly troubled by angina pectoris, to which he succumbed not long after he had given his last paper on Wallerian degeneration.[10] His son, Augustus D. Waller, was also a distinguished physiologist. Bartelmez relates how, on one occasion, with the mention of his father's name, the younger Waller said, "I am *the* Wallerian degeneration!"

SOUTHBOROUGH, MASSACHUSETTS   D. DENNY-BROWN

References

[1]Philos. Tr. R. Soc. London, 1850, p. 423–429.   [2]C. rend. Acad. sci. Paris, 1851, *33*:370–374 *et seq*.   [3]Med. Zeitung, Berlin, 1852, *21*:161–162 (Budge).   [4]C. rend. Acad. sci. Paris, 1853, *36*:378–382.   [5]*Ibid.*, 1862, *55*:425–427.   [6]Arb. a. d. physiol. Inst. Leipzig, 1868, *3*:62–77. [7]Pflügers Arch., 1876, *12*:219–277.   [8]Arch. Neur. Psychiat., Chicago, 1936, *35*:1081–1115 (Sheeman).   [9]C. rend. Acad. sci. Paris, 1851, *33*:606–611.   [10]Proc. Roy. Soc., London, 1870, *18*:339–343 (abstract of the Croonian Lecture).

References to Biography and Works: 1) Proc. Roy. Soc., London, 1871, *20*:xi–xiii (not signed).   2) *Some apostles of physiology.* London, privately printed, 1902, p. 123–126 (Stirling).   3) J.A.M.A., 1969, *208*:2469–2470 (anon.)

THOMAS WILLIS (1621–1675)

*T*HOMAS WILLIS introduced the experimental approach to the study of the nervous system, as William Harvey, just before him, had done for the circulatory system. The most famous of his seven books, *Cerebri anatome,* published in 1664—with the striking illustrations by Christopher Wren and Richard Lower—surpassed anything that had appeared up to that time and marked the transition between medieval and modern notions of brain function.[1,2] In it, Willis used the term "neurology" for the first time, meaning by that the knowledge of the cranial, spinal and autonomic nerves. "Willis put the brain and the nervous system on their modern footing so far as that could be then done."[3]

Willis was born in Great Bedwin, a Wiltshire village. His mother died when he was ten, and the family moved to North Hinksey, across the Thames from Oxford. As a schoolboy he was known by the villagers for giving away his lunch to the poor, "so that . . . his father would often say 'this boy will starve himself' and would latterly, on that account, make him eat his meat at home before he went to school." His medical studies were made difficult because of the upheaval of the Civil War between Charles I and Cromwell, during which Willis was in the Oxford University Legion on the side of the King. He graduated Bachelor of Medi-

ÆTATIS SVÆ, 45.

Thomas Willis

cine in 1646, and spent the next twenty years in Oxford where he became much sought after as a physician. At the restoration of Charles II in 1660, he was appointed Sedleian Professor of Natural Philosophy at Oxford and given the M.D.

Willis had as students Robert Hooke, the inventive physicist

Dr. Thomas Willis, by David Loggan. From the frontispiece of his *Pathologiae Cerebri* (1667).

and microscopist; John Locke, the physician-philosopher; Richard Lower and Edmund King, who performed the first blood transfusion in man; Thomas Millington, later physician to the King; and Christopher Wren. Willis was thus the senior member of what appears to have been one of the earliest neurological research teams. In 1663, Willis became one of the original Fellows of the Royal Society and in the following year a Fellow of the Royal College of Physicians. Influenced by Gilbert Sheldon, Archbishop of Canterbury, he moved in 1667 to London where he soon became noted for his medical skill and his charitable works. He died of pleurisy. He is one of the few medical men, including Joseph Lister and John Hunter, who are buried in Westminster Abbey.[4]

The bibliography of Thomas Willis covers a formidable range of topics, including fermentation, fevers, urine, scurvy, muscular motion, anatomy of the brain and nerves, convulsive diseases, headache, apoplexy, and the comparative anatomy of some dozen species ranging from the earthworm to man. He published numerous clinical and autopsy reports, particularly on neurological problems.

His name has been associated with the syndrome of paracusis, and of narcolepsy, with the spinal assessory nerve, the first division of the fifth nerve, the connective tissue septa in the dural sinuses and, of course, the arterial circle at the base of the brain. The clinical observations of Willis include a description of the sweetness of diabetic urine and a lengthy discussion of various types of diabetes, or "chamber pot dropsy." He recorded epidemic typhoid fever among the troops in the Civil War, described and named puerperal fever, wrote about whooping cough and asthma, and pointed out that the intermittent pulse was not invariable associated with a bad prognosis. He first devised the *probang*, an ingenious instrument to treat a stricture of the esophagus.

As Cushing and Symonds have surmised, Willis was among the first to present the notion of a circulating hormone from the pituitary and from the gonads. His classification of the cranial nerves according to function, published in 1664, was in use for more than a century.[5] He described the branches of the vagus nerve and the nerves to the diaphragm, discovered the basal ganglia, the pyramids and depicted other structures of the brain stem in such detail as never presented before. He reported what appears to have been myasthenia gravis in a woman who temporily lost her power of speech and became "mute as a fish." The term "reflex" can be ascribed to Willis. He wrote on mental retardation and, most important, explained hysteria not as a disorder of the uterus but as a nervous affection. Some of his speculations were far beyond the physiological basis available at that time and these views as well as some of the details of his figures were subject to criticism, for example, by Stensen, the contemporary Danish anatomist.

Of all Willis' observations, the most significant to us were those relating to the cerebral circulation, because he recognized the functional importance of this unique vascular anastomosis in maintaining collateral blood flow to the brain. He reports how he had "squirted oftentimes into either artery of the carotides, a liquor dyed with Ink" so that "the vessels creeping into every corner and secret place of the Brain and the Cerebel" were "imbued with the same colour." Moreover, he records the clinical histories of two patients where this anatomical arrangement, he argues, had prevented apoplexy. For although "the Right Arteries, both the Carotid and Vertebral, within the Skull, were become bony and impervious and did shut forth the blood from that side," the remaining large vessels ("the fourfold chariot") running to the arterial circle at the base of the brain were able, by way of their "mutual conjoynings," to "supply or fill the channels and passages of all the rest." This sequence—anatomical description, clinical reporting, and pathological observation—exemplifies the originality and insight he brought to medical problems.

The man and his work can perhaps best be summed up in the words of a contemporary, Anthony Wood: "Dr. Willis left behind him the character of an orthodox, pious, and charitable physician. . . . The truth is tho he was a plain man, a man of no carriage, little discourse, complaisance or society, yet for his deep insight, happy researches in natural and experimental philosophy, anatomy and chymistry, for his wonderful success and repute in his practice, the natural smoothness, pure elegancy, delightful, unaffected neatness of Latin stile, none scarce hath equall'd much less out-done him, how great soever."[6]

MONTREAL, CANADA   WILLIAM FEINDEL

References

[1]*The remaining medical works of that famous and renowned physician, Dr. Thomas Willis* (etc.). Transl. into English by S. Pordage. London, Dring, Harper & Leigh, 1681. [2]*Practice of physick. Two discourses concerning the soul of brutes.* London, Dring, Harper & Leigh, 1683. [3]*Man on his nature.* London, Cambridge U. P., 1951 (Sherrington). [4]Brit. Med. J., 1962, *1:*552–553 (Feindel). [5]Mayo Clin. Proc., 1966, *41:*453–461 (Rucker). [6]*Athenae oxoniensis.* 3rd ed., edited by Bliss; vol. 3. London, Potter, 1817, p. 1048–1053 (Wood).

References to Biography: 1) *Disciples of Aesculapius.* Vol. 2. London, Hutchison, 1900 (Richardson). 2) *Dictionary of national biography.* Vol. 62. London, Oxford U. P., 1900, p. 25–26 (Moore). 3) Bull. Soc. Med. Hist., Chicago, 1923, *3:*215–232 (Miller). 4) Med. Life, 1934, *41:*177–191 (Rolleston). 5) Ann. Med. Hist., 1940, *2:* 181–199 (Dow). 6) Powell (Ed.), *Brief lives and other selected writings.* London, Cresset, 1949 (Aubrey). 7) Brit. Med. J., 1955, *1:*119–124 (Symonds). 8) Notes and records of the Royal Society of London, 1960, *15:*91–97 (Symonds). 9) Brit. Med. J., 1962, *1:*552–553 (Feindel). 10) Canad. Med. Ass. J., 1962, *87:*289–296 (Feindel). 11) Proc. Roy. Soc. Med., London, 1964, *57:*682–687 (Dewhurst). 12) Feindel (Ed.), *Thomas Willis. The anatomy of the brain and nerves.* Tercentenary Edition. 2 vol. Montreal, McGill U. P., 1965; with facsimile of Pordage's 1681 English transl. of *Cerebri anatome,* and bibliography. 13) *Thomas Willis, 1621–1675. Doctor and Scientist.* New York, Hafner, 1968 (Isler). 14) Scherz (Ed.), *Nicolaus Steno's lecture on the anatomy of the brain.* Copenhagen, Nyt Nordisk Forlag, Busck, 1965. 15)J. neurol. Sci., 1966, *3:*109–116 (A. Meyer).

II

NEUROANATOMISTS IN MORE RECENT TIMES

KORBINIAN BRODMANN (1868–1918)

*K*ORBINIAN BRODMANN was born in Liggersdorf, Hohenzollern (Württemberg). He studied medicine in Munich, Würzburg, Berlin and Freiburg i.B. and received his license to practice medicine in 1895. For a year thereafter he worked in the Universitäts-Kinderklinik und Poliklinik in Munich with the intention of settling down, eventually, as a general practitioner in the Schwarzwald. He contracted diphtheria, however, and in order to recuperate from its sequelae took a position as assistant in a sanitarium for nervous diseases in Alexanderbad in Fichtelgebirge (northern Bavaria), which was directed at that time by Oskar Vogt. This contact with Vogt, in the summer of 1896, induced Brodmann to devote himself to the study of neurology and psychiatry. In 1898 he received the M.D. at Leipzig.

During the period 1900–01 Brodmann worked at the Städtische Irrenanstalt at Frankfurt-am-Main, where he came in contact with Alzheimer; it was under his influence that he became interested in the anatomical problems which were to occupy him exclusively for the remainder of his life. In 1901, he accepted a position with Vogt at the Neurobiologisches Institut in Berlin. Here he remained until 1910. During this period Brodmann accomplished virtually everything for which he later became known.

In a series of papers,[1-9] Brodmann established the basis upon which the present-day science of comparative cytoarchitectonics of the mammalian cortex rests. His famous map of the human cortex appeared in 1908.[6,7] Brodmann's broad comparative-anatomic approach, his recognition that the cortex is organized anatomically along the same basic principles in all mammals, and his idea of utilizing the morphogenesis of the cortex as a basis for the classification of cortical types and for the nomenclature of the layers, were all instrumental in dispelling the almost hopeless confusion which existed before Brodmann entered the field. His studies culminated in his famous book, *Vergleichende Lokalisationslehre der Grosshirnrinde* (Leipzig, Barth, 1909; reprinted 1925) which re-

mains the only comprehensive work ever published on this subject. After Brodmann left Berlin he began a series of investigations
dealing with the size and development of mammalian cortical
fields. However, the lack of adequate laboratory facilities curtailed
greatly his productivity, and the outbreak of World War I interrupted his research altogether.

Despite the fact that the significance of his work was recognized
early by leading German scientists, Brodmann faced great obstacles in his academic career. The opposition to his work was so
strong that the medical faculty of the University of Berlin refused

Portrait, courtesy of Prof. Dr. Hugo Spatz, Giessen, Germany.

to admit him as a Privatdozent. His personal relations at the Neurobiologisches Institut were also strained.

The economic insecurity of his position at the Neurobiologisches Institut induced him to leave Berlin in 1910 and to accept a position with R. Gaupp at Tübingen, where he was made titular professor in 1913. Gaupp, now 82, was one of his staunchest friends. Only in 1916, when he became Prosector at the Irrenanstalt Nietleben near Halle, did Brodmann achieve for the first time in his life an economically secure position which offered him at the same time an opportunity for research. When, in Munich, the Deutsche Forschungsanstalt für Psychiatrie was established, an institution where Kraepelin, Nissl and Spielmeyer had taken up their abode, Brodmann was appointed head of its topographic-histologic division. W. Scholz relates that Spielmeyer spoke of Brodmann as an intense and earnest man who was reserved almost to the point of timidity, but who could flare, on occasion, into a temper. A few months after the appointment, Brodmann died of acute sepsis following an attack of influenza. He was survived by his wife, whom he had married less than two years previously, and by a baby daughter, Ilse, who was taken into the home of her maternal grandmother.

MADISON, WISCONSIN   JERZY E. ROSE

References

[1]J. Psychol. Neur., Lpz., 1903, 2:79–107.   [2]Ibid., 1903, 2:133–159.
[3]Ibid., 1905, 4:177–226.   [4]Ibid., 1905, 6:108–120.   [5]Ibid., 1906, 6:275–400.   [6]Ibid., 1908, 10:231–246.   [7]Ibid., 1908, 10:287–334.
[8]Verh. anat. Ges., 1912, 26:157–216.   [9]Verh. Ges. deut. Naturforsch., 1913, 85:I.Theil.:200–240.

References to Biography: 1) J. Psychol. Neur., Lpz., 1918, 24:I–X (O. Vogt).   2) Münch. med. Wschr., 1920, 67:75–78 (Kraepelin). 3) Zschr. ges. Neur. Psychiat., 1919, 45:329–349 (Nissl).

WALTER CAMPBELL (1868–1937)

*A*LFRED WALTER CAMPBELL was born in his father's "station" at Cunningham Plains, near Harden, in the hills of New South Wales, Australia. He studied medicine in Edinburgh, receiving the degrees of M.B. and Ch.M. in 1889. Here he showed athletic prowess which won him the captaincy of the cricket and soccer teams, and when not thus engaged he was shooting grouse. From Edinburgh he went to Vienna as assistant to Krafft-Ebing, and later studied in Prague. In 1892 he obtained his doctorate in medicine with a thesis on *The pathology of alcoholic insanity,* for which the University of Edinburgh accorded him a gold medal.

He spent the next thirteen years as resident medical officer and director of the laboratory of pathology at Rainhill Asylum near Liverpool, and it was in that laboratory that he conducted the studies for which he is famous. Campbell owed much to Sir Charles Sherrington who gave him—as he stated—"not only valuable specimens, but counsel and encouragement when energy flagged."

In 1905 Campbell returned to Sydney, N.S.W., where he took up the practice of neurology and mental diseases. He was married in 1906 to a young lady he had grown up with in Cunningham Plains, and they had two daughters. In 1914 he volunteered for the Army and was sent to Egypt. Back in Sydney after the war, he carried on with great distinction until he retired in 1937. He lived on a steep hillside, the house hidden by trees through which an occasional flash of the loch-like waters of the bay could be seen; his grouse-shooting capabilities were now diverted to providing a sanctuary for birds, and he got to know all their names and their habits.

Those who knew him say he was a fine speaker, his enunciation infinitesmally studied in making his point, a gleam always appearing from under his deep brows. In private life he was reserved but not hard to know. He had a keen and "pleasantly sardonic" sense of humor. He was reticent about his scientific accomplishments but ready to talk more freely when it came to sporting achievements.

Alfred Walter Campbell

Although some spadework had been done, "it is safe to say that architectonics of the cerebral cortex started with Campbell in England and Brodmann in Germany." Campbell's magnum opus, *Histological studies on the localization of cerebral function* (Cambridge, University Press, 1905), has become a classic, and his map of the human brain has been reproduced in virtually every textbook on neuroanatomy.

While Broadmann thought mainly as a comparative morphologist and evolutionist, Campbell thought fundamentally in terms of function. "Not until the ground is prospected and prepared by the physiologist and clinician can the histologist hope to step in and work with any real measure of success" (*Histological studies* etc.,

Portrait, courtesy of Dr. C. J. Cummins, Sydney, and Dr. Sydney Sunderland, Melbourne, Australia.

p. xix). He worked up three normal human hemispheres, a tremendous task in itself, and studied with the same thoroughness the hemispheres of the chimpanzee, the orang (he later described the brain of a gorilla[1]), and the dog, cat and pig. Fifteen other brains, with pathological changes, were studied for special purposes, such as to clarify the finer organization of the motor cortex and the visual area. Most brains were examined for both cells and fibers. Campbell's subdivisions of the primate cortex were not as fine as those of the German school, but modern architectonics has time and again decided in favor of his sober views.

Other works which have earned for him the respect of the scientific world were those on radicular fields in herpes zoster (with Henry Head)[2] and cerebral sclerosis.[3]

Among his later contributions, his address on *Dr. John Hughlings Jackson*[4] was a model of charm and clarity.

SAN FRANCISCO, CALIFORNIA   GERHARDT von BONIN

References

[1]Rep. Path. Lab. Lunacy Dep., N. S. Wales, 1916, *3:*19–36.   [2]Brain, London, 1900, *23:*353–523.   [3]*Ibid.,* 1905, *28:*367–437.   [4]Med. J. Australia, 1935, *2:*344–347.

References to Biography: 1) Med. J. Australia, 1938, *1:*181–185 (contains bibliography; Parker, Dawson, Wallace).   2) Arch. Neur. Psychiat., Chicago, 1938, *40:*566–568 (Fulton).

GEORGE COGHILL (1872–1941)

*B*ORN and reared on a farm near Beaucoup, Illinois, where incessant toil and even hardship were his lot, George Ellett Coghill early developed a seasoned character, honesty, tenacity of purpose, and inflexibility when it came to dealing with persons of less lofty standards. His education was received at Shurtleff College (Illinois), the University of New Mexico, and Brown University (Rhode Island). In the summer of 1902 he studied with Th. Boveri at Würzburg. After teaching zoology in Oregon at Pacific

University and Willamette University, and in Ohio at Denison University, he became, in 1913, Professor of Anatomy at the University of Kansas, and was head of the department from 1918 to 1925. During the next ten years he was research professor of comparative anatomy at the Wistar Institute of Philadelphia. He was a member of the editorial board of the *Journal of Comparative Neurology* from 1904 until his death, and managing editor from 1927 to 1933.

Coghill's most important contribution was the secure foundation he laid for study of the embryology of behavior. Anatomy did not reach maturity as a science until the origins and relationships of adult structures were revealed by embryology. So also the data

Portrait, courtesy of Dr. O. Larsell, Portland, Oregon.

of animal and human behavior were not knit together into a consistent fabric of firm texture until certain basic principles were discovered by Coghill and validated by him through a rigorous program of embryological research. For intensive study he chose the
salamanders, because their patterns of behavior and their bodily
structure are generalized and yet comparable with those of man.

Coghill's objective was a record of the exact sequence of changes
in patterns of behavior from first motility to the adult, based on
statistically adequate numbers of specimens, and a description of
the correlated stages in the growth of the nervous system. This inquiry was the first, and so far the most complete, account of the
relationships between the progressive differentiation of bodily
structure and the operation of that structure as manifest in overt
behavior. His most fundamental principle was the demonstration
of the primacy of an integrated "total pattern" of organization and
the progressive individuation of local "partial patterns" within
and under the dominance of the integrated whole. This was validated by detailed descriptions of the growth of the mechanisms of
both the total and the partial patterns.[1-6] Up to Coghill's time it
was generally believed that the reflex constituted the unit of behavior, but Coghill showed that efficient movement occurs prior to
the development of reflex mechanisms. In the larvae of Amblystoma, he demonstrated repeatedly that the first movements are
adaptive ones (such as those used in swimming), the coordination
of which is governed by tegmental and other motor centers,[6-8] that
coordinated movements occur before the sensory fibers reach the
periphery, and that only later, when the sensory fibers have
spanned the gap between periphery and central motor fields, do
partial patterns or reflexes come into being. An epitome of his
views and a detailed historical background of neuro-embryology,
in which are discussed the contributions of some of the founders
of neurology with which this volume deals (Vulpian, Remak, His,
Schilder, Pavlov), were presented in his presidential address before the American Association of Anatomists in 1933.[3]

The impact of Coghill's views, which undermined the then current assumptions of behaviorism, not only profoundly influenced
subsequent research in biology and psychology, but also awakened
much controversy. Studies of behavior patterns in mammalian and

human embryos undertaken by several of Coghill's students and others led to divergent interpretations but left his own results on salamanders intact.

An ambitious program for carrying on his investigations on pouch young of the opossum, unimpeded by the difficulties in maintaining an adequate oxygen supply to which experimental work on living non-marsupial mammalian embryos are subject, failed to develop at the Biological Farm of the Wistar Institute, established in 1929 near Fallsington, Pennsylvania. Difficulties arose and frictions developed which caused him to move back to the Institute laboratory in Philadelphia, where he continued his work on Amblystoma. In December, 1935, his connection with the Institute was severed and Coghill, in poor health and facing an uncertain future, saw the collapse of his program.

From 1936 until his death, Coghill lived in retirement at Gainesville, Florida, where, although partially disabled, he established a private laboratory and opossum colony, supported by a small farm. Here his program was revived and he continued his studies on individuation of limb movements in Amblystoma and the opossum. Several younger investigators came to his laboratory from time to time to work with him on various aspects of development of behavior, and a number of papers resulted. Coghill himself published a translation of part of W. Preyer's *Specielle Physiologie des Embryo,* a critical review of the literature on early somatic movements in birds and mammals other than man, and several briefer papers. Although handicapped by physical infirmity and the necessity of providing for his immediate needs and for old age from his farm, he continued his investigations almost to the end, which came on July 23, 1941.

O. LARSELL

References

[1]Correlated anatomical and physiological studies of the growth of the nervous system (Papers I–XII). J. Comp. Neur., 1914–36, vol. 24–64.
[2]*Anatomy and the problem of behavior.* Cambridge, U. P., 1929.
[3]Science, 1933, *78:*131–138.   [4]J. Genet. Psychol., 1936, *48:*3–19.
[5]*Early embryonic somatic movements in birds and in mammals other*

than man. Monogr. Soc. Res. Child Development, National Research
Council, Washington, D.C. Vol. 5, No. 2, 1940.   [6]J. Comp. Neur.
1943, *79:*463–486.   [7]*Ibid.,* 1926, *40:*47–94; *41:*95–152; *42:*1–16; 1931,
*53:*147–168.   [8]Arch. Neur. Psychiat., Chicago, 1929, *21:*989–1009.

*Reference to Biography: George Ellett Coghill, naturalist and phi-
*o o*her.* Chicago, U. of Chicago, 1949 (C. J. Herrick).

ALEXANDER DOGIEL (1852–1922)

*A*LEXANDER STANISLAVOVICH DOGIEL was born in
Panevezys, district of Kaunas, Lithuania. He studied medicine at the University of Kazan where in 1883 he obtained the
M.D., and two years later became instructor in embryology. In
1888 he was appointed lecturer in histology at the University of
Tomsk, and in 1892, professor of histology at the Women's Medical Institute in St. Petersburg, where he remained for the rest of
his life. Here he succeeded in organizing a laboratory of histology,
the products of which attracted world-wide admiration.

Of the Russian investigators who distinguished themselves with
their neurohistological work (Babukin, Yakulovich, Oviasnikov,
Doinikov, Bekhterev) from 1850 to the turn of the century, Dogiel was probably the most outstanding. Boeke regarded him as a
"master of the technique of staining the elements of the nervous
system." He was extraordinarily versatile, prolific, and inspired
throughout his life by a strong belief in the inductive method, the
"réunir des faits pour se donner des idées" of Buffon. Having exceptional linguisitic ability, he published his scientific papers in
Russian, German and French. He had the highest esteem for
Cajal, Golgi and Retzius, to all three of whom he dedicated his
classical monograph on the structure of the spinal ganglia of man
and animals.[1] The magnificent illustrations in this volume are
from his own hand.

Besides his contributions to various medical fields, Dogiel excelled particularly in his studies on the histological structure of
nerve fibers, their somatic distribution, and the functional correlations of motor, and especially sensory, nerve endings. Important

Portrait, courtesy of Dr. Leon Roizin, New York City.

also were his papers on the histology of the sympathetic nervous system and the neuroglia of the retina. But he is best known for his description, in 1889, of the sensory end-corpuscles in skeletal muscle, external genital organs, salivary gland, conjunctiva, and cornea,[2-4] and as an authority on the germane work of Pacini, Merkel and Meissner, Kühne, Ruffini, Golgi, Retzius and Cajal, in the earlier part of the nineteenth century. In ingenuity, Marcello Malpighi (1628-1694) was on a par with this distinguished group. His device in seeking nerves was to separate tissues by boiling—essentially the same procedure used by a cook in peeling a boiled tongue while still hot and steaming. It was thus that he studied first the tongue, then the skin, showing that nerves proceed into papillae (which he likened to the horns of snails). But he erred on two counts: that papillae are terminal expansions of a branching nerve, and that papillae and nerve constitute a hydrostatic system, pressure on the papillae being directly transmitted through the hollow nerve to the brain.[5,6]

Dogiel's classification of the neuron types in the spinal, sympathetic, cardiac and intestinal ganglia (in 1899)[7] has been confirmed by many leading neurohistologists (Marinesco, L. R. Müller, de Castro, Ranson and Billingsley, Terni, Harting), and remains a classical contribution to neurocytology. His demonstration of the presence of sensory fibers in the three extraocular nerves, based on animal experiment,[8] has been widely quoted.

Thanks to his unlimited enthusiasm, he was able to face and overcome the many obstacles he encountered. In 1915, after frequent delays, he succeeded in founding the *Russian Archives of Anatomy, Histology and Embryology*. As editor-in-chief, he was regarded by his collaborators (Kolossov, Mislavsky, Severtsov, Tonkiv, Zavarin, Deineka) as the most critical and accurate of them all. Even during the revolution, he did not relax his efforts, until he was stricken by a fatal cerebral hemorrhage while preparing a manuscript on a favorite subject in histology.

He will always be known for his works on histology, distinguished by their precise and rich documentation, their superb drawings, and their lucid thought.

NEW YORK CITY   LEON ROIZIN

References

[1]*Der Bau der Spinalganglien des Menschen und der Säugetiere.* Jena, Fischer, 1908. [2]Arch. mikr. Anat., 1890, *35*:305–320; 1893, *41*:585–612; 1893, *41*:612–623; 1894, *44*:15–26; 1895, *46*:305–344. [3]Anat. Anz., 1890, *5*:483–494. [4]Arch. russes d'anat., d'hist. et d'embr., 1917, *1*:3. [5]Arch. Derm. Syph., Chicago, 1968, *97*:101–109 (Belloni). [6]Analecta Med.-Hist., vol. 3, *Steno and brain research in the seventeenth century.* Oxford, Pergamon, 1968, p. 193–206 (Belloni). [7]Arch. Anat. Physiol., Anat. Abt., 1899, p. 130–158. [8]Arch. mikr. Anat., 1906, *68*:501–526.

Reference to Biography: Bolshaia meditsinskaia entsiklopediia. Vol. 9. Moscow, 1929 (Semashko).

LUDWIG EDINGER (1855–1918)

E DINGER, founder of modern comparative neuroanatomy, was born in Worms on the Rhine, the eldest son of a self-made, well-to-do textile merchant. When he was fourteen, his mother arranged that he be given a microscope: "I shall never forget my ecstasy. . . . Corkstoppers, flies, house-dust . . . nothing was safe . . ." He learned to embed and mount his own preparations. But he was judged a poor student; on finishing the Gymnasium he flung his books over the garden wall—then went and rescued Homer, Horace, and Sophocles' *Antigone* after all.

At Heidelberg he found the anatomist, Friedrich Arnold (1803–1890), successor to Friedrich Tiedemann, pathetic in his theories and speculations. Old Bunsen, the physicist, he decided not to listen to at all. When examined by Theodor Schwann he forgot whatever he had known of that professor's cell theory. But with Carl Gegenbauer (1826–1903) he caught on. And the one book he chose to take along on his vacation was on comparative histology by E. Leyden (1832–1910), so deeply impressed was he by the lectures on clinical neurology Leyden gave.

At Strassburg, working in the tower over the hospital gate, Edinger found an immense stimulus in Wilhelm Waldeyer

Portrait, courtesy of Mrs. Dora L. Lindley, Pearl River, New York.

(1834–1921). Under his guidance, Edinger finished in 1877 his first neurological paper, *Die Endigung der Hautnerven bei Pterotrachea*.[1] During that year he was assistant to the internist Adolf Kussmaul (1822–1902)—precise, astute (his clinical diagnosis of a tuberculoma in the Rolandic area was later proved correct and his book on aphasia became a classic), always complaining that colleagues could not write decent German. He saw much of Recklinghausen (1833–1910), the gifted pathologist, got to know Stilling's work, and became a friend of Goltz.

Edinger's academic career began in Giessen in 1879 under Franz Riegel (1843–1904). Röntgen was the physicist there, still unknown. In 1881, only twenty-six years old, Edinger was awarded his habilitation. A year he spent in travel, visiting Berlin (with Ehrlich, Wernicke, Westphal), Leipzig (Erb, Strümpell, Möbius, Kraepelin, Flechsig), and Paris (Charcot); in 1883 he settled down in Frankfurt-am-Main as a practising neurologist. But he preferred the laboratory. The microtome he had purchased was set up in his kitchen and his mother's jelly glasses put to use for staining sections. Working on human fetuses in the winter of 1883/84 he identified the spinal course of a fiber group,[2] a forerunner of his later discovery (in 1889) of a "tractus spino-bulbo-thalamicus,"[3,4] a pathway traced previously (in 1885) by Bekhterev only as far craniad as the bulbar reticular formation. In 1885 appeared Edinger's famous text on the structure of the nervous system,[5] an outgrowth of lectures given before the Frankfurt medical society. The world success of the book lay in Edinger's ability to interconnect structure, function, and clinical experience. His attitude toward comparative neurology, so similar to Broca's, was summed up as follows: "Once the configuration of a given structure has been studied in detail in some forms, one can generally easily discover it in other forms even when it is more or less obscured by new additions."

In 1885 he came under the spell of Carl Weigert, who had just perfected his myelin stain, and for the next 20 years hardly a day would pass without some contact between them, often at Edinger's home, with discussions lasting well after midnight. Starting from a work desk at Weigert's Senckenbergisches Pathologisches Institut Edinger built up and financed a Neurological Institute. Married in 1886, his wife became an assistant in the laboratory. He was made Ordinarius in neurology at the newly founded Goethe University of Frankfurt in 1914, and his institute was now financed by a "Ludwig Edinger Stiftung," as part of the University.

His appeal as the foremost teacher of functional anatomy is explained by his dictum that "to investigate brain anatomy alone [and not function] is to pursue a sterile science." He was the first to describe and verify postmortem the syndrome of thalamic pain,[6] a splendid contribution not overshadowed by that of Roussy and Dejerine fifteen years later. In 1909 appeared his volume on the clinical application of neuroanatomy, *Einführung in die Lehre vom Bau und den Verrichtungen des Nervensystems* (Leipzig, Vogel).

Distinguished scientists of many countries joined him in his work. Van Gehuchten and Streeter cooperated in demonstrating the phylogenetic development of the forebrain; Franz and Röthig did the same for the diencephalon, as did also Kurt Goldstein (1878–1965).[7] With Gordon Holmes and Wallenberg, Edinger described the avian brain. Comolli and Shimazono were his co-workers in formulating the modern concept of the cerebellum, while Wallenberg and Ariëns Kappers collaborated in expanding the idea that the olfactory system is related to an oral sense, operative in the recognition, assessment and ingestion of food. It was Edinger who laid the main groundwork for Ariëns Kappers' later contributions, although Th. Ziehen and A. Bethe assisted materially. Ariëns Kappers was working with Edinger particularly on the striatum. "Being with him," he later remarked, "lingers in my memory as the most delightful experience of my life . . . [he] opened up for me the field of comparative fiber anatomy—*his* field." Yet Edinger was perhaps more aware than most of us are today that from the structure of the brain one cannot reach all the conclusions with respect to phylogenesis.

Discoveries he made and terms he coined became household words within one generation. He was the first to describe the ventral and dorsal spinocerebellar tracts and to distinguish between paleo-encephalon and neo-encephalon, between paleo-cerebellum and neo-cerebellum. Other terms he coined were "gnosis" and "praxis," later adopted by Freud and by Liepmann in their descriptions and agnosia and apraxia. The Edinger-Westphal nucleus (identified in fetal human material by Edinger in 1885[8] and in the adult by Carl F. O. Westphal in 1887[9]) became well known to every student of neurology, as did the nucleus in the oculomotor cell complex described in 1889 by his associate in Frankfurt, Perlia.[10] By that time, the presence of a neighboring cell aggregate, the nucleus of Darkschewitsch—which Darkschewitsch called the "upper small-celled oculomotor nucleus" (1885,[11] 1889[12]) had become known. Only much later (in 1911) did Cajal describe an adjacent cell group, the interstitial nucleus, now named after him.[13] While Darkschewitsch apparently described both nuclei as one and the same, Zeri (1895),[14] then Panegrossi (1904),[15] recognized that each was a separate and distinct nucleus.

Profound scientist, brilliant teacher, and able organizer, Edinger also was noted as a hypnotist. A fine artist, too, Edinger would delight his students by simultaneously drawing the intricate structures of the brain with his left hand while writing their legend with his right. His daughter, Dr. Tilly Edinger, relates that while sitting for his portrait at a table, dissecting a brain, he noticed that the artist, Lovis Corinth, was having difficulties in portraying its convolutions and forthwith came to the canvas and painted them himself. He was as devoted to art as he was to science and, like Freud, he always had on his desk some exquisite antique Grecian figurines.

While still at the very height of his powers, full of plans and ideas for the future, he died of a heart attack a few hours after undergoing an operation. A study of his brain, which he often said he hoped someone would undertake, was made by Riese and Goldstein; extraordinarily well-developed occipital lobes as well as other unusual features were observed.[16]

At the centenary jubilee, Wilhelm Krücke, the Director of the Edinger Institute, reminded the guests of the remark Edinger had made at the inaugural of the Institute: "In my work two motives always impelled me. One was my wish to serve clinical neurology as I came to know it under Leyden, Kussmaul and Erb. The other was the attempt to understand better its anatomical substratum, and impart of it what I could to my associates."

F. H. LEWEY

References

[1]Arch. mikr. Anat., 1877, *14*:171–179.   [2]Neur. Cbl., 1885, *4*:73–76. [3]Anat. Anz., 1889, *4*:121–128.   [4]Deut. med. Wschr., 1890, *16*:421– 426.   [5]*Zehn Vorlesungen über den Bau der nervösen Centralorgane des Menschen und der Thiere.* Leipzig, Vogel, 1885 (8th ed., 1911). [6]Zschr. Nervenh., 1891, *1*:262–282.   [7]Neuropsychologia, 1966, *4*:293– 297 (biography of Goldstein, by Denny-Brown).   [8]Neur. Cbl., 1885, *4*:309.   [9]Arch. Psychiat., Berlin, 1887, *18*:846–871.   [10]Arch. Ophth., Berlin, 1889, *35* (Abth. 4):287–308.   [11]Neur. Cbl., 1885. *4*:100–101.   [12]Arch. Anat. Entwcklngsgesch., Lpz., 1889, p. 107–116. [13]*Histologie du système nerveux.* Vol. 2. Paris, Maloine, 1911, p. 262, 263.   [14]Riv. sper. freniat., 1895, *21*:580–641.   [15]Mschr. Psychiat. Neur., 1904, *16*:268–281.   [16]J. Comp. Neur., 1950, *92*:133–168.

References to Biography: 1) Fol. neurobiol., Lpz., 1915, *9*:343–366 (contains bibliography; Ariëns Kappers).   2) Deut. Zschr. Nervenh., 1918, *59*:I–XXXV (contains bibliography; Wallenberg).   3) *Ibid.,* 1915, *53*:425–448 (Ariëns Kappers).   4) Klin. Wschr., 1925, *4*:841– 842 (not signed).   5) Deut. med. Wschr., 1918, *44*:302–303 (Oppen- heim).   6) Münch. med. Wschr., 1918, *65*:272–275 (Dreyfus).   7) Zschr. ges. Neur. Psychiat., 1918, *44*:114–149 (Goldstein).   8) *Lud- wig Edinger 1855–1918.* Wiesbaden, Steiner, 1959 (Krücke, Spatz, Goldstein, Flesch-Thebesius, Lauche; with complete bibliography).

CHARLES FOIX (1882–1927)

CHARLES FOIX, the son of a physician, was born at Salies-de-Béarn, near Bayonne, France. He embarked on the study of medicine in Paris and became interne in 1906, médecin des hôpitaux in 1919, and agrégé in 1923. During his Salpêtrière days he was a pupil of Pierre Marie. Later he gave courses at Guillain's clinic at the Salpêtrière and at Achard's at the Hôpital Beaujon, always distinguishing himself by his wide knowledge and rational approach.

When Foix died at the age of forty-five, France lost one of her finest neurologists. He had approached the problem of focal lesions of the brain by a novel method, namely, the arterial supply.

Charles Foix

Instead of designating lesions by topographic location, he established syndromes that were due to thrombosis of specific arteries. He studied in detail the syndromes produced by occlusion of the posterior[1] and anterior[2] cerebral arteries and their branches and of the pontile arteries,[3] describing among the latter the syndrome of the lateral artery of the bulb,[4] which up to that time was thought due exclusively to occlusion of the posterior inferior cerebellar artery. He was at work on the much larger field of infarction in the regions supplied by the middle cerebral artery when his life was cut short. From a vast material gathered at the Salpêtrière and later at Ivry he compared in minute detail the findings during life and those after death. His clinical perception was swift and sure,

Portrait, courtesy of Dr. Maurice -Levy, Paris, France.

and with an almost photographic memory for detail he could draw from past experience the knowledge to fit the case under discussion.

While lesions of vascular origin were Foix's particular domain, he was also deeply interested in those most intricately constructed regions, the midbrain and interbrain. With Jean Nicolesco (1895–1957),[5] he published an imposing treatise on the anatomy and blood supply of these regions.[6] In 1921, he and his colleagues established histologically in the substantia nigra the lesions considered specific for Parkinsonism,[7] an observation in line with the earlier discovery (in 1913) by Frederic H. Lewy (or Lewey) (1885–1950),[8] then in Breslau, of cytoplasmic inclusion bodies in the substantia nigra and locus coeruleus.[9] Hallervorden, in 1933,[10] opened a new vista by finding neurofibrillary tangles in nerve cells at various sites; but non-specific as were the "Lewy bodies" they too added, in time, to the enigma of Parkinson's syndrome.

Foix described intracerebral centrolobular sclerosis at about the same time that Schilder's work on the subject appeared, so that in some quarters the disorder became known as Schilder-Foix disease. His and Alajouanine's introduction of subacute necrotic myelitis[11] attracted much attention. But their view that the cause was "local endomesovasculitis" was discarded when others found that the myelopathy was due to systemic vascular disease in which the spinal veins also become distended and tortuous.

Another disorder which bears the imprint of Foix is rhythmic myoclonus of the palate, larynx, pharynx and other brain-stem-innervated structures. Described originally by Kupper[12] and by Spencer,[13] and shown postmortem by Klien[14] to be associated with a lesion of the cerebellar hemisphere, Foix and his associate Hillemand[15,16] hit upon a case in which there was degeneration of the central tegmental tract and the reticular formation and pseudohypertrophy of the inferior olivary nucleus. Papers in collaboration with Tinel[17] and Chavany[18] appeared soon afterward. Subsequently, van Bogaert[19,20] raised the question whether one and the same disorder may not arise from lesions at different sites, the genesis of the myoclonus depending on the interruption of functional systems having synapses either in the inferior olivary or in the dentate nucleus. He and Bertrand[21] came a step nearer the solution in their report of a case in which the inferior olivary and dentate nuclei were degenerated and the central tegmental tract and the reticular formation as well. This concept introduced, it was but a short step for Guillain and Mollaret[22] to provide evidence that a break in any part of the olivo-dentato-rubro-olivary triangle could produce the disorder, a view since refuted in part by the observation that a rubro-olivary pathway does not exist. The importance of the pseudohypertrophy of the inferior olivary nucleus in development of the myoclonus was later stressed by Lhermitte and Trelles.[23]

To return to Foix, he was a versatile individual. Although primarily interested in neurology, he was placed in charge of a tuberculosis service after World War I and acquitted himself well. When the time came for his inaugural lecture, he was given four hours in which to prepare a discourse on the splenic anemias, and did so brilliantly. Outside the field of medicine his chief interest was poetry, and some of his longer poems dealing with classical subjects ranked well with those of his literary contemporaries. Even better were his lyrics, which preserved for posterity a certain grace of expression that stamped the author as a man of understanding, sympathy and poetic vision.

He was of medium height, with mobile expression and dancing eyes. He let his hair grow in ringlets over the left side of his head, and would sweep the unruly locks away from his face when bending over a patient. His voice was warm, vibrant, and captivating. Gentleness and kindness endeared him to his friends and students. Some of them imitated his brisk walk, his staccato speech, and his quick reponses which, although they seemed superficial in others, were exact and to the point in Foix.

SAN FRANCISCO, CALIFORNIA   WALTER FREEMAN

References

[1]Presse méd., 1923, *31(1)*:361 365 (with Masson).   [2]Encéphale, 1925, *20*:209–232 (with Hillemand).   [3]Rev. méd., Paris, 1926, *43*:287–305 (with Hillemand).   [4]Rev. neur., Paris, 1925, *1*:160–179 (with Hillemand and Schalit).   [5]*Nicoleso. Travaux scientifiques.* Paris, Masson, 1959, p. 5–9 in Preface (biographies of Nicolesco by van Bogaert and

Nicolau).   [6]*Anatomie cérébrale. Les noyaux gris centraux et la région mesencephalo-sous-optique; suivi d'une appendice sur l'anatomie pathologique de la maladie de Parkinson.* Paris, Masson, 1925.   [7]Rev. neur., Paris, 1921, *28*:593–600.   [8]A.M.A. Arch. Neur. Psychiat., Chicago, 1951, *66*:114–115 (biography of Lewey; anon.).   [9]Deut. Z. Nervenh., 1913, *50*:50–55.   [10]Klin. Wschr., 1933, *12*:692–695. [11]*Ibid.*, 1926, *33*:1–42.   [12]Arch. Ohrenh., 1873, *1*:296–297.   [13]Lancet, London, 1886, *2*:702.   [14]Neur. Cbl., 1907, *26*:245–254.   [15]Rev. neur., Paris, 1924, *1*:451–452 *et seq.*   [16]*Ibid.*, 1924, *2*:501–503. [17]*Ibid.*, 1924, *2*:503–506.   [18]*Ibid.*, 1926, *1*:942–956.   [19]*Ibid.*, 1925, *2*:189–200.   [20]*Ibid.*, 1926, *1*:977–988.   [21]*Ibid.*, 1928, *1*:203–214. [22]*Ibid.*, 1931, *2*:545–566.   [23]Encéphale, 1933, *28*:588–600.

References to Biography: 1) Rev. neur., Paris, 1927, *34*:441–446 (Roussy).   2) Aesculape, Paris, 1927, *17*:243–251 (Vinchon).

ARTHUR van GEHUCHTEN (1861–1914)

*P*IERRE LOUIS ARTHUR van GEHUCHTEN was born in Antwerp. As a student, he was trained in the laboratory of the biologist, Jean-Baptiste Carnoy, in Louvain. After studying in Berlin and Frankfurt-am-Main, he returned, at the age of twenty-six, to the Catholic University of Louvain to take charge of descriptive anatomy.

In 1890 appeared his first paper, which dealt with the olfactory mucosa of mammals as revealed by the Golgi method. This was the beginning of years of research on the olfactory bulb, optic lobes, cerebellum, spinal cord, innervation of the hair follicles, etc., an account of which is to be found in Lewellys F. Barker's classic volume on *The nervous system and its constituent neurons* (New York, Stechert, 1909). Van Gehuchten's work on the structure of nerve cells and his promulgation of the theory of dynamic polarization in 1891[1] helped to establish the neuron doctrine.

In 1900 he began the publication of his journal, *Le Névraxe,* in which many of his papers appeared. His early work had laid the foundations for his first textbook, *Anatomie du système nerveux de l'homme* (Lierre, In, 1893), which went to several editions; the second edition, published in 1897, ranks with the greatest anatomic works of our time. The journal and textbook had a lasting

influence on neurological teaching and research in other countries, as did also his *Les centres nerveux cérébro-spinaux* (Louvain, Uystpruyst-Dieudonné, 1908). These were fruitful years in the de-

Portrait, courtesy of the National Library of Medicine, Bethesda, Maryland.

lineation of nerve tracts: Probst[2-5] carried out monumental studies on the course of tracts from the brain stem to the thalamus, including the termination there of the medial lemniscus and brachium conjunctivum; Wallenberg[6] elucidated the trigeminal lemniscus; von Monakow,[7] Held[8] and Lewy[9] traced the course of auditory pathways through the brain stem; and Mott,[10] Choroschko,[11] Goldstein[12] and Collier and Buzzard[13] charted the course of the lateral spinothalamic tract to its termination. Van Gehuchten worked in all these fields, providing new facets here, dissenting there, always evaluating what was new and giving it proper perspective.

As time went on, van Gehuchten became more preoccupied with clinical neurology, contributing papers on a variety of subjects, including poliomyelitis, syringomyelia, and aphasia, which culminated in 1941 in a textbook of neurology.[14] His interest in clinical neurology had, indeed, always been keen. In 1897 he entered the controversy on the nature of the motor disturbances in cerebral palsy,[15] but he added nothing substantially new to the knowledge of the disorder which the pioneer English orthopedist William John Little (1810–94)[16] had described in 1862 under the term "spastic rigidity" and which he considered to be due to asphyxia neonatorum. In 1884 von Strümpell attempted to distinguish acquired from congenital forms[17] and in 1893[18,19] and 1897[20] Sigmund Freud's important work on the subject appeared.

Van Gehuchten's habits were those of an ascetic and as regular as clockwork: he would lecture in the early morning hours, work in his laboratory until late afternoon—singing all the while—then take a long walk with his dog, after which he would return to the laboratory. His friendliness and diligence in research made him a favored scholar and attracted many investigators to his laboratory. The anniversary of his twenty-fifth year of service to the University on December 1, 1912, was the occasion for a great ceremony in Louvain, at which scientists from every quarter of the globe gathered to do him honor. But the homage paid him was not the usual two-edged weapon, for he continued to find full support for his work.

Van Gehuchten's work and his journal came to an untimely end in 1914 when World War I broke out. His laboratory, country home and manuscripts destroyed, he sought refuge in England. He was received at Cambridge, where he was given a position and the use of laboratory facilities in the Research Hospital. There, with a hopeful spirit, he set himself the task of repeating the work on which he had been engaged at Louvain, but the sudden development of volvulus interrupted his studies as they were recommencing. He died of a heart attack shortly after an emergency operation for appendicitis. He had done an immense amount of pioneer work in his fifty-three years.

JAMES W. PAPEZ

References

[1]Cellule, Louvain, 1891, 7:81–122.   [2]Mschr. Psychiat., 1900, 7:387–404.   [3]Arch. Psychiat., Berlin, 1900, 33:1–57.   [4]Ibid., p. 721–817. [5]Mschr. Psychiat., 1901, 10:288–309.   [6]Anat. Anz., 1900, 18:81–105. [7]Arch. Psychiat., Berlin, 1891, 22:1–26.   [8]Arch. Anat. Physiol., Anat. Abt., 1891, p. 279–299.   [9]Folia neurobiol., Lpz., 1909, 2:471–518. [10]Brain, London, 1895, 18:1–20.   [11]Mschr. Psychiat., 1909, 26:534–545.   [12]Neur. Cbl., 1910, 29:898–911.   [13]Brain, London, 1903, 26:559–591.   [14]Les maladies nerveuses. Louvain, Librairie Universitaire, 1914 (4th ed., 1936).   [15]Rev. neur., Paris, 1897, 5:558–559. [16]Tr. Obst. Soc. London, 1862, 3:293–344.   [17]Jahrb. Kinderh., 1884, 22:173–178.   [18]Rev. neur., Paris, 1893, 1:177–183.   [19]Neur. Cbl., 1893, 12:512–515 et seq.   [20]Die infantile Cerebrallähmung. Wien, Hölder, 1897.

References to Biography: 1) Bull. Acad. méd. Belgique, 1920, 4.sér., 30:961–978 (Henrijean).   2) Med. tschr. geneesk., 1914, 50:2071–2075 (Winkler).

ROSS HARRISON (1870–1959)

*R*OSS HARRISON belongs to the small international group that, beginning in the 1890's, prepared the channels in which the science of development now runs. He was the most medically oriented of the great experimental embryologists; probably also the most rigorous not only in framing physicochemical expla-

nations, but also in seeking mathematical expressions for the phenomena of development.

Ross Granville Harrison was born in Germantown, Pennsylvania, and grew up mainly in Baltimore. He entered Johns Hopkins University in 1886 and received the Ph.D. in 1894. In 1892–93 he spent a highly important year in the laboratory of Moritz Nussbaum in Bonn, Germany. There he returned for several shorter periods in the following years; in 1896 he married a German wife, Ida Lange. He eventually took the M.D. at Bonn in 1899; he never practised medicine.

After obtaining the Ph.D., Harrison taught biology for a year at

Portrait, courtesy of Dr. Dorothea Rudnick, New Haven, Connecticut.

Bryn Mawr College, then joined the Anatomy Department of Johns Hopkins Medical School, with F. P. Mall. In 1907 he was called to Yale to revivify Zoology there; his bringing together undergraduate and graduate instruction with research facilities in a single Department—a novelty in the administrative history of that university—was soon given material form by the construction of the Osborn Laboratories in 1913. He remained at Yale for the rest of his life, a highly admired figure both locally and internationally. After his retirement, Harrison served as Chairman of the National Research Council (1938 to 1946).

Harrison's first role in neuroembryology was a classical one. If today the cellular origin of the components of the vertebrate nervous system, central and peripheral, is accepted dogma, the reason is that Harrison, during his years in Mall's laboratory, performed and analyzed the necessary experiments. His German sojourns had brought the microsurgical methods of Born to his attention; he rapidly mastered the required manipulations, the culture methods, and the selection of the most favorable local species of Amphibia. He showed[1] that removal of the neural crest just after closure of the embryonic neural tube would eliminate spinal ganglia, dorsal roots, and sensory components of the spinal nerves, as well as sheath cells. Similarly, removal of the ventral half of the neural tube would eliminate the motor component. In another set of experiments[2] he showed that skeletal muscle can undergo histogenesis in the absence of innervation. Further, by raising tadpoles in anaesthetic solutions he demonstrated that motor activity during development is not necessary either for morphological differentiation or for coordinated reflex function in the larva.

Harrison's earliest studies, on the morphogenesis of fins in bony fish, had faced him with the question of peripheral innervation. His first transplantation studies on nerves regenerating in tadpoles, or developing in abnormal situations, had early convinced him of the correctness of the view of His and Cajal, that nerve fibers are outgrowths of single neurons, and do not originate in cell chains or organize by means of protoplasmic bridges. To test this view conclusively, he transferred bits of Amphibian medullary tube to sterile hanging drops of clotted frog lymph, where he could observe their development continuously in a noncellular environment. In 1907 he announced the first successful animal tissue culture.[3] His elegant figures showing outgrowth of unmistakable nerve fibers from neuroblasts *in vitro*,[4] together with his thoroughly documented analysis, left no room for further questioning the neuron principle; and his conclusions as to the stereotropism of the growing nerve fiber have yet to be improved on.

On completing the neuroblast studies, Harrison returned to the investigation of more complex units of the embryo: organ rudiments such as the ear, the eye, and regions of the central nervous system. This analysis was carried out by means of systematic transplantations, over relevant developmental stages, involving critical orientation of the axes of the rudiment with reference to those of the host. This was an approach foreshadowed in his early grafting experiments with the tail and the lateral line system. The analysis focussed not only on the regulative or mosaic properties of differentiation within the rudiment, but also on its polarity and symmetry relative to its host surroundings, to the regulation of its growth, and to patterns of regeneration. His studies of the Urodele forelimb furnish the model for these organ-studies.[5]

It seems fair to say that Harrison's tissue-culture experiment and the work that led up to it ended a controversy and closed a chapter in embryology, whereas his later studies belong among the great seminal contributions to biology. None of Harrison's original articles and review lectures,[6] nor his gallant if premature attempt to ascertain molecular orientation in the embryo,[7] have lost any of their power to stimulate inquiry, even though the experiments themselves seem to leave nothing more to do for his successors.

Harrison's work and personality attracted a number of highly able students and research fellows. Many of these in turn have made impressive contributions to neural science: for example, Davenport Hooker's monumental assemblage of material on the development of reflexes in the human fetus, or the imposing analyses of early development of the Amphibian nervous system that we owe to S. R. Detwiler, L. S. Stone, and their students.

Harrison influenced all biology in this century also by the powerful fascination of his humane and creative scholarship. There was a high-precision analytic drive, balanced against the broadest synthetic view of his material; a sober devotion to fact, balanced against an uncompromising aesthetic in execution. He had been born into a fortunate situation: the American universities were coming of age, so that an academic career was open; and the solid uncluttered education of his place and period left scope for independent individual development. Harrison came to his profession with a sound scientific and mathematical background; he also was a skilled draftsman, a good outdoor naturalist, had the habit of wide reading, and a fine feeling for words and logic. He spoke and wrote an excellent German, had literary command of Latin and the Romance languages, and even some knowledge of Slavic tongues. His diversions were travelling, walking, sailing, mountain climbing, gardening, music, good cheer, and good company.

The fascination was that this versatile, rather salty, genial character was covered by a cloak of gentle self-effacement or even total withdrawal. His figure, often judged the epitome of scholarly asceticism, was slight and spare; the face long, narrow, and generously modelled, with near-sighted gray eyes that could twinkle disarmingly. Despite the perfection of his manners, he was capable of interminable silences in company and famous for not answering letters. When he was in a talking mood, his conversation was unhurried, his sentences well composed. The precision and extent of his memory were prodigious, but his use of it always discreet; his stories at the laboratory lunch-table were invariable light and ironic; he excelled in the epigrammatic and quietly revealing *mot de situation* or the gnomic Goethean quotation. It was almost impossible to induce Harrison to talk about his own work in company: one had to catch him unawares. He quite obviously enjoyed the racy talk of young people in the laboratory; perhaps the most telling commentary on his character is that, once the ice of shyness was broken, the students saved their best stories for him.

NEW HAVEN, CONNECTICUT   DOROTHEA RUDNICK

References

[1]Amer. J. Anat., 1906, *5*:121–131.   [2]*Ibid.*, 1904, *3*:197–220.   [3]Proc. Soc. Exp. Biol., N.Y., 1907, *4*:140–143.   [4]J. Exp. Zool., 1910, *9*:787–846.   [5]*Ibid.*, 1918, *25*:413–461; *ibid.*, 1921, *32*:1–136; Arch. Entwmech., 1925, *106*:469–502.   [6]Wilens (Ed.), *Organization and development of the embryo.* New Haven, Yale, 1969 (Harrison).   [7]J. Exp. Zool., 1940, *85*:337–363.

References to Biography and Works: 1) *Of scientists and salamanders.* San Francisco, Freeman, 1966 (Twitty).   2) *Biographical memoirs of the National Academy of Sciences,* 1961, 35:132–162 (contains bibliography; Nicholas).   3) *Biographical memoirs of Fellows of the Royal Society,* 1961, 7:111–126 (Abercrombie).

CORNELIUS ARIËNS KAPPERS (1877–1946)

*I*N GRONINGEN, the Netherlands, Cornelius Ubbo was born into the scholarly Kappers family. His father liked to call himself Ariëns, that is "the son of Ariën" (Kappers), Ariën being a fairly common Dutch forename. And so, semiofficially, the patronymic Ariëns got attached to the Kappers family name—a bane ever after to registrars and compilers of indexes.

Cornelius attended schools at Leeuwarden, then entered the University of Amsterdam, where Winkler and van Rees were among his teachers. Here he soon found his life work and followed it consistently. His doctoral thesis, based on his research at the Marine Biological Station at Naples, on the structure of the brain of teleosts and selachians, won honors in 1904. He then received an appointment in neuropathology at the University Hospitals in Amsterdam, but in 1906 joined Edinger's Senckenbergisches Pathologisches Institut at Frankfurt-am-Main, and shortly was made chief of the laboratory. Here a great part of his future thinking was determined, and in many ways he followed and expanded Edinger's methods and concepts, particularly in regard to the neo-, archi-, and paleo-subdivisions of the various parts of the brain.

In 1907 he published his first paper on neurobiotaxis,[1] and as years went by he continued to develop this theory of nuclear position which so greatly intrigued him. Although the early postulates as to the mechanisms involved have not been verified, and a number of exceptions to the rule are now apparent, the theory, as restated in 1927,[2] has been of great use in stimulating research and in drawing attention to certain general principles in comparative neuroanatomy.

In 1908 Kappers was unanimously elected director of the Central Institute for Brain Research in Amsterdam, which was

founded, in part for him, by the Royal Dutch Academy of Science; the Institute was patterned after the Edinger Institute in Frankfurt. He remained loyal to the Institute in spite of invitations to professorships of much greater personal advantage from the Universities of Leiden and Yale. A just reward came in 1929 when he was elected to the chair of comparative neuroanatomy at the University of Amsterdam. He held these two positions for the rest of his life. Many honors were accorded him; among them were de-

Portrait, courtesy of A. Ariëns Kappers, Jr., Amsterdam. (Photograph taken in 1928 on receiving Honorary Doctorate of Science at Yale University.)

grees from the Universities of Dublin, Glasgow, Yale and Chicago. He was a member of the Royal Dutch Academy of Science, and a Fellow of the Royal Society of Edinburgh.

Ariëns Kappers was a tall, well-built man, courteous and dignified in bearing, with a genial twinkle in his eye, and a friendliness which could be relied on. He welcomed students at the Institute without regard to race or creed. His contacts with students and colleagues at the Institute, on numerous lecture tours, and as visiting professor at the Peiping Union Medical School and the American University at Beirut, developed in them a sound interest in and respect for comparative neuroanatomy.

In his researches, which covered all parts of the nervous system, he clearly demonstrated the continuing usefulness of the comparative method for elucidating the complexity of the structure and functions of the brains of the higher mammals and of man. His concepts were presented in an encyclopedic treatise published in German in 1920[3] and reissued in a much enlarged English edition in collaboration with G. Carl Huber and Elizabeth Caroline Crosby in 1936.[4] A second treatise, in French, prepared in collaboration with E. H. Strasburger, was published posthumously.[5] In the latter he included a summary of his more recent interests on the fissuration of the cortex in modern and prehistoric man and its anthropologic bearing. These interests were stimulated by his visit to China in 1924 and intensified while in Syria in 1929 and led him naturally into the field of anthropology during his later years.

During World War II he worked for his country with intense patriotism and lived to see peace and freedom again established. His end came suddenly while working in his garden on July 28, 1946.

ROCKVILLE, MARYLAND   DAVID McK. RIOCH

References

[1]Neur. Cbl., 1907, 26:834–840.   [2]Acta psychiat. neur., Kbh., 1927, 2:118–145.   [3]Die vergleichende Anatomie des Nervensystems der Wirbeltiere und des Menschen. 2 vol. Haarlem, Bohn, 1920–21 (with Fortuyn).   [4]The comparative anatomy of the nervous system of vertebrates, including man. 2 vol. New York, Macmillan, 1936. [5]Anatomie comparée du système nerveux, particulièrement de celui des mammifères et de l'homme. Haarlem, Bohn, 1947.

References to Biography: 1) J. Comp. Neur., 1946, *85:*309–311 (Crosby). 2) Med. tschr. geneesk., 1946, *90:*1917–1927 (van Valkenburg). 3) Yearb. Roy. Soc. Edinb., 1947, p. 19–21 (Dott).

VITTORIO MARCHI (1851–1908)

*M*ARCHI was born in Novellara (Reggio Emilia), Italy. He studied at the University of Modena where, in 1873, he obtained the Ph.D. in chemistry and pharmacology, and in 1882 the M.D. Soon thereafter he was appointed assistant in anatomy at the University of Modena and prosector at the Mental Hospital of San Lazzaro in Reggio Emilia. In 1883 he obtained a fellowship under Golgi (in Pavia), and after the completion of a year's work he stayed on as Golgi's assistant.

In 1885, Marchi became assistant to Luciani, who at that time was directing the Istituto di Fisiologia at the University of Florence. Although Luciani encouraged him to concentrate on cerebellar physiology, Marchi's heart was in histological problems. Consequently, in 1887, he competed for the chair of histology at the University of Palermo, and was placed third among the elegible candidates. This hurt him deeply; he renounced the academic career and decided to become a country doctor in San Benedetto del Tronto. In 1890 he was appointed chief of the Hospital of Jesi, where he was successful in organizing a neurological clinic and a histological laboratory.

There Marchi finally made his permanent residence and continued to work until his premature death, which occurred under tragic conditions: he had just returned from a visit to his old master, Luciani, with whom he had made arrangements to do some experimental investigations, when his middle ear became infected; symptoms of meningitis ensued, and in agonizing pain he correctly diagnosed his condition, called in a friend to whom he accurately predicted the time of his death—which came three days later.

Marchi's name became internationally known in connection with his and Algieri's observation in 1885[1] and 1886[2] that the products formed in degenerating myelin sheaths could be stained specifically by osmic acid after mordanting with a chromic salt. The year 1885 was an auspicious one in neurohistologic research.

Vittorio Marchi

for it marked the discovery of the aniline staining method by Nissl. As Rasmussen reminds us, osmic acid as a staining agent was used first by Fr. Schultze in 1849 and was popularized by Max Schultze in 1864, who employed it in the staining of myelin sheaths, as did Rudneff in 1865. But the method as devised by Marchi was immediately recognized as a new approach for histopathologic studies, for it now became possible to follow myelinated fibers from their source almost to their termination; his method "set the stamp of final approval." Through its use, investigators of many countries have been able to determine accurately the anatomo-topographic distribution of various degenerative processes involving the central and peripheral nervous pathways. The Swank-Davenport modification of the Marchi method is one of the most widely used today.[3]

Marchi's most outstanding contributions to neuroanatomy were those based on descending degeneration following experimentally induced lesions of the various regions of the cerebral cortex[2] and the origin and destination of fibers in the cerebellar peduncles.[4,5] He published, in all, twenty-one papers.

Marchi was a modest and persevering investigator who, due to ill-fated circumstances, was unable to use to full extent the staining technique he discovered; but it served other investigators in making fundamental contributions to the normal and pathologic histology of the central and peripheral nervous systems.

NEW YORK CITY   LEON ROIZIN

References

[1]Riv. sper. freniat., 1885, *11*:492–494.   [2]*Ibid.*, 1886, *12*:208–252. [3]Stain Techn., 1934, *9*:129–135.   [4]*Sull'origine e decorso dei peduncoli e sui loro rapporti cogli altri centri nervosi.* Firenze, LeMonnier, 1891. (Publicazioni del R. Ist. studi sup. pratici. Sez. scienze fisiche e naturali. No. 18.)   [5]Nota prev. lab. fisiol. R. Ist. studi sup. Firenze, 1886.

References to Biography and Works: 1) Arch. Ital. biol., 1908, *49*:149–152 (contains bibliography; Luciani).   2) *Some trends in neuroanatomy.* Dubuque, Brown, 1947 (Rasmussen).

JEAN NAGEOTTE (1866–1948)

*N*AGEOTTE was born in the picturesque old French city of Dijon. His medical studies, undertaken in Besançon, were completed in Paris, where in 1889 he became interne des hôpitaux. He received his medical degree in 1893, and was appointed physician to the Bicêtre in 1898. After more than a decade there, he

Jean Nageotte

joined (in 1912) the staff of the Salpêtrière and succeeded Ranvier in what then became the chair of comparative histology in the Collège de France. His training as a physician and his study of pathological anatomy, carried on as opportunity offered, provided splendid training for the field of normal histology.

His doctoral thesis and some later contributions dealt with tabes dorsalis.[1-5,10] From the study of the nervous system of tabetics he concluded that the initial lesion occurs in the dorsal root component of the mixed spinal (or radicular) nerve, since called the "radicular nerve of Nageotte." His masterly technique also brought out *boutons terminaux* of the spinal cord in great profusion.[6] Further, in a unique case of tumor confined to the facial nerve in which degenerated nerve fibers proceeded centralward, he found (in Marchi preparations) that fibers of the nervus intermedius traverse the spinal tract of the trigeminal nerve, and termi-

Portrait from Presse médicale (vol. 69, p. 837, 1948), redrawn by Van Cott.

nate in a bulbo-pontile nucleus that blends with the nucleus soli-
tarius; he called this the "gustatory nucleus"[7]—a conclusion only
recently confirmed. With Babinski, he formulated a clinical syndrome resulting from lesions of the medulla oblongata (the syndrome of Babinski-Nageotte),[8] and the two of them also collaborated in writing a book on the cerebrospinal fluid.[9]

As his interest in normal histology increased, Nageotte, employing what were then new techniques, undertook a comprehensive
study of the structure of the nerve fiber, particularly the myelin
sheath.[6,10-12] Like other observers he believed that the myelin sheath
was a derivative of the axis cylinder and that it consisted of living
protoplasm teeming with mitochondria: according to him this
sheath had "vegetative" function. The sheath of Schwann (the neu-
rolemma of modern terminology), he observed, was composed of
neuroglia that had migrated peripherally and taken on a syncytial
form; to him it was concerned with nutrition of the axis cylinder.
Subsequently he studied the various stages of degeneration following injury of the peripheral nerves, and then turned his attention
to the problem of nerve regeneration; in this field he was successful
in grafting into dogs heteroplastic nerves previously fixed in alcohol.[13] On the basis of these results, Nageotte advocated the use of
alcohol-fixed heteroplastic transplants for human nerve repair, believing them to be superior to fresh autoplastic transplants. This
was during World War I. Most workers today do not share this
opinion.

Nageotte's interest in the nerve fiber, and particularly in the
myelin sheath, continued throughout his academic career. He became absorbed in the chemical constitution of myelin and presented an interesting theory of its molecular structure.[14] It was his
belief that the anatomical characteristics of this sheath, for instance, its discontinuity at the nodes of Ranvier, are manifestations of its chemical composition. He devoted a great amount of
energy also to a study of connective tissue.

From Thiébaut we learn that Nageotte was not only a talented,
conscientious physician and investigator, but also a devotee of classical literature. The pleasures which Paris so liberally provides did
not seem to interest him. Though inclined to be sarcastic and slow
to make friends, he deeply admired such prominent men of his
day as Ramón y Cajal, Ross Harrison, Gombault, Babinski, Ray-

mond, Chaslin, and Caullery. He greatly valued the assistance and councel of his wife, a distinguished pediatrician, who, for a time, presided over the Société de Pédiatrie. Together they reached as lofty a pinnacle as did the Dejerines and the Vogts. In 1923, as the result of an accident, Nageotte became paralyzed and thereafter was seldom free from pain. Gradually he became deaf. The occupation of his country by the German Army during World War II brought him much sorrow, for his wife died during this period, one of his daughters was imprisoned, and his son-in-law was deported by the Germans. However, he lived to see his country liberated.

ANN ARBOR, MICHIGAN   ELIZABETH C. CROSBY
BIRMINGHAM, ALABAMA

References

[1]*Tabès et paralysie générale.* Paris, Steinheil, 1893.   [2]Bull. Soc. anat. Paris, 1894, *69*:808–820.   [3]C. rend. Soc. Biol., Paris, 1900, 2.sér., *52*:354–356.   [4]*Ibid.,* 1902, 4.sér., *54*:1226–1228.   [5]*Pathogénie du tabès dorsal.* Paris, Naud, 1903.   [6]*La structure fine du système nerveux.* Paris, Maloine, 1905.   [7]Rev. neur. Psychiat., Prague, 1906, *4*:473–488.   [8]Rev. neur., Paris, 1902, *10*:358–365. [9]*Contribution à l'étude du cytodiagnostic du liquide céphalo-rachidien dans les affections nerveuses.* Tours, Maretheux, 1901.   [10]Nouv. Iconog. Salpêtrière, 1906, *19*:217–238.   [11]C. rend. Soc. Biol., Paris, 1910, *68*:39–42.   [12]Arch. mikr. Anat., 1911, 77:245–279.   [13]C. rend. Soc. Biol. Paris, 1918, *81*:761–764.   [14]*Morphologie des gels lipoides, myé'ine, cristaux liquides, vacuoles.* Paris, Hermann, 1937.

References to Biography: 1) Presse méd., 1948, *69*:837–838 (Thiébaut). 2) Bull. Soc. méd. hôp. Paris, 1948, 4.sér., *64*:1264–1266 (anonymous).

FRIDJHOF NANSEN (1861–1930)

STATEMENTS are common that Nansen shares with Wilhelm His and August Forel the priority in establishing the anatomical independence of the nerve cell. But the statements are desultory, and considering Nansen's eminence in other fields, as well as the need to complete the record, something more definite

The inscription reads: "Fritjof Nansen. Madame Golgi et M-. le Prof. C. Golgi. Souvenir. Bergen 9.3.87."

Portrait, courtesy of Madame Carolina Papini Golgi, Rome.

ought to be said about his actual contributions to the understanding of the neuron. All three men published their key observations in 1887—His on human embryos, Forel on anterograde and retrograde degenerative changes resulting from lesions in the human central nervous system, Nansen on invertebrates and lower vertebrates. The story takes some poignancy from the fact that as a disciple of Golgi, Nansen was reared in the enemy camp, so to speak, and in most points was not unfaithful to his master. It turns out that any generalizations one wishes to make about neurohistologists, or, for that matter, about polar explorers, he must take into account the life of Fridjhof Nansen.

From the time of his enrollment in the University at Christiania[1] (later Oslo), in 1880, Nansen concentrated his efforts on zoology. In the spring of 1882 he joined a six-month expedition into the seas near Greenland on the sealing-ship *Viking* and in the vicinity of Spitzbergen obtained some of his most prized Myzostomes (short, indistinctly segmented, disk-shaped ectoparasitic annelid worms, closely related to polychaets; they are found on echinoderms, such as crinoids and starfishes). On return, he was offered the post of Curator of the Zoological Division of the Natural History Museum at Bergen. He had few qualifications for the position aside from enthusiasm, but accepted. He was twenty-one at the time.

For weeks on end during the next five years Nansen worked in his laboratory at peak intensity, hardly raising his eyes from his microscope, then would set out into the mountains. In 1884 he once did what even his most adventurous friends thought foolhardy: in deep winter he crossed the mountains from Bergen to Christiania and back again, mostly by ski, 220 miles each way. This brought fame to him in Norwegian circles and enabled him to settle down again for a time with his Myzostomes. In this he persisted, turning down an offer of a post at Yale University tendered by a frequent visitor, Professor Marsh. Perhaps the factor that influenced him the most to stay in Norway was what he read one morning in the newspaper (in 1883), bearing the headline: *Nordenskiöld Back from Greenland gives Vivid Account of Interior.*

In his earliest publications[2,3] on the central nervous system of

Myzostomes and the hag-fish, *Myxine glutinosa,* Nansen raised
more questions as to histology than he could answer. "We have
such great technical difficulties to contend with that . . . for some
time to come we shall probably have to content ourselves more or
less with assumptions."[2] He felt frustrated and was later to remark
that he regretted that he did not select physics as his field; the
years spent as zoologist, he felt, could have been used better.

The year 1884 was the turning point. He had had the good fortune, as he related, of coming upon some articles by Camillo
Golgi. Finding that Golgi's *réaction noire* (silver chromate
method) brought solutions to his questions, he decided that he
must visit Golgi. The Director of the Museum, Dr. Daniel C. Dan-
ielsen, concurred that he had earned a vacation. The gold medal
he had been awarded for his work on the Myzostomes he cashed in
for railroad tickets. In February, 1886, he set out on a journey of
about six months, touring the natural history museums in Germany, then spending some weeks in Naples at the Marine Zoological Station with Professor Dohrn, and sending his impressions of
the station to the Norwegian journal, *Naturen.*[4] Finally he ended
up with Golgi in Pavia, where, for a month or so, he examined sections prepared, as he stated, by a method [silver chromate] that far
surpasses any hitherto known.

Back again in Bergen, Nansen soon acquired a great store of
new specimens ranging from mollusks to small mammals. Observations made on this array resulted in a paper on "The natural history of lower vertebrates"[5] and another on "The 3rd eye of the
vertebrates, cyclops."[6] But his most important was a monograph
entitled, *The structure and combination of the histological elements of the central nervous system* (in English) (Bergens
Museums Årseberetning, 1886–87), in which many species were
dealt with. An abbreviated version[7] went to the University at
Christiania as a thesis for the Ph.D., an ordeal for which he was
preparing himself. Another publication,[8] noted, as were his others,
for his elegant drawings of nerve cells and nerve fibers, is equally
imposing.

The monograph carries the description and the illustrations, of
an important detail (in *Myxine glutinosa*), which Nansen was the
first to note: each dorsal root nerve fiber ("nerve tube," "nerve

cylinder"), just after entering the spinal cord, or even before entering, divides into an ascending and a descending branch, both of which give off numerous collaterals to various cord segments.

The central nervous system of the Myzostomes, Nansen found, is much like that of other Annelids and that of Arthropods. Parts of it are made up of ganglionic cell-masses which contain nerve and glial cells—isolated or in groups—while other parts are devoid of cells. The components free from nerve cells were called "central fibrillary masses," "the *Punktsubstanz* of Franz von Leydig" (1857), "and the reticular fibrillary net of Béla Haller" (1858).

Nansen's account of the components of the nerve cell—dendrites, cell body and axon (or neurite), for the central nervous system, and ganglion cell and central and peripheral processes (neurites) for the peripheral nervous system—does not deviate materially from the present-day concept. Neurites, he stated, fall into two groups (as Golgi had also observed): the neurites of *motor nerve cells*, which traverse the fibrillary masses and emerge in the peripheral nerves as "nerve cylinders" (the homologue of axis cylinders of vertebrates) and the neurites of *sensory nerve cells*, which do not traverse the masses, but, instead, enter the masses, then divide into a multitude of fibrillary branches, and participate in the formation of "fibrillary plexuses." The axons of motor cells give off, along their course—stated Nansen—fine collaterals which merely mingle with the sensory fibrillary plexuses.[7]

In Nansen's time, anastomoses between nerve cells or their processes as they related to the central fibrillary masses no longer needed to haunt histologists, as that issue had finally been laid to rest by the rarely quoted investigator Buchholz in 1863 and by Solbrig in 1872 (though, Hardesty and Held reverted to the syncytial idea in 1902–1904). Nerve cells, Nansen re-emphasized, are never in direct continuity with one another, neither through their axonal nor their dendritic processes.[7] To him, nerve fibers, both central and peripheral, were made up of longitudinally oriented "primitive tubules," the latter containing "hyaloplasm," which is "the real nervous substance." Each primitive tubule was enveloped by sheaths of "spongioplasm," and each nerve tube (in the peripheral nerves) was surrounded by a "neurilem-sheath." So-called neurofibrils, he stated, represent an optical illusion when a nerve fiber is viewed in the fresh state, and an artefact in fixed materials; Nansen expressed surprise that investigators should display such anxiety in trying to find them.

The reflex arc ("reflex-curve"), as Nansen saw it, had three components: centripital fibers, the centrum to be traversed, and centrifugal fibers. This was at a time when the significance of dendrites in impulse conduction was not known. Golgi had concluded that the dendrites are solely a source of nutrition for the cell, and that only in this way do they participate in cell function. Nansen echoed Golgi on this point. Nansen, much like Golgi, felt it correct to assume that the nerve-cell body (likewise nutritive to the axon) is also not a part of the reflex arc; instead, the discharges coming via sensory fibers reach collateral branches of the motor-cell neurites through the medium of the central fibrillary plexus, the "centrum."[7,8] The meeting place of the terminals of dendrites and of collaterals of axons, he wrote, is in the fibrillary centrum.[2] (Fig. 11)

There was a freshness in many of Nansen's observations. In his monograph, Nansen remarked following his summation of the enormous literature, that he could scarcely agree with any author, though his views, he thought, were most closely related to those of Franz von Leydig (1821–1908), of Tübingen, later of Bonn. Kuhlenbeck[9] sizes up Nansen's writings thus: Nansen expresses views that to a certain degree could be interpreted as implying the neuron theory. Certainly, some of his concepts were identical with those formulated in this theory. It is thus not without some justification that Nansen is regarded as a co-founder of the neuron theory with His and Forel.

Nansen's defense of his thesis was reported in the daily Christiania newspaper, *Aftenposten,* on 28 April 1888. As a preliminary, three lectures were required, one of his own choice, the other two specified by the Faculty. These behind him, Nansen launched into the defense of his thesis, ordinarily a ceremony but not on this occasion. A rough session ended in Professor Heiberg's remark that Nansen's anatomical observations would survive, but that his theories would be forgotten. The decision was in his favor, nevertheless.

He left Christiania by boat two days later, and on June 4, 1888, sailed out of Isafjord, Iceland, aboard the *Jason,* leader of an expedition to take him and his party of five across the vast ice field of Greenland, from east to west.

In later years, back from his explorations, he became Curator of the Zoological Museum in Christiania. During the winter of 1891–92, with Nansen's collaboration, Professor Gustav Guldberg, Director of the Anatomical Institute, got out a monograph on the whale embryos Nansen had brought back from an expedition.[10] In 1896 Nansen was appointed Professor of Zoology to the University, and in 1908, Professor of Oceanography.

The rest belongs to the annals of polar exploration, oceanography, geology, geophysics, and post-World War I reconstruction, which in 1923 won him the Nobel Prize for Peace. A heart condition brought his end.

MOFFETT FIELD, CALIFORNIA
PAVIA, ITALY
OSLO, NORWAY
BERGEN, NORWAY

WEBB HAYMAKER
PIERA LOCATELLI
AAGOT LÖKEN
ERIK WAALER

References

[1]Det Kongelige Frederiks Universitet, now Universitetet i Oslo. [2]Forelöbig meddelelse om undersögelser over centralnervensystemets histologiske bygning hos Ascidierne samt hos Myxine glutinosa. Bergens Mus. Årsberetn., 1885, p. 55–78. Transl. into English: Ann. Mag. Nat. Hist., London, ser. 5, 1886, 18:209–226.   [3]Bidrag til Myzostomernes Anatomic og Histologi. Bergens Mus. Årsberetn., 1885 (resumé in English).   [4]Naturen, 1887, 11:39–46 (in Norwegian). [5]Ibid., 1887, 11:12–21 (with Brunchorst; in Norwegian).   [6]Ibid., 1887, 11:65–71 (with Brunchorst; in Norwegian).   [7]Nord. Med. Ark., 1887, 19:1–24 (in Norwegian).   [8]Jena Zschr. Med. Naturw., n.F. 14, 1886, 21:267–321 (in German).   [9]The central nervous system of vertebrates. Vol. 3. Basel, Karger, 1969, p. 203–205 (Kuhlenbeck).   [10]Bergens Mus. Skrifter, no. 5, p. 1–70 (in English).

References to Biography and Works: 1) Fridtjof Nansen. Nordens Kalender, 1931, p. 5–20 (Helland-Hansen).   2) Fridtjof Nansen og hans videnskapelige insats. Oslo, Norske Videnskapsakad. Årbok, 1930, 65–84 (Helland-Hansen).   3) The nervous system and its constituent neurones. New York, Stechert, 1909 (Barker).   4) Die Langen Reisen. Eine Nansen-Biographie. München, Kindler, 1956 (Bauer). 5) Naturen, 1961, no. 7–8, 387–421 (Brinkmann, Jr.; in Norwegian).

JAMES PAPEZ (1883–1958)

*I*N HIS secluded laboratory at Cornell University, in Ithaca, where he was Professor of Anatomy (1920–1951), James Wenceslaus Papez used to take every hour he could spare from his teaching to look at serial sections of brains. Ceaselessly he would put section after section under the microscope, and bubble over in excitement when something new to him appeared. After evening dinner his indulgent wife, Pearl, and their three children, would excuse him so that he could go back to the laboratory and view some more sections. In sensing fiber connections, he often relied upon nuances in the way in which "normal" material took the stain. To what he saw he would add a liberal dash of imagination, which was his forte, and the mechanisms involved in the performance of this or that function would emerge.

This is the background on which Papez conceived a "mechanism of emotion" (the hippocampo-mamillo-thalamo-cingulate-hippocampal circuit), which eventually made him famous. His paper was published in 1937.[1] At the time, obscurity prevailed as to the significance of the human hippocampus: it might have an olfactory liaison and it might be involved in epilepsy and in hydrophobia. Papez was convinced that the basis of emotion is phylogentically evolved through the medium of the gustation and the olfaction mechanisms concerned in nutrition and reproduction, and he thought that the taste of potential foods and the odors associated with rutting form the guides for feeding and mating drives. "The central emotive process of cortical origin," wrote Papez, "may be conceived of as being built up in the hippocampal formation and as being transferred to the mamillary body and thence through the anterior thalamic nuclei to the cortex of the gyrus cinguli. . . . Radiation of the emotive process from the gyrus cinguli to other regions in the cerebral cortex would add emotional coloring to psychic processes occurring elsewhere. . . . It is evident that [the proposed mechanism of emotion] will have to stand the test of experimental and clinical experience if it is to be useful in science."

As late as 1942 Papez commented to a friend that it seemed that no one took his concept seriously; he had had very few requests for

Portrait, courtesy of Mrs. Pearl Papez, Lancaster, Pennsylvania.

reprints. Somehow the paper was lost sight of. Klüver and Bucy, in 1939,[2] in a report delivered before the American Neurological Association, described how bilateral extirpation of the greater part of the hippocampal formation together with the temporal lobe in monkeys led to "psychic blindness," etc., Papez's paper was not mentioned. With customary modesty, Papez made no mention of it in the discussion. Only later did the magnitude of Papez's contribution become recognized.

At Cornell, Papez had at his command a large assemblage of vertebrate material, including the Wilder Collection of primate brains, and it was from this array that many other contributions came. Among them was his description of the reticulospinal tracts in the cat.[3] The structure, evolution and connections of the thalamus received much of his attention: in the turtle (1932), armadillo (1932), *Pithecus (Macacus) rhesus* (1939),[4] and man.[5] Papez was convinced that a pathway runs from the retina to the supraoptic nucleus (the optico-supraoptic tract). In viewing serial sections Papez would exclaim: "That elusive pathway! It stops right at the edge of the nucleus! It must be that the fibers lose their myelin as they enter the nucleus." Experimentalists do not believe that retinal fibers terminate in any part of the hypothalamus. Yet a radioactive tracer introduced into the eye has recently been shown to accumulate in the hypothalamus.[6]

James W. Papez was born in a small community in Minnesota— Glencoe—the site of an early Moravian settlement. It was to this area that his father had emigrated from his native Austria-Hungary (the part which was later to become Czechoslovakia). The young James Wenceslaus had his schooling in nearby Hutchinson. He received the M.D. from the University of Minnesota College of Medicine and Surgery (1911), where he had been provided a fellowship in neurology on the recommendation of J. B. Johnston. It was by working with this great comparative neuroanatomist that Papez got his start. During the next decade (1911–1920) he taught anatomical sciences at Atlanta College of Physicians and Surgeons (later, a part of Emory University). Then, at Cornell, his famous course of comparative neuroanatomy emerged. Dr. Elizabeth C. Crosby relates that while some neuroanatomists were experts on this or that phylum, Papez was an authority on all of them. This is evident in his *Comparative neurology* (New York, Crowell, 1929) for which his wife was the artist, as she was also for his other publications. Besides lecturing on comparative neuro-anatomy, he later gave courses on Human Growth and Development, Physical Anthropology, and Cerebral Mechanisms, which attracted scholars from at home and abroad. Teaching was perhaps his greatest contribution. A student, Herman A. Schwartz, recently remarked: "I remember him dryly lecturing. His words weren't particularly exciting. But his intense preoccupation and fascination . . . made the identification of nuclei and tracts and their significance an absolutely exciting occupation. I'll always remember Papez coming over to me after the final exam (on which my grade was 99) and, with a slightly raised eyebrow, asking: 'What went wrong?' "

Throughout his tenure at Cornell, Papez was consultant to the Reconstruction Home, Ithaca, an institution for the treatment of infantile and spastic paralysis. This was the main source which sharpened his acumen in the field of neuropathology. A clearer exposition than his on pubertas precox (due to infundibuloma)[7] would be hard to find. In a case of classical double athetosis due to hypoxemia at birth he made the surprising observation that the globus pallidus (of the two sides) was severely atrophied and the "cortico-nigral tract" degenerated. The surprise was that the striatum was entirely normal.[8]

Dr. Papez was an early riser and would have a poem written before he and his wife had breakfast. In 1957 some were brought together in a volume entitled, *Fragments of verse* (Los Angeles, New Age Publ. Co.). Like another Mr. Chipps, Dr. Papez was close to the students and, as one of them has since liked to reminisce, his clothes seemed never quite to fit. He could often be seen surrounded by students conversing in his usual tone of suppressed excitement. With a smile and a chuckle he would argue but never get into an argument; at a certain point he would simply cease talking. His silence was eloquent.

This gentle, unassuming man, with whom all were at ease, had not an ounce of malice in him. As Fred A. Mettler, Papez's assistant, put it: "Being totally devoid of vanity or guile his only reaction to stupidity or avarice [in others] was a momentary, surprised unhappiness with shortcomings that had no corollary in his own makeup. . . ." Because of these qualities and the flow of his ideas, meetings never seemed quite complete if one hadn't had a chance to discuss things with Dr. Papez.

Upon retirement from Cornell University (in 1951), Papez moved to Columbus, Ohio, where he took up the post of Director of Biological Research at the State Hospital. One Sunday morning, while finishing breakfast with his wife, he felt ill (precordial distress) and remarked calmly: "This is it." He went to the couch, brushed away the newspaper, lay down, and was soon gone.

MOFFETT FIELD, CALIFORNIA   WEBB HAYMAKER

References

[1]Arch. Neur. Psychiat., Chicago, 1937, *38*:725–743.   [2]Trans. Amer. Neur. Ass., 1939, *65*:170–175.   [3]J. Comp. Neur., 1926, *41*:365–399. [4]Arch. Neur. Psychiat., Chicago, 1934, *32*:1–44 (with Aronson). [5]*Ibid.*, 1939, *41*:277–289.   [6]Brain Res., 1968, *8*:209–212 (O'Steen and Vaughn).   [7]J. Neuropath., 1947, *6*:15–23 (with Ecker).   [8]Arch. Neur. Psychiat., Chicago, 1938, *40*:789–799 (with Hertzman and Rundles).

References to Biography and Works: 1) Proc. Amer. Ass. Anatomists, Anat. Rec., 1958, *131*:279–282 (Mettler).   2) *National Cyclopedia of American Biography,* 2d ed., New York, White, 1937.   3) Cornellian, 1958.   4) Necrology of the Faculty, Ithaca, Cornell Univ., 1958, p. 27–29.

SANTIAGO RAMÓN Y CAJAL (1852–1934)

*T*HIS eminent Spaniard was born in a little pueblo in Petilla de Aragon, a melancholy village in the Pyrenees, hard to find on a map, in a region traditionally said to be occupied by *baturros* (people who are not very bright). His father, Justo Ramón Casassús, was a struggling barber surgeon, second class, who by his own tireless efforts had succeeded in obtaining an academic degree from the medical faculty of the University of Zaragoza, whereupon he became a country doctor. The father long feared that his artistically inclined son would never earn his salt. A wandering artist said that he had no talent; his teachers declared him a dolt; a barber and shoemaker, to whom he was apprenticed, said he was lazy; a grandee called him a criminal, and sent him to jail, for having taken shots at his palace with a cannon which he impro-

Portrait, courtesy of the National Library of Medicine, Bethesda, Maryland.

vised by hollowing-out a tree trunk. Salvation came on hunting trips with his father and through his love of drawing, first of bones collected on judicious visits to cemeteries. This led him to anatomy and thence to medicine.

Once through medical school (1873), he served as regimental surgeon in Cuba. In his short military service he acquired a breadth of experience, a deeper love for his own soil, but also a mixture of pulmonary tuberculosis and malaria which almost cut short his medical career. On his return to Spain he was appointed assistant, then professor of anatomy at the University of Zaragoza (1877), where he began the histological studies which were destined to make him famous. Having almost no funds, Cajal (to use his mother's family name) put as many sections as he could on each slide. What he saw under his rickety Verick microscope excited him enough that he got a paper off to *The Catholic Daily* in Zaragoza; a nerve cell by its emergent fiber, he found, "groped to find another." He sent reprints to the crowned heads of Europe, but received no enthusiastic acknowledgments. He became Professor of Anatomy at Valencia (1884), then at Barcelona (1887), and finally received an assignment on the medical faculty at the University of Madrid (1892), where the greater part of his life's work was accomplished.

At Zaragoza he was ridiculed for his egotism in sending papers beyond the Pyrenees for publication, but they were accepted. Later, editors were seeking him out. Once he had received recognition through a demonstration of silver-impregnated brain sections before a meeting of the German Anatomical Society at the University of Berlin (1889) (of which von Kölliker was chairman), other honors came to him. Through Sherrington's recommendation, he delivered the Croonian Lecture before the Royal Society in London (1894) and received honorary degrees from Oxford and Cambridge. Sherrington tells of a dinner in Cajal's honor in London, where Cajal gave a little oration, followed by a peroration, capped by a final dramatic gesture: a pyramid of crumbled bread, carefully piled up beside his plate, was grandly swept onto the carpet, with a challenging look, as the final word resounded. The trick of rhetoric shocked none more than the housemaid.

Cajal's travels included a trip to the United States, only a year after the Spanish-American war, to give a series of lectures at the Clark University. As expected, he received the Nobel Prize, jointly with Golgi. Meanwhile Cajal had established his Laboratorio de Investigaciones Biológicas at the University and a school of followers had begun to form. Much of his work and that of his illustrious pupils appeared in Spanish journals. In addition to well over 250 articles concerned largely with the normal and pathological histology of the nervous system in animals and man, he published monographs on the cerebral cortex,[1] the retina, and on degeneration and regeneration of the nervous system. He was no mean neuropathologist: his manual of pathological anatomy,[2] which he wrote in 1887–88, went through seven editions. His textbook on histology of the nervous system, with its thousand original illustrations,[3] still remains the outstanding classic on the subject. Where His, Forel, von Kölliker and Nansen demonstrated the anatomical independence of the nerve cell, Cajal more than any other was instrumental in establishing that the neuron theory was not theory, but fact.[4] His autobiography,[5] his philosophical cogitations,[6] and his observations on the development of the spirit of research[7] reveal the breadth of his thinking; his work on color photography[8] portrays something of the catholicity of his interests.

Cajal has been characterized as a man of "furious enthusiasm," of intense industry, and of deep philosophical reflection. He was also in the best sense a national zealot—a patriot jealous for his nation's reputation; he was, in fact, the source of the renaissance of the scientific spirit in Spain. He inspired a number of pupils who later became famous. His favorite was the brilliant, shortlived Nicolás Achúcarro.[9] Others among his pupils who were great were Jorge Francisco Tello (1880–1958),[10] Fernando de Castro (1896–1967),[11] Gonzalo Rodriguez Lafora (1887–   ), and especially Pío del Río-Hortega (1882–1945).

Cajal once wrote: "In the intricate warp of the brain one can advance only step by step, and if one is to do so safely, the front trenches must be those dug by men like Meynert, Golgi, Edinger, Flechsig, Kölliker, Forel, and the other great ones. . . ." And he went on to conclude: "I threw myself into the task with sure faith that in that dark thicket where so many explorers had been lost, I should capture, if not lions and tigers, at least some modest game scorned by the great hunters."

CYRIL B. COURVILLE

References

[1]*Studies on the cerebral cortex [limbic structures]*. Chicago, Year Book Publ., 1935 (transl. from the Spanish by Kraft).   [2]*Manual de anatomía patológica general*. Barcelona, 1890. (7th ed. Madrid, Moya, 1922.)   [3]*Histologie du système nerveux de l'homme et des vertébrés*. 2 vol. Paris, Maloine, 1909–11 (transl. from the Spanish by Azoulay).   [4] *Neuron theory or reticular theory? Objective evidence of the anatomical unity of nerve cells*. Madrid, Consejo Sup. d. Invest. Cientificas, Instituto "Rámon y Cajal," 1954 (transl. from the Spanish by Purkiss and Fox.)   [5]*Recuerdos de mi vida*. 3rd ed. Madrid, Pueyo, 1923.   [6]*Charlas de café*. 4th ed. Madrid, Tipografía Artística, 1932. [7]*Reglas y consejos sobre investigación científica*. 6th ed. Madrid, Pueyo, 1923. (Engl. trans. by Sanchez-Perez and Courville: *Precepts and counsels on scientific investigation. Stimulants of the spirit*. Mountain View, Pacific, 1951).   [8]*La fotografía de los colores: fundamentos científicos y reglas prácticas*. Madrid, 1912.   [9]Haymaker (Ed.), *The founders of neurology*. 1st ed. Springfield, Thomas, 1953, p. 5–7 (biography of Achúcarro, by Polak).   [10]Arch. Med. Panam., 1959, *8*:2–6 (biography of Tello, by Herrera).   [11]J. Neurol. Sci., 1968, *6*:189–190 (biography of de Castro, by Moya).

References to Biography: 1) *Recuerdos de mi vida*. 3rd ed. Madrid, Pueyo, 1923 (contains bibliography; Cajal). (Engl. trans. by Craigie and Cano: *Recollections of my life*. Amer. Philosophical Soc. Memoirs VIII. Phila., U. of Pa., 1937).   2) Grote (ed.), *Die Medizin der Gegenwart in Selbstdarstellungen*. Vol. 5. Leipzig, Meiner, 1925 (autobiography).   3) Arch. Neur. Psychiat., Chicago, 1926, *16*:213–220 (Penfield).   4) Anat. Anz., 1935, *80*:46–75 (contains bibliography; Tello).   5) Tr. Lab. invest. biol. Univ. Madrid, 1935, *30*:1–210 contains annotated bibliography; Tello).   6) *Explorer of the human brain. The life of Santiago Ramón y Cajal (1852–1934)*. New York, Schuman, 1949 (Cannon, with foreword by Sherrington).   7) *Young endeavour*. Springfield, Thomas, 1958 (Gibson).   8) *The world of Ramón y Cajal with selections from his nonscientific writings*. Springfield, Thomas, 1968 (Craigie and Gibson).

STEPHEN RANSON (1880–1942)

S TEPHEN WALTER RANSON, the son of a physician in a small community in Minnesota, was one of the foremost of a generation responsible for the flowering of neurological investigation in the United States. His career as professor of anatomy at Northwestern University, and later as director of its Institute of Neurology, was marked for some forty years by a series of basic contributions, initially anatomical but gradually more concerned with the functional significance of neural structures.

Ranson's interest in neurology was developed during his student years by his association with J. B. Johnson of Minnesota and H. H. Donaldson of Chicago. In his doctoral investigation, Ranson began a long-term study which revealed the prevalence of nonmyelinated afferent fibers in peripheral nerves.[1] Their distribution and their origin from the small cells of sensory ganglia, their central course in Lissauer's and the spinal trigeminal tracts, were systematically determined, and their importance for pain conduction ascertained.

His ever increasing interest in neurological function drew him to the study of visceral and somatic reflexes, and next, brain stem centers involved in spinal integration. The chance observation that a "hypothalamic cat" could walk brought him into a second major program of investigation. It occupied the latter part of his career, in which he revived the Horsley-Clarke instrument to reach, with facility, this hitherto inaccessible part of the brain.

With closely knit teams of associates, he clarified the hypothalamic innervation of the pituitary gland and established its importance for the regulation of water exchange and for gonadotrophic control. The role of the hypothalamus in initiating the objective features of emotional excitement and in preserving a constant body temperature was elucidated,[2] and the profound hypokinesia and somnolence resulting from basal diencephalic injury were described.[3] Thus, Ranson, through his many contributions—well over two-hundred—was one of the most distinguished of a long line of pioneers whose efforts were directed in one way or another toward clarifying the problem of hypothalamic function.

In 1933 and again in 1936 Ranson sought the anatomical expla-

Stephen Walter Ranson

nation of the Argyll Robertson pupil and found that an important part of the neural mechanism concerned is the pretectal region.[4,5]

Toward the end of his career, in collaboration with his son and daughter, Ranson began investigations of the corpus striatum which led to a disclosure of the structural basis of recurrent striatal influences exerted on the cerebral cortex.[6]

At Northwestern University, Ranson was director of an institute created to provide him full time opportunity for research, with his

Portrait. courtesy of Dr. H. W. Magoun, Los Angeles, California.

only teaching responsibility that of training numerous graduate students, in whose subsequent independent progress he took a personal interest. Edition after edition of his *The anatomy of the nervous system* (1st ed., 1920, Philadelphia, Saunders) engaged his careful attention. Merited honors came to him—invitations to lectureships, the dedication of a volume of contributions on the hypothalamus by the Association for Research in Nervous and Mental Disease (1940), membership in the National Academy of Sciences, and the presidency of the American Association of Anatomists. Nevertheless, he remained to the end an unremitting worker, of keen mind and quiet dignity, who vastly preferred the satisfaction of investigative accomplishments in his laboratory and the enjoyment of his charming family, to the pursuit of recognition and acclaim. A duodenal ulcer plagued him for years, but a heart attack caused his death.

LOS ANGELES, CALIFORNIA   H. W. MAGOUN

References

[1]Amer. J. Anat., 1911, *12*:67–87.   [2]Bull. N. Y. Acad. Med., 1937, *13*: 241–271 (Harvey Lecture).   [3]Arch. Neur. Psychiat., Chicago, 1939, *41*:1–23.   [4]Arch. Neur. Psychiat., Chicago, 1933, *30*:1193–1204 (with Magoun).   [5]Brain, Lond., 1936, *59*:234–239 (with Magoun, Atlas and Hare).   [6]Arch. Neur. Psychiat., Chicago, 1941, *46*:230–249 (with S. W. Ranson, Jr., and M. Ranson).

References to Biography and Works: 1) Q. Bull. Northwest. Univ. Med. School, 1942, *16*:302–310 (contains bibliography; Magoun and M. Ranson).   2) Anat. Rec., 1943, *86*:3–10 (Arey).   3) List of Ranson's graduate students, research assistants, fellows and colleagues: vol. 15 of Publ. Inst. Neurol., Northwestern Univ. Med. School, 1943.

PÍO DEL RÍO-HORTEGA (1882–1945)

"*H*ISTOLOGY is an odd-tasting dish, repulsive as a medicament to students who must be examined in it, and little liked by physicians who consider their schooling finished. Taken in large quantities under compulsion it is not absorbed, but if

tasted in little sips it finally becomes a delight to the palate and even a cause of addiction." So wrote Hortega (in 1933),[1] at the repeated urging by students of the University of Madrid, for *Residencia,* their monthly publication. Under his eyes and pen "dendrites would sometimes display graceful, plumed forms. . . . Neither the ugliness of the toad nor the stench of his intestine can be

Portrait of Hortega in 1936, in Madrid, courtesy of Dr. William C. Gibson, Vancouver, Canada.

suspected in the fan formed by its intestinal epithelial cells. . . . In the cephalic cartilage of the squid, the cells lead a life of repose and gather together as a family to exchange confidences. . . . Even in the most malignant tumor the cells are grouped harmoniously." Such read the legends for the imaginative drawings he had made.

Don Pío had studied the masters. Weekends found him in Toledo, with the El Grecos. Hung in his home, Penfield relates, was a full length saint, an oil he himself had done. In Madrid, he had the habit of taking his sketches each night to a *tertulia* at the Spedium Coffee House, and when his friends had left he would work on them until closing time at 2 A.M. Only Goméz—Nicolas Goméz y del Moral—remained with him to the end. An intense admirer and champion of Hortega, he was a business man more interested in the amenities than in business or science. As to Don Pío, he was a dapper and shy person; sensitive, highstrung and proud, with a quick, nervous smile, and words as rapid as a whirlwind. He was tremendously fastidious: when asked to sign the portrait reproduced here, he vacillated, gesticulated, murmured to himself, and we wondered whether he had decided not to; next day he came with a bottle of white ink. With his narrow head, aquiline profile, and long, slender fingers, he could have been out of an El Greco canvas.

Hortega was born, one of eight children, in Portillo, near Valladolid, once the capital of Castille. The family lived for a time in a castle in that little town, but when the mother died (when Pío was five) and the castle began falling into ruins, his father, del Río, moved the family to Valladolid. Here their home faced one whole side of the principal plaza. From a balcony Pío would watch the bull-baiting at the festival each year, a harmless sport he enjoyed as much as he frowned upon professional bull fighting, which he refused to witness. Here, in Valladolid, he received his medical education, graduating in 1908. After practicing medicine for two years in Portillo and finding it not his vocation, he accepted a position as assistant in anatomy and histology to Professor López Garcia at his alma mater. Thanks to his outstanding gifts—he was working on his thesis on tissue changes in brain tumors—he was awarded a fellowship by the Spanish Cancer Committee for study in Paris (with Prenant), London, and Berlin.

On his return to Spain, Cajal accepted him, but turned him over for a time to Achúcarro, just returned from the U.S.A. After improving some of the techniques of Achúcarro, Hortega introduced in 1919 his ammoniacal silver carbonate method.[2,3] With this he succeeded in staining a spidery element which he designated "microglia" (soon called the "Hortega cell" by Spatz). The method also yielded his "oligodendroglia." On the latter he withheld publication because his discoveries ran counter to the views of his master, Cajal. Persuaded by his colleagues to publish, Hortega finally yielded (1921).[4] He had gone too far. One morning he found a notice from Cajal attached to the door of his laboratory: his presence was no longer desired. There had been whisperings into Cajal's ear that visitors had been seeking out Hortega rather than him, and anyway, was this Hortega cell anything more than the one already described by Robertson of Edinburgh?

Through his friend, Juan Negrín (Professor of Physiology to the University, later the Prime Minister and leader of the ill fated Republican forces in the Civil War), he set up a small laboratory in the Student's Residence in the Pinar district of Madrid. Here he demonstrated that microgliocytes and cells of the reticuloendothelial system are identical. Soon he also became Chief of the Department of Experimental Research at the Instituto de Oncología (Cancer Institute), later Director of an imposing laboratory established by the Junta. He proceeded to study and classify the tumors of the nervous system, publishing superb monographs in 1933 (translated into English in 1962[5]) and 1945.[6] For relaxation he would freeze and section a whole slab of a human hemisphere, impregnate sections with silver, and, almost unbelievable, would mount the sections so skillfully that not a flaw could be found. It delighted him to see nerve fibers extending several inches across the section without interruption.

At the height of his activity, the Civil War broke out in Spain (1936). Hortega watched as his Cancer Institute was demolished by the Luftwaffe, and by the Moor's and Italian's gunfire; his books and histological treasures were used as bulwarks against snipers. He stayed in Madrid for a time, then left for Valencia, at the bid of the Government, which had moved there. Gómez was with him when, the military situation deteriorating, he departed for

Paris, both hollow-eyed. He worked for about a year in the laboratory of Clovis Vincent at the Pitié, then proceeded to Hugh Cairns' laboratory at Oxford (1938), where he spent three years. At Oxford, according to McMenemey, "he would learn to be 'very English' in time and with grim determination would request a tea of fish and chips. . . The rooks' nest in the elms reminded him of senile plaques . . . This nervous, lonely, little man would say, 'I love you all but, oh God, not your draughts and your everlasting mutton.' " The quietude was new to him; he would hum Spanish folk songs while he worked, and sometimes the haunting American Negro song, "Water Boy." On top of it all came the diagnosis of cancer of the penis, a diagnosis known only to himself through the series of biopsies he secretly obtained.

The incorruptible Hortega refused General Franco's invitation to return to Spain. So, in 1940, he left for Buenos Aires (accompanied by Gómez) to become director of a new laboratory just established there to the memory of Cajal.

During his five years in Buenos Aires, he succeeded (with Prado and Polak) in discovering the glia of the sympathetic nervous system and the perispinal ganglia. In a series of papers on brain tumors (the last in 1944), he announced new techniques which only recently have become available to the outside world.[7] Pain developed in his back, yet he could not bring himself to tell the surgeon he secretly visited in Montevideo what was basically wrong. Finally the cancer forced him to bed. He dictated on the biography of Cajal he was preparing after he could no longer hold a pen. Gómez was with him to the end, unwilling to delegate to a nurse the menial tasks of caring for this ill and dying man.

.   .   .   .

Del Río-Hortega's name was to glia what the names of many others included in this volume were to the nerve cell. His key articles on the microglia appeared in 1921[7a] and in 1932.[8] The Scotsman, Ford Robertson (1867–1923), by placing sections in platinum bichloride and formalin for some months, had managed to bring out (in 1899) certain cells (some probably microglia, others oligodendroglia) which he called "mesoglia" because he was not sure that they were neuroglia. That mesenchymal cell which, during fetal life, migrates in amoeboid form from the region of blood vessels and subsequently takes on the appearance of the Hortega microglial cell was discovered by Shinkishi Hatai[9]; he referred to this cell as "one type of the neuroglia elements . . . the mesoblast." They are not unlike the cells found in more recent times[10,11] to migrate from the blood stream in pathological states. Neuroglial elements that seemed to originate from blood vessels, to which they were attached, were known to Golgi and also to Andriezen (in 1892), who called them "vascular satellites," but it was Lenhossék (1863–1937), then in Basel, who (in 1891) named them "astrocytes." Cajal, using a gold chloride-sublimate technique (published in 1913[12]), brought them out in great clarity. Hortega, with his methods, demonstrated several different kinds[13] (also later, in a definitive article, he included an account of the relation of astroglial processes to the vessel, on the one hand, and to nerve cells, on the other [the "angiogliona"][14]). Cajal recognized two elements, the nerve cell and the neuroglial cell; but he knew there was a third, the one that failed to take his stains. That third element, Hortega found, was, in fact, two cells: the microgliocyte and the oligodendrocyte. Not only that, but Hortega proceeded to show that the oligodendrocyte was related to the nerve fiber (a system which he called the "neurogliona"), including its role in myelination.[15]

MOFFETT FIELD, CALIFORNIA   WEBB HAYMAKER

References

[1]Residencia, Madrid, 1933, *4*:191–206. (Engl. transl., Texas Rep. Biol. Med., 1949, *7*:363–390 (Wolfe, Butler and Haymaker).   [2]Tr. Lab. invest. biol. Univ. Madrid, 1919, *17*:229 *et seq*.   [3]Bol. Soc. Españ. Biol., 1919, *7*:19–25.   [4]Bol. Real Soc. Españ. historia nat., 1921, *21*:63–93.   [5]*The microscopic anatomy of tumors of the central and peripheral nervous system*. Springfield, Thomas, 1962 (transl. by Pinedá, Russell and Earle).   [6]*Nomenclatura y clasificación de los tumores del sistema nervioso*. Buenos Aires, López y Etchegoyen, 1945. [7]*Blastomas del sistema nervioso central y periferico. Patología y ordenación histogenética*. Buenos Aires, López Libr. Ed., 1966 (Polak). [7a]Mem. Soc. Esp. Hist. Nat., 1921, *11*:213 *et seq*.   [8]Penfield (Ed.), *Cytology and cellular pathology of the nervous system*. New York, Hoeber, 1932, vol. 2, p. 483–534.   [9]J. Comp. Neur., 1902, *12*:291–296.

[10]Arch. Neurol. Psychiat., Chicago, 1947, *57*:673–692 (Haymaker and Sabin). [11]J. Neuropath., 1963, *22*:643–676 (Konigsmark and Sidman). [12]Trab. Lab. invest. biol. Univ. Madrid, 1913, *11*:219–237. [13]*Ibid.*, 1916, *14*:1 *et seq.* [14]Arch. hist. norm. pat., B. Aires, 1945, *1*:5–71. [15]*Libro de oro dedicado al Dr. Mariano R. Castex* etc. Buenos Aires, Buffarini, 1938, vol. 2, p. 369–377.

References to Biography and Works: 1) Arch. hist. norm. pat., B. Aires, 1947, *3*:377–421 (contains bibliography; Polak). 2) J. Neurosurg., 1946, *3*:275–284 (Prados and Gibson). 3) Arch. Neur. Psychiat., Chicago, 1945, *54*:413–416 (Penfield). 4) Lancet, 1945, *2*:222 (McMenemey). 5) Tr. Lab. invest. biol. Univ. Madrid, 1945, *37*:VII–XVIII (de Castro). 6) Rev. neur. psiquiat., Lima, 1945, *8*:262–387 (with bibliography; Encinas). 7) Ciencia, Méx., 1945, *6*:193–197 (Costero). 8) An. Rev. med., Mex., 1945, *3*:29–36 (Perrín). 9) J. Hôtel-Dieu de Montreal, 1945, *14*:405–416 (Masson).

GRAFTON ELLIOT SMITH (1871–1937)

$\mathcal{G}$RAFTON ELLIOT SMITH was named after Grafton, New South Wales, where he was born. "Grafton . . . Grafton?" even King George V muttered with knitted brow as he was about to knight him in 1934. (The "Elliot" part of his name came through some relationship with George Elliot.) As a boy, he used to collect sharks and other fishes on the near-by beaches, and dissect the nervous system with his penknife, but he would never offer any reasons for this preoccupation; his school-fellows nicknamed him "Broody," feeling that he must be hatching something. He would draw and paint his specimens under the tutelage of his father, a pupil of Ruskin in London prior to emigration of the Smiths to Australia. When sixteen, he flunked the Junior Public Examination because of his originality in spelling. His father, a schoolmaster, wanted him to enter an insurance office, but by that time Grafton had become excited about T. H. Huxley's *Elementary lessons in physiology* and decided on his own future.

At the age of seventeen Smith entered the medical school at University of Sydney, and graduated M.B. at twenty-one (1892).

Grafton Elliot Smith

Soon he was about to work on cats, but Charles Martin (later Sir Charles), of the Physiology Department, reminded him that almost the whole world of monotremes and marsupials was right here at his disposal. His first neurological paper, on the cerebral commissures (in 1894),[1] was called a classic by Edinger. He won the M.D. with his thesis on *Anatomy and histology of the cerebrum of the nonplacental mammal* (1895).

When he was twenty-five, he obtained a travelling fellowship

Portrait, courtesy of Lady Elliot Smith, Oxford, England. (Photographer: F. W. Schmidt, Manchester.)

from the University of Sydney and, sailing on the R.M.S. Himalaya, reached the British Isles. Because Oxford demanded proficiency in Latin and Greek, he entered Cambridge University. Under the stimulus of Macalister, and stirred by contact with Gaskell, Horsley, Langley, Mott, E. A. Schäfer (later Sharpey Schaffer), Elliot Smith continued his work on cerebral morphology. He was so pestiferous about getting a microtome that Macalister, in desperation, pulled fifty sovereigns from his pocket and told his protégé to buy one himself—a Cambridge "rocker." On Macalister's recommendation Smith was invited to the chair of anatomy in the newly organized Government Medical School in Cairo. The prospects bright, he moved to London to work for a time at the Royal College of Surgeons on a Catalogue, and married Kathleen Macredie, who ruefully recalled how brief the honeymoon in their Bloomsbury flat was, for he had spent day and night on that Catalogue!

In Cairo, he soon began to learn Arabic, as the students spoke no English. The teaching hospital was named "The Palace of the Howling Dervishes." But mummies and paleopathology fascinated him most, and he ended up preparing some 20,000 reports on anatomical phases of burials in Nubia (4000 B.C.–2000 B.C.). Analysis of this material was presented in books.[2-5] On finding advanced calcific arteriosclerosis of the heart in a mummy, the story goes, he remarked to his assistant: "Remember the Biblical passage, And the Lord hardened the heart of Pharaoh?" His conclusion that culture had spread by diffusion from Egypt startled the thinking world; protests from all over came pouring in. In addition Elliot Smith managed to publish forty-two papers on neuroanatomical subjects during his stay in Egypt—including the celebrated one on the cortical pattern of the human brain (1907).[6]

In 1909 he returned to England, to the chair of anatomy at Manchester, where he continued his studies on ethnology, anthropology and the evolution of the brain, the last of which formed the basis of his Arris and Gale Lectures in 1910.[7] World War I forced his attention to subjects such as shell shock.[8] At the conclusion of the War he delivered the Croonian Lectures on the cerebral cortex[9] and published his chief paper on the corpus striatum[10] —his last original work in neuroanatomy. In 1919 he was invited to the chair of anatomy at University College, London; here he had another unique opportunity, for the Rockefeller Foundation made possible the founding of an Institute of Anatomy. At University College, Elliot Smith made the teaching of anatomy attractive and encouraged a succession of brilliant pupils to vivify that discipline in the medical school curriculum. Among them was R. A. Dart who, in 1923, took the chair at Johannesburg; he acquired that controversial skull of an intermediate creature—*Australopithecus africanus*—and naturally brought it back to London to show to Elliot Smith, only to have his wife leave it in a taxi cab; Scotland Yard, however, was able to still the panic.

In 1932, after revising the section on neuroanatomy in the 6th edition of Cunningham's *Text-Book of anatomy,* he was partially incapacitated by a stroke but returned to work after some months. Diabetes supervened; he remained his own self. At the International Congress of Anthropology and Ethnology held at University College in 1934—when Europe was beginning to undergo turmoil, he demolished any claims to a "Nordic race" or an "Aryan people." In 1935 he suffered another stroke, which affected his speech. As if this were not enough, their youngest son was fatally asphyxiated by car fumes. Then Lady Elliot Smith was badly burned in an explosion of a gas stove and was put into the hospital for several months. In 1936 he retired from the chair of anatomy. His end came a few months later.

Elliot Smith's main contributions were in the field of comparative anatomy and evolution of the nervous system. His analyses of the fissural pattern of the brain in mammals have been the basis of our homologies of cerebral configuration. He gave meaning to the phylogenetic changes in surface topography by his studies of the subcortical and cortical factors that influence the elaboration of the pallium,[7,9] and he was an important contributor to the understanding of the development of speech and of binocular vision.[11]

Elliot Smith's hair turned white when he was about thirty. This gave him a somewhat pontifical appearance; indeed, there was a kind of solemn serenity about the man with the ever lit cigar. Nothing seemed to perturb him except in Egypt, when, throwing the hot calipers into the burning sand, he perforce left no doubt as to what he thought about the flies, the dust, the heat, the village of Shellal, and even the ancient dead. Despite it all, together with

Wood Jones and others from England, Elliot Smith accomplished the most massive anthropological investigation of all time. His contributions to neuroanatomy and ethnology were no less prodigious. He was a shy man, but over tea he would exchange yarns and be ready to discuss Biblical prophecies or the University rugger match. When dealing with students he could—as Abbie relates—completely forget that he was supposed to be a famous man. He did not live long enough to enjoy the leisure of retirement.

BALTIMORE, MARYLAND   A. EARL WALKER

References

[1]Proc. Linn. Soc. N.S.W., Ser. 2, 1894, *9*:635–657.   [2]*The migration of early culture*. Manchester, Univ. Press, 1915.   [3]*Human history*. New York, Norton, 1929.   [4]*Egyptian mummies*. London, Allen & Unwin, 1924 (with Dawson).   [5]*The ancient Egyptians and the origin of civilization*. New York, Harper, 1923.   [6]J. Anat. Physiol., 1907, *41*:237–254.   [7]Lancet, 1910, *1*:1–6 *et seq.*   [8]*Shell shock and its lessons*. Manchester, Univ. Press, 1917 (with Pear),   [9]Brit. Med. J., 1919, *1*:758 (abstract of Croonian Lecture).   [10]J. Anat., London, 1919, *53*:271–291.   [11]*Essays on the evolution of man*. London, Oxford U. P., 1927.

References to Biography and Works: 1) J. Anat., London, 1936, *71*:1–6 (J.T.W.)   2)Man, London, 1937, *37*:51–53 (Young).   3) Brit. Med. J., 1937, *1*:99–101 (anon.).   4) Bull. Post-Grad. Committee in Medicine, Univ. of Sydney, 1959, *15*:101–150 (with bibliography and reproduction of some of Elliot Smith's drawings; Abbie).   5) J. Anat., London, 1938, *72*:280–294 (with bibliography; Woollard).

III

NEUROPHYSIOLOGISTS

VLADIMIR BEKHTEREV (1857–1927)

*V*LADIMIR MIKHAILOVICH BEKHTEREV, the son of a low-ranking Government official, was born in Sarali, a small village in the forests of Viatka Territory between the great bend of the Volga and the foothills of the Ural Mountains. There was a notable conformity in the physique and the personality of the man and the rugged austerity of the country whence he came. As seen in his middle fifties, Bekhterev was an arresting figure. Rather heavy-set, square-shouldered, with massive head slightly thrust forward, piercing black eyes under black, bushy brows, and clear-cut, characterful features framed by a silvery beard and grey locks of hair swept to one side, he could well serve as a prototype for a romanticized painting of a northern woodsman.

At the age of sixteen, Bekhterev entered the Military Medical Academy in St. Petersburg, and graduated when he was twenty-one (in 1878), with a degree comparable to Bachelor of Medicine. He remained at the Academy as assistant to the psychiatrist Merzheievsky, a distinguished teacher, widely traveled, who had been influenced by the great French organic school of psychiatry (headed by Magnan, of Paris) and by Darwin.

The last quarter of the nineteenth century was the grand period in the history of neurology. The foundation upon which the edifice of anatomy, physiology and pathology of the nervous system rests was largely being laid by many of the men whose memory is honored in this volume. During that period the river of European civilization seemed rather definitely to shift its flow toward the countries of central Europe. Those on the periphery of the cultural watershed also fed generously their youthful, creative energies into that common stream. In 1884 Bekhterev, then twenty-six years old, received a traveling scholarship for approximately eighteen months. During the winter of 1884–85 he worked under Flechsig, who was then applying his myelogenetic method to the study of nervous pathways. Young Bekhterev put his shoulder to the task with telling effect. It was while with Flechsig in Leipzig

that Bekhterev described the superior vestibular nucleus[1] which bears his name. Among many subsequent contributions, the first descriptions of the central tegmental tract, the connections of the inferior olive, the component fibers of the cerebellar peduncles, and the nuclear complexes in the reticular formation of the tegmentum were made by Bekhterev.[2] While on his scholarship abroad, Bekhterev also visited du Bois-Reymond, Meynert, Westphal, Charcot, and studied under Wundt. Yet it seems that Flech-

Portrait, courtesy of Prof. Dr. Hugo Spatz, Frankfurt a.M., Germany.

sig influenced him the most. Developmental momenta and myelogenesis remained the cardinal frame of reference in Bekhterev's
scientific thought and method.

On returning to Russia in 1885, his accomplishments had been
such that the "grey-beards" at the University of Kazan could offer
him nothing less than the professorship of psychiatry. Manuscripts
he sent to Germany for publication now bore *von* before his name.
In 1893 he succeeded his old teacher, Merzheievsky, in St. Petersburg. During the following twenty-one years Bekhterev showed
the full measure of his stature as a thinker, investigator, teacher,
and organizer of research in neurology and social biology. Functional anatomy of the brain, experimental psychology, and clinical
neurology were three fields in which Bekhterev carved out a place
for himself as his ancestors must have cut the clearings in the pri-
meval forest beyond the Volga. He was extremely versatile in his
academic interests and fields of research, which embraced hypnosis
and even psychosurgery (with Puusepp).[3,4] He was, in fact, a cory-
phaean figure, being prominent even in public affairs. He had
phenomenal endurance; he needed at the most only five hours of
sleep. Everywhere and always—when sitting in conferences, riding
in a carriage, at night sitting in bed, his wife sleeping beside him
—he worked on galley proofs and new manuscripts. More than six
hundred publications had accumulated by the end of fifty years.

During these fifty years the lives of Bekhterev and Pavlov ran
parallel and their paths frequently crossed. Bekhterev was the
younger of the two—by eight years. They were faculty colleagues.
Bekhterev approached the problem of the relationship between
the brain and behavior as an anatomist, experimental psychologist
and clinician rather than as a single-purposed physiologist, which
Pavlov so eminently was. Bekhterev used the method of conditioned reflexes extensively in his work. As a pupil of Wundt and
Flechsig, he called them "associative reflexes." Instead of the visceral response (salivation) which Pavlov employed as a natural development from his earlier studies on the physiology of the digestive tract and whose interest in "psychical secretion" led him to
the study of higher nervous activity, Bekhterev chose to use the somatic response (skeletal movement). In this choice of the "indica-

tor," Bekhterev probably put himself at a methodologic disadvantage, for a somatic motor response is less readily amenable to quantitation than a visceral response, such as drops of saliva. There was a keen and at times spirited competition between the two masters and their schools. In the long run, Pavlov came out the better of the two, but Bekhterev, although his work was publicly denounced,[7] made, nevertheless, a great contribution. In his elaboration of what he came to call "psychoreflexology,"[5] he and his pupils produced an impressive amount of factual data, many of which gained a peculiar relevance in application to present-day problems of neurology. For example, the cortical representation of visceral functions of blood pressure, of pupillary, gastrointestinal, urovesical and anorectal motility, and of glandular secretory activity, was intensely explored by Bekhterev during the period between 1890 and 1910.[2,5]

From 1913 on he devoted most of his time to the Psychoneurological Institute in Leningrad, which he had founded in 1907. After 1905 the problems of abnormal social behavior, "mass" behavior and "collective" reflexology became his absorbing interests. Amidst his research and teaching activities, he was a widely sought practitioner and consultant. His close friend and pupil, Ludwig Puusepp (1875–1942),[6] able Estonian neurosurgeon, related that it was customary for Bekhterev to make appointments at his office as late as midnight or even in the small hours of the morning. Some of his former patients tell of the dramatic experience they had of being ushered into the heavily draped and carpeted library and beholding, behind a huge desk laden with books and manuscripts, the grey-locked, bearded head of a mystic who silently transfixed them with his glance as they approached him.

Following the fateful ten days in 1917 that "shook the world," Bekhterev, like Pavlov, was left alone; he kept his peace and adapted. His Institute was renamed State University of Medical Sciences. He aged greatly. He was close to seventy-one when he died, the day after his return from the All-Union Neurological Congress in Moscow, over which he had presided—the last act of his extraordinarily diversified and fruitful life as a scientist.

BOSTON, MASSACHUSETTS   PAUL I. YAKOVLEV

References

[1]Neur. Cbl., 1885, *3*:145–147.   [2]*Die Leitungsbahnen im Gehirn und Rückenmark; ein Handbuch für das Studium des Nervensystems.* Leipzig, Besold, 1894 (trans. by Weinberg from Russian original, 1877–78). [3]Arch. internat. neur., Paris, 1912, 10.sér., *2*:1–17 *et seq.*   [4]*Die Funktionen der Nervencentra.* 3 vol. Jena, Fischer, 1908–11 (trans. by Weinberg from Russian original, 1903–07).   [5]*Objective Psychologie oder Psychoreflexologie: die Lehre von den Assoziationsreflexen.* Leipzig, Teubner, 1913.   [6]Walker (Ed.), *A history of neurological surgery.* Baltimore, Williams & Wilkins, 1951 (biography on Puusepp, by A. F. Thomson), p. 270–271.   [7]Science, 1951, *114*:227–233 (London).

References to Biography: 1) Arch. Psychiat., Berlin, 1928, *83*:677–886 (Pines).   2) Brazier (Ed.), *The central nervous system and behavior.* Tr. First Conf., Feb. 23–26, 1958. New York, Macy Found., 1958, p. 187–210 (Yakovlev).

HANS BERGER (1873–1941)

W ITH a physician father, a much quoted poet grandfather (Rückert), and a mother who read books on the relationship of mind and body, Johannes Berger seems to have been oriented by heredity toward the study of that strange alchemy by which the brain turns physical energy into psychic function. Moreover, there was something metronomic in his circadian rhythm: both for work and for leisure the synchrony of his days was phased to the exact minute.

As he was born in Neuses near Coburg (Thuringia), the closest university was at Jena, and so it was natural that this should be the geographical center of his life work. In 1900 he joined the psychiatric clinic as assistant to Otto Binswanger (1852–1929), where Oskar Vogt and Korbinian Brodmann were also assistants. The ideas of these two men on localization of brain function found an absorbed listener in Hans Berger. In 1906, he was made Ausserordentlicher Professor to the University, in 1912 physician-in-chief at the clinic. In spite of the objections raised that he was a "true" psychiatrist, he was named successor to Binswanger in 1919. He

even served as Rector of the University in 1927–28 and as Prorector from 1935 to 1938, when he became Professor Emeritus.

His publications show how sharply he focused on what he considered the central problem of psychiatry—the physical basis of psychic phenomena. His more important contributions were on intracranial blood circulation,[1] bodily manifestations of psychic states,[2] psychophysiology,[3] and the temperature of the brain,[4] the latter of which had been recorded through the intact and the perforated skull for diagnostic and "psychophysiological" purposes, beginning with Broca and Lombard, and Schiff and Mosso in the 1870's.

But the studies which crowned Berger's career were based on electrical recordings, the electroencephalogram of man. Berger was

Portrait, courtesy of Dr. Frederic A. Gibbs, Chicago, Illinois.

fully aware that Richard Caton (1842–1926), a Liverpool surgeon, had succeeded in 1875 in leading off action potentials from
the brains of animals (rabbit and monkey),[5] and that he was thus
the discoverer of the electrical activity of the brain. Berger also
knew of the further successes along this line achieved by the Polish
physiologist Adolf Beck (1863–1939) in 1891, and of the findings
of Russian workers. In 1902 Berger noted the "spontaneous" fluctuations in the electrical activity of animal brains which these
other workers had reported, but he was unable to detect a change
on sensory stimulation. Failure after failure to evoke an electrical
response in the animal brain came over the next eight or ten years.
In 1912 a paper by the Russian physiologist, Pravdich-Neminsky
(1879–1952) for the first time illustrated a photographic record of
the electrical activity of the brain. He called it an "electrocere-
brogram." Berger's reaction to this demonstration was that he
should work harder.

During all these years Berger's experiments were carried on in
his spare time in utter secrecy. Never did he mention what he was
doing, nor would he ever admit anyone to the laboratory located
in a small building on the grounds of the clinic in which he
worked. As a diversionary measure he would give public discourses
on telepathy, in which he was a firm believer, offering hypotheses
of wave propagation to explain it. Increasing inflexibility in his attitude toward his assistants went hand in hand with his increasing
isolation, so that people began to shun him.

In 1924 Berger made the first EEG recording in man (he called
it an "Elektrenkephalogramm"). He did this not only in normal
subjects but also in the brain-injured, thereby laying the foundation for the application of the technique to clinical neurology. In
the following year, using a Siemens double-coil galvanometer, he
found a decrease in activity on sensory stimulation—thus duplicat-
ing the results obtained by Beck and Pravdich-Neminsky in animals and he also found the counterpart of two of Pravdich-Neminsky's categories of waves, the alpha and beta ranges. Still he kept
his discoveries totally in the dark. His paper announcing that variations in voltage could be recorded through the intact cranium
appeared in 1929,[6] five years after he had conceived the idea. The
others that followed were also epoch-making.[7,8]

Although at first the importance of his work went generally un-recognized and was even ridiculed, he was reserved but undis-mayed, and greatly pleased when in 1937 he was invited to preside with Adrian at the symposium on electrical activity in the nervous system at the Congress of Psychology in Paris. They hailed Berger as the most distinguished of all the visitors. Tears came to his eyes as he said: "In Germany I am not so famous." Plans were made to have him visit the United States to inspect laboratories where elec-trical studies on the brain were in progress and to lecture on his work. He began to polish his English, and wrote: "I will come as soon as the international situation permits."

As a front-row witness of the rise of Hitler and World War II, and forced by old age merely to wait and watch, he decided in a fit of melancholia—to which he was subject—that he had seen enough and on June 1, 1941, ended his life. He had entered the hospital on the medical service, and terminated his existence by hanging.

To his psychodynamically oriented fellow-psychiatrists Berger seemed unimaginative and plodding; they were inclined to patron-ize him. To his students he seemed rather dry and aloof, except on occasions when he would storm and fume if their knowledge of the fundamentals of neuroanatomy was inadequate. Such were the attitudes toward a scholar who was one of the greatest innovators of all time.

Hans Berger is called the father of electroencephalography. He was also a founder of psychophysiology.

CHICAGO, ILLINOIS   FREDERIC A. GIBBS

References

[1]*Zur Lehre von der Blutzirkulation in der Schädelhöhle des Menschen, namentlich unter dem Einfluss von Medikamenten.* Jena, Fischer, 1901.   [2]*Über die körperlichen Äusserungen psychischer Zustände.* Jena, Fischer, 1904–1907.   [3]*Psychophysiologie in 12 Vorlesungen.* Jena, Fischer, 1921.   [4]*Untersuchungen über die Temperatur des Gehirns.* Jena, Fischer, 1910.   [5]Brit. Med. J., 1875, 2:278.   [6]Arch. Psychiat., Berlin, 1929, *87*:527–570.   [7]*Ibid.*, 1931, *94*:16–60; 1932, *97*:6–26; 1933, *98*:232–251; 1933, *99*:555–574; 1933, *100*:301–320; 1933, *101*:452–469; 1934, *102*:538–557; 1935, *103*:444–454; 1936, *104*:678–689; 1937, *106*:165–187.   [8]Nova Acta Leopoldina, 1938, *6*:173–309.

References to Biography and Works: 1) Arch. Psychiat., Berlin, 1941, *114*:17–24 (contains bibliography; Böning).   2) Nervenarzt, 1941, *14*:481–484 (Wawrzik and Jung).   3) J. Hist. Med., N. Y., 1949, *4:* 361–371 (Ginzberg).   4) *Essays in the history of Italian neurology.* Milan, Ist. di storia della med., 1963 (Belloni, ed.), p. 237–254 (Fischgold).   5) *A history of the electrical activity of the brain. The first half-century.* London, Pitman, 1961 (Brazier).

CLAUDE BERNARD (1813–1878)

C LAUDE BERNARD'S birthplace, an old farmhouse in St. Julien (Rhône, France), is now a carefully preserved monument. It stands on a hill, surrounded now, as then, by vineyards; to this quiet spot Claude Bernard returned each summer of his retirement to perform a few additional experiments in an improvised laboratory, but especially to think over the results of the work he had done in Paris, its significance for the science of experimental medicine, and particularly its philosophical implications.

When he had finished his early education in the local schools he went to work for a pharmacist in nearby Lyon. The composition of a romantic drama in his leisure moments led him to try his hand at authorship in Paris; but when he showed his efforts to a prominent literary critic in the capital, he was advised to return to a career more nearly related to his experience as a pharmacist's assistant. It was not until he was thirty that he obtained the M.D.

The great influence in his life was François Magendie (1783–1855), who may be termed the father of experimental physiology in France. Magendie was Claude Bernard's sponsor and patron from the younger man's student days to the older scientist's death, when he bequeathed his chair of medicine at the Collège de France to his assistant who, by that time, was giving the courses for him. Although Claude Bernard held a professorship of general physiology first at the Sorbonne, and later at the Muséum d'Histoire Naturelle, his heart really belonged to the Collège de France where Magendie and he had worked so long together. In the course of his life he touched with an illuminating hand almost every phase of physiology, so that Pasteur characterized him not as a physiologist but as physiology itself.

Cl. Bernard

His first paper (1843) concerned the origin and functions of the tiny chorda tympani nerve, but after this came the discovery of the fat-splitting enzyme of the pancreas and the glycogenic function of the liver before he returned to the nervous system for the most spectacular of all his discoveries (1849),[1,2] *viz.*, that a slight wound in the floor of the fourth ventricle of the brain would ren-

Portrait, courtesy of the National Library of Medicine, Bethesda, Maryland.

der an animal temporarily diabetic. From his observation in 1852[3] that cutting the cervical sympathetic nerve of the rabbit causes not only constriction of the pupil of the eye but also flushing and rise of temperature in the ear, came the discovery of the control over blood flow exerted by the nervous system through vasomotor nerves, constrictor and dilator. Johann Friedrich Horner (1831–1886), Swiss ophthalmologist, described in man his famous triad of miosis, ptosis and enophthalmos in 1869;[4] in France the disorder is still referred to as the Claude Bernard-Horner syndrome. Actually the line of this syndrome stretches from Pourfour du Petit (1727) over Stilling (1840), Weir Mitchell (1864) and others.[4]

The old question whether voluntary muscle can be influenced otherwise than by way of its motor nerve was settled in the affirmative by Claude Bernard with the use of curare (1849), and the principles he discovered were immediately applied for treating tetanus, and again, since the 1940's, in anesthesia and convulsive therapy.

Physiology during the middle of the nineteenth century was dominated by Claude Bernard, perhaps his only peer being Carl Ludwig (1816–1895). Pupils came to him from Russia, Germany and America. The succeeding generation of French physiologists, d'Arsonval, Paul Bert, Dastre, and a host of others all owe much to him. Even today his *Introduction à l'étude de la médecine expérimentale* (Paris, Baillière, 1865), available in English,[5] is an inspiration to laymen as well as to the profession.

Claude Bernard was always rather solitary. His moments of greatest happiness came when he had found a neat solution to some problem arising from his physiological investigations. The intransigent Paul Bert (1830–86), author of the incomparable *La pression barométrique* (Paris, Masson, 1878), was his favorite pupil and his successor at the Sorbonne in 1868. Bert, acknowledging his debt to the master, described him as a man of "great kindliness, simplicity of soul, and possessed of a naive generosity."

J. M. D. OLMSTED

References

[1]C. rend. Soc. biol., 1849, *1*:13–15 *et seq.*   [2]*Leçons sur la physiologie et la pathologie du système nerveux.* 2 vol. Paris, Baillière, 1858.   [3]C.

rend. Acad. sci., Paris, 1852, *34:*472–475.   [4]Klin. Mbl. Augenh., 1869, *7:*193–198. See also Arch. Surg., 1929, *18:*2025–2039 (Fulton), Bull. Hist. Med., 1951, *25:*284–288 (Kisch), and Anesthesiology, 1968, *29:*623–624 (Leake).   [5]*An introduction to the study of experimental medicine.* New York, Schuman, 1950 (trans. by Greene). Also Dover, 1957 (paperback).

References to Biography: 1) *Claude Bernard.* London, Unwin, 1899 (Foster).   2) *Claude Bernard, physiologist.* New York and London, Harper, 1938 (Olmsted).

EMIL du BOIS-REYMOND (1818–1896)

W HETHER the lines of progress in electrophysiology be traced backward over a century or forward from an earlier time they are found to meet in the work of one great figure. The half century which had elapsed since Galvani's great discovery had been one of expectancy completely frustrated by lack of methods, until the impasse was broken in 1819 by Oersted, who demonstrated the connection of electricity and magnetism. Thus galvanometers were made possible, but until their sensitivity could be made equal to that of the rheoscopic frog they were useless. In the competition the two had just begun to come alongside when du Bois-Reymond* started his studies. Deflection by the frog current had already been seen. However, the conditions of the experiments were such that no decision could be reached with respect to the famous controversy that arose between Volta and Galvani.

First du Bois-Reymond gave clear descriptions of the resting currents observed in excised muscles and nerves. He postulated electromotive forces pre-existent in the tissues, a view the sound-

---

* Bois-Reymond, Emil Heinrich, du, is the form given in Poggendorff's *Biographisch-Literarisches Handwörterbuch zur Geschichte der exacten Wissenschaften* (Leipzig, Barth, 1863) , in Hirsch-Hübotter's *Biographisches Lexikon der hervorragenden Ärzte aller Zeiten und Völker,* edit. 2 (Berlin, Urban & Schwarzenberg, 1929) , and in Garrison. But it is Du Bois-Reymond in the Index Catalogue (Nat. Libr. Medicine) , the New York Academy of Medicine portrait catalogue, and the Grand Larousse. His father was a watchmaker in Neuchâtel, a Swiss canton at that time still under partial Prussian sovereignty. He came to occupy a civil service position in Berlin. Hence perhaps the aristocratic spelling and spacing of the name.

Emil du Bois-Reymond

Portrait, courtesy of the National Library of Medicine, Bethesda, Maryland.

ness of which has only been strengthened by its ability to withstand worthy opposition.

Next there followed the observation which is basic to the understanding of the changes taking place during activity. He found by direct galvanometric methods that during a tetanus the current flowing at rest from an intact surface to an injured region is decreased, and proved indirectly that this negative variation must be made up of a series of individual variations. It is the magnitude and time-course of these variations and their sequelae that have occupied the attention of physiologists ever since.

The third contribution of high importance was introduced in connection with the term "electrotonus," which was coined to refer to the potential changes produced by an externally applied current. In recent years the findings have been correlated with the potential changes known to occur during activity. It is quite possible that future historians will attribute a greater significance to electrotonic influences than we can at present.

The difficulties with which du Bois-Reymond had to contend are now hard to realize. That he could work at all was only made possible by his ingenuity in the improvement of methods: notably his astatic galvanometer evolved to a high sensitivity, his introduction of nonpolarizable electrodes and potentiometric measurement by the compensation technique, and his appreciation of the need to keep tissues in contact with physiological fluids. For excitation he invented a form of induction coil still in use. His original law of excitation satisfied physiologists during the long period before the re-evaluation of the time parameter which he introduced.

Du Bois-Reymond became one of the remarkable coterie around Johannes Müller; and he succeeded the master in the chair of physiology in 1858. Like many brilliant people he suffered from migraine and thought it was produced by irritation of the cervical sympathetic nerves, a "vasomotor neurosis" causing constriction (Arch. Anat. Physiol., Lpz., 1860, p. 461–468). Growing responsibilities came more and more to occupy du Bois-Reymond's time: his teaching, his permanent secretaryship of the Prussian Academy of Sciences, and his duties at the Physical Society (of which he was a co-founder) and at the Physiological Society. In connection with his official positions he became instrumental in the promotion of the welfare of science and the author of numerous occasional lectures. The latter are notable because of his nationalism, his vigorous opposition to vitalism, and for other reasons of interest to the student of epistemology, including his oracular *Ignorabimus* regarding the mind-brain relationship.

From du Bois-Reymond and his friend and contemporary, Helmholtz, our great heritage is a directive influence: their inspired welding of physics with physiology.

HERBERT S. GASSER

References

Reference to Chief Work: Untersuchungen über thierische Electricität. 2 vol. in 3. Berlin, Reimer, 1848, 1849, 1884.

References to Biography: 1) Rev. sci., Paris, 1897, 4.sér., 7:385–394 (Rosenthal).   2) *Emil du Bois-Reymond.* Wien, Springer, 1922 (Boruttau).   3) *Zwei grosse Naturforscher.* Leipzig, Barth, 1927 (Diepgen).

ÉDOUARD BROWN-SÉQUARD (1817–1894)

B ORN as he was on the British island of Mauritius of a French mother (Charlotte Séquard, a vivacious young lady) and an Irish-American father (a Philadelphia captain who was lost with his ship [piracy?] soon after the marriage), Brown-Séquard was a British subject who spent much of his life traveling back and forth between Mauritius, France, England and the United States. In Paris they called him Brown. This was natural, as he was born Charles Édouard Brown and did not take his mother's name until 1846, and not until 1858 did he legalize it. Like Claude Bernard, he went to Paris with the intention of becoming a dramatic author. But he, too, soon destroyed his plays and enrolled as a medical student. By 1842 he was working under Trousseau and Rayer, the ablest clinicians of the time; again like Claude Bernard he preferred not to settle down to practice but to continue his physiological investigations. When in 1843 his mother,

who had accompanied him to Paris and eeked out a living for the two of them, suddenly died, the blow was such that he rushed back to Mauritius in an almost delirious state of confusion. Finding that the island had no proper niche for him, he returned to Paris— on borrowed money.

Portrait, courtesy of the National Library of Medicine, Bethesda, Maryland.

He was interested in digestion, and would swallow sponges, pull them up, saturated, by a string, and analyze the gastric juice. Soon he turned to the nervous system. His doctoral thesis (1846)[1] foreshadowed the discovery always associated with his name: the syndrome following hemisection of the cord. The ideas in vogue regarding the functions of the different parts of the spinal cord were those of Sir Charles Bell in England, extended by F. A. Longet in France, who maintained that all sensation was carried in the dorsal columns. In his thesis, Brown-Séquard stated that after sectioning the dorsal columns of the cords of cold-blooded vertebrates, birds and mammals, sensation in every case persisted in the parts situated below the section. He also commented on the ease with which he had found sensory impressions to be transmitted from one side of the cord to the other. The thesis was shortly followed by a series of papers in which he clearly established that hemisection of the cord was succeeded by sensory loss on the opposite side of the body and retention and even increase of sensation on the same side.[2]

His second important neurological observation completed Claude Bernard's discovery of vasomotor nerves, for Brown-Séquard was the first to show, in 1852,[3] that stimulation of the cervical sympathetic nerve in the rabbit causes blanching of the ear.

All this time (from 1843 to 1852) he was living in desperate straits. His experiments were carried on in his apartment, and his animals were housed there. To reduce the need for much food he drank coffee incessantly; some eighteen hours of his day were spent writing, reading, experimenting; he became seriously ill from an infection following a wound in the dissecting room. Realizing the poor state of his health and position, and having become involved in revolutionary activities, he decided that he must go to America. He knew hardly a word of English.

He boarded ship armed with a letter from his young friend and partisan, Broca, addressed to the University of Pennsylvania: ". . . Brown-Séquard . . . has imposed upon himself incredible sacrifices . . . and today has nothing left save an honorable character, profound erudition, and scientific articles which everyone can appreciate." In Philadelphia he eked out his earnings giving lectures, delivering babies at cut-rate prices, teaching French. The year not having brought him an appointment, he was again on the high seas in July, 1853, accompanied by his new American wife. Again

Paris was unheeding, and he and his wife continued on to Mauritius, there to find, in May, 1854, an epidemic of cholera which was to take the lives of 8000 people. Immediately he helped organize a hospital. He ingested material vomited by victims to test the efficacy of opium as a cure. Imagining that he himself had the symptoms—as the story goes—he took so large a dose of laudanum that he almost died.

Fortune for once favoring him, he received an offer of a professorship, again on Broca's recommendation, from the Medical College of Virginia, which he accepted. But he was to stay only about four months. To the faculty he had a "surplus of honesty" (he disapproved of slavery), with a lack of energy; his lectures were "not very unlike an attack of spasmodic asthma"; the agony of trying to make himself understood was, if anything, topped by the agony of his listeners, trying to comprehend. His demonstrations, by contrast, were "like wonders wrought by a stage magician." Something was wrong, for in Paris this short wiry person had always been in constant motion and he had had a great gift of elocution.

Back again in Paris, in 1855, his practice as a neurologist began in earnest with the loan by Rayer of an electrical stimulator which he proceeded to apply with great skill to human patients. But observing convulsions in the guinea pigs upon the spinal cords of which he had performed various operations, he spent much of his subsequent life in the attempt to discover the causes and treatment of epilepsy. Later on, he was instrumental in introducing bromide for epilepsy, as suggested by Locock in 1857. His inquiring mind early led him into another field, endocrinology. Addison had published in 1855 his observations on the clinical effect of disease of the suprarenal capsules, and a year later Brown-Séquard showed how fatal adrenalectomy is.[4] Toward the end of his life Brown-Séquard became uncritically enthusiastic over organotherapy—he had repeatedly injected into himself crude extracts of animal tissues—so that his career ended on a note of extravagant claims: attempts to isolate an effective testicular hormone to counteract senescence made him a laughing stock in some quarters. But he had greater vision than they knew.

In 1858 he undertook a course of lectures in several University centers in Great Britain, and in 1860 was appointed physician to the newly founded National Hospital, Queen Square—the second appointment on its professional staff (Jabez S. Ramskill received the first). Here he remained for about 4½ years. The young Hughlings Jackson fell under his spell. Honors and a lucrative practice came. But asked to see a patient in Liverpool for a fee of £200 he insisted that his ordinary fee would do; offered a fee of £10,000 to see a boy in Italy, he declined, saying he was not the right person to advise on the case.

Restless, his wife having died, he again set out for America, in 1864. Now a chair at Harvard was waiting for him. In 1866 he delivered the address opening the Medical Lectures at that school.[5] "I would urge upon you," he said, "to make good use of those low creatures, endowed with so little sensibility,—the frogs, the fishes, and the turtles; to which list I might add the rabbits, animals whose sensibility is indeed so dull, that they will hardly stop eating a carrot (even when not particularly in need of food) while you are cutting their flesh . . ." Arguing that the use of such animals for experimenting was for the good of mankind he said, "I am selfish enough to prefer mankind to frogkind, rabbitkind, etc." In 1868 he was back in France, probably for the sake of his twelve-year-old son. But since he could not be accorded professorial rank in Paris—he was still not a French citizen, not to speak of his libertarian leanings—he returned to America again, in 1870. The next eight years, in New York, though interrupted by trips to Europe, were his unhappiest: his second wife died after the birth of a daughter. He acquired a third, the widow of a painter.

Another sailing ship returned him to Paris in 1878, the only city he really cared for. Claude Bernard had just died. Taking out naturalization papers he became, finally, a real Frenchman, also Bernard's successor at the Collège de France, an office he happily fulfilled until his death from apoplexy fifteen years later.

During his Paris years he founded three journals devoted to physiology and published hundreds of articles. One of them, in 1876, dealt with his observation that cerebral-cortical ablation in certain regions was succeeded by gastric ulceration, an observation previously made (in 1844) by Moritz Schiff, who considered the ulceration due to local vasomotor paralysis (from lesions of the corpus striatum or cerebral peduncle); Brown-Séquard, disagreeing, contended that contraction of gastric arteries and veins was at fault.[6] He dwelled on his view that neural activity at one level is always colored and conditioned by what is happening at another, remote level, a notion independently elaborated by Sherrington later on. His public discourses became famous: at the International Congress of Medicine in Paris in 1867—the first of its kind —he was the most eagerly awaited speaker; however, owing to the sudden illness and death of a fellow Mauritian, he did not appear.[7]

Brown-Séquard left an enthusiastic group of young workers, the best known of whom were d'Arsonval and François-Franck; upon his passing, the great French school of experimental physiology— belonging to Magendie, Flourens, Claude Bernard and himself— was never the same again.

J. M. D. OLMSTED

References

[1]*Recherches et expériences sur la physiologie de la moëlle épinière.* Thèse de Paris, 1846.   [2]C. rend. Acad. sci., Paris, 1850, *31:*700–701. [3]Med. Exam., Phila., 1852, n.s., *8:*481–504 *et seq.*   [4]C. rend. Acad. sci., Paris, 1856, *43:*422–425 *et seq.*   [5]*Advice to students: An address delivered at the opening of the medical lectures of Harvard University. Nov. 7, 1866.* Cambridge, Wilson, 1867.   [6]Progr. méd., Par., 1876, *4:*136–137.   [7]Brit. Med. J., 1967, *3:*487–489 (McMenemey).

References to Biography and Works: 1) *Charles-Édouard Brown-Séquard, a nineteenth century neurologist and endocrinologist.* Baltimore, Johns Hopkins Press, 1946 (Olmsted). 2) Lancet, 1952, *1:*760 (Jefferson).   3) *Young endeavour.* Springfield, Thomas, 1958, p. 222–223 (Gibson).   4) *The National Hospital. Queen Square.* Edinburgh, Livingstone, 1954 (Holmes).   5) *Notice sur les travaux scientifiques.* Paris, Masson, 1878 (Brown-Séquard).

JOANNES GREGORIUS DUSSER DE BARENNE
(1885–1940)

*T*HE sudden death of Professor Dusser de Barenne on June 9, 1940, occurred at a time when international communications were seriously disrupted, and many of his colleagues in Europe were therefore long unaware that his brilliant career had

Joannes Gregorius Dusser de Barenne

been brought to a premature close when he was but fifty-five years of age and at the height of his powers.

Dusser de Barenne was born in the village of Brielle in The Netherlands. His father was a municipal official of Amsterdam, and Dusser de Barenne, after preliminary education in the public schools, entered Amsterdam University and received his medical qualification in 1909. His professional career began that year as a teaching assistant in the Laboratory of Physiology at Amsterdam where he commenced the work on the effect of strychnine on the

Portrait, courtesy of Dr. John F. Fulton, New Haven, Connecticut. (Donated to Yale Medical Library by Dr. Paul E. Rekers.)

reflex activity of invertebrate ganglia.[1] After two years he was appointed psychiatrist to the Meerenberg Lunatic Asylum where he was engaged until the outbreak of World War I in the physiological analysis of decerebrate rigidity and also of tonic neck and labyrinthine reflexes.

During the War he served as a medical officer in the Dutch Army and found time while stationed at a military establishment at Delft to continue his studies on the tonus of skeletal muscle. In 1918 he became an assistant to Rudolf Magnus at Utrecht and participated actively for twelve years in investigations on the physiology of posture which brought widespread recognition to the Utrecht School. His most important paper during this period, however, was the result of a visit in 1924 to the laboratory of Sir Charles Sherrington where he studied the sensory symptoms which followed on local application of strychnine to the cerebral cortex of rhesus monkeys, a practice that won him the nickname, "Strychnine," an appelation he enjoyed. The paper embodying his findings, now regarded as a classic, demonstrated for the first time the major functional subdivisions of the sensory cortex.[2]

By common consent, Dusser de Barenne had now become the foremost of the younger generation of Dutch physiologists. With the deaths of Einthoven and Magnus in 1927 and the retirement of Zwaardemaker, the three most eminent chairs of physiology and pharmacology in Holland became vacant almost simultaneously. Dusser de Barenne would have filled any one of them with distinction and he no doubt would have been called but for the religious restrictions in the Dutch universities; these were intolerable to a free-thinking man of Dusser de Barenne's outspoken tendencies, and thus the United States was able to claim one of the most distinguished physiologists ever to appear on the continent of Europe.

Dusser de Barenne arrived in New Haven, Connecticut, in September, 1930, to join the faculty of the Yale School of Medicine, and for the next ten years he engaged in a program of research which for sustained productivity has had few parallels. A succession of men, attracted by his presence in the States, became associated with him as pupils and assistants—Percival Bailey, Warren McCulloch, Leslie Nims, and Arthur Ward, to mention only a few. His primary contribution during this period lay in the introduction of the new technique of physiological neuronography which has made possible a vast research endeavor involving analysis of the interaction of various cortical and subcortical regions of the brain; it also led to the discovery of many hitherto unsuspected fiber connections and projections (chiefly nonmyelinated). One of his techniques came to him in a dream. His wife, who had borne him three daughters, had suddenly died, an event so depressing that he thought of quitting science. He lay awake night after night realizing that he was at an impasse in the laboratory for lack of a method to determine which layers of a cortex were requisite for sensation. Finally, in the middle of one long, lonely night he thought of getting up and having breakfast, but dozed off. He saw in his dream an egg cooking slowly. He jumped from his bed, rushed to the laboratory, heated a brass rod in boiling water, and applied it to the cortex. In twenty minutes the method of laminar thermocoagulation was at his fingertips!

With some he was quick tempered, even explosive, also blunt, and toward an outsider he tended to be suspicious until satisfied that he was not scheming and insincere. He had had repeated heart attacks, and those who worked with him sensed the increased pressure under which he worked as he realized that his labors must soon come to an end. This was evident both in the laboratory and as co-editor of the *Journal of Neurophysiology:* more light danced in his eyes; fewer words served him for more sense; he would accomplish in minutes what previously had taken him hours; he worked more continuously. "He would go dogishly on," Warren Sturgish McCulloch (1898–1969) related, "for fifty-five hours, repeating an observation every three minutes on a single point on a single hemisphere before he was satisfied." His stature as a man and as a scientist continues to grow as time affords perspective against which to appraise his immediate contributions and his subsequent influence.

JOHN F. FULTON

Reference

[1]Fol. neurobiol., Lpz., 1910, *4:*467–474 *et seq.*   [2]Proc. R. Soc., London, 1924, ser.B, *96:*272–291.

References to Biography: 1) J. Neurophysiol., 1940, *3*:283–292 (contains bibliography; Fulton and Garol). 2) Yale J. Biol. & Med., 1940, *12*:743–746 (McCulloch).

JOSEPH ERLANGER (1874–1965)

*T*HE fact that in 1944 Joseph Erlanger received the Nobel Prize for discoveries in the field of neurophysiology has doubtless caused a later generation to overlook the significant contributions he made in somewhat distant areas. His important work on the circulatory system was alluded to when, in 1947, he was awarded an honorary degree by the Johns Hopkins University, and afterwards he expressed appreciation of this recognition in a manner which indicated his pride in that earlier work.

Erlanger was born in San Francisco, the sixth of seven children of a German-Jewish immigrant who, having arrived after an arduous trip via Panama, had unsuccessfully taken part in the gold rush. Not an apt pupil in public school, Joseph had to be prodded by his mother into getting an education. In 1895 he graduated with a B.S. from the University of California in Berkeley. Wavering between Harvard and Johns Hopkins in his choice of a medical school, he decided on Hopkins. In the summer season following his first year there, not having the wherewithal to return to San Francisco for vacation, he took on the problem of the location of the cells supplying the facial muscles in the rabbit, also the whereabouts in the spinal cord of the anterior horn cells which supply the soleus muscle. Lewellys Barker, who oversaw this work, later reproduced four of Erlanger's drawings of nerve cells with retrograde changes, in his classic, *The nervous system and its constituent neurones* (New York, Stechert, 1909).

Graduating in the uppermost fraction of his class at Johns Hopkins, Erlanger was awarded an internship under Osler. Receiving no salary, he managed to get along on the $10 a month his brother sent him. The next year he received a coveted fellowship in the Department of Pathology under W. H. Welch (despite Welch's complaint that he could not read Erlanger's handwriting), but soon obtained a release when offered an assistantship in Physiology

Joseph Erlanger

by W. H. Howell. Accidently breaking a Mosso instrument just imported from Italy, he constructed a device of his own for measuring arterial pressure in the arm; soon he became a key figure in establishing the principles and in developing the instruments for the indirect measurement of human arterial pressure.[1,2]

In 1904 Langley and Anderson had stated that "the central end of any *efferent somatic* fibre can make functional union with the peripheral end of any *preganglionic* fibre. . . ." But it was left to Erlanger to provide the evidence (in 1905)[3]: after suturing a spi-

Portrait, courtesy of Dr. James W. Woods, Oklahoma City, Oklahoma. (Photographer: C. F. Dieckman, St. Louis, Missouri.)

nal nerve to the peripheral end of the cut vagus he found that the regenerating spinal-nerve fibers may make such functional cardiac connections that their stimulation will produce inhibition of the heart. "This results," he concluded, "from the action of ordinary nerve impulses upon a peculiar end-apparatus."

Sometime in 1904 William Osler asked the young physiologist to see a patient with Stokes-Adams disease. Physiological recordings, Erlanger found, revealed complete auriculoventricular block, and gradual return to normal. Extensive animal studies on the transmission of excitation in the mammalian heart from the pacemaker to the ventricles followed. In the course of this work, by means of a special clamping device and a technique of cardiac surgery remarkable for that day, Erlanger produced the first *chronic* heart block. These experiments[4-6] made it clear that no cardiac structure can vicariously assume the function of the bundle of His, and they went far toward substantiating the view, then in dispute, that conduction in the mammalian heart is myogenic.

Meanwhile he had advanced to an associate professorship at Johns Hopkins, but in 1906 the work on heart block was temporarily interrupted by his acceptance to head the Department of Physiology at Wisconsin, a position he left in 1910 to assume the same chair at Washington University, St. Louis, where he was prominent in the reorganization of the Medical School. During these years he turned his attention to the pacemaker of the mammalian heart. "The localization of impulse initiation and conduction in the heart," his Harvey Lecture of 1912, sets forth in masterly fashion the views and conclusions possible at that time, many of them originating in his own work.

That experience doubtless provided a splendid background for the work on nerve for which he is now best known. Meanwhile the exigencies of the first World War had led him to collaborate with Walter Meek, his successor at Wisconsin, and with Herbert Gasser, his former student (who had joined him in St. Louis in 1916), in a study of secondary traumatic shock, especially the changes in blood volume and the effect which gum acacia had on the development of the changes.[7]

The "discoveries relating to the highly differentiated functions of single nerve fibers," as the Nobel Prize citation for Erlanger

and Gasser ran in 1944, began in 1921 shortly after Gasser had returned to Washington University from war service to become Professor of Pharmacology. The discoveries resulted from the cou-
pling of a cathode ray oscillograph, of greater sensitivity than any
of its forerunners, with an improved three-stage amplifier. This
equipment made it possible not only to record the action potentials of a nerve trunk with greater accuracy than had previously
been possible but also to detect its compound nature. At the meeting of the American Physiological Society in 1921, they presented
the plot of an action current "of striking clearness." A full report
in 1922[8] mentioned secondary waves on the catacrotic limb of the
potential wave, in frog nerves and the tibial nerve of cat and rabbit but, significantly, not from the phrenic of the dog. A classic
paper with George Bishop, on the compound nature of the action
current of nerve as disclosed by the cathode ray oscillograph,[9]
showed that these "catacrotic waves" signalled conduction at different velocities in different groups of nerve fibers and that the
several groups have different thresholds of stimulation and different durations of refractory phase. Related studies followed.[10-12]

The next step in the joint Erlanger-Gasser investigation seems
to have stemmed from the suggestion of Lapicque and Legendre
(1913) that since chronaxie is shorter the larger the fiber, and
since there is a relation between chronaxie and velocity of conduction, the velocity of impulses is greater in large than in small
fibers. During his European sojourn of 1923–1925 Gasser, with
Lapicque and Desoilles, had obtained histological evidence that
the fibers of the saphenous nerve vary widely in size whereas those
of the phrenic, whose action potential had been found free from
secondary waves, are relatively homogeneous. Shortly after Gasser's
second return to St. Louis he and Erlanger presented (in 1927)[13]
definite evidence that it is the size of the constituent fibers in a
given nerve trunk which determines the form of its action potential: "at least to a first approximation the velocity in a fiber is determined by its diameter." Histological examination of a nerve
trunk allowed them "to predict with some accuracy the form of
the action potential it will yield." Thus began the development of
the present standard classification into A fibers, thickest and fastest
(with subgroups alpha, beta, delta, and gamma); C fibers, unmye-

linated, and carrying impulses at the slowest rates; and B fibers, of intermediate velocities, myelinated, small, and confined to the autonomic system. Erlanger and Gasser[14,15] further showed how these different types are distributed in the motor and sensory spinal roots and what other properties vary with the speed of conduction: duration, size and rate of rise of the action potential; refractory period; threshold; and sensitivity to asphyxia and to local anesthetics. The last two variables were especially employed by Gasser and others to analyze somatic sensation in terms of different types of afferent fibers.

After Gasser left St. Louis in 1932 for New York, Erlanger with various collaborators, especially E. A. Blair, devoted his attention chiefly to analyses of the changes in the excitability of single fibers caused by constant currents and thereby disclosed some significant differences between motor and sensory fibers. His Nobel Lecture dealt chiefly with this subject.

After retirement in 1946 Erlanger, as Professor Emeritus of Physiology, continued to work in his St. Louis Laboratory until a year before his death in 1965. A little detail concerning him during this period spotlights one aspect of his character. He had applied to the National Institutes of Health for a research grant. His application was for $900. The study section, all academic physiologists, who had before them as many requests for twenty times that amount, voted to recommend a grant of $1,000. But they were troubled; the thought haunted them that the supplement might offend Dr. Erlanger; they knew how meticulous he was about his every act. He was undemonstrative but affable, critical but never contentious. In giving intellectual aid and continued loyalty to students and colleagues, he was most generous. "Joseph Erlanger's students," wrote one of them, "and their students will bear the imprint of this great teacher—an academician of the highest order—a friend of lasting loyalty who shall always live in memory."

BALTIMORE, MARYLAND   PHILIP BARD

References

[1]Johns Hopk. Hosp. Rep., 1904, *12*:127–378 (with Hooker).   [2]Amer. J. Physiol., 1916, *40*:82–125.   [3]Amer. J. Physiol., 1905, *5*:372–395. [4]J. Exp. Med., 1905-06, *7–8* (parts 1, 2 and 3), 7:675–724; 8:8–58.

[5]Amer. J. Physiol., 1906, *15*:153–206 (with Hirschfelder).   [6]Heart, London, 1910, *1*:177–230 (with Blackman).   [7]Amer. J. Physiol., 1919, *50*:51–53 (with Gasser and Meek).   [8]*Ibid.*, 1922, *62*:496–524 (with Gasser).   [9]*Ibid.*, 1924, *70*:624–666 (with Gasser and Bishop). [10]*Ibid.*, 1925, *72*:613–635 (with Gasser).   [11]*Ibid.*, 1926, *78*:574–591 (with Bishop and Gasser).   [12]*Ibid.*, 1926, *78*:630–657 (with Bishop). [13]*Ibid.*, 1927, *80*:1522–1547 (with Gasser).   [14]*Electrical signs of nervous activity*. Eldridge Reeves Johnson Foundation Lecture. Philadelphia, U. of Pa., 1937 (with Gasser).   [15]Some observations on the responses of single nerve fibers. *Les Prix Nobel en 1947*. Stockholm, Nobelstiftelsen, 1949.

References to Biography and Works: 1) Annual Rev. Physiol., 1964, *26*:1–14 (with selected references) (Erlanger).   2) *The human brain and spinal cord. A historical study illustrated by writings from antiquity of the twentieth century.* Berkeley, U. of Calif., 1968 (Clarke and O'Malley).

DAVID FERRIER (1843–1928)

*F*ERRIER was born near Aberdeen, and was educated at the Universities of Aberdeen and Edinburgh. His most influential teachers were Alexander Bain, logician and psychologist at Aberdeen, and William Image, F.R.C.S. and general practitioner in Suffolk, whom Ferrier assisted while writing the thesis for his M.D. in 1870. That year Ferrier moved to London, where he lived the rest of his life.

He was connected chiefly with the National Hospital from 1880 and with the Medical School of King's College where he occupied the chair of neuropathology created for him in 1889. He was a charter member of the Physiological Society and in 1878 joined with Hughlings Jackson, Sir John Bucknill and Sir James Crichton-Browne in founding the journal, *Brain*. He was elected Fellow of the Royal Society in 1876, Fellow of the Royal College of Physicians (London), 1877, Laureate of the Institut de France, 1878, and received many other honors throughout his long, active life, including knighthood, 1911, the Hon. ScD. from Cambridge, 1914, and the Hon. LL.D. from Birmingham in 1927.

As Stanley Cobb has pointed out,[1] Ferrier was probably the

Sir David Ferrier

link between Hughlings Jackson and Sherrington, for he worked
with Jackson in the 1870's and Sherrington worked with him in
the 1890's. Ferrier will be remembered primarily for his pioneer
work in neurophysiology and especially the experiments by which
he established the concept of localization of function in the cere-

Portrait, courtesy of Dr. John F. Fulton, New Haven, Connecticut. (Photographer:
Maull & Fox, London, England.)

brum. In this connection, it may be mentioned that Friedrich Albert Lange (1828–75) in his *Geschichte des Materialismus und Kritik seiner Bedeutung in der Gegenwart* (1866), was the first to propose such a concept and to distinguish localization of function from localization of symptoms.[2]

Ferrier's studies were begun in 1873[3] and were published during that year and the three following years.[4-7] They were undertaken ". . . to put to experimental proof the views entertained by Dr. Hughlings Jackson . . ., and to follow up the path which the researches of Fritsch and Hitzig . . . indicated . . ." In this introduction to his first publication he gave warm credit to others, as was typical of him; the words, "to put to experimental proof," were an expression of his basic scientific philosophy.

He was one of the rediscoverers of the experimental method, and his work was marked by simple, direct practicality, careful control, and precise, full recording. By means of comparative studies he established general principles of the functions of the brain in mammalian species from rodents to apes. He continued his work in the clinic, applying these principles to his observations on man,[8] and on the basis of his experience with animals, strongly urged the surgeons to operate for intracranial disorders. Indeed, Rickman Godlee felt that Ferrier was one of the principal figures in opening the field which is now neurosurgery.

Ferrier was more than an experimenter; he was, rather, a philosopher who did not philosophize but who experimented. He is to be credited with the discovery that removal of the precentral gyrus leads immediately to paralysis of the limbs of the opposite side, and that in the monkey the hemiplegic position is soon assumed.[6,7] Although his work established the "motor area" and certain "sensory areas," he was not himself misled by the concept of localization. For him the functions of the cerebrum were "sensorimotor" and he stated: "From the complexity of mental phenomena and the participation in them of both motor and sensory substrata, any system of localization of mental faculties which does not take both factors into account must be radically false." He thus presaged the present view which regards the brain as the organ *par excellence* of interaction.

Ferrier was a slight, erect man, quiet of manner, direct of

speech, and of great energy. His life was that of a busy consultant, but he took time to continue some research in collaboration with others, effectively encouraging younger men. He attended scientific meetings assiduously, but avoided scientific polemics. His modest hope that he was "not in the way" while watching an experiment expressed by implication more forcibly than any protestation could have done, his feeling for the importance of the experimenter and the experiment. His vigorous defense of animal experimentation when he was taken to court by antivivisectionists at once won his case and made his name famous throughout England.

ROCKVILLE, MARYLAND   DAVID McK. RIOCH

References

[1]Arch. Neur., Psychiat., Chic., 1948, 59:63–98.   [2]J. Hist. Med., N. Y., 1950, 1:50–71 (Riese and Hoff).   [3]West Riding Lun. Asyl. Rep., London, 1873, 3:1–50.   [4]Proc. Roy. Soc., London, 1874, 22:229–232. [5]Brit. Med. J., 1874, 2:766–767.   [6]Philos. Tr. Roy. Soc., London, 1875, 165:433–488.   [7]The functions of the brain. London, Smith, Elder, 1876.   [8]Brit. Med. J., 1878, 1:399–402 et seq. (Goulstonian Lectures).

References to Biography and Works: 1) Proc. Roy. Soc., London, 1928, ser.B., 103:vii–xvi (Sherrington).   2) Lancet, London, 1938, 1:627–629 (not signed).   3) J. Ment. Sci., London, 1928, 74:375–380 (Grainger Stewart).   4) Arch. Neur. Psychiat., Chic., 1948, 59:63–98 (Cobb)   5) Bull. Inst. Hist. Med., Balt., 1938, 6:477–487 (Viets). 6) Neurosurgical Classics. New York, Johnson Reprint, 1965, p. 119–128 (Wilkins).

PIERRE FLOURENS (1794–1867)

$\mathcal{F}$ LOURENS' birthplace was the castle of La Trésorière, at Maureilhan, in the South of France. A friend of the family, a priest returned from exile after the revolution, offered to take the boy; and little Marie Jean Pierre, aged nine, installed in front of the curé on a donkey, rode to Payguerolles, about 60 km north,

Marie Jean Pierre Flourens

where he worked at his education for the next seven years. Distinctly bright, he was sent to the medical faculty at Montpellier. There de Candolle, the famous botanist, made him join the Society for Natural History and even become its secretary. After graduation, Flourens went to Paris with letters of recommendation to Cuvier, Lamarck, Portal, and E. Geoffroy Saint-Hilaire. When he was twenty-four, Cuvier charged him with writing reviews for the *Revue encyclopédique*.

Two years later Flourens lectured on the physiological theory of sensations. This made him turn to the central nervous system; by 1824 he published *Recherches expérimentales sur les propriétés et les fonctions du système nerveux dans les animaux vertébrés;*[1] Soury, the great neurohistorian, lauded "la sûreté, la précision, la clarté, la simplicité lumineuse de son style," not without criticizing a certain excess of elegant simplification. Flourens recognized three properties of the nervous system: (1) intelligence, i.e., perception and striving; (2) sensibility, i.e., reception and transmission of impressions; (3) excitation of muscular contractions. Immediate contractions issue in the spinal cord, mostly its anterior column; co-ordination in the cerebellum; sensation in the posterior column. Intellectual faculties reside in the cerebral lobes, as seen in birds and reptiles (which for him included the frog); mammals he studied less. He describes his ablation experiments on which rest most of his work and fame, as well as much of subsequent neurophysiology. Work on the cerebellum was largely performed on pigeons. The sense of vision in the pigeon he placed in the quadrigeminal bodies, where, in this bird, we still place the centers that control the movement of the iris and the movement of the body around the longitudinal axis. He also showed that the medulla oblongata contains the center for respiration and called it *noeud vital,* a name which is still used.

Flourens' work is two-sided. On one hand he was the first to ascribe different functions to different parts of the brain: they all have "des propriétés spécifiques, des fonctions propres, des effets distincts" (p. 110). On the other hand he never went further in his subdivisions. He felt that vision, hearing and tactile sensations were experienced to the same degree in the whole cortex. But then only mammals have a fully developed cortex, with a pyramidal tract (of which Flourens knew nothing) and definite regions to which visual, acoustic and tactile sensations go. Flourens cheerfully talks about frogs, birds, and mammals as though they had similar brains.

He was strongly and effectively opposed to Gall's doctrine.[2] As to Gall's cranioscopy he was certainly correct; as to cortical function he was, it must be admitted, wrong.

Cuvier chose him to give his course at the Collège de France in 1828; two years later he lectured on comparative anatomy at the Musée du Jardin; when Portal died in 1832 he was given his chair. In 1855 he was professor at the Collège de France, in the next year and to his death a permanent secretary of the Académie des Sciences. He joined the "Immortals" in 1840 after many months of balloting for the single vacant seat, by defeating Victor Hugo.

Flourens' second great work of the 1820's concerns the inner ear in birds where he made a clear distinction between the organ of hearing and the equilibratory organ by extirpating separately the cochlea, the vestibulum and the semicircular canals. By destroying only one semicircular canal at a time he even disentangled the function of the three canals.[3] Menière's paper of 1861, on the disease which bears his name, is based on Flourens' crucial experiments.[4]

We will merely mention an evidently large work on the skin and mucous membranes (1843)[5] and one on bones (1847) in which he showed that bone is formed by the periosteum, and thus paved the way to some surgical advances. He also undertook important and lasting work on surgical anesthesia showing that ether and chloroform extinguish the action of the cerebral lobes first, then that of the cerebellum, the spinal cord next, and finally the medulla oblongata with the *noeud vital.*

No doubt a strong individuality, sensitive, erudite and eloquent, he interspersed his discourse with anecdotes about others and could hold an untiring audience. A militant conservative, he was elected deputy for his home arrondissement in 1838; in 1846 he was created a peer of France. The revolution of 1848 made him withdraw from political life and society.

Married perhaps not before he was in his forties, he had, in 1838, a son, Gustave, who for a while helped his father at the Collège de France but was abruptly dismissed on account of revolutionary ideas, fled to Crete, was elected in 1867 to the Greek parliament, but soon returned and fell in 1871 as a member of the

Commune in an attack against the conservative troops of the Versailles government. Pierre Flourens died in 1867, just before the dismissal of his prodigal son. According to his own wishes his grave has merely the words *P. Flourens, physiologiste*. As such he was one of the most important figures of the nineteenth century.

SAN FRANCISCO, CALIFORNIA   GERHARDT von BONIN

References

[1]*Recherches expérimentales sur les propriétés et les fonctions du système nerveux dans les animaux vertébrés.* Paris, Crevot, 1824. [2]*De la phrénologie et des études vraies sur le cerveau.* Paris, Garnier, 1863.   [3]Mém. Acad. Sci., Paris, 1828, *9*:450–477.   [4]*Menières Originalarbeiten ins Deutsche übersetzt.* Göttingen, Meisterschmidt, 1955, p. 69 (Blumenbach).   [5]*Anatomie générale de la peau (particulièrement dans les races humaines colorées) et des membranes muqueuses.* Paris, Gide, 1843.

References to Biography: 1) Rev. Sci., Paris, 1887, *39*:1–11 (Vulpian). 2) *Le système nerveux central, structure et fonctions; histoire critique des théories et des doctrines.* Paris, Carré & Naud, 1899 (Soury).

FELICE FONTANA (1730–1805)

*T*HE greatness of this man lies in his many-sided contributions:[1] to physiology, anatomy, botany, toxicology, chemistry and experimental pathology. For neurologists, there is special interest in his giving the first accurate description of the nerve fiber, and in the role he took regarding the eighteenth century preoccupation with the irritability of tissues; for this was the idea that lay behind the emergence of electrophysiology at the end of that century.

The conception of irritability developed by Haller dominated physiology for over one hundred years. "Irritability" was the product of a growing restlessness with the centuries-old Galenic doctrine that nerves were hollow tubes carrying the animal spirits from the ventricles of the brain to the muscles, causing them to balloon during contraction.

Felice Fontana

Even before the publication of Haller's famous *Mémoires sur les parties sensibles et irritables du corps animal* (1760), the ingenious Leopoldo Marc Aurelio Caldani (1725–1813) reported to Haller his experiments with Fontana in a series of letters—especially their failure to find evidence of irritability in the intestines and lungs, and their attempts to convince themselves of the insen-

Portrait from the Accademia degli Agiati at Rovereto, Italy, by courtesy of Dr. Luigi Belloni.

sibility of the dura mater. Both in animals and in conscious tre-
phined men, what produced convulsions was not irritation of the
dura but pressure on the brain. Fortunately, Haller included these
letters from Bologna in his *Mémoires,* and so the physiological
world learned of the experiments currently in progress there. We
find Fontana at first strongly opposed to identifying the nervous
principle with electricity, as he himself also wrote to Haller in
1757.[1]

Seven years after the publication of Haller's *Mémoires,* in 1767,
Fontana brought together his own views on irritability in the treatise *De irritabilitatis legibus.*[2] Hallerian irritability has raised so
much dissension among Italian scientists, he says in an opening
phrase, that it might well be called "an irritation to all Italy."

Contractility and irritability were, in Haller's opinion, identical. In Fontana's view, however, each muscle fiber was, by its elasticity, attempting to restore itself after a contraction. He sought
the explanation for voluntary sustained contraction in the fine
tremor he observed during the effort, and interpreted the tremor
as an extremely rapid alternation of irritability and elasticity. By
now he also was more receptive to the idea that electricity might
be playing a part. In his treatise on the nerve we find him writing:
"The mechanism of muscular movement is unknown, we cannot
even imagine how to explain it. It seems as though we shall be
compelled to adopt some other principle—if not of ordinary electricity, then something analogous to it."[3] Here, perhaps, is the first
suggestion that the production of electricity might be excited by
the nerves rather than merely conducted by them, as by wires.

To the prior discovery by Caldani, by Haller, and by Whytt, of
the pupillary reflex to light, Fontana added that in a state of fear
or excitement the pupils remained dilated in spite of light reaching the eye. In an experiment on his cat, he held the eyelids open
for a very long period and noted that when the animal finally slept
the pupils became extremely narrow, narrower even than when
awake in the light. These observations of the pupil in sleep and
wakefulness cannot be bettered in modern times; they include the
consensual light reflex.[4]

In his work with the microscope, Fontana was the first to spot a
"body" within a "vesicle," in other words the cell nucleus. He de-

scribed the tubules of the kidney, the axon cylinder and the nerve sheath. Some of these as well as his pharmacological studies are immortalized in the famous book on the *Venom of the viper.* At the end of the edition in French[3] we find the short treatise on the nerves. It is a little gold mine of ideas, for his time, on the frontier of this science. Not only did he describe and illustrate the solid axis "cylinder" of the "primitive nerve fiber," but also the degeneration of nerve, as it loses its function when separated from its center.[3] He proceeded to cut the sciatic nerve in several different species and by stimulating the distal cut end made the muscles contract although the animal could no longer spontaneously move its foot. These observations were published in 1775[5]; in 1799 he was to work on nerve regeneration.[6]

The treatise on the venom of the viper includes studies of many plant poisons and the first description of the ciliary duct that now bears his name. Botanists remember him for the rust parasite of grain. The active interest he took in optical instruments extended to those used in astronomical work and, in order to have Sisson make some for the Observatory of the Grand Duke of Tuscany, he journeyed to London. There, in 1775, he wrote his piece on the structure of nerves.

An enduring monument is the vast collection of wax figures he had made, on instructions from the Grand Duke, for the teaching of anatomy and, in lieu of the life-class, for the students of art, both in Bologna and Florence. When the Emperor Joseph II happened to see them there he immediately asked Fontana to have some copied for his Military Medical Academy in Vienna: forty cases of them loaded on twenty mules went over the Alps in due course.

Fontana was born in Pomarolo, a village of the Trentino near Rovereto, and educated at Verona and Parma; he then studied in Padua and Bologna, and had a brief period in Rome. Appointed to the Chair of Philosophy at Pisa in 1765, he was later called by the Grand Duke of Tuscany to take charge of the Cabinet of Physics and Natural History at Florence. There he spent thirty fruitful years traveling abroad from time to time to add to the collections of the famous Accademia del Cimento.

Trained not for medicine but the church, and though wearing

the garments of a lay abbot, he never engaged in religious activities. Toward the end of his life he fell foul of religious and political controversies: his sentiments lay with France in her revolutionary struggle. As a result he was imprisoned by Austria but rescued
by Napoleon and able to return to Florence. In recognition of this
help he reproduced for France some of his famous wax figures; several of them can still be seen at Montpellier.

He was honored by burial in Santa Croce, the pantheon of Florence. A fitting epitaph would be this, taken from his dedication to
the treatise on irritability: *"The reward for my effort in that matter is to have read the animal Spirits out of office, forever. . . ."*

LOS ANGELES, CALIFORNIA   MARY A. B. BRAZIER

References

[1]Letter to Urbain Tosetti. In *Mémoires sur les parties sensibles et
irritables du corps animal.* Vol. 3. Lausanne, d'Arnag, 1760; p. 159
(Haller).   [2]*De irritabilitatis legibus.* Lucca, Riccomini, 1767.
[3]*Traité sur le venin de la vipère.* 2 vol. Florence, 1781.   [4]*De' moti
dell'iride.* Lucca, 1765.   [5]*Ricerche filosofiche sopra la fisica ani-
male.* Florence, Cambiagi, 1775.   [6]*Principes raisonnés sur la généra-
tion.* Florence, 1799.

References to Biography: 1) Symposium Ciba, 1960, 7:84 (Belloni).
2) Archeion, 1930, *12*:296 (Bilancioni).   3) Physis., 1959, *1*:307
(Zanobio).

CHARLES ÉMILE FRANÇOIS-FRANCK (1849–1921)

*F*RANÇOIS FRANCK was a Parisian by birth. His initial
medical studies were carried out in Bordeaux, and in
1870 he became assistant in the Hôpital Saint André. His work toward a medical degree was interrupted by the Prussian attack on
France. He volunteered his services to the French army, and because of his excellent horsemanship he sometimes served as liaison
officer. It was during one of his attempts to carry an official dispatch that he was wounded and taken prisoner by the Prussians.
Being a physician, the carrying of dispatches constituted a viola-

Charles Émile François-Franck

tion of the Geneva Convention: he was tried, convicted, and sentenced to death, but after a miraculous escape he made his way back to Bordeaux.

With the war over, François-Franck returned to Paris to continue his medical education. He was recognized as a brilliant student and was made chef de clinique and prosector in 1872. Upon receiving his doctorate in medicine in 1875 he was appointed assistant to Marey in the laboratory of pathologic physiology of the Collège de France. Marey, because of frail health and a desire to devote all his energy to research, soon placed the responsibility of the lectures on François-Franck. This annual series of forty lec-

Portrait from *Nos grands médecins d'aujourdhui,* Paris, 1891, by H. Bianchon.

tures he conducted brilliantly for thirty years. Original experiments formed the foundation of these discourses, the principal subject of which was the physiology of the circulation. Marey[1] and François-Franck[2,3] were responsible for showing, for instance, that when variations of carotid-cephalic arterial pressure occur, cardiac and vasomotor compensatory reactions immediately set in. Thus these men may be considered forerunners of Heinrich Ewald Hering (1866–1948), whose discovery of the carotid sinus mechanism in 1924 opened up the modern study in this field.[4,5]

During 1884–86 François-Franck's lectures were devoted almost entirely to a study of the cerebral circulation.[6] He played a large part in Marey's work on sphygmography, and he was especially skillful in adapting Marey's graphic method to experimental research.

A friendship had grown up between Pitres and François-Franck when both were studying for their doctorates. Pitres was later to become the professor of neurology at Bordeaux, but in the meantime he was working at the Salpêtrière under Charcot, who was then concentrating on cerebral localization of function. Pitres acquired the enthusiasm of his master and he, in turn, engaged the interest of François-Franck in this field of work.

These two young men initiated a series of experiments which François-Franck terminated alone, experiments noted for their originality and precision. Among their contributions was the observation that after removal of the motor region of the cerebral cortex—simian and canine—not only the crossed fasciculi of the pyramids, but also the homolateral, undergo degeneration.[7] The direct result of this collaboration was François-Franck's important book on motor functions of the brain,[8] in which he reported on the excitability of the cortex and the localization of cerebral function. In this book, to which Charcot wrote the preface, François-Franck included the following dedicatory note: "A mon cher ami le professeur Pitres—nous avons recueilli ensemble la plupart des documents utilisés dans ce volume: je te prie d'en accepter la dédicace, comme un juste hommage, et un souvenir de notre vieille amitié."

But François-Franck's life was not spent entirely in the laboratory. He was a beloved pupil of Potain and it was under this inspiration that François-Franck became also a clinician of the first rank. His opinions were much sought as a heart specialist, for which his physiological training and experiments under Marey had well prepared him.

As early as 1885—he was then thirty-six—François-Franck became the director of the laboratory of pathologic physiology of the Collège de France. In 1887 he was elected to membership in the Académie de Médecine, Paris, and in 1905 he succeeded Marey to the chair of physiology. On this occasion, Hallion, speaking for François-Franck's pupils, collaborators, and friends, addressed these words to him: "Solicitude for the public good, generosity, unshakable faith in friendship, scrupulous observance of the pledged word, come what may—it was through such qualities as these that you conquered our hearts."

Following a long illness, François-Franck died in Paris.

NEW YORK CITY   DOROTHY GOODENOW
NEW YORK CITY   FRED A. METTLER

References

[1]*La circulation du sang à l'état physiologique et dans les maladies.* Paris, Masson, 1881.   [2]Trav. Lab. Marey, 1877, *3:*273–292.   [3]*Ibid.,* 1878, *4:*73–98.   [4]Arch. ges. Physiol., 1924, *206:*721–723.   [5]*Die Karotissinusreflexe auf Herz und Gefässe vom normal-physiologischen, pathologisch-physiologischen und klinischen Standpunkt.* Dresden, Steinkopf, 1927.   [6]*Cours du Collège de France, de 1880 à 1904, et travaux du laboratoire de 1875 à 1904.* Paris, Doin, 1940.   [7]Arch. physiol. norm. path., Paris, 1885, 3.sér., *5:*7–50 et seq.   [8]*Leçons sur les fonctions motrices du cerveau (réactions volontaires et organiques) et sur l'épilepsie cérébrale.* Paris, Doin, 1887.

Reference to Biography: Bull. Acad. méd., Paris, 1921, 3.sér., *86:*148–151 (Richelot).

WALTER GASKELL (1847–1914)

W ALTER HOLBROOK GASKELL, the son of a barrister, was born at Naples; his family home, however, was in the north of England. He entered Trinity College, Cambridge, in 1864, and took up the study of medicine at University College, London, in 1870. On the advice of his teacher, Sir Michael Foster (1836–1907), Gaskell interrupted his medical course in 1874 to undertake physiologic work in Carl Ludwig's laboratory. Called to the University of Cambridge in 1883, he continued there as lecturer on physiology, praelector on natural science, and fellow of Trinity Hall.

Gaskell's accomplishments in the field of the autonomic nervous system from the time he became associated with Ludwig until 1889 have assured him a lasting position of prominence among physiologists. In 1874 he published a significant paper on the vasomotor nerves of striated muscle,[1] and in 1882 his great memoir on the muscular activity of the heart and its innervation appeared.[2] The latter, in which the theory of the myogenic nature of cardiac contractions was supported, constitutes a model of neatness and finality.

Gaskell's establishment of the histologic foundation of the autonomic nervous system, upon which Langley built so substantially, is among the great achievements of English physiology. His innervation studies in different animals led to the mapping and interpretation of the nerve supply to the visceral organs, including the cardiovascular system. The results of this study, first announced in 1885, were incorporated in an exhaustive treatise published in 1886.[3]

One of the major contributions of this work was the delimitation of the preganglionic outflow to the thoracic and the first two lumbar segments. His work was based on the study of osmic acid-stained serial sections through the anterior and posterior spinal roots and the rami communicantes of the dog, and although in the light of subsequent findings based on silver impregnation methods many of his observations have been proven incorrect—for instance he asserted that no nonmyelinated fibers leave the spinal cord by

Walter Holbrook Gaskell

way of spinal roots, but that all such fibers are branches of cells lying in the sympathetic ganglia—his fundamental conclusions have stood the test of time and have formed the basis of our present-day knowledge. In his 1886 paper, Gaskell referred to three separate outflows of fine myelinated fibers to peripherally situated motor ganglion cells: bulbar, thoracolumbar and sacral, and some years later (1916) included all three in the "involuntary nervous system" (see below). Claude Bernard was the first to make a sharp distinction between visceral and vascular nerves, but it was Gaskell to whom we are indebted for first distinguishing among the

Portrait, courtesy of the National Library of Medicine, Bethesda, Maryland.

visceral and vascular nerves two antagonistic groups (collateral and lateral), one excitatory, the other inhibitory; and thus he anticipated Langley's subdivision of the autonomic nervous system into sympathetic and parasympathetic divisions.

Another significant contribution was his pioneer work[3,4] in formulating the doctrine of functional nerve components, subsequently established on a firm basis by Herrick (1889, 1931),[5,6] Strong (1895),[7] Johnston (1901),[8] and Coghill (1902).[9] There was, in fact, hardly any phase of the existing knowledge of the physiology of the nervous system to which he did not add materially. The results of his long years of study are embodied in *The involuntary nervous system* (London, Longmans, Green & Co., 1916), the last pages of which were revised the night before he was fatally stricken with cerebral hemorrhage. In recognition of his scholarship, the University of Edinburgh and McGill University conferred upon him the honorary LL.D. He was also a Marshall Hall prizeman and was awarded a medal by the Royal Society.

During his later years, Gaskell developed a theory of the origin of vertebrates from invertebrate ancestors, one of the chief tenets being that the central canal of the nervous system was originally the lumen of the primitive gut.[10] Although this theory has not met with approval, Gaskell, in its elaboration, accumulated a wealth of data which merits serious consideration.

As a tribute to his kindly, unassuming, sympathetic character, it has been said of Gaskell that every physiologist who worked in the Cambridge laboratories during his time was his personal friend, and that all recognized his home as their favorite meeting place.

ALBERT KUNTZ

References

[1]Proc. Roy. Soc., London, 1876, *25:*439–445.   [2]Philos. Trans. Roy. Soc., London, 1882, part 3, *173:*933–1033 (The Croonian Lecture). [3]J. Physiol., London, 1886, 7:1–80.   [4]*Ibid.*, 1889, *10:*153–211.   [5]J. Comp. Neur., 1899, *9:*153–455.   [6]*An introduction to neurology.* ed.5. Philadelphia, Saunders, 1931, p. 417.   [7]J. Morph., 1895, *10:* 101–230.   [8]Zool. Jahrb., 1901, 25:1–204.   [9]J. Comp. Neur., 1902,

*12:*205–289.   [10]*The origin of vertebrates.* London, Longmans, Green, 1908.

References to Biography and Works: 1) Proc. Roy. Soc., London, 1915, ser.B., *88:*xxvii–xxxvi (Langley).   2) Science, n.s., 1914, *40:*802–807 (Garrison and Pike).   3) Arch. Neur. Psychiat., Chic., 1936, *35:*1081–1115 (Sheehan).

HERBERT GASSER (1888–1963)

*I*NSPIRED though he was as a medical student by Erlanger's lectures during those two years at Wisconsin (1911–13), Herbert Spencer Gasser did not for a moment conceive the idea that he would one day share with him the Nobel Prize in Physiology. He was also bewildered by these lectures and had no realization that Erlanger was aware of his attendance. After graduation at Johns Hopkins in 1915 and a year spent as Instructor in Pharmacology under A. S. Loevenhart back in Wisconsin, Gasser to his surprise was invited by Erlanger, now at Washington University in St. Louis, to join him. From 1916 until 1932—when Gasser left for New York—the two remained in closest professional contact.

World War I interrupted Gasser's principal pursuits in neurophysiology, but it served to make him widely known as the resourceful young man heading a special pharmacological laboratory of the Chemical Warfare Service, where he worked mainly with Lewisite. This was as a civilian, as for physical reasons (a mumps infection) he was not accepted by the Army. By 1920 Gasser, back at St. Louis, was helped toward the materialization of his dream to record the details of nerve action potentials. At lunch, he and Erlanger would ponder over Bernstein's remark in the Appendix to his *Electrobiologie* (1912), that deflections of a cathode beam would allow a recording of the oscillations of bioelectric currents with complete accuracy. Realization came about, first of all through his friend and fellow medical student H. S. Newcomer, a physicist who built a three-stage amplifier with the advice of friends at the Western Electrical Company. But its response to the electrical changes in the nerve was still too slow. A recording de-

Herbert Gasser

vice that would not introduce a lag due to inertia was needed. In 1920 a chance suggestion by a friend led him to attend the meeting of the Physical Society at Chicago, where J. B. Johnson of Western Electrical was to describe an oscillograph tube with a hot cathode, operating at a low voltage and with correspondingly high sensitivity. Back home again, Gasser was not long in obtaining a similar tube from Western Electrical. Thanks to his and Erlanger's ingenious adaptations, the exact pattern of the nerve impulse could now be recorded. In 1922, Gasser and Erlanger revolutionized electrophysiology with their paper, "A study of the action currents of nerve with the cathode ray oscillograph" (Amer. J. Physiol., *62:496–524*).

In the preceding fall Gasser, then only thirty-two, had accepted a promotion to the professorship of pharmacology at Washington

Portrait, by Bachrach, Washington, D.C.

University, where Abraham Flexner, a powerful catalyst of medical progress, was a frequent visitor negotiating support of full-time teaching and research. On such a visit, the Dean, Nathaniel Allison, gave a dinner to display the excellence of his faculty. "What are you doing," Flexner asked the Dean with a glance at Gasser, "making freshmen full professors?" And turning to Gasser: "How would you like to go to Europe for two years and learn some languages?" On a Rockefeller travelling fellowship, Gasser spent 1923–25 abroad, working in England with the physiologist A. V. Hill, the engineering genius W. J. Hartree, and with Henry Dale; also with Hermann Straub in Munich, and with Louis Lapique at the Sorbonne. Meanwhile (and subsequently) at St. Louis, George H. Bishop, Peter Heinbecker and Helen T. Graham contributed heavily to the improvement of the oscillographic equipment, and to the knowledge of nerve conduction made possible by it.

In 1932 Gasser went to the New York Hospital-Cornell Medical Center to succeed Graham Lusk as Professor of Physiology. Three years later he was called to succeed Simon Flexner as Director of the Rockefeller Institute. During World War II, he organized the facilities of the Rockefeller Institute for the war effort. He served as chairman of a civilian committee charged with the direction of research into chemical warfare. During the period of his directorship, there was a gradual transition of emphasis from infectious diseases to the nervous system. Gasser became master of a new tool, the electron microscope. Upon retirement as Director in 1953, he resumed his work in neurophysiology, in a new laboratory especially equipped for him. Freed from administrative responsibilities, he could devote his full energies to defining nerve fibers and relating them to specific sensory and motor functions—the work for which he is most famous.

Gasser suffered from migraine headaches but refused all these years to let them incapacitate him. On April 17, 1961, he had a stroke. Although largely recovered, he resided in the New York Hospital most of the time until his death from respiratory involvement on May 11, 1963.

In addition to receiving the Nobel Prize (in 1944), he was awarded the Kober Medal of the American Association of Physicians (in 1954), an honor conferred by his close friend, Detlev W. Bronk, who succeeded him at the Rockefeller Institute. Gasser was elected a member of the American Philosophical Society, the National Academy of Sciences, and of many scientific, professional and honorary societies both at home and abroad.

He had grown up in Platteville, a small town in southwestern Wisconsin. His mother was a descendant of one Edward Griswold, a settler in Connecticut in 1639. His father, an Austrian born in Vorarlberg, was brought to America as a boy and studied medicine at Northwestern University. (Presumably he was no relative of Johann Laurentius Gasser [1702–1777], the Austrian anatomist after whom the trigeminal ganglion is named.) Herbert was the eldest of three children. He would recall the ruins of the old blockhouse at the edge of town burned down during the Black Hawk War, relish telling of fishing for minnows in summer, skating in winter, and reading the adventure tales in lurid covers which he found displayed in the local store. He took up playing the violin, but soon found that it was not for him. Financing of his education came hard owing to his father's misadventures in the local zinc mines.

In later years, Herbert Gasser's interests knew no bounds; his hobbies involved music, literature, the theater, travel. Whatever he undertook, he did with thorough care and devotion, in the laboratory, the classroom, the administrative office, the conference hall. Although shy and modest in his relations with his fellows, he was intensely interested in their welfare. His mind was razor-sharp, his information prodigious, his memory keen. Integrity was his passion, seconded by impatience with sham and pretense. What he and his colleagues have done has shaped the destiny of biological science in this century.*

NEW YORK CITY   JOSEPH C. HINSEY

* Let us add the tale of the platinum ruble. This coin was picked up in Paris in 1839 as a chemical curiosity by Dr. Robert Peter who had been sent abroad to gather up books for Translyvania University, Lexington, Kentucky. On Dr. Peter's death, his son passed the coin, with a complete set of his father's reprints, to Professor J. H. Kastle, Peter's designated favorite and most distinguished pupil. Kastle continued what was to become a tradition. The requisites, as stipulated by him for transmission of ruble and reprints, were personal affection for the recipient, who also must be teaching and be scientifically productive. A. S. Loevenhart was next in line; he designated as his choices (1) Dr. H. S. Gasser, (2) Dr. C. D. Leake, (3) Dr. A. L. Tatum. Following Gasser's passing, the Executor gave notice that Dr. Joseph C. Hinsey was the new possessor. (The Editors)

Selected References

1) Physiological action currents in the phrenic nerve. An application of the thermionic vacuum tube to nerve physiology. Amer. J. Physiol., 1921, *57*:1–26 (Gasser and Newcomer).   2) The components of the action currents obtained from nerves. *Ibid.*, 1922, *63*:417 (Gasser and Erlanger).   3) The compound nature of the action current of nerve as disclosed by the cathode ray oscillograph. *Ibid.*, 1924, *70*:624–666 (Erlanger and Gasser, with Bishop).   4) The dynamics of muscular contraction. Proc. Roy. Soc., London, 1924, *96*:398–437 (Gasser and Hill).   5) Plexus-free preparations of the small intestine. A study of their rhythmicity and of their response to drugs. J. Pharm. Exp. Ther., 1926, *27*:395–410 (Gasser).   6) The component of the dorsal root mediating vasodilation and the Sherrington contracture. Amer. J. Physiol., 1930, *92*:679–689 (Hinsey and Gasser).   7) Electrical signs of nervous activity. In *Eldridge Reeves Johnson Found. for Med. Physics Lectures*. Philadelphia, U. of Pa., 1937, p. 194 (Erlanger and Gasser).   8) Mammalian nerve fibers. Nobel Lecture, December 12, 1945. In *Les Prix Nobel en 1940–1944*. Stockholm, Nobelstiftelsen, 1945, p. 128–141 (Gasser).   9) Comparison of the structure, as revealed with the electron microscope, and the physiology of the unmedullated fibers in the skin nerves and in the olfactory nerves. Exp. Cell Res., suppl., 1958, *5*:3–17 (Gasser).

References to Biography and Works: 1) Exp. Neurol., 1964, suppl. 1, p. 1–38 (with bibliography; Hinsey).   2) Lancet, London, 1963, *1*:1167–1168 (Adrian, Hill).   3) Tr. Assoc. Amer. Physicians, 1954, *67*:39–42 (Bronk).

FRIEDRICH GOLTZ (1834–1902)

*F*RIEDRICH LEOPOLD GOLTZ was born in Posen, in East-Prussia (now Poland), the son of a police inspector. A few years later the family moved to Danzig, where Friedrich had his first schooling. When his father died in 1846, Friedrich left Danzig for Thorn (now in Poland), to live with his uncle, Bogumil Goltz, who was widely recognized as a naturalist, philosopher and poet.

In 1853 Goltz entered the University of Königsberg. In time he

Friedrich Goltz

became Assistant in the surgical clinic, then Prosector. His heart, however, was in physiology and when he could find the time he would steal to his modestly furnished room to conduct experiments on frogs which he himself caught, his laboratory armamentarium consisting only of scissors, tweezers, and thread. No wonder then that in describing his experiments before learned societies, he often began by saying, "Man nehme zwei Frösche . . ."

At the age of thirty-six, aided by a recommendation from Helmholtz, he was made Ausserordentlicher Professor of physiology at Halle (1870). After two years he was appointed Ordentlicher Pro-

Portrait, courtesy of Prof. Dr. W. Krücke, Frankfurt-am-Main, Germany.

fessor of physiology at the newly-founded University of Strassburg, a position which he occupied until 1900 when he was forced to retire because of a severe chronic illness.

Goltz and Sechenov, of Russia, were among those who initiated the modern study of reflexology, carrying on where Marshall Hall (1790–1857) and Johannes Müller (1801–1858) had left off. Early in his career, while a Prosector at Königsberg, Goltz demonstrated that when rapidly repeated blows were struck on the belly of a frog its heart stopped beating ("Klopfversuch"), and he concluded that this shock-like state was the result of reflex inhibition mediated through the vagus nerve.[1,2] In 1869 he turned to decerebration and ablation of the spinal cord in the frog, with telling effect.[3,4] He found that decerebrated (or "spinal") frogs could still croak "like the frogs in Aristophanes," and that they could be made to do so reflexly ("Quakversuch"). At the Hannover Meeting of Physiologists in 1865 he was asked by a fellow-physiologist to make each of the frogs he had brought along croak five times, and he did so, much to the astonishment of his audience. His frogs could respond in an intelligent way to certain stimuli; they could hop, swim, crouch, and slither from the hand that grasped them. However, when left alone they would sit motionless, and although surrounded by food would die of starvation. When the thalami were left intact, the frogs retained sexual instinct and were able to eat.

His work on mammals began in 1874. He had human physiology always in mind, and would say, "Auch meine Gehirnuntersuchungen werden einmal der leidenden Menschheit zu gute kommen." At first his cerebral ablations were small, but later he removed more and more of the brain until eventually he was successful in accomplishing subtotal decerebration, producing "Hunde ohne Grosshirn." He concluded that a direct relation existed between the amount of cerebral cortex removed and the degree of resulting dementia, and thus he anticipated the holistic concepts formulated by S. I. Franz (1874–1933) and K. S. Lashley (1890–1958), namely, that except for the visual area there are no well-defined functional centers. Goltz's "spinal" dogs, which he succeeded in keeping alive for as long as eight months, were incapable of purposive movements or actions[5,6] and, to use Bernard Shaw's phrase, they "blundered into death" (Garrison). His decorticated dogs were able, on the other hand, to walk with adequate coordination, indicating that the pallium was not a requisite to the walking reflexes. However, the animals with frontal decortications were extremely restless, pacing the floor most of the time, and at the slightest annoyance growling and snapping viciously (sham rage).[7] From these experiments he drew the conclusion that the site of integration of pseudoaffective mechanisms is subcortical. In this realm Goltz was the forerunner of Bard,[8] who in 1928 noted from his famous ablation experiments in cats that neural structures in the hypothalamus made possible the expression of angry behavior, as did Walter Rudolph Hess (1881–   ), in 1948, by means of implanted electrodes.[9,10]

A debate with Ferrier was brewing, an echo of an earlier one (during 1861) in which the prestigious Gratiolet countered Bouillaud's and Auburtin's ideas on the cerebral localization of function, by exclaiming, "I do not hesitate to conclude that all attempts at localization which up to now have been tried, lack any foundation. They are no doubt great efforts, titanic efforts! But when one attempts to grasp the truth at the height of these babbles, the edifice crumbles."[11] The debate took place at the International Medical Congress in London in 1881.[12] "I will prove beyond the shadow of a doubt," challenged Goltz, "that Ferrier's theory [of localization of function] is completely false." Operated (decorticated) dogs Goltz had brought along performed astonishingly well. Ferrier, in reply, remarked: "If I cannot argue with him—and I must differ with him widely—it is not because I dispute his facts. . . . But I reject his conclusions." Ferrier's demonstrations on monkeys left no doubt in the minds of the referees. The verdict was unanimously in Ferrier's favor. But Goltz, in his demonstrations, had left a strong impression. Sherrington, then twenty-four, decided then and there to enter the field of physiology. His first publication (with Langley) was on the anatomical aspects of spinal degeneration observed in Goltz's dogs.[13,14] He was a frequent visitor in Goltz's laboratory during the ensuing ten years.

Goltz's private life was one of even tenor. At thirty-four he entered into a happy marriage. To his colleagues he was brusque and blustering, but among his rather narrow circle of friends he was noted for his ability as a raconteur and for his refreshing informality. The cut of his jaw and the intentness of his expression revealed a man of determination and persistence: it was these qualities of his character which helped to elevate him into the company of the great physiologists of the past century.

MOFFETT FIELD, CALIFORNIA   WEBB HAYMAKER

References

[1]Königsb. med. Jahrb., 1862, *3*:271–274.   [2]Virchows Arch., 1863, *26:* 1–33.   [3]*Beiträge zur Lehre von den Functionen der Nervenzentren des Frosches.* Berlin, Hirschwald, 1869.   [4]Pflügers Arch., 1872, *5*:53– 76.   [5]*Ibid.,* 1874, *8*:460–468 (with Freusberg).   [6]*Ibid.,* 1896, *63:* 362–400 (with Ewald).   [7]*Ibid.,* 1892, *51*:570–614.   [6]Amer. J. Physiol., 1928, *84*:490–515.   [9]Helv. Physiol. Acta, suppl. 5, 1948. [10]*Die funktionelle Organisation des vegetativen Nervensystems.* Basel, Schwabe, 1948.   [11]Bull. Soc. anat. Paris, 1861, *36*:330–357, 398–407 (Broca, with discussion by Auburtin and Gratiolet).   [12]Trans. Internat. Med. Congr., London, 1881, *1*:218–228, 234–237.   [13]J. Physiol., London, 1884, *5:vi.*   [14]*Ibid.,* p. 49–65.

References to Biography and Works: 1) Pflügers Arch., 1903, *49*:1–64 (contains annotated bibliography; Ewald).   2) *An introduction to the history of medicine.* Philadelphia, Saunders, 1929, p. 540–541 (Garrison).   3) *Reflex action. A study in the history of physiological psychiatry.* Baltimore, Williams & Wilkins, 1930 (Fearing).   4) Bull. N. Y. Acad. Med., 1954, *30*:559–578 (Stookey).   5) *Neurosurgical Classics.* New York, Johnson Reprint, 1965, p. 119–128 (Wilkins).

MARSHALL HALL (1790–1857)

*T*HE reflex concept as we understand it today owes much to Marshall Hall, English physician and physiologist, born at Basford, near Nottingham. The son of the cotton manufacturer who first used chlorine for bleaching, he studied chemistry, as well as anatomy, and entered Edinburgh Medical School in 1809, where he was graduated three years later. After spending two years

Marshall Hall

as Resident House Physician to the Edinburgh Royal Infirmary
and visiting the medical schools of Paris, Göttingen, and Berlin, he
returned to Nottingham. Here he established himself as a very
able physician, mainly known for a book on diagnosis[1]—a new
topic in 1817—and for his advocacy of P. C. A. Louis's plea to re-
frain from excessive blood-letting.[2] Ten years later he moved to
London where he conducted a large private practice, but he was
never on the staff of a hospital and carried out his researches at
home. He was made Fellow of the Royal Society in 1832 and of
the Royal College of Physicians of London in 1841. Having retired from practice in 1853 he died four years later of a cancerous

Portrait from *Pettigrew's medical portrait gallery,* vol. 4, courtesy of the Wellcome
Historical Medical Museum, London.

oesophageal stricture. He married at the age of thirty-nine; his only son became an eminent barrister.

Opinions differ concerning the personality of Marshall Hall. Some thought he was an unduly conceited little man, and indeed he did not suffer injustice without protest. No doubt brilliant, but overaware of his gifts, he could not establish the usual personal contacts. Yet Thomas Wakley (1795–1862), the outspoken Editor of *The Lancet,* supported Hall's claim that his contribution was equivalent to that of William Harvey;[3] others maintained that Hall's opponents were mostly envious of his ability. His wife's biography of him, as might be expected, is wholly laudatory.

Hall published nineteen books and over 150 papers; they teem with refutations, attacks, defensive arguments, and claims for priority. He did not always refer to the work of others, and on one memorable occasion he was accused of blatant plagiarism.[4]

His major researches, beginning in 1832 and extending over twenty-five years, concerned the physiology of the reflex: he claimed that he had devoted 25,000 leisure hours to them![5] The concept of the reflex has its roots in antiquity and Hall's work was a direct extension of that of Robert Whytt of Edinburgh (1714–1766), Albrecht von Haller of Göttingen (1708–1770), Georg Procháska of Prague (1747–1820), J. J. C. Legallois of Paris (1770–1840), and of many more. By 1830 there existed considerable experimental data on the reflex and the isolated spinal cord but little on the latter's reflex function. Hall's contribution to neurophysiology was to postulate an independent reflex system in the cord and spinal nerves, an "excito-motory system,"[6] or afferent-efferent in modern terminology. This system was in "the true spinal marrow," not in the "spinal chord" which contained the connections between brain and body. The nerves of the reflex system were distinct, and unrelated to volition, sensation, consciousness, or physical influences. Reflex activity was *through* the cord, and he therefore called the system "diastaltic"[7]—a term like others of his now long-forgotten. Nevertheless, Hall was the first to provide a basis for the concept of the neural arc in the spinal cord.

Opposition to it was widespread, partly on account of the man's personality and partly because he had excluded the soul, in certain quarters still deemed essential for all human activity. Support, however, came from abroad where personality factors were not operative and where mechanistic views had displaced the need for the soul. The name of Johannes Müller of Berlin (1801–1858) is often linked with that of Hall, for his findings were similar.[8] The studies of these men were thus of vital importance in the evolution of the reflex concept and led directly to the significant advances of Sir Charles Sherrington of Oxford (1857–1952), I. M. Sechenov of St. Petersburg (1829–1905), and of F. L. Goltz of Strassburg (1834–1902) later in the nineteenth century.

Hall also described the grasp reflex,[9] though without appreciating its significance, and he studied the effects of drugs such as strychnine and opium on reflex activity. Furthermore he indulged in broad, if frequently erroneous, applications of the latter to diagnosis and treatment. But he was the first to make a clear reference to spinal shock,[9] also recognized by Whytt almost a century earlier and he observed muscle tone, especially that of the sphincters.

An original, postural method of artificial respiration[10] is one of the many topics Hall dealt with in the field of general medicine. The critical attitude displayed in his experimental work was often absent from his clinical investigations and his books on diseases of the nervous system[11] were never very popular. Epilepsy he thought was due to cervical cord irritation,[12] a view probably based on a misinterpretation of adversive seizures. Outside the medical field Hall demonstrated his versatility in papers on algebra and Greek grammar, and he was always ready to attack the evils of his day, such as American slavery (after a journey to the United States), flogging in the army, defective sewerage, and inadequate railway safety.

LONDON, ENGLAND   EDWIN CLARKE

References

[1]*On diagnosis, in four parts.* London, Nottingham (printed), 1817.
[2]*Researches principally relative to the morbid and curative effects of loss of blood.* London, Thames Ditton (printed), 1830. *Observations on blood-letting, etc.* London, 1836. Practitioner, 1909, *82:*320–331.
[3]Lancet, London, 1846, *2:*154–157, 186–189, 244–247, 250. *Ibid.,* 1857, *2:*172–175.   [4]*London Med. Gaz.,* 1838, *2:*40–47, 72–73, 93–96, 128,

160, 218–219, 252–254. ⁵Philos. Trans. Roy. Soc., London, 1833, 123:635–665. ⁶*Memoirs on the nervous system. Memoir II. On the true spinal marrow and the excito-motory system.* London, Sherwood, Gilbert & Piper, 1837. ⁷*Synopsis of the diastaltic nervous system or the system of the spinal marrow and its reflex arcs, as the nervous agent in all the functions of ingestion and of egestion in the animal oeconomy.* London, Mallett, 1850 (Croonian Lecture). ⁸London and Edinburgh, Phil. Mag., 1837, 10:187–193. ⁹See G. Jefferson in *Science, medicine and history . . .* in honour of Charles Singer, edit. by E. A. Underwood. Vol. 2. London, Oxford U. P., 1953, p. 303–320. ¹⁰*Prone and postural respiration in drowning,* etc. London, 1855. ¹¹*Lectures on the nervous system and its diseases.* London, Sherwood, Gilbert & Piper, 1836. *On the diseases and derangements of the nervous system, etc.* London, Baillière, 1841. ¹²*Essays on the theory of convulsive diseases.* London, 1848. *On the neck as a medical region,* etc. London, 1849.

References to Biography: 1) *Memoirs of Marshall Hall, M.D., F.R.S.,* by his widow. London, Bentley, 1861. 2) Lancet, London, 1850, 2:120–128. 3) Lancet, London, 1857, 2:172–175. 4) *Great doctors of the nineteenth century.* London, Arnold, 1935, p. 85–105 (Hale-White). 5) *Autobiographical recollections of the medical profession.* London, Churchill, 1874 (Clarke), p. 327–330. 6) *Reflex action.* London, Baillière, Tindall & Cox, 1930 (Fearing). 7) *Medical portrait gallery.* Vol. 4. London, Fisher, 1840 (Pettigrew). 8) Med. Hist., 1958, 2:120–133. 9) *J.A.M.A.,* 1962, 181:1132–1133; 18:1341.

HERMANN von HELMHOLTZ (1821–1894)

*H*ERMANN LUDWIG FERDINAND von HELMHOLTZ was born at Potsdam of a respected academic father and a mother who was descended from William Penn. He was a weakling as a boy. Early interested in physics, he undertook the study of medicine rather than pure science because it was his only opportunity to get an education in at least a related field without forcing pecuniary sacrifices on his parents, who had to take care of five boys. He entered the army medical school in Berlin and served for some years after graduation as an army surgeon. In Ber-

Portrait, courtesy of the National Library of Medicine, Bethesda, Maryland.

lin he became one of the twelve disciples of Johannes Müller (1801–58), who, in 1826, had developed the theory of specific nerve energies. Helmholtz's thesis, written in Berlin in 1842, *De fabrica systematis nervosi evertebratorum*, demonstrated the integral connection between nerve cell and nerve fiber more convincingly than had his predecessors Remak and Hannover. With Ludwig (1816–95), du Bois-Reymond (1818–96) and Brücke (1819–92)—neurophysiologists with a background in physics—Helmholtz began a new era of medical investigation based on the application of physical principles. In 1847 these audacious youngsters issued a manifesto to the effect that all living processes, including consciousness, are explainable in terms of physics and chemistry, a proposition only now becoming demonstrable.

From 1842 to his death from cerebral hemorrhage, Helmholtz published 217 contributions of prime significance. His early studies on the generation of heat in muscles led to his great generalization, *Ueber die Erhaltung der Kraft,* in Berlin, 1847, in which he demonstrated his mathematical skill and established a physical principle of fundamental importance, the indestructibility of energy. This resulted in his appointment as professor of physiology at Königsberg, where he remained until 1856. He then obtained the chair in the same field at Heidelberg, where he was succeeded by Willy Kühne (1837–1900), the discoverer of the motor endplate and the muscle spindle. In 1871 Helmholtz became professor of physics at Berlin and from 1888 to 1894 was president of the Physikalisch-technische Reichsanstalt, the prototype apparently of the Bureau of Standards in Washington, D.C.

Helmholtz's most influential practical work in neurology was done at Königsberg. Here he first successfully measured the velocity of nerve conduction,[1] a feat Müller had thought impossible, although A. von Haller in the eighteenth century had more or less guessed it. Helmholtz accomplished this with a special pendulum-myograph which he invented. Medicine as a whole is indebted to him for the invention of the ophthalmoscope, designed first to demonstrate to his students how light is reflected from the retina of the eye. The little volume describing the invention appeared in 1851.[2] The instrument was a result of the careful mathematical and physical considerations involved, a thrilling example of the practical significance of an academic proposal.

Helmholtz's work on accommodation, color vision, and the sensation of tone is profoundly important not only in neurology but also in psychology. His view, expressed in 1867, that the position of the eyes is not *consciously* perceived through the mediation of proprioceptor nerve fibers coming from the extraocular muscles, holds true today; his contributions to the nervous reflexes of equilibrium are also significant. It is not pertinent to indicate here Helmholtz's supreme contributions to physics. It was his suggestive influence, for instance, which led his pupil, Heinrich Herz, to demonstrate the existence of electromagnetic waves as predicted by Clerk Maxwell, and thus to make possible the development of modern radiation theory.

Helmholtz's one weakness was lecturing. Max Planck[3] relates: "It is obvious that Helmholtz never prepared his lectures properly. He spoke haltingly, and would interrupt his discourse to look for the necessary data in his small notebook; moreover, he repeatedly made mistakes in his calculations at the blackboard, and we had the unmistakable impression that the class bored him at least as much as it did us. Eventually his classes became more and more deserted, and finally they were attended by only three students . . ."

In other ways the influence of the Jovian Helmholtz was profound. He was remarkable as a scientist, as a philosopher, and as a personality which was majestically reflected in his splendid appearance. He was fond of mountaineering and travel, but most of all enjoyed his scientific friendships. Max Planck, one of those three students staying to the last, says: "With his well-rounded personality, integrity of convictions and modesty of character, he was the very incarnation of the dignity and probity of science . . . supplemented by a true human kindness, which touched my heart deeply. When during a conversation he would look at me with those calm, searching, penetrating, and yet so benign eyes, I would be overwhelmed by a feeling of boundless filial trust and devotion. I would feel that I could confide in him, without reservation, everything I had on my mind, knowing that I would find him a fair and tolerant judge; a single word of approval, let alone praise, from his lips would make me as happy as any worldly triumph."

On the other hand, with shallow or trivial persons Helmholtz was apt to invest himself with "the subtle ether of potential disapprobation," which, as some have testified, made them feel as if they were dealing with the fourth dimension of space (Garrison).

It is not surprising that a biographer, J. G. M'Kendrick, called him one of the greatest geniuses of the nineteenth century.

SAN FRANCISCO, CALIFORNIA   CHAUNCEY D. LEAKE

References

[1]Arch. Anat. Physiol., Lpz., 1850, p. 71–73; 1852, p. 199–216.   [2]*Beschreibung eines Augen-Spiegels zur Untersuchung der Netzhaut im lebenden Auge.* Berlin, Förstner, 1851.   [3]*Scientific autobiography and other papers.* New York, Philosophical Lib., 1949 (trans. by Gaynor), p. 15, 24.

References to Biography: 1) *Hermann von Helmholtz.* 3 vo'. Braunschweig, Vieweg, 1902–03 (Königsberger). (Engl. trans. by Welby: *Hermann von Helmholtz.* Oxford, Clarendon, 1906.)   2) *Hermann Ludwig Ferdinand von Helmholtz.* London, Unwin, 1899 (M'Kendrick).   3) Proc. Mayo Clin. 1951, *26:*209–231 (Keys, Rucker, N. M. Keith, Woltman).

EDUARD HITZIG (1838–1907)

H ITZIG, a native of Berlin, came of a distinguished family. His grandfather was a criminologist, writer and poet, and his father was one of Europe's most renowned architects. Hitzig at first embarked on the study of law, then turned to medicine. After some semesters at Würzburg, he completed his studies at Berlin, where, in 1862, he received his doctorate. He then engaged in the practice of medicine in Berlin. Called to Zürich in 1875, he became professor of psychiatry and director of the Burghölzli Asylum. Here, a year later, von Monakow became one of his pupils. Hitzig held this position until 1879, when he was made a member of the faculty of the University of Halle and director of the psychiatric clinic of the Irrenanstalt Nietleben. Later, in 1885, he was appointed director of the newly founded neuropsychiatric clinic of

Eduard Hitzig

the University of Halle. He remained in this position until 1903 when he retired because of failing vision, correctly diagnosed by himself as atrophy of the optic nerves complicating diabetes.

Among his fellow students in medicine were Cohnheim and Karl Schröder. Exerting an important influence on Hitzig's scientific career were Romberg in neurology, Traube and Virchow in pathology, du Bois-Reymond in physiology, and Griesinger and Carl Westphal in psychiatry.

Portrait, courtesy of Dr. Maurice Genty, Académie de Médecine, Paris, France.

Hitzig's epochal studies of the electrical excitability of the cerebral cortex were initiated during the 1860's with experienced Gustav Theodor Fritsch (1838–1927) as his collaborator. At that time there were no laboratories available at the Physiological Institute in Berlin for work on warm-blooded animals, and as a consequence Hitzig and Fritsch did their first studies on dogs in Hitzig's home, operating on Frau Hitzig's dressing table. Their joint paper in 1870,[1] of which Fritsch was the senior author, marked the beginning of a new era in the study of brain physiology. According to Percival Bailey, the legend goes that Fritsch discovered in dressing a wound of the brain during the Prussian-Danish war in 1864 that irritation of the brain causes twitching of the opposite side of the body. Earnest[2] states that Weir Mitchell was aware as early as 1860 that one side of the brain innervates the opposite side of the body; this was just before the time that Mitchell took up his study of the war-wounded in Philadelphia. (In this connection it should be mentioned that Roberts Bartholow, of Cincinnati, Ohio, was the first to apply electrodes to the human cortex [1874], using as his subject a servant of his household who had cancer of the scalp. Weak faradization of the cortex produced muscular contractions of the limbs of the opposite side of the body and turning of the head to that side.[3] On publication of this observation, Bartholow was forced to leave Cincinnati.) Fritsch's work with Hitzig was his only important contribution. Fritsch was a man of wealth, a globe-trotter, who spent about ten years in South Africa. Some time after 1870 he was made Ausserordentlicher Professor of physiology at the University of Berlin. He never became Ordinarius.

Working subsequently without the aid of Fritsch, Hitzig defined the limits of the motor area in the cerebral cortex of dog and monkey, and using this discovery as a starting point, he[4] disproved the holistic theory of the equivalence of all parts of the cerebrum proposed in 1842 by Marie Jean Pierre Flourens (1794–1867)[5] and adopted by Goltz. He also struck a blow at Munk's view[6] that the property of intelligence is discretely distributed through the cortex in aggregates (rather than uniformly as contended in the holistic theory of intelligence), a view supported by Monakow[7,8] and Kleist[9-11] on the basis of brain injuries in man. "I believe," wrote Hitzig[3] (p. 261), "that Munk is correct in his view that intelligence—or better, the store of ideas—is a property of all parts of the cortex, or rather of all parts of the brain, but I contend that abstract thought must require particular organs, and these I find in the frontal lobe" (translation by Halstead, 1947).

As a pioneer in experimental investigation, much of Hitzig's work was carried out under conditions which would have discouraged less ardent investigators. He had even to battle with the Ministry of Finance for oil paint to brighten the walls of his laboratory. In all of his investigative work and his teaching he constantly emphasized the importance of exact data obtained under controlled conditions; he held no brief for philosophic speculations. His comprehensive grasp of the problems involved in the physiology of the brain and his capacity to evaluate the data at hand are particularly evident in his Hughlings Jackson Lecture on the motor cortex[12] and in his *Welt und Gehirn* (Berlin, Hirschwald, 1905).

His contributions to medical education, particularly in the fields of neurology and psychiatry, were also noteworthy. Through his influence, psychiatrists became increasingly aware that the brain is the instrument of the mind and that the treatment of mental patients must be placed on a more scientific basis. He also brought to public attention the need for more adequate provisions for the care of mental patients.

Hitzig was a stern man—sharp, abrupt, disagreeable. It was hard to win from him either affection or dislike, but toward those whom he disliked he could be most caustic. He was a lover of polemics, and took great relish in his long controversy with Munk on localization of function in the brain of the dog. To him, controversy was necessary if science was to progress. When Forel arrived at Burghölzli in March, 1879, to succeed Hitzig, he found the institution in a topsy-turvy state, with an atmosphere of confusion and agitation reigning. Hitzig, with the soul of a jurist, actually reveled in his lawsuit against the economist Schnurrenberger, but nonetheless was burning to be off. He left Zürich with the air of a martyr, thanks to his "incorrigible conceit and vanity complicated by Prussianism."

Near the end of his life, Hitzig became almost blind, and thus was forced to put his sword in its scabbard. He often said that he did so with the greatest reluctance.

ALBERT KUNTZ

References

[1]Arch. Anat. Physiol., Lpz., 1870, p. 300–332.   [2]*S. Weir Mitchell, novelist and physician*. Philadelphia, U. of Pa., 1950.   [3]Amer. J. Med. Sci., 1874, *67*:305–313.   [4]*Untersuchungen über das Gehirn. Abhandlungen physiologischen und pathologischen Inhalts*. Berlin, Hirschwald, 1874.   [5]*Recherches expérimentales sur les propriétés et les fonctions du système nerveux*. Paris, Baillière, 1842.   [6]*Ueber die Funktionen der Grosshirnrinde: gesammelte Mittheilungen mit Anmerkungen*. Berlin, Hirschwald, 1890.   [7]*Gehirnpathologie*. Wien, Hölder, 1905.   [8]*Die Lokalisation im Grosshirn und der Abbau der Funktion durch kortikale Herde*. Wiesbaden, Bergmann, 1914. [9]Mschr. Psychiat., 1931, *79*:338–350.   [10]Jahrb. Psychiat. Neur., Wien, 1933, *50*:23–34.   [11]*Gehirnpathologie*. Leipzig, Barth, 1934. [12]*Hughlings Jackson und die motorischen Rindencentren im Lichte physiologischer Forschung*. Berlin, Hirschwald, 1901.

References to Biography and Works: 1) Kirchoff (ed.), *Deutsche Irrenärzte*. Berlin, Springer, 1924, 2:148–156 (Wollenberg).   2) *Brain and intelligence. A quantitative study of the frontal lobes*. Chicago U. of Chicago, 1947 (Halstead).   3) *Auguste Forel mémoires*. Neuchatel, Baconnière, 1941.   4) *Neurosurgical classics*. New York, Johnson Reprint, 1965, p. 15–27 (Wilkins).

Biographies of Fritsch: 1) J. Comp. Neur., 1892, 2:84–88 (C. L. Herrick) 2) Deut. med. Wschr., 1908, *34*:605–606 (Benda).

LUIGI LUCIANI (1840–1919)

*L*UCIANI, a pioneer in cerebellar physiology, was born in Ascoli Piceno, Italy. At the age of twenty he graduated from the Gymnasium, where his intelligence and industry had greatly impressed his Jesuit teachers. Italy was then undergoing political upheaval, and the young man—a nephew of the great pa-

Luigi Luciani

triot Candido Augusto Vecchi—became deeply engrossed in its causes; instead of continuing his studies at the University, he lingered at home absorbing what he could of politics and statesmanship—and their basis, philosophy. When twenty-two, he began his medical studies at the University of Bologna, his "mind still filled with the *Critique of pure reason*" (as he says in his unpublished autobiography). After an interlude at the University of Naples and a year or so as assistant at the Eye Clinic of Magni, he received the M.D. at Bologna (1868). Soon thereafter he became Vella's assistant at the Physiological Institute, a position which he held until 1874. In this period falls what he considered a crucial event:

Portrait, courtesy of the National Library of Medicine, Bethesda, Maryland.

his year and a half period of study at the Physiological Institute of the University of Leipzig (1872–73). "This stay in Germany is the most important period of my life as a scientist; it has left in me deep and lasting impressions. In a feeling of gratitude and justice which I shall harbor forever, I recognize Ludwig as my real teacher."

It was quite natural that Luciani's mind greatly profited by the sceptical and practical attitude of this German physiologist. His increased stature soon gained him recognition: successively he became Privatdozent in general pathology in Bologna (1873), Extraordinarius in the same field in Parma (1875), and Ordinarius of physiology at Siena (1880), Florence (1883) and finally Rome (1893–1917). There he died from a chronic disease of the genitourinary tract.

High honors had been bestowed upon him both at home and abroad. In 1895 the Accademia dei Lincei received him as *socio nazionale,* he was elected Rector of the University of Rome, and from 1905 until his death he was a senator. From academies and societies in Leipzig, London and Göttingen came honorary memberships.

As early as 1864, while a second-year medical student, Luciani presented his first paper, *Vom vergleichenden organischen Plastizismus,* to his teacher, Giovanni Franceschi, who found so much of merit in it that he had it printed without consulting Luciani. His first important discovery was made in the laboratory of Ludwig. Observations based on the earlier experiments of Stannius had enabled him to distinguish three phases of cardiac activity preceding heart failure: the phenomena of the attack, the periodic rhythm, and the crisis (collectively "Luciani's phenomenon"). These experiments led him to important theoretical conclusions on the nature of the automatic activity of the heart; later he succeeded in applying them to the activity of the respiratory centers, the periodic rhythm of which he studied (Cheyne-Stokes phenomenon).

On returning to Italy he centered his interests on physiology of the nervous system. In Parma, his friend Tamburini provided the opportunity for him to work at the insane asylum at near-by Reggio. The fruits of this period were the classical studies on cerebral localization of function,[1] undertaken together with Tamburini and Seppilli. In 1878, he established the theory of the cortical pathogenesis of epilepsy.[2] But it was during his Florentine period that he wrote the two monographs on which his fame securely rests: the physiology of starvation in man (in which he distinguished three stages—hunger, physiological inanition, pathological inanition),[3] and the physiology and pathology of the cerebellum.[4] In the latter monograph he described his observations on decerebellated dogs and apes. While Ferrier had thought it impossible to keep mammals alive after destruction of the cerebellum, he now conceded his error and asserted that Luciani "was the first to examine the consequences of partial or total extirpation of the cerebellum in higher mammals by skilfully planned and executed experiments." Thanks to his extraordinary skill, Luciani was able to keep decerebellated dogs and monkeys alive for as long as one year. This work initiated the modern study of cerebellar function; it led him to the classic theory that the cerebellum serves as a center for tonic, sthenic and static functions, a theory now accepted as fact.

His last years were devoted to the completion of his five-volume treatise on human physiology,[5] which was brilliantly conceived and written with great clarity and fluency. The text reached five editions in Italian, and was translated into several foreign languages including English.

His keen and paternal interest in the guidance of young workers and his contagious enthusiasm and excellence as a speaker gained him such pupils as Marchi, De Sanctis and Baglioni. His fundamental belief, often expressed in his teaching and writing, was that the physician should think physiologically and that physiology and pathology are inseparable.

HIALEAH, FLORIDA   ARMANDO FERRARO

References

[1]Riv. sper. freniat., 1879, 5:1–76 (with Tamburini).   [2]Ibid., 1878, 4:617–646.   [3]Fisiologia del digiuno: studi sull'uomo. Firenze, Le Monnier, 1881.   [4]Il cerveletto. Nuovi studi di fisiologia normale e patologica. Firenze, Le Monnier, 1891.   [5]Fisiologia dell'uomo. Milano, Societa edit. libraria, 1901–11 (ed. 5, 1919–21) (Engl. trans. by Welby. London, Macmillan, 1911–21).

References to Biography: 1) Arch. Ital. biol., 1920–21, *70*:228–244 (contains bibliography; Baglioni).   2) Personal communication from Prof. Gozzano, Bologna.

FRANÇOIS MAGENDIE (1783–1855)

*T*HE son of a surgeon, François Magendie was born in Bordeaux. In 1791, during the revolution, the family moved to Paris where the father was active in politics and soon also in the administration of hospitals. The son's formal education began at the age of ten, and he entered the hospital service as a student of medicine when he was sixteen. He first worked at the Hôtel Dieu with Boyer, the surgeon, and also at the Charité; other strong influences were Fr. Xavier Bichat (1771–1802) and Guillaume Dupuytren (1777–1835). In 1803 he was appointed Lecturer in Anatomy; in 1808 he received his doctorate in Medicine. All his life he remained a practicing hospital physician; in addition, and especially from 1816 on, he turned more and more to experimental physiology. Twenty years later he was Professor of Physiology and General Pathology at the Collège de France, while continuing to practice and teach at the Hôtel Dieu. Amicable and witty in private, he was formidable and impulsive as a teacher and as an opponent. He was married to a rich widow but left no offspring and died of coronary artery sclerosis on October 7, 1855, at Saunois near Paris, seventy-two years old. Services were held at the Madeleine; he was buried at the Père Lachaise.

Opposed to tradition, Magendie yet owed much to two trends then current in France: on one hand, vitalism, as championed by Stahl, Sauvages, Bordeu and Barthez on through to Bichat, and on the other, idealism and sensualism, espoused by those who denied that the primary causes of phenomena can ever be known, whereas observation and experiment are possible and, indeed, necessary in the analysis of secondary effects. Vital energy primarily underlies the life process just as gravitational force rules the cosmic worlds. According to Magendie (1809), the secondary effects of gravity as also the manifestations of vital energy are in all respects analyzable. Both are stringently determined. One should attempt there-

fore to explain the mode of action of vital force through experiment and analysis instead of through verbal argument. Physiology must parallel physics in method and precision; in fact the distinc-

Portrait, courtesy of the National Library of Medicine. Bethesda, Maryland.

tion between "vital" and "physical" properties is "one of the most childish absurdities." Magendie was the tutor and spiritual father of Claude Bernard, who in turn contributed the greatest share to the revolution in French clinical and experimental medicine.

Physician and physiologist, Magendie derived his problems from both the bedside—where he was a therapeutic nihilist—and the laboratory bench. Nearly every branch of physiology profited by his discoveries. His *Précis élémentaire de physiologie* (1816/17)[1] was based entirely on animal experiment. He began by investigating emesis and emetics; tartor emetic injected intravenously yielded diaphragmatic contraction as the basis of vomiting in the dog (1813). Next he analyzed the role of the epiglottis in swallowing; the mechanism of digestion; the action of alkaloids: strychnine, morphine, veratrin, etc. (1821). Heart action, heart murmurs, the temperature variables of the blood, the discovery of normal blood sugar, were next. From 1822 on and for many years the nervous system stayed in the foreground. He furnished proof of the functional division of the spinal nerves into motor anterior and sensory posterior roots. In England, Charles Bell (1774–1842), himself an eminent neurologist, challenged in 1824 the priority for this discovery. Bell pointed to his pamphlet, "Idea of a new anatomy of the brain, submitted for the observation of his friends," privately distributed in 1811. An unfair claim, for without knowing of Bell's work, Magendie in 1822[2] divided the anterior and posterior spinal nerve roots in eight puppies; stimulation of the posterior roots, he found, elicited an expression of pain, a sensory phenomenon; stimulation of the anterior roots produced motor effects. The controversy was hard to die; the verdict of history is in Magendie's favor (see Olmsted, 1944, p. 83–122). Bell and Magendie also disagreed on the respective role of the 5th and 7th cranial nerves. In experiments similar to those undertaken by P. Flourens, Magendie examined the effect of dividing the various cerebellar connections, of severing the olfactory lobe (1826), and of removing both cerebral hemispheres. He investigated the origin and significance of the cerebrospinal fluid (1825/27), but erred in regarding it as a product of the arachnoid and so missed the actual direction of its flow. Yet he described the *apertura medialis ventriculi quarti*—the foramen of Magendie—and was again mistaken in the belief that the pineal gland functioned by opening and closing the aqueduct of Sylvius (1828). Clearly, while neuroanatomy and neurophysiology were still much at their difficult beginnings, Magendie, during that first half of the nineteenth century, showed the way which the experimental method was to take in the rise of neurology.[3]

MÜNSTER, WESTPHALIA, GERMANY   K. E. ROTHSCHUH

References

[1]*Précis élémentaire de physiologie.* 2 vol. Paris, Méquignon-Marvis, 1816/17.   [2]J. physiol. expér. et path., 1822, 2:276, 366.   [3]*Leçons sur les fonctions et les maladies su système nerveux, professées au Collège de France.* Paris, Ébard, 1839/41.

References to Biography: 1) *François Magendie. Pioneer in experimental physiology and scientific medicine in XIX century France.* New York, Schuman, 1944 (with bibliography; Olmsted).   2) Bull. Hist. Med., 1943, *14*:341–351 (Olmsted).   3) *Éloge sur Fr. Magendie.* Première Leçon in: *Leçons sur les effets des substances toxiques et médicamenteuses.* Paris, Baillière, 1857 (with bibliography; Claude Bernard).

RUDOLF MAGNUS (1873–1927)

*M*AGNUS was born in Braunschweig, Germany, into a family rich in medical tradition. At first he was attracted by literature and philosophy, but acting on the advice of a friend of the family, the chemist Richard Meyer, he undertook the study of medicine. At Heidelberg, where he pursued most of his medical studies, he was influenced particularly by the physiologist W. Kühne, and the chemist Victor Meyer. It was here that his enduring friendship with Jakob von Uexküll and Otto Cohnheim (later Kestner) began.

While still a medical student he presented a paper at the meeting of the International Congress of Physiology at Bern in 1895, on a method of measuring the blood pressure of an exposed artery. In his doctoral thesis in 1898 the technique of measuring blood

Rudolf Magnus

pressure was further expounded. During the time he was associated with Gottlieb in Heidelberg—first as Assistant (1898) and later as Privatdozent (1900)—his interests were in water balance in tissues and renal function. A sojourn in Schäfer's laboratory in Edinburg resulted in their joint discovery of the diuretic action of pituitary extracts. In 1904, at Heidelberg, he devised a new technique for studying the surviving small intestinal loop, now used in almost all pharmacologic laboratories, and from its use came a host of important observations on automatic rhythm, local reflexes, and the responses to certain alkaloids. His demonstration that the de-

Portrait, courtesy of the National Library of Medicine, Bethesda, Maryland.

gree of stretching of the intestinal muscle determines the direction of conduction of the stimulus was a fundamental discovery.

Magnus gained much from his association with Langley in 1905; and in 1908, attracted by Sherrington's epochal research on the neural regulation of movement, he went to Liverpool, where, in collaboration with Sherrington, he undertook the study of reflex mechanisms of the central nervous system. In the same year he accepted the chair of pharmacology at Utrecht. His inaugural address on *Ziele und Aufgaben des pharmakologischen Unterrichts* remains a masterpiece.

A chance observation, made independently by Magnus and by Sherrington—that rotation of the head in a decerebrated animal alters muscle tonus in the limbs—led to innumerable experiments and to eighty-two publications by Magnus and his small and happy group of gifted workers.[1-5] Among the notable works which came from his laboratory was one by de Kleijn in which it was shown that proprioceptive impulses arising in the neck influence the position of the eyes.[6] These many joint studies culminated in 1924 in his greatest work, *Körperstellung* (Berlin; Springer). As Cameron Prize Lecturer (1926) he related the now classical experiment performed in an effort to determine the function of the otolithic mechanism as compared to that of the semicircular canals: anesthetized guinea pigs were centrifugalized at high speeds, thereby detaching the otolithic membranes but leaving the canals, the ampullae, and the cristae intact, with the result that all labyrinthine reactions evoked in the animals by angular and rectilinear acceleration were retained, but reflexes resulting from static posture were abolished.[7] What is now known of the function of the otoliths, postural reflexes, tonic neck reflexes, tonic labyrinthine reflexes, righting and supporting reflexes, the centers and pathways for regaining and maintaining body position—in short, the complicated system by which the brain stem and cervical cord control the body musculature—is the fruit of Magnus' genius. No one knew better than Magnus that though his data were final and conclusive, his work on body position was just the beginning of much further research on the problems of body movements as a whole.

Three hundred publications by Magnus and his Utrecht colleagues, de Kleijn, Le Heux, Rademaker and others, testify to the abounding energy of this man of small physical stature but gigantic intellect. In supervising virtually every detail of the many research projects under way in his laboratory, he was able to grasp immediately the significance of any of his associates' observations.

A series of ten lectures which he delivered in 1906 on *Goethe als Naturforscher* (Leipzig; Barth), translated into English,[8] indicates the many aspects of his mind. He was an historian, philosopher, botanist and anatomist in addition to being a physiologist of the first rank. Also he was a gifted speaker and teacher.

In need of a vacation before undertaking the Lane Lectures at Stanford University, San Francisco, he journeyed to the high Alps. He wrote to a friend of the great vistas from Pontresina and of the beauty of the flowers. Soon afterward he suddenly died. Had he lived two months longer he would have witnessed the inauguration of a magnificent laboratory built for him in Utrecht by the Rockefeller Foundation.

NEW YORK CITY   IGN. NIC. W. OLNINCK

References

[1]Pflügers Arch., 1912, *145*:455–548 (with de Kleijn).   [2]*Ibid.*, 1912, *147*:403–416 (with de Kleijn).   [3]*Ibid.*, 1913, *154*:163–177 (with de Kleijn).   [4]Münch. med. Wschr., 1913, *60*:2566–2568 (with de Kleijn). [5]Pflügers Arch., 1916, *163*:405–490.   [6]*Ibid.*, 1921, *186*:82–97. [7]Lancet, London, 1926, 2:531–536 *et seq.*   [8]*Goethe as a scientist.* New York, Schuman, 1949 (trans. by Norden).

Reference to Biography: Stanford Univ. Pub., Med. Sci., 1930, 2:241–277 (contains bibliography; Dale).

JOHANNES MÜLLER (1801–1858)

*J*OHANNES PETRUS MÜLLER was born at Coblenz on the Rhine, the eldest of a shoemaker's five children. At school he excelled at mathematics and drawing; Latin, his masters vouched, he wrote better than his native German. When Johannes was eighteen years of age, he went up to the University of Bonn to

Johannes Müller

study medicine. In his second year at Bonn he won the prize for his essay *De respiratione foetus*. He was M.D. at twenty-one.

For the next two years, at the University of Berlin, the romantic youth came under the sobering influence of Rudolphi, Professor of Anatomy and Physiology (also Purkyně's protector and his fu-

Portrait, courtesy of the National Medical Library, Bethesda, Maryland.

ture father-in-law); but in 1826 Müller was appointed Assistant in human and comparative anatomy back at Bonn. One year later he was Privatdozent and married. In 1833 he returned to Berlin where he was appointed successor to Rudolphi—on his own suggestion to the Minister of Education. He was the last one there to teach anatomy and physiology as a combination of subjects, in an institute that offered a single microscope, in addition to Müller's own. In the same year (Müller was only thirty-two), the first part of his famous *Handbuch der Physiologie* appeared. Completed by 1840 and translated into English from 1838 on, this was the standard reference of the age, the great impetus given to the investigation of biological problems by physical and chemical method. His writings encompassed the physiology of motion and sensation; fetal life, as observed by dissections of invertebrates, and the comparative anatomy of vertebrates; histology, human anatomy, to some extent also animal chemistry; and he was interested in systematic zoology, ethnology and paleontology. Goethe's blend of feeling and science exerted an irresistible influence, as seen in Müller's "Comparative physiology of the visual sense of man and animals with an investigation of the movements of the eyes and of human vision" (1825), and "On fantastic visual appearances" (1826), a little volume treating such pathological topics as hallucinations, illusions, and visions. It is in the former work that the fundamental law of the specific energies of the senses (or nerves) first appears in his writings, to be definitely formulated in the *Handbuch* of 1838. Its ancestry goes back to Aristotle, Descartes, Locke, Charles Bell, and Goethe. But Müller's "ten laws" had a powerful effect on Helmholtz and all subsequent sensory physiology. Pressure on the eye produces the sensation of color, he argued; in fact, all stimuli excite in the organism not what they are themselves, but something else. "The things we know are only the essences of our senses: of outer objects we only know their actions on us in terms of our own energies." This shifts the emphasis from *objective* data to *subjective* experience, a concept rooted in Müller's vitalistic and animistic heritage. Although the ultimate frame of reference is a metaphysical rather than a physical one, nobody will deny Müller's law its scientific character—and never mind the imposing simplicity of the experimental procedure.

Whether he was acknowledging the priority of Marshall Hall's work on the spinal reflex, which barely preceded his own, or claiming the universality of science and its ethics ("A German, French, English school of medical science is barbarism"), or defining the role of fact finding vs. philosophy, his break with romantic *Naturphilosophie* established a bridgehead for modern physiology in general, and for the dreamy parochialism of his country toward its leadership in particular.

He explains his attitude in the preface to the *Bildungsgeschichte der Genitalien* (p. VIII): "I have always been in favor of discussing the subject methodically, thoughtfully . . ., or what amounts to the same thing, philosophically. . . . But by that I do not mean the type of insight which is apt to reach results without sufficient experiential proof—or in the manner of the so-called *Naturphilosophie* . . . which sets us back to the times of Ionic philosophy. . . . I request above all *that one be indefatigable in observing and experiencing,* and this is the first demand that I make upon myself . . ."

His personality must have been tremendously attractive, evidenced by his success as a lecturer (occasionally he seemed to deliver a sermon, Virchow felt) and the charm of his style. The scientific ardor he inspired and sustained in his assistants is reflected by practically all the great names in 19th century German biological science: Remak, Schwann, Henle, Bischoff, Virchow, Helmholtz, du Bois-Reymond. Yet, this esteemed man, with the massive head and shoulders looming above a short body, suffered several depressive episodes. Presumably they were not unrelated to the introspective type and the excessive amount of his investigations. On April 26, 1858, he was found dead in his bed. He was known to have taken large does of opium in his last years. Alexander von Humboldt, now eighty-nine years old, godfather and statesman of a new world science, spoke at his friend's open grave.

GLEN ALLEN, VIRGINIA   WALTHER RIESE

(Editorially condensed, this investigation was supported by Research Grant RO1-MN 12875 from the National Institute of Mental Health, USPHS, Washington, D.C.)

References

References to Biography: 1) Arch. Ophth., Chic., 1944, *32*:395–402 (Chance).   2) *Johannes Müller (1801–1858).* Stuttgart, Wiss. Verlagsges., 1958 (Koller).   3) *Johannes Müller—eine Gedächtnisrede (held 24 July 1958 at the University of Berlin)* (Virchow).   4) *Studies in romanticism.* Graduate School, Boston Univ., 1962, 2:11–22 (Riese).   5) Bull. Hist. Med., 1963, *37*:179–183 (Riese and Arrington).

HERMANN MUNK (1839–1912)

*C*ORTICAL localization, we know, was inaugurated in the 1860's and 1870's: by Broca for speech, by Fritsch and Hitzig for motor functions, by Jackson for a general philosophy. Who then supplied the correct evidence for the sizable rest, the visual, acoustic, and somatosensory functions of the brain's convexity? There is only one answer: Hermann Munk. The fact is half-remembered but three-quarters forgotten, in accordance with some of the wayward accounting of tradition. Neglect of this sort is likely to have its roots in personalities and nationalism. It must be sought in the tense controversies that surrounded the work of Munk and the other men concerned with brain research. From the turn of the century, neurophysiology branching out into neurosurgery also became increasingly identified with the achievements of English speaking teams. After a start in France, the leadership had passed to Germany, to England, eventually to the United States. More than about the "also-ran" Munk we naturally hear about Ferrier, for it was Ferrier who established the line West of the Channel which leads to Horsley, Sherrington, Cushing, Fulton, and Penfield.

Occupying a middle but always original position, Munk fought on two, or rather three, fronts. He had no mercy for Ferrier's concepts of a visual center in the angular gyrus, a center for touch in the hippocampus, and a hunger center in the occipital lobe; he opposed Flechsig, Hitzig, and Ferrier (at loggerheads themselves) on their localization of intelligence in the frontal lobe (to Munk, in-

Hermann Munk

Portrait, courtesy of Dr. Mary A. B. Brazier, Los Angeles, California.

telligence was an attribute of the whole association cortex). On the other hand he defended localization against Goltz, the common enemy whose wholesale jeers were directed at all this "cartographer's physiology." According to Fritsch, who used to have lunch with Munk in the early days, Munk was an imaginative but cool, cautious and infinitely painstaking worker, a man also of great self-confidence and strong intransigence. Stern and sterling, but hardly popular, we gather, and rather lonely. He may have relaxed in the company, not of his colleagues, but of the painters and sculptors he admired and supported.

Like Goltz, Munk was a native of Posen (East-Prussia). He was proud of having been one of Johannes Müller's last students in Berlin. There he returned and remained after a stay in Göttingen; M.D. in 1859, Privatdocent in 1862, Extraordinarius in 1869, soldier in the war of 1870. In 1876 the Berlin Veterinary School appointed him Full Professor to its small but new physiological laboratory. Here, assisted by his younger brother Immanuel, he performed those deft, cortical excisions, about fifteen millimeters in diameter, two millimeters deep, on dogs and macaques, and learned how to make them survive for months as he soon gave up Lister's fashionable but lethal carbolic acid spray. Most of his early work Munk reported in the Berlin Physiologische Gesellschaft which he helped found in 1875; on the intervention of Helmholtz he became a regular member of the Prussian Academy of Sciences in 1880. The government ignored the medical faculty's recommendation to have Munk succeed du Bois-Reymond to the chair of physiology; he died Ordentlicher Honorarprofessor, and as if on a sidetrack.

Munk's publications of his work spanning three decades consist of the communications he made to the two learned societies mentioned; the most outstanding ones are collected in a couple of rather modest volumes;[1-3] they make difficult reading. His merit regarding the brain's role in vision goes far beyond Meynert, Panizza, Luciani and Tamburini for establishing the facts of cortical blindness and mind blindness. In unilateral lesions of the occipital lobe he uncovered the fact of "hemiopia" where his precursors had only thought of blindness of one eye; his insight was just falling short of Henschen's focus on the calcarine fissure. His observations about the type of sensory (and motor) loss due to excisions in the parietal area were equally ingenious, precise and fundamental, as were his experiments about temporal lobe functions. Sherrington quoted Munk as his forerunner in assigning an essential role to inhibition in reciprocal innervation.[4] For these reasons, notwithstanding the somehow ascetic grayness that adheres even to the very sound of his name, and despite the paucity of personal facts that barely seem to fill a life, we must include Hermann Munk here as one of the most dedicated and solid builders of our neurological foundations.

SAN FRANCISCO, CALIFORNIA   FRANCIS SCHILLER

References

[1]*Über die Functionen der Grosshirnrinde.* Berlin, Hirschwald, 1881. [2]*Some papers on the cerebral cortex.* Springfield, Thomas, 1960, p. xiii-xiv, 97–117 (trans. by von Bonin). [3]*Über die Functionen von Hirn und Rückenmark.* Berlin, Hirschwald, 1909. [4]*The discovery of reflexes.* Oxford, Clarendon, 1960, p. 134 (Verhandl. Berlin Physiol. Gesellsch., Oct. 1881). (Lidell).

References to Biography: 1) Deut. med. Wschr., 1909, *35*:258–259 (Rothmann). 2) *Ibid.,* 1912, *38*:2085–2086 (Fritsch).

IVAN PAVLOV (1849–1936)

*Pavlov is a star which lights the world, shining down on
a vista hitherto unexplored . . .* WELLS

*B*ORN on the other side of the tracks of science, as the son of a peasant priest in the village of Riazan in central Russia, Ivan Petrovich Pavlov was educated for the priesthood. Perhaps it was this, too, that made him, as he said, "able to renounce the practical side of life, with its cunning and not always irreproachable methods." However, when twenty-one years of age he began to study medicine at the University of St. Petersburg under Mendeleyev, Buttlerov, and Tsyon, and won a two-year fellowship for study in Germany upon graduation. He worked with Carl Ludwig

at Leipzig and Heidenhain at Breslau, investigating circulation with
the former, pancreatic and gastric secretion with the latter. Back
in St. Petersburg, he ventured into experimental pharmacology with
Botkin, a clinician. Lewes' *Practical physiology* and Sechenov's
Reflexes of the brain were now always at his bedside.

Pavlov's contributions fall into four fields: cardiac physiology,
digestion, central nervous system, and psychophysiology. He discovered independently of Gaskell the special trophic nerves of the
heart. In his investigation of the digestive glands,[1] for which he

Portrait courtesy of Dr. J. R. M. Innes, Falls Church, Virginia.

was awarded the Nobel Prize in 1904, he succeeded, where others had failed, through the method of the chronic fistula, in bringing to the surface of the skin the salivary, pancreatic and choledochus ducts. For the study of the gastric secretion he devised a miniature stomach (the "Pavlov pouch") differing from that of Heidenhain in that the vagal nerve branches were preserved. His substitution of the chronic experiment for the acute was an important advance in physiology, enabling him to observe an animal over its life span. He was probably the first to apply modern surgical techniques and asepsis in physiology—techniques which were equal even at that time (1890) to the best in use in hospitals today.

The use of salivary and gastric fistulae in the long-term study of secretion, using healthy animals, led to the discovery of the conditional reflex.[2] This determined the main line of his research concerning higher nervous activity after he had become fifty-five. At the age of eighty he began to study psychiatry, and applied his physiological studies to that field. His book on conditional reflexes, translated into English in 1941,[3] has been called the greatest book on psychiatry ever written (G. Sutherland).

His professional career in Russia was frequently halted owing to vehement altercations on matters of principle with institutional as well as national politicians. Nevertheless his laboratory was endowed by members of the Russian nobility. He suffered the vicissitudes of war and revolution, stoutly refusing personal privileges from a government whose actions in general he opposed, and fearless in his denunciation of principles of which he disapproved. Pavlov fared better than others; with the gathering clouds of war his patriotism became dominant; he acknowledged his gratitude to the Soviet Government for its sponsorship of science. Gratitude, too, for man's best friend, then also science's most tried martyr, motivated Pavlov to erect a stone dog in the courtyard of the Institute for Experimental Medicine.

Until the death of Stalin in 1953, Pavlov was the Aristotle of Russia from whom it was heresy to disagree. Since then his valuation in Russia has become more realistic. Abroad, the interest in his methods and concepts has been steadily growing, though in 1969 there were only six or seven of his former collaborators still alive and working, among them Asratyan, Anokhin and Vasiliev in

Russia, Konorski in Poland, Hayashi in Japan, Gantt in the U.S.A.

Pavlov was one of the most dynamic, brilliant, and zealous scientific figures of all time. His genius rested on his ability to design an experiment so as to eliminate extraneous factors, on his keen powers of observation, and on his use of imagination in developing concepts. His extreme skill at the operating table and in devising new procedures placed him in the front rank of the most eminent surgeons. By nature he was simple in his tastes and home loving, but vehement in his likes and dislikes, fearlessly honest, ferocious in defending his principles. "To meet him," Yerkes said, "was like meeting a fresh breeze from the sea."

After the death of his son Victor (in the White Army) Pavlov had trouble sleeping. Mme. Pavlov viewed his insomnia with alarm, for his habits had always been as regular as clockwork: he would sit down to lunch exactly at twelve o'clock; he would play the same records on his phonograph on the same night of each week, month after month; he would retire at precisely the same time each night; and he would always leave St. Petersburg for Estonia on an extended summer vacation on the same day each year, settling down on his estate, there to play strenous games and read French novels. Pavlov's scientific zeal persisted to the end: despite his sleeplessness he worked on full schedule in his laboratory until a week before he died, at the age of eighty-six: in the last hour of his life he discussed the meaning of the symptoms of his obscure illness and of the complicating pneumonia with a neurologist. Pavlov was appealing to students everywhere, not only the Komsomol (a Soviet youth organization), when he wrote: "First of all, be systematic . . . learn to do the drudgery. . . . Second . . . comes modesty; pride . . . will deprive you of the ability to be objective . . . The third thing necessary is passion . . . be passionate in your work and in your search for truth."

BALTIMORE, MARYLAND   W. HORSLEY GANTT

References

[1]*The work of the digestive glands.* Philadelphia, Lippincott, 1902 (transl. by Thompson) (1st ed. in Russian, 1897).   [2]*Lectures on*

conditioned reflexes. London, Lawrence, 1928 (transl. by Gantt).
³*Conditioned reflexes and psychiatry.* New York, Int. Publ. Co., 1941
(transl. by Gantt).

References to Biography and Works: 1) *Lectures on conditioned reflexes.* London, Lawrence, 1928 (Pavlov) (transl. by Gantt), p. 11–31.
2) Canad. Med. Assoc. J., 1929, *21*:582–583 (Babkin).   3) *Pavlov.*
Chicago, U. of Chicago Press, 1950 (Babkin).   4) Science, 1951,
114:227–233 (London).   5) *Ivan Pavlov. The man and his theories.*
London, Souvenir, 1964 (Cuny) (transl. by Evans).

JAN PURKYNĚ (1787–1869)

*J*AN EVANGELISTA PURKYNĚ was born in Libochovice
in Bohemia, to Czech parents of humble peasant stock. As
the result of a German priest's entry of his name as "Purkinje"—
pronounced *poor′kin·ye*—into the birth registry, he himself used
that German phonetic spelling until 1850. (Hence *per·kin′jay,*
that English phonetic abomination.) When he was ten years old,
his father died, leaving the family poor. Educated by Piarist monks,
he taught school as a novice for three years, but in 1808 left the
order in protest "against a continuous slavery to the superiors
whose lives and dignity did not always come up to my expectation"
(John). He decided in favor of philosophy. With this in mind he
walked the 200 miles to Prague. In 1810 he became tutor in the
home of Baron Hildprandt, at Blatná, who enabled him to begin
the study of medicine.

As a medical student, Purkyně observed the effects of drugs
upon himself and, having "eine starke Natur," continued to do so
for years. His descriptions of acute poisoning with ipecac, belladonna, etc. are classics. It was his conviction that experiment in
one's own body ("in corpore nobili") gave more practical results
than those in animal experiment ("in corpore vili") or in fatally
ill patients. The alarming symptoms he experienced after taking
large quantities of camphor started the unfounded rumor that he
was an epileptic.

Stimulated by Goethe's *Farbenlehre,* he wrote his doctoral dis-

JAN PURKYNĚ
Profesor w léčitelstwj na uniwersitě Wratislawské (Breslau).
Narozen 1787, 17 prosince w Libochowicjch.

Od jeho ctjtelu.

Pokud i kde Bůh žíti poweli,
Buď wěren wlasti, wjře, přjteli.
Jan Purkyně

Where and how long God lets you stay, my friend,
Stay faithful both to Him and to your land.
Jan Purkyně

Portrait, courtesy of the National Library of Medicine, Bethesda, Maryland.

sertation (1818) on the subjective aspects of vision,[1] a study which was to occupy him for many years. The second volume on entoptic phenomena (1825) included the celebrated chapter on after-images and the different thresholds of various colors. His inaugural dissertation (1823) dealt with visual and cutaneous sensibility and with differences in the dioptic media, establishing a basis for objective optometry and the ophthalmoscope. It happened to include the earliest data on the individuality of finger prints. His appointment as professor of physiology at Breslau was arranged by Geheimrat Rust, who had met him in 1817, and by K. A. Rudolphi, professor of anatomy at Berlin, whose daughter he married in 1825; it was Goethe, however, who had introduced him to Rudolphi and to many other notables in Berlin, such as Hegel, Freiherr von Stein, Varnhagen von Ense and the Humbolt brothers. The faculty at Breslau was opposed to the appointment of a Czech, and for years picayune jealousy prevented any effective cooperation with his colleagues. When he introduced demonstrations and laboratory work into his teaching, procedures new to biology, the faculty recommended that he be demoted. The Ministry of Education replied by commending his methods.

Important discoveries in histology came after Purkyně obtained his compound microscope (1832). The development of technical methods helped materially to make his laboratory the "cradle of histology," a place where he and his assistants investigated animal and plant tissues "with the hunger of wolves." Cholera carried off two of his children in 1835, and to add to the tragedy, his beloved wife fell victim to a typhoid epidemic three years later. After that the laboratory was moved to his home. The detailed histological studies were all published under the names of his students, except for the monograph on ciliary epithelium and its function in mammals; this appeared in 1934[2] under co-authorship with the highly gifted Gabriel Gustav Valentin (1810–83), Purkyně's favorite pupil, who in 1835 received the Grand Prix des Sciences Physiques of the Institut de France for his work on a comparison of the development of tissues in animals and plants. Later, at Bern, Valentin was acknowledged as "the most prominent physiologist of his time."[3]

In 1837 Purkyně presented to the German Men of Science and

Physicians in Prague a brief resumé of his microscopic survey of the human brain.[4] It included the first adequate description and illustrations of myelinated fibers, nerve cells (Körnchen) with their nuclei and dendrites, and the layers of a cerebellar folium, including the row of "flask-shaped ganglionic bodies" that have become a household word in neurohistology. They usually, he said, have two branches extending almost to the pia.[5]

These observations contributed basic facts for the development of the cell theory. In 1839 he introduced the term "protoplasma." In the same year appeared his work on the cardiac fibers which were to be named after him. His pioneering autognostic studies on vertigo, begun in 1820, enabled him to distinguish the ocular from other factors involved. His basic experiments in this field were carried out on the swings and carrousels in a Prague amusement park. In 1846 he wrote on the value of dreams as an index to personality. He was also instrumental in the development of the animated cartoon and hence in movie making altogether.

In 1850, at the age of sixty-three, Purkyně received the call he had long hoped for—the chair of physiology at Prague. This was only two years after the Czech national aspirations had been squashed after an abortive uprising (in 1848). Purkyně was provided with an adequate laboratory, but his nationalistic interests brought to a halt his avalanche of original scientific observations. He was elected to the Czech provincial Parliament, and coedited the leading Czech daily newspaper. With amazing energy he campaigned constantly for the cultural and political emancipation of his countrymen. The Austrian police authorities could not be certain whether the man who had written: "It is not right that one nation should rule another nation," was a dangerous "subversive element" or "an eccentric humanist who does not constitute a danger to State interests."

When we consider the acclaim and confirmation that greeted the discoveries for which the time was ripe, it would seem that many of the leading biologists of the day were Purkyně's followers. His enduring monuments are the cells, the fibers and the phenomena which bear his name. His massive contribution, which included translations from Schiller, Shakespeare, and Tasso, and many popular essays on science, enthroned him in the hearts of all Czechs.

Goethe, referring to his own theories on light and color perception, once advised his readers:

> "And should you fail to understand,
> Let Purkyně give you a hand!"[6]

G. W. BARTELMEZ

References

[1]*Beiträge zur Kenntniss des Sehens in subjectiver Hinsicht.* Prag, Calve,
1819. (ed. 2, 1823.)   [2]Müllers Arch., 1834, *1:*391–400.   [3]Kagan
(ed.), *Victor Robinson memoria' vo'ume. Essays on the history of medicine.* New York, Froben, 1948 (Kisch), p. 193–212.   [4]Ber. ü. d. Versamml. deut. Naturf. u. Aerzte, Prag, Hasse, 1838, *15:*174–175 *et seq.*
[5]Bull. Hist. Med., 1940, *8:*1397–1398 (Viets and Garrison).   [6]Bull.
Hist. Med., 1951, *25:*159–168 (Baer), Gesnerus, 1949, *6:*105 (Fischer).

References to Biography: 1) Vierteljahresschr. f. d. prakt. Heilk., Prag,
1859, *63*(Beilage):1–20 (contains bibliography; Eiselt).   2) Osiris,
1936, *2:*464–483 (Hykeš and Studnička).   3) *J.A.M.A.,* 1899, *32:*812–
814 (Opitz).   4) Presse méd., 1938, *1:*681–682 (Karasek).   5) *Jan
Evangelista Purkyně,* Philadelphia, Amer. Philosoph. Soc., 1959 (John).
6) Brit. Med. J., 1969, *3:*107–109 (Posner).

MORITZ SCHIFF (1823–1896)

S CHIFF's name is hardly ever remembered in connection
with any of the great discoveries in neurology, yet a close
look at his work shows him as one of the pioneers in experimental
neurophysiology. He was born in Frankfurt-am-Main, into a well-
to-do Jewish family. As a boy, he marvelled at the natural history
collections of the Senckenberg Institut. As a young man he went
to Heidelberg, where he distinguished himself in anatomy under
Tiedemann, later in Berlin under Johannes Müller, and in 1884
he obtained his M.D. in Göttingen. Next he took up ornithological
problems, and others concerning the fauna of the South American
Continent, at the Jardin des Plantes in Paris. He met Magendie
whose teachings made physiology his passion, especially the physiology of the nervous system.

Portrait, courtesy of the National Library of Medicine, Bethesda, Maryland.

Success in the study of birds led to Schiff's appointment as Director of the Ornithological Section back at the Senckenberg Institut in 1847. Then, like so many liberal intellectuals of his day he took part in the revolutionary events of 1848, and enlisted as a military surgeon. With Carl Vogt, the famous zoologist, he escaped the fate of another militant friend, the son of Professor Tiedemann, who was executed in Prussia. Political and perhaps religious reasons foiled Schiff's attempt (in 1855) at getting a "Habilitation" at the University of Göttingen, despite the support of the Faculty. The more liberal Swiss appointed him to the chair of Anatomy and Pathological Physiology in Bern, still in the same year. His fame as a teacher having spread, he was invited by the newly constituted Italian Kingdom, in 1863, to the chair of physiology at the Istituto di Studi Superiori in Florence.

After more than a decade (in 1876) he again was on the move: the government had forbidden any further experimentation. Was it lack of understanding of its purpose? Or the protest of antivivisectionist ladies, especially those in the British colony? Paradoxically, his writings stress all the precautions he took during operations (including ether anesthesia) in order to avoid pain and terror for the animals. They were his pets. His pockets were always messy with tidbits for them, bones or crumbs saved from his meals, and served with a cajoling word or tune. Before leaving Florence he had taken his noble revenge by vindicating priority in electrotherapeutics for Italian medicine.[1] Amends from the Italian government came only in 1894.[2]

So it was again Switzerland—Geneva this time—and there he remained from 1876 on as Professor of Physiology. Germany, where he belonged, seems to have been closed to him. He also refused to change his religion. In these final twenty years practically no more publications came—none until 1884, when some of his ideas on the thyroid erupted, on hearing of the "discoveries" of thyreoprivic syndromes in man, produced by the Swiss surgeons Reverdin (1882) and Kocher (1883) after thyroid surgery. From experimental thyroidectomy carried out by him in 1856–58 (communicated to the Royal Society of Science in Copenhagen,[3] then buried in a work on the formation of sugar in the liver in 1858[4]), he had concluded that the thyroid was a gland of internal secretion, a general concept proposed by Claude Bernard in 1855. Consequently, Schiff repeated his earlier experiments and (in 1884)[5] published them together with his account of intra-abdominal transplantation of the gland following thyroidectomy—a classic in modern endocrinology.

Many of Schiff's contributions are described in his *Muskel- und Nervenphysiologie* (Lahr, Schauenburg, 1858–59), the first volume of a projected comprehensive *Lehrbuch der Physiologie*. Take his experiment of compressing the carotid artery (page 107): after 2 to 3 seconds paresthesias appeared in the contralateral side of face, extending after 20 seconds to what we today would call a "Jacksonian march," i.e., hemianesthesia and hemiparalysis, and sometimes focal seizures. Bilateral compression he called "unsuccessful" because of doublesided paresis.

In 1845, the Weber brothers had announced their exciting discovery of the inhibitory action of the vagus nerves on the heart. Schiff, from his studies of vagotomy (in 1849) concluded that the inhibition was paradoxical, that the vagus was a cardioexcitatory nerve, a paradox which, in part, has been confirmed recently.[6] Severance of the vagus resulted in respiratory embarrassment and disturbances of gastric function,[7] and of its splanchnic branch, in inhibition of intestinal motility—work which Lord Lister found cause to praise. He discovered other autonomic influences: section of the trigeminus resulted in suppression of vasomotor function in the face and in neuroparalytic keratitis; when either the hypoglossal or the lingual nerve was sectioned, the vessels of the tongue became dilated.[8] Much work also went into his demonstration of vasomotor fibers in spinal peripheral nerves,[9] and from the results of sectioning at spinal and higher levels he concluded[10] that all fibers running along vessels are controlled from a center in the medulla oblongata—again, a major discovery. Of special interest was his basic work on the regeneration of nerves. He pointed out the nonspecificity of Meissner's corpuscles and nerve endings in general.[11] He performed lobectomies, even total cerebrectomies, in birds and mammals, and described the symptoms long before Goltz and others did, but was unable to keep the preparations alive sufficiently long to examine the chronic defects. He repeated Claude Bernard's piqûre of the fourth ventricle, but in frogs; for his demonstration that the sugar came from the liver[3] he received a prize from the Academy of Sciences in Copenhagen. A more comprehensive discourse on the subject appeared later.[4]

This was at about the time Brown-Séquard was making the observations (1846, 1850) that were to establish his fame, on the hemidestruction of the spinal cord in man. While in Paris, Schiff had become acquainted with F. A. Longet (1811–1871) and his doctrine extending Magendie's law of the spinal roots to the cord, placing all motor function in its anterior half of the cord, all sensory function in its posterior half. In 1849 Schiff showed, against Longet, that pain and temperature sensations ("aesthsodic") cross the midline in the gray matter of the cord, and are independent from posterior column sensations ("kinaesthsodic"—i.e., concerned with the awareness of movement).[12] But his findings, made on an even broader scale of experiments, did not fit—he thought—with Brown-Séquard's interpretation, especially not with the latter's view that "nervous energy" flowed through the nervous system regardless of fiber or other connections. It is worth-while to read of Schiff's efforts in investigating "conduction" (from the frog to the dog, the highest mammal he had a chance to work on): section of one or both posterior columns, one or more segments on one or both sides with or without inclusion of the anterior columns, isolation of the gray substance by sectioning all the white pathways. Every pattern was minutely examined, interpreted, and compared with findings in man. He was noted not least for his honesty. Never would he describe observations, he wrote, unless they were made repeatedly and witnessed by some members of the Senckenberg Society.

Schiff was talented in many ways. In Florence he so rapidly acquired the language that even the natives thought him Italian. His bon mots and his gifts as a raconteur earned him the social standing that made his home—wherever that happened to be—an international center. Judging from his portrait, taken at the celebration of his seventieth birthday in Geneva, his troubles had taken none of the sparkle from his eyes, nor had his ardor left him. His week in the laboratory continued to have seven days, the year no holidays. (To a New Year's well wisher: "What's so new? What's so different from yesterday?" And he gave a little jump.) But his

maxim that rest consisted in switching tasks made his work somewhat erratic. He never failed a student, but there was a shade of
contempt in this benevolence. As a host, too, he was unconvention-
ally relaxed, making an appearance among his dinner guests at
10:30, his tiny figure in a dressing gown, and in slippers, to exchange some jokes with the company and retreat to his study with
a worthy admirer of some specimen.

He was married twice; to a cousin, and to a statuesque Italian
beauty. They bore him three sons; all three became professors—in
Italy.

It would seem that neither time nor place was favorable for
Schiff; first he had too few influential backers and followers, later
also too many influential competitors. In the historical evaluation
of a scientist his merit and his position are not independent variables. But who would dare speak of him in faint praise for all the
Gordian knots of speculation he cut?

SAN FRANCISCO, CALIFORNIA   FRANCIS SCHILLER
MOFFETT FIELD, CALIFORNIA   WEBB HAYMAKER

Acknowledgement: This biography was prepared with the invaluable
assistance of K.-J. Zülch, Cologne, Germany.

References

[1]Lancet, 1876, 2:117–118, 150–151 (transl. by Steele).   [2]*Ibid.*, 1894,
1:382 (anon.).   [3]Nachr. Georg-Augusts Univ., 1856, p. 243–247.
[4]*Untersuchungen über die Zuckerbildung in der Leber, und den Einfluss des Nervensystems auf die Erzeugung des Diabetes.* Würzburg,
Stahel, 1859.   [5]Arch. exp. Path., Lpz., 1884, 18:25–34.   [6]J. Physiol.
London, 1957, 138:172–177 (Burn and Rand).   [7]*Neue Untersuch-
ungen über den Einfluss des Nervus vagus auf die Magenthätigkeit.*
Bern, Haller, 1860.   [8]Arch. Physiol. Heilk., 1853, 12:377–391.
[9]Proc. Acad. Sci. Paris, 1862, 55:425–427.   [10]*Untersuchungen zur
Physiologie des Nervensystems mit Berücksichtigung der Pathologie.*
Frankfurt, Rütten, 1855.   [11]*Muskel- und Nervenphysiologie.* Lahr,
Schauenburg, 1858–59, p. 166, 206, 238.   [12]*Ibid.*, p. 234.

References to Biography and Works: 1) Wien. klin. Wschr., 1896, 9:
1008–1010 (Biedl).   2) *J.A.M.A.*, 1968, 203:131–132 (anon.)
3) Lancet, 1894, 1:282 (anon.).   4) *Ibid.*, 1896, 2:1198 (anon.).

5) *The Jews and medicine. Essays.* Vol. 2. Baltimore, Johns Hopkins Press, 1944, p. 503–513 (Friedenwald).   6) *The endocrine organs in health and disease with an historical review.* London, Oxford U. P., 1936, p. 23, 151, 178 (Rolleston).

IVAN SECHENOV (1829–1905)

*I*VAN MIKHAILOVICH SECHENOV, the "father of Russian physiology," was well built; he had a lined, pale, almost greenish face, penetrating eyes that would dart around when he was indignant (he hated undue praise); but normally gentle and pleasant, he would hold forth in his rich baritone voice and with convincing arguments, enslaving any audience. Although he disliked parties and kept urging his wife to go home, his song to the bitter end was heard above the din. His "reflexology of the mind" did not prevent him from displaying noble and strong emotions. One day in 1894 he appeared at his lecture paler than usual, dressed in mourning, bursting repeatedly into sobs, finally retreating to the anteroom; finding there a towel to wipe away his tears, he moaned: "Such a fine man to have to go to the grave." Helmholtz had died, seventy-three years old.

Sechenov was born in the province of Simbirsk, on the Volga. At the age of fourteen he entered the St. Petersburg School for Military Engineers, but quickly gave up military ambitions to study medicine at the University of Moscow (1851). He received his medical degree in Vienna (1856), following which he worked with Helmholtz, du Bois-Reymond, Hoppe-Seyler, and Carl Ludwig, his lifelong friend.

On return to Russia, armed with du Bois-Reymond's galvanometer and induction coil, Sechenov introduced electrophysiology into laboratories and teaching. In 1860 he successfully defended his dissertation[1] and was appointed assistant professor of physiology at the Imperial Medico-Chirurgical Academy of St. Petersburg. For a time he worked with the famous Russian chemist, Mendeleyev, but soon had to leave St. Petersburg because of the upsurge of reactionary forces. He took this occasion to go to Paris and study under Claude Bernard. Quiet restored, he returned to St. Petersburg. From 1870–76 he transferred his activities to the University

Ivan Mikhailovich Sechenov

of Odessa, but came back six years later to St. Petersburg as professor of physiology at its University. In 1888 he resigned for personal reasons and moved to Moscow, where he was active first as lecturer, and three years later became professor (until 1901). He died there of pneumonia.

The early contributions of Sechenov were to general physiology and physiological chemistry, but his life work was centered on neurophysiology. His most noteworthy contribution, the result of studies carried out in Claude Bernard's laboratory, was that on cerebral reflex activity.[2-6] His major work, *The reflexes of the brain,* which was a classic, appeared in 1863. In this field he stands with Goltz as a pioneer. Sechenov considered cerebral reflex activity the

Portrait from *Avtobiograficheskie Zapiski.* Moskva & Leningrad, Academy of Sciences, U.S.S.R., 1945.

source of voluntary actions. Stimulations, according to him, arise in the peripheral sense organs and are mediated to the psychic realm, which determines the nature of muscular response. Absence of all senses would thus make psychic life impossible. However, the reflex activity itself is regulated by other cerebral centers (especially that in the mid-brain), which serve in an inhibitory capacity.[7] His assertion that "the initial cause of any human action lies outside the person" ran counter to the point of view of the Czarist government, who regarded the concept as materialistic, anti-religious, immoral, and therefore dangerous to society. For a time the Government considered destroying Sechenov's monograph and indicting him under the penal code. In spite of this he went even farther and claimed that "physiology possesses a number of data that establish the affinity of psychic phenomena to those purely somatic acts which are called the nervous processes of the body."[7]

Sechenov's independence as a thinker was also demonstrated by his opposition to Virchow's dominant teaching that only the cell is responsible for disease. He maintained, as did Lasègue, that physicochemical factors in the environment of the cell are of equal if not greater importance, a view which brought him in conflict with numerous contemporary worshippers of Virchow. This and the government's hostility toward him were the causes of his frequent changes in academic residence. Wherever he went, the ablest physiologists (Voroschilov, Tarkhanov, Spiro, Pashutin, Kravkov, Vvedensky, to mention only a few) flocked to his laboratory. His work was also a great inspiration to Pavlov. He was successful in recording "spontaneous fluctuations of current" in the medulla and spinal cord of frogs (1882).[8]

Sechenov was admired not only for his intellect and scientific achievements, but even more for his idealism, exceptional honesty, and fearlessness in fighting injustice and stupidity. In 1861, when only thirty-two years old, he declined the invitation to become a member of the Imperial Academy of Sciences, though assured of election. The reason given was that his contributions to science were, in his opinion, not of sufficient importance to entitle him to so great an honor. When twenty-five years later he was elected— this time not against his objections—his appointment was vetoed by the government.

The scientific world, and especially the intellectuals in Russia, held him in high esteem and revered his memory. Each of the members of the 15th International Physiological Congress held in Russia (1935) was presented with a special edition of selected works of Sechenov and a Sechenov medal. In 1943 the Academy of Science of the U.S.S.R. republished a volume by him on *Elements of thought*. The *Russian Journal of Physiology* was named the *"Sechenov Journal,"* which is only proper, for Sechenov's school of physiology achieved a fame equivalent to that of any of the great schools of Western Europe.

GEORGE B. HASSIN

References

[1]*Materialy dlia buduschei fiziologii alkogolnogo opianieniia.* St. Petersburg, Treja, 1860.   [2]C. rend. Soc. biol., Paris, 1863, *63*:50–53 *et seq.* [3]Ann. Sci. Nat., 1863, *19*(Zool.):109–134.   [4]Ztsch. rat. Med., 1865, *23*:6–15.   [5]*Ibid.,* 1866, *26*:292–294.   [6]*Selected works of Sechenov.* Moscow, State Publ. House of Biol. Med. Literature, 1935 (articles in English and German).   [7]*Physiologische Studien über die Hemmungsmechanismen für die Reflexthätigkeit des Rückenmarkes im Gehirne des Frosches.* Berlin. Hirschwald, 1863.   [8]Arch. ges. Physiol., 1882, *27*:524–566.

References to Biography: 1) *Selected works.* p. vii–xxxvi (Shaternikov). 2) *Avtobiograficheskie zapiski.* Moskva & Leningrad, Izd. Akad. U.S.S.R., 1945.   3) *Sechenov.* Moskva, Izd. Akad. Nauk., 1945 (Kozhtioants).   4) *Soviet psychiatry.* Baltimore, Williams & Wilkins, 1950 (Wortis).   5) *A history of the electrical activity of the brain. The first half-century.* London, Pitman, 1961 (Brazier).

CHARLES SCOTT SHERRINGTON (1857–1952)

*T*HE life of Sir Charles Sherrington spans a long period of the most active growth in the medical sciences, during which he himself gave enormous impetus to neurophysiology. Although best known for his long series of studies on spinal reflexes, he made equally great strides in the physiology of perception, reaction, and behavior, and with remarkable clarity succeeded in con-

927   R S Eves

Charles S. Sherrington

trasting these with the properties of the mind. His style was in
every way elegant. He was the last of the magnificent Victorians.

   He was born in London, the son of a country physician who
died when Charles and his two younger brothers were still in early
childhood. They were brought up in Ipswich in the home of their
stepfather, a physician of wide cultural interests. His brothers William and George subsequently became successful lawyers. Following a traditional English education, Charles was at first deeply in-

Portrait, courtesy of Dr. D. Denny-Brown, Southborough, Mass.

terested in the classics. One of his schoolmasters, Thomas Ashe, was a poet of considerable distinction, who imbued the young Sherrington not only with a great fondness for poetry but also for literature and travel. From his stepfather, Caleb Rose, came his interest in science and medicine. After a brief introductory period as medical student in London and Edinburgh he transferred to Cambridge University in 1879. There he was strongly influenced not only by Michael Foster—the "father of British physiology"—but also by Foster's already remarkable pupils Langley and Gaskell.

Following graduation in medicine Sherrington became assistant in anatomy for a year during which he began a series of studies of Marchi degeneration of corticospinal fibers, at first with Langley and later independently. As part of this investigation Langley and Sherrington[1] reported on the anatomical changes in the cord and brain stem of a decorticate dog exhibited by Goltz at the International Congress in 1881. This led to the first of many visits to Goltz' laboratory in Strasbourg.

Following the discoveries of Pasteur and Koch, Sherrington, caught up in the enthusiasm of the day, devoted his whole effort to bacteriological studies for a time between 1884 and 1887. With C. S. Roy he set out to establish the cause of cholera, but not much came of it. Traveling in Spain in pursuit of outbreaks of the disease he met Cajal and later persuaded him to lecture in England. His travels also took him to Berlin, where he met Robert Koch and worked for a time in the laboratory of Virchow (1886–87).

In 1887, at the age of thirty, Sherrington was appointed lecturer in physiology at St. Thomas' Hospital Medical School in London and continued his studies of degeneration of spinal tracts. In 1891 he succeeded Victor Horsley as Professor of Pathology at the Brown Institution, a verterinary institute, an appointment that provided facilities for observation of animals with chronic spinal lesions.

Though general observations on spinal reflex activity had been made in the chronic spinal dog by Goltz and Freusberg in 1874, by Haycraft in 1890 and by Goltz and Ewald in 1896, the systematic analysis of their patterns and interaction awaited the inquiry of Sherrington. Liddell's memoir of Sherrington[2] eloquently describes the painfully slow evolution of his ideas of reflex transmission and interaction prior to 1890. That the nervous system consisted of a congregation of separate units had become accepted from the neurone theory of Waldeyer. Cajal had demonstrated the "end-feet," or "boutons terminaux," but it was Sherrington who provided the evidence for a one-way transmission at the "synapse" and the concept of convergence of reflex channels on a "final common path." This for the first time provided an explanation for flexibility and adaptation in nervous function. He began with a systematic delineation of the innervation of muscles and skin by the nerve roots, published in three large papers: in 1892,[3] 1894,[4] and 1898.[5]

In 1895 Sherrington was appointed professor of physiology in Liverpool, where he did much of his best work. By 1900, when he wrote the sections on sensation, spinal cord and mid-brain in Schäfer's *Textbook of physiology,* he had amassed an enormous amount of information on reflex activity. In addition he had commenced studies on the interaction of various reflexes, revealing their use of neurones shared in common, and the inhibitory effects resulting from conflict between them. Inhibition was found to be an active process; not the simple absence of activity. Concepts of facilitation and reciprocal innervation emerged. In his chance observation of decerebrate rigidity in 1896 he found a background against which to demonstrate the presence of reciprocal inhibition even when no conflicting reflex discharge was evident. The patterns of excitation and inhibition inherent in neuronal connections, deduced from these studies, were the subject of his Silliman Lectures, published in 1906 as the *Integrative action of the nervous system*[6] and reprinted five times. This was and will remain a classic of neurophysiology.

In following years Sherrington established the nature of postural reflexes and demonstrated their dependence on the anti-gravity stretch reflex, tracing the afferent stimulus to the proprioceptive end-organs, of which he had shown the sensory nature many years earlier.[7] In 1913 he was appointed to the chair of physiology in Oxford University, where he stayed until retirement in 1935. In these years his investigative talent turned to more quantitative studies of the interaction of reflexes, enabled by this development of recording by isometric myograph. (The principle of this instrument is that, provided the rate of neuronal discharge is high, the amount of muscular contraction recorded represents the number of active motor neurones ["motor units"]; overlapping and subliminal effects could be recorded precisely.) These studies indicated the activity of cumulative excitatory and inhibitory transmitter substances at the synapse, in distinction to the electrical theories of transmission favored by others. In this period he was President of the Royal Society, and the recipient of many honors, including knighthood in 1922, the Order of Merit in 1924, and the Nobel Award (shared with Adrian) in 1932. With all this, he retained his kindly, courteous ways, his gentleness in criticism. In 1925 he published a modest volume of his collected verse.[8]

In 1935 he retired to live in Ipswich where he wrote the philosophical study of dualism, *Man on his nature*[9] (the Gifford Lectures at Edinburgh University for 1937–38). His fascinating historical and bibliographical study, *The endeavor of Jean Fernel*,[10] published in 1946, was his last major contribution. By 1941, when he was eighty-four, he was becoming greatly disabled by painful arthritis, which he endured with extraordinary courage. Even so, his capacity as raconteur was not lessened. Nor his perceptiveness, judging from his contribution to a radio symposium on brain and mind shortly before his death.

SOUTHBOROUGH, MASSACHUSETTS   D. DENNY-BROWN

References

[1]Proc. Physiol. Soc. J. Physiol., London, 1884, 5:vi.   [2]*The discovery of reflexes*. Oxford, Clarendon, 1960 (Liddell).   [3]J. Physiol., London, 1892, 13:621–772.   [4]Philos. Trans. Roy. Soc. London, 1894, 184B:641–763.   [5]Philos. Trans. Roy. Soc. London, 1898, 190B:45–186.   [6]*The integrative action of the nervous system*, New Haven, Yale, 1906. (Revised, with a new foreword by the author and a final bibliography, 1947.)   [7]*The selected writings of Sir Charles Sherrington*. London, Hamish Hamilton, 1939 (Denny-Brown, ed.).   [8]*The assaying of Brabantius and other verse*. Oxford U. P., 1925.   [9]*Man on his nature*. Cambridge U. P., 1940.   [10]*The endeavour of Jean Fernel, with a list of the editions of his writings*. Cambridge U. P., 1946.

References to Biography: 1) *Sherrington, physiologist, philosopher and poet.* Liverpool U. P., 1958 (Lord Cohen of Birkenhead).   2) Obituary Notices of Fellows of the Royal Society, 1952, *8*:241 (Liddell). 3) *Charles Scott Sherrington, a biography of the neurophysiologist.* New York, Doubleday, 1967 (Granit).   4) Amer. J. Psychol., 1952, *65*:474, also J. Neurophysiol., 1957, *20*:543 (Denny-Brown).   5) Brain, London, *80*:402–410 (Penfield).

ALFRED VULPIAN (1826–1887)

*B*ORN in Paris, Edmé Félix Alfred Vulpian was descended from the aristocracy, the legal profession, and a father who also wrote wittily for the stage, refused vaccination, died of small-pox, and left four children to poverty. Despite his brilliance, Alfred failed in the entrance concours to the École Normale (the top teacher's college). By this accident neurology gained a great scientist who also was a stylist. To make a living, Vulpian obtained a technician's job; it was at the *Muséum* and with Flourens; through his influence the promising nineteen-year-old was matriculated in medical school. While an interne Vulpian taught natural history at a high school. Perhaps this hard, mixed upbringing accounted for the unusual success of his doctoral thesis (1853) on the still somewhat vague origin of the cranial nerves III to X.

He became médecin des hôpitaux in 1857, agrégé in 1860, and continued to teach physiology of the nervous system until 1866 when he was named to the chair of pathological anatomy vacated by Cruveilhier, its first occupant. Vulpian was seated only over violent opposition, because he had written a memoir on the higher functions of the brain that had aroused the wrath of the bishops and barons in the Senate. In 1862 he took over, with Charcot, that chaotic welfare institution for the chronically sick, known as the Salpêtrière.

Vulpian was more restrained and perhaps even more learned than his great friend, and he was an experimenter. He worked out the principles of degeneration, and particularly the regeneration, of nerves; he established the principles and added many new facts concerning the vasomotor[1] and sudomotor apparatus, and he made

Edmé Félix Alfred Vulpian

them common knowledge. He discovered the chromaffin system of the adrenal marrow by the application of chromium salts; he showed that curare had its effects at the point between nerve and muscle; he wrote magisterially about the action of various drugs upon the nervous system—strychnine, pilocarpine, anaesthetics, and nicotine.[2] With unprecedented conscientiousness he went over

Portrait, courtesy of Dr. Maurice Genty, Académie de Médecine, Paris, France.

and over his experiments, checking and controlling them until he could be certain of the results. The effect on his students was profound. Mme Dejerine spoke of his kind, nobly Hippocratic head, of the gentle warnings with which he met her pleas to be allowed to study medicine—and of the extension of the big toes in paraplegics Vulpian had pointed out to her (before Babinski).

Entering upon his teaching duties in pathological anatomy, Vulpian found that microscopy had been neglected in France, whereas the Germans with men like Virchow were making vast strides. He undertook to overcome this handicap settling, for example, the acrid dispute among his colleagues concerning the various lesions of tuberculosis. With the crude sectioning and staining methods available he was nevertheless able to describe the lesions of poliomyelitis and spinal muscular atrophy, the retrograde changes that take place in the spinal cord after amputation or nerve section, and he was the first (1879) to repudiate the prevalent view that tabes dorsalis is primarily a dorsal column disease—for how could posterior column degeneration lead to atrophy of the posterior roots?[3] He was equally important as a clinical physiologist.

Those who knew Vulpian spoke of his prodigious labors (he rose at 4 A.M.; his day, he said, was ruled like a music sheet), his memory for detail, his encyclopedic knowledge, his administrative ability, his artistry in presenting a subject. When the centenary of his birth was celebrated an international gathering in Paris fêted him together with Pinel.

Through his 225 published papers and through his lectures, in word and print, Vulpian had a profound and salutary effect upon neurological thought—more in France, perhaps, than abroad, mainly because he was overshadowed, first by Charcot, and next by his own followers, the Dejerines. How much of Vulpian there was in Charcot's achievement is hard to know, given their daily cooperation. Vulpian, as permanent secretary of the Academy of Sciences (a singular honor even among the "immortals"), did much to further Charcot's public career. Vulpian's influence upon his many followers in several fields of knowledge made him the intellectual leader of his day; his probity and kindness were much revered. A man of unusual merit whom you may discover with some surprise, in dignified stone, against the soft background of a few trees, at the top of a short flight of stairs, on a small street near the old École de Médecine—recessed, reserved, impressive, and in perpetual shade.

SAN FRANCISCO, CALIFORNIA   WALTER FREEMAN

References

[1]*Leçons sur l'appareil vaso-moteur (physiologie et pathologie) faites à la Faculté de Médecine de Paris.* 2 vol. Paris, Gerner-Baillière, 1874–75.
[2]*Leçons sur la physiologie générale et comparée du système nerveux faites au Muséum d'histoire naturelle.* Paris, Germer-Baillière, 1866.
[3]*Maladies du système nerveux; leçons professées à la Faculté de Médecine.* 2 vol. Paris, Doin, 1879–86.

References to Biography: 1) Arch. physiol. norm. path., Paris, 1887, 3.sér., *9*:345–352 (Charcot).   2) *Ibid.,* p. 353–355 (Brown-Séquard). 3) Paris méd., 1913, *12*(suppl.):733–747 (Camus).   4) Bull. Acad. méd., Paris, 1927, *97*:724–738 (Hayem and Gley).   5) Rev. neur., Paris, 1927, *1*:1087–1187 (Centenaire de Vulpian) (Roger, Lacroix, Rathery, Mme. Dejerine, *et al.*).

IV

INVESTIGATORS OF NEURAL TRANSMISSION
AND NEUROCHEMISTRY

WALTER CANNON (1871-1945)

W ALTER BRADFORD CANNON was born in Prairie du Chien, Wisconsin. Both parents belonged to pioneering families that had pushed westward from Massachusetts early in the nineteenth century to settle eventually in the upper Mississippi valley. Cannon's career appears to have been largely determined by this genetic and social background, for throughout his life he displayed those traits which are found in the successful frontiersman and explorer—unusual energy of body and mind, resourcefulness, curiosity motivated by the spirit of adventure but directed by a keen intelligence, and a desire to be of help to one's fellows.

In retrospect the place of Cannon's birth seems most auspicious, for Prairie du Chien had grown up on the site of Fort Crawford where in the 1820's William Beaumont had made those classic observations on the fistulous Alexis St. Martin, that constituted the most important work on gastric digestion before the investigations of Pavlov. In 1896, after he entered medical school, Cannon demonstrated for the first time by means of the newly discovered Roentgen rays the movements of the alimentary tract. Thus began observations and experiments that placed him beside Beaumont and Pavlov as one of the great contributors to our knowledge of digestion. On his graduation in medicine at Harvard (1900) he became an instructor in physiology and six years later he succeeded Bowditch as professor. His studies of the gastrointestinal tract, summarized in *The mechanical factors of digestion* (London, Arnold, 1911), terminated in 1912 with the demonstration that the pangs of hunger are due to cramp-like contractions of the stomach.

It was the observation that the movements of the stomach and intestines ceased whenever his animals became excited that aroused Cannon's interest in the autonomic nervous system. Gaskell and Langley had beautifully detailed the origins, distribution and local effects of autonomic neurons. It remained to determine the conditions of their activity. Over a period of more than twenty

279

years, which began in 1911, Cannon and his many students published a long series of papers in which was set forth evidence that
under conditions of physiological stress the sympathetic system
and its constituent part, the adrenal medulla, act to produce visceral adjustments which are nicely adapted to the preservation of
the individual. The earlier results were reported and interpreted
in the first edition of *Bodily changes in pain, hunger, fear and
rage* (New York, Appleton, 1915); a second edition (1929) presented much new evidence bearing on the general theme and included an account of notable experiments on thirst and a discussion of the central mechanisms involved in emotional behavior
and emotional experience. The validity of the emergency theory
of the sympatho-adrenal system was dramatically confirmed in
1929 when Cannon and four collaborators showed that cats from
which both chains of ganglia had been removed are capable of

Portrait, courtesy of Dr. Philip Bard, Baltimore, Maryland.

normal life under uniformly serene circumstances, but exhibit deficiencies when exposed to conditions of physiological stress.[1] A facility for seeing the different facets of a physiological problem led Cannon to a broader interpretation of these experimental facts, namely that the sympatho-adrenal system is important in the maintenance of what he termed "homeostasis," the relatively steady state of the *milieu interne*. His accounts of the bodily organizations for homeostasis, particularly his book, *The wisdom of the body* (New York, Norton, 1932; also 1939), have had a widespread influence.

From the use of the denervated heart as an indicator of medulliadrenal secretion came the discovery that *sympathin* is produced in the normal animal. This disclosure led Cannon into the territory of the chemical mediation of nerve impulses where he became pioneer. Two stimulating monographs on this subject were written in collaboration with Rosenblueth.[2,3]

In his extraordinary autobiography,[4] Cannon tells us that "It is probable that if, while a first-year student of medicine, I had not undertaken research on the physiology of the digestive tract by use of the then newly discovered x-rays, I would have become a neurologist." The reference is to clinical neurology.

BALTIMORE, MARYLAND   PHILIP BARD

References

[1]Amer. J. Physiol., 1929, *89*:84–107 (with Newton, Menkin and Moore).
[2]*Autonomic neuro-effector systems.* New York, Macmillan, 1937.
[3]*The supersensitivity of denervated structures. A law of denervation.* New York, Macmillan, 1949.   [4]*The way of an investigator. A scientist's experiences in medical research.* New York, Norton, 1945.

References to Biography: 1) Psychol. Rev., 1946, *53*:137–146 (Yerkes). 2) Amer. Rev. Soviet Med., 1946, *4*:155–62 (Leibson).   3) *Young endeavour.* Springfield, Thomas, 1958, p. 113–118 (Gibson).

HENRY DALE (1875–1968)

$\mathcal{S}$ IR HENRY DALE, past-president of the Royal Society and of the British Association for the Advancement of Science, and pioneering director of England's National Institute for Medical Research, was probably the most influential physiologist-pharmacologist of the twentieth century. His development of the concept that nervous impulses are chemically transmitted makes him not only a great neurologist, but also one of those rare geniuses who can demonstrate the unity of science by showing the interdependence of the sciences. His discovery and analysis of the action of histamine is of great neurological importance since this chemical agent and the allergy which may release it are intimately associated with nervous disorder.

Henry Hallett Dale was born in London. During his early education he was a Scholar at Leys School, and then Coutts-Trotter Student at Trinity College, Cambridge. Here, in 1898, he worked under Langley, who so thoroughly demonstrated the details of the autonomic nervous system. Dale reported well on the neuroanatomy of infusoria, but failed to get the fellowship he wanted. In 1900 he went to finish his medical training at St. Bartholomew's Hospital in London. After qualifying in 1903, he obtained the George Henry Lewes studentship at University College, with the great cardiologist-physiologist Ernest Henry Starling (1866–1927). The following year he married, and was chosen by Sir Henry Wellcome to be director of the Wellcome physiological research laboratories. From here came his studies on ergot and the isolation of ergotoxine, which he found would reverse the pressor action of adrenaline. In studying this effect, and using post-pituitary extracts as controls, he discovered the uterus-contracting action of such extracts, which led to their wide use in obstetrical practice.

From the same laboratory came Dale's great report in 1910 on "Chemical structure and sympathomimetic action of amines" (*J. Physiol.*, *41*:19–59) with the chemist, George Barger (1878–1939), who synthesized the many compounds studied. In their actions, these agents mimic the effects of stimulation of the sympa-

thetic system. This study later resulted in bringing into clinical medicine many useful drugs, including the amphetamines. As the first director of the National Institute for Medical Research he studied histamine in relation to anaphylaxis, and began work on nerve transmission.

Portrait, courtesy of Dr. Chauncey Leake, San Francisco, California.

The theory of neurohumoral transmission was developed by the joint efforts of Otto Loewi (1873–1961) and Henry Dale, who accordingly shared the Nobel prize in 1936. According to this theory, the electrical impulse (probably reflecting underlying chemical phenomena), on reaching the nerve ending, discharges pharmacologically active compounds, such as acetylcholine and noradrenaline which activate the next excitable neuron. While Loewi made the crucial experiments, using the vagus nerve, Dale showed that the actions of acetylcholine are both muscarinic and nicotinic, and that at different synapses there are different effects which can be differently antagonized. This led to work on curarines, which block acetylcholine, and from there to the clinical use of curarine derivatives to give muscle relaxation in surgery. Another application came in the recognition of drugs such as physostigmine, drugs that block the enzymatic destruction of acetylcholine, and so allow this substance to accumulate in cases of deficiency, as in myasthenia gravis. Again, Dale's ideas led to the clinical use of adrenergic blocking agents, such as guanethidine.

Dale was knighted in 1932. He gave many distinguished lectures in England and in the United States, and received many special honors. He was president of the Royal Society from 1940 to 1945, and during these bitter war years his unfailing good cheer served as a beacon of hope to his scientific colleagues. He was Fullerian professor and director of the Davy-Faraday Laboratory of the Royal Institution from 1942 to 1946. Busy though he was during the war years, Dale always found it possible to take special pains to be hospitable to visiting scientists, especially those from the United States. He became chairman of the Wellcome Trust in 1938, and continued to guide the growth of the great Wellcome Medical History Museum and Library until 1960.

Dale was a charming gentleman. After his witty and wise dinner remarks at the Zurich International Physiology Congress in 1938, I couldn't help dubbing him "benedictorial," and so he was: kindly, yet firm, a brilliant and popular speaker, often featured at the dedication of significant new research laboratories both in England and in the United States. His writings are lucid and extremely well organized, with a wealth of detail to support the points being made. They contain much thought about logical development of his ideas, and the chain of physiological adventures they recall will long be studied with intellectual profit.

SAN FRANCISCO, CALIFORNIA   CHAUNCEY D. LEAKE

References

Dale collected his best writings in two volumes. The first, *Adventures in Physiology*, London, Pergamon, 1953, contains thirty of his most important scientific reports. Included are later comments on these reports. The volume lists 253 of his publications. The second, *An autumn gleaning*. London, Pergamon, 1954, contains fourteen of his occasional addresses, ranging from "Viruses and heterogenesis," through several biographical sketches, the "The freedom of science." An obituary notice appeared in *The Lancet* of August 3, 1968, with several warm appreciations from those who knew him well.

JOHANN THOMAS HENSING (1683–1726)

*T*HE first specific monograph on the chemical examination of the brain[1] was published in 1719 by Hensing, professor extraordinarius of medicine at the University of Giessen, in the Landgraviate of Hesse-Darmstadt. In his preface Hensing alludes to the successful investigations on the brain by such sagacious anatomists as Willis, Malpighi and Ruysch, and contrasts them with the speculations by such investigators as Thomas Bartholin, Burrhus, Leeuwenhoek, and Lémery on the "temperament" of the brain and its fatty nature. Hence he deems it wise to identify its nature more closely with fire, "per ignem,"—then the chemist's most powerful tool. As a result we also have the first report on the isolation of a specific substance from brain tissue: phosphorus.

Hensing had come to Giessen from Frankfurt-am-Main, where his father was a skilled surgeon. At first inclined toward theology, he changed to medicine because of a bout of poor health which affected his voice and lungs. His studies, begun at Leipzig in 1704, were interrupted shortly by the Swedish incursions into Saxony, forcing him to return home by way of the universities of Halle, Wittenberg and Jena. Studies in chemistry, anatomy and botany

together with instruction in practical medicine under Georg Christoph Möller, physician to the Imperial Tribunal at Wetzlar, led to graduation from the University of Giessen in 1709. Hensings' doctoral thesis was entitled: *Dissertatio inauguralis chymico-medica de Vitriolo,* in which he extolled the virtues of various sulfates as therapy for many diseases including epilepsy.[2](p. 41-46)

In 1710 Hensing married the daughter of the vice-chancellor of

From portrait (*ca.* 1723) in the Aula of the University of Giessen, courtesy of the Rector (author's photograph). Signature is from a letter to Landgraf Ernest Ludwig in 1717, in which Hensing sets forth his religious beliefs as required for appointment to the faculty.

Giessen University, and nine children were born of the marriage. As "Land-Physikus" (provincial medical officer) he supplemented his practice with private lectures on medicine and chemistry and was appointed professor extraordinarius of medicine in 1717. Six years later as ordinarius of Natural and Chemical Philosophy, he was permitted to organize a laboratory according to his own design in the local royal castle, and allocated an annual supply of coal (a royal monopoly) to fuel his chemical furnaces. Unfortunately the laboratory never achieved its potential, for Hensing died shortly thereafter of a "malignant catarrhal fever." A bibliography of some twelve publications plus some "programmata" and "schediasmata" summarize his scientific career.

Hensing lived during the ravages left by the Thirty Years' War and repeated epidemics of plague and dysentery. The university was dependent upon the whims of the reigning Landgraf and on the religious climate of the moment. The chemistry of his day, especially in Germany, reflected the alchemical approach aimed at separating mixtures into their pure principles by means of distillation, digestion, rectification, calcination and the like. Thudichum wrote of Hensing's brain analyses:[3] "This ingenious work gives a clear summary of the state of our subject at that time. . . . The first part describes the chemical operations which were carried out in the separation of water, oil, salt and earth. The products lost on burning, gases, were not examined." Hensing was clearly aware of the work of other scientists: his monograph on chemical analysis of the brain provides an excellent review of contemporary knowledge of phosphorus and phosphorescence. For his isolation, Hensing utilized the method of Wilhelm Homberg, physician and chemist to the Duc d'Orléans and director of the chemical laboratories of the Académie Royale des Sciences in Paris. Homberg had adapted the method of Kunckel as demonstrated by Robert Boyle, for the isolation of phosphorus from dung.[4]

As he investigated that small, black cake of "so mournful a countenance," which he had isolated from 12 ounces of beef brain, Hensing described his own discovery:[1(p. 24)] "When taken out of the glass, however, the little cake remains quiescent for a longer time, unless it is divided into smaller pieces; then, to be sure, it glows like a coal and splits into reddish-yellow ashes, but at night it gives forth a visibly conspicuous and luminous radiance. Once it is glowing, if the powder is thrown vigorously into the air, it hisses and bursts into myriads of sparks, forming a most glorious beam of fire." He concludes: "By this experimental confirmation, we have no doubt at all about the product of our investigations being a phosphorus . . ." Like many of the brain chemists who followed him, Hensing speculated on the role that his phosphorus might play in the functioning of the brain. This very theme recurs in most of the important nineteenth century studies of brain chemistry—Vauquelin, Couërbe, and Thudichum—the latter by coincidence also having been a Hessian and a graduate of Giessen.

It would be presumptuous to suppose that Hensing had any major impact upon succeeding investigators, although his discovery was known to many in Germany and cited by Sömmerring in his *Vom Baue des menschlichen Körpers.*[5] It was also cited by J. F. John, who translated into German[6] the paper on analyses of brain and nerve by Vauquelin, but it was not known to the latter. Evidently Thudichum had not seen Hensing's monograph until shortly before he revised the second edition of his book, though it contains a comprehensive review of Hensing's findings. Appropriately, the present sketch marks the 250th anniversary of the first publication on the composition of the brain, a cornerstone of modern neurochemistry.

BETHESDA, MARYLAND   DONALD B. TOWER

References

[1]*Cerebri examen chemicum ex eodemque Phosphorum singularem omnia inflammabilia accendentem.* . . etc. Giessen, Vulpius, 1719. [2]Published at Giessen, Vulpius, 1710.   [3]*Die chemische Konstitution des Gehirns des Menschen und der Tiere.* Tübingen, Pietzcker, 1901, p. 318–319 (Thudichum).   [4]Mém. Acad. roy. d. sci. Paris, 1711, p. 238–245. In *Hist. Acad. roy. d. sci.* Paris, 1714,   [5]Pt. 5, sect. 1: *Hirn- und Nervenlehre.* (2d ed.) Frankfurt a.M., Varrentrap u. Wenner, 1800.   [6]Schweiggers Jour. f. Chem. u. Phys., 1813, *8*:430; footnote, p. 431–432.

References to Biography and Works: 1) *Exequias . . . Joh. Thomae Hensing.* Giessen, Vulpius, 1726 (Rüdiger).   2) *Grundlage zu einer*

Hessischen Gelehrten und Schriftsteller Geschichte. Vol. 5. Cassel, 1785; p. 458–461 (Strieder).   3) *Biographisch-Literarisches Handwörterbuch zur Geschichte der exacten Wissenschaften.* Vol. 1. Leipzig, Barth, 1862, p. 1073 (Poggendorff). (Reprinted: Ann Arbor, Edwards, 1945.)

JOHN NEWPORT LANGLEY (1852–1925)

*L*ANGLEY, English physiologist, was born at Newbury. He was educated partly at home by his father, who was headmaster at a private school. In 1871 he matriculated at St. John's College, Cambridge, and in 1874 graduated with honors. During his second year at the College he abandoned his program leading to a civil service career and began the study of natural science, a change of purpose largely due to the influence of Sir Michael Foster, whose classes in physiology Langley attended. For nine years, beginning in 1875, Langley was demonstrator for Foster and during this time collaborated with him in writing *A course of elementary practical physiology and histology* (ed. 7, London, Macmillan, 1899). While still a student, he had already begun to observe, under Foster's keen tutelage, the action of pilocarpine on the heart, giving the results in his first published paper in 1875. This led to a study of its effects on secretion, and opened the first phase of the work which occupied him for almost fifteen years. These studies, histological and chemical, were correlated with the effects on vasomotor and secretory activity.

Beginning in 1877, Langley held a series of posts at Trinity College, including a lectureship along with Gaskell and Sheridan Lea, and ultimately succeeded Foster in the chair of physiology in 1903. In 1889 Langley showed with Dickinson that on painting a sympathetic ganglion with nicotine, the passage of impulses across it is blocked;[1] thus, when nicotine was applied to the superior cervical ganglion (of the rabbit), stimulation of sympathetic fibers distal to the ganglion still caused pupillary dilatation and constriction of vessels of the ear, whereas stimulation proximal to the ganglion produced no such effects. This observation refuted the view of Hirschmann (1863) and Heidenhain (1872) that the site of ac-

J. N. Langley.

tion of nicotine as far as the pupil was concerned was in the nerve endings of the pupillodilator fibers. What Langley had shown with nicotine was the location of the short postganglionic fibers of the

Portrait, courtesy of the National Library of Medicine, Bethesda, Maryland.

parasympathetic system and the long postganglionic fibers characterizing the sympathetic system.

Through this discovery Langley entered in 1890 the most notable phase of his work on the autonomic nervous system. With H. K. Anderson he demonstrated the unity of postganglionic neurons.[2-4] It was shown that visceral efferent neurons are not present in the dorsal root ganglia. Langley's "axon reflexes" explained what others thought were true reflex actions obtained from peripheral ganglia. His observations led him to introduce the terms "preganglionic" and "postganglionic" nerves in 1893[5] and "autonomic nervous system" in 1898,[6] the latter to replace "vegetative nervous system," coined by Marie François Bichat (1771–1802). The autonomic nervous system, Langley emphasized, was essentially efferent. The cells of the plexus of Meissner[7] and Auerbach[8] he referred to as the "enteric nervous system" since he could find no proof that they were part of the autonomic nervous system. Langley worked on the segmental distribution of the sympathetic fibers of the white rami. It was in 1905 that he coined the term "parasympathetic system" to signify the cranial and sacral outflows of the autonomic system; he separated them from the orthosympathetic outflow by their differing responses to adrenaline, pilocarpine, and other drugs.[9] He never gave consideration to the problem of integration of central and peripheral autonomic pathways.

From 1905 on, Langley was concerned with functional relations between nerve fiber and muscle, and again made effective use of drugs, such as nicotine, curare and adrenaline. His observations led him to conclude that the region just under a nerve ending is especially excitable, due probably to the presence of "receptive substances," with which most poisons react specifically.[9]

During World War I, he studied regeneration of nerves and the effect of stimulation and massage on degenerated muscle. After the war he returned to the study of the autonomic nervous system, concentrating on vasomotor reflexes and the control of the capillaries. During this period he completed a classic in physiology, *The autonomic nervous system* (Cambridge, Heffer, 1921). Of his works, Fletcher has stated: "They stand permanently in their place not merely as additions here and there to knowledge, but as indispensable stepping stones along which, at this point or that, the progress of knowledge has actually made its way." He edited the *Journal of Physiology* with great distinction for more than thirty years. As editor he had an uncanny skill in condensing the papers of verbose authors, detecting their fallacies, and clarifying their arguments; it is to him that credit goes for making this journal a model of scientific achievement for all other physiological journals to follow.

Langley was elected Fellow of the Royal Society in 1883 and became its vice president in 1904. He received many honors, among them the Retzius Medal of the Swedish Society of Physicians. His pupils included Elliot Smith, A. V. Hill, Barcroft, and Adrian.

Langley had very wide interests outside the field of science. He was one of a close-knit circle concerned with the humanities. He participated actively in outdoor sports, and for 20 years was manager of the Trinity Lawn Tennis Club. Following a brief illness, during which he contracted pneumonia, Langley died at his home in Cambridge.

NEW YORK CITY   WILLIAM F. WINDLE

References

[1] Proc. Roy Soc., London, 1889, *46:*423–431.   [2] J. Physiol., London, 1895, *19:*71–84 *et seq.*   [3] *Ibid.,* 1896, *20:*372–406.   [4] Schäffer, E. A. (ed.), *Text-book of physiology.* Vol. 2. Edinburgh & London, Pentland, 1900, p. 616–696.   [5] Proc. Roy. Soc. London, 1893, *52:*547–556. [6] J. Physiol., London, 1898, *23:*240–270.   [7] Zschr. rat. Med., 1857, ser.2, *8:*364–366.   [8] Virchows Arch., 1864, *30:*457–460.   [9] J. Physiol., London, 1905, *33:*374–413.

References to Biography and Works: 1) J. Physiol., London, 1926, *61:* 1–27 (contains bibliography; Fletcher).   2) Arch. Neur. Psychiat., Chic., 1936, *35:*1081–1115 (Sheehan).   3) Anesthesiology, 1968, *29:* 623–624 (Leake).

OTTO LOEWI (1873–1961)

*O*TTO LOEWI was the son of a wine merchant in Frank-furt-am-Main, whose country manor in the Harz Mountains provided the boy with many happy summers. The nine years of Latin and the six years of Greek at the Gymnasium, too, he always regarded as having had a profound influence on his attitude towards life. He wished to take up the history of art as a career, but for practical reasons, medicine was considered better by the family. At Strassburg he found most of the lecturers boring except those in anatomy—and in philosophy. During a year in Munich he again gave most of his attention to music, the theatre and the art galleries. Only in the last year of his course, again in Strassburg, was his interest in the medical sciences suddenly awakened through the inspiring lectures of the great physician, Naunyn, and through his experiences in the laboratory of Schmiedeberg, one of the fathers of pharmacology.

Considering his education in biochemistry inadequate he spent some months with Hofmeister; next he dutifully underwent, as an assistant of von Noorden in Frankfurt, his exposure to patients, mostly young and mostly dying of tuberculosis or pneumonia, to decide that the laboratory rather than the clinic was for him. He joined the Department of Pharmacology in Marburg under Professor H. H. Meyer, as an assistant, later as Privatdozent. After seven happy years he followed Meyer to Vienna, and in 1909 was made Professor of Pharmacology at Graz. In 1938, as a Jew, sixty-five years old and a Nobel Prize winner, he was thrown into jail by the Nazis but released two months later. After a period in England and Belgium, spent, in part, on uncomprehending U. S. immigrant benches, he became Research Professor at New York University on the invitation of Professor Wallace. The summers, to his great delight, he spent at Woods Hole. This and the Engadine in Switzerland were the two places he loved most; in the Engadine he also met the future Mrs. Loewi who became the mother of a daughter and three sons, his constant help and the gracious hostess of their homes in Graz and New York until her death in 1958. Loewi was eighty-eight when he died on Christmas Day 1961.

His scientific interests were quite varied. An early major contribution was the demonstration that animals could be maintained in
nitrogen equilibrium by an enzyme hydrolysate of the pancreas,
against the current belief that animals could not synthesize pro-
teins from smaller molecules.

In Vienna, with Alfred Fröhlich, of syndrome fame, he demonstrated that small doses of cocaine potentiate the responses of sym-

Portrait, courtesy of The Johns Hopkins Institute of the History of Medicine,
Baltimore, Maryland.

pathetically innervated organs to epinephrine and sympathetic nerve stimulation. Perhaps his interest in the vegetative nervous system was aroused in 1902 by a visit to Cambridge where T. R. Elliott was conducting his classical work on the action of epinephrine. In Graz with his long-time assistant Adolph Jarisch, Loewi elucidated the mechanism of Claude Bernard's *piqûre,* and the hyperglycemic effect of epinephrine. Alone, or with many visiting collaborators and students (Walter Fletcher from England, Velyan Henderson from Toronto, Franklin C. McLean later of Chicago, and many others), throughout many years, he also demonstrated the part played by cations. Thus he concluded that the effects of digitalis glucosides are due to sensitization of the frog's heart to calcium.

His greatest contribution, published in 1921[1,2] was, of course, the demonstration of the chemical transmission of the nervous impulse. He often had to tell the story how in 1920, on Easter Sunday morning, he awoke in the wee hours with the idea that the vagus worked by means of a chemical substance, and the conception of an experiment to prove it. He scribbled this down and fell asleep. When he finally got up he could not read what he had written. The importance of the forgotten something haunted him all day. When he awoke the next morning both idea and experiment were clear in his mind: stimulating the vagus of an isolated frog's heart containing Ringer's solution would produce a slowing effect on a second denervated heart by the transfer of the Ringer solution to it. Here it was, his *Vagusstoff.* In addition he demonstrated the respective effect on the accelerator nerve. The experiments had not taken long. It was still early in the morning. He tried to arouse the assistants who slept in the Institute: "Come, come, I have found something marvelous!" "Sorry, Herr Hofrat . . . the holiday . . . not before 8 o'clock. . . ." Nine years later, Walter M. Fletcher quoted Loewi an entry in his diary to the effect that in 1903 while the two were taking a walk in the hills near Marburg he had remarked how beautiful the village looked in the sunset, when Loewi said: "Don't bother me with the sunset, I am thinking the vagus may work by means of a substance." In the hey-day of Freud it all had for seventeen years disappeared from his conscious mind to be resurrected in the middle of an Easter night.

The discovery that the nervous impulse is transmitted by a chemical agent has led to thousands of germane ideas and experiments. In 1937 Loewi and his old friend Sir Henry Dale received the Nobel Prize. He continued to work on various aspects of this subject and on many of his older interests.

Loewi was an inspiring teacher, lively and voluble in public and in private, a man who found something of interest in everybody he met and always something interesting to say, whether they were students or eminent scientists, great artists, or humble people. I believe that his greatest characteristic was the continued youthful attitude to changes in science, art or life—"he never ceased to wonder." Hence his magnificent adaptation in 1938, his eager embracement of American culture. He was seventy-six when, after listening to Rosalyn Tureck, the pianist, he discovered Bach, having previously favoured only Beethoven and Brahms. After the Nobel Prize he received many honours and honorary degrees: University of Graz, Frankfurt and New York University, but the one he valued most was the Foreign Membership of the Royal Society of London to which he was elected in 1954. Albert Einstein wrote to him on his eightieth birthday: "I hope you have now reached such an age that you will no longer be bothered by the stupidities of others and will have developed a sense of humour about your own." He had not hoped in vain.

MONTREAL, CANADA   J. S. L. BROWNE

References

[1]Pflügers Arch., 1921, *189*:239–242.   [2]*Ibid.*, 1921, *193*:201–213.

References to Biography: 1) *An autobiographic sketch.* In *Perspectives in biology and medicine,* autumn issue, 1960 (Loewi).   2) *Biographical memoirs of Fellows of The Royal Society,* vol. 8, 1962 (with bibliography; Dale).   3) *Otto Loewi. Ein Lebensbild in Dokumenten.* Berlin, Springer, 1968 (Lembeck and Giere).

JOHANN LUDWIG WILHELM THUDICHUM
(1829–1901)

E VEN if one hesitates to designate Thudichum as *the* founder of neurochemistry, one must still credit him with the most important single contribution to the field. This was his monograph, *A treatise on the chemical constitution of the brain—based throughout upon original researches,* published in 1884 (London, Baillière, Tindall & Cox),[1] translated into Russian in 1885,[2] and republished as a revised German edition in 1901.[3] At the time of the original reports, his brain analyses were the center of bitter controversy, and only after several decades did the full import and significance of his contributions begin to be appreciated.

Thudichum was born in Büdingen, in the Grand Duchy of Hesse-Darmstadt, then, as now, a small and delightful "Wasserburg" surrounded by medieval moats, between Frankfurt-am-Main and Giessen. One can still see the old Pfarrhaus where Thudichum was born and the Rektorathaus (*ca.* 1560) where he lived as a small boy. He was an eldest son, his father the rector of the Lutheran church and founder and principal of Büdingen Gymnasium.

Young Thudichum matriculated in medicine in 1847 at the University of Giessen, where his teachers included Bischoff in anatomy and Liebig in chemistry. In 1850 he matriculated at Heidelberg where he studied under Bunsen and Henle, and won a medal for a research paper, "On urea in amniotic fluid," disputing the views of Wöhler. He openly supported the Revolution of 1848 and did volunteer service during the "Danish" war, waged by Prussia, in a field hospital at Kiel under Surgeon-General von Esmarch, but managed to graduate from Giessen in 1851. Following his failure to secure the post of Conservator of Pathology in Giessen (presumably because of his revolutionary past), Thudichum emigrated in 1853 to London, became a naturalized British citizen, and married a distant cousin, Charlotte Dupré—a marriage blessed with eight children.

Over the next two decades Thudichum held posts as professor of chemistry at the Grosvenor Place Medical School, St. George's

Johann Ludwig Wilhelm Thudichum

Hospital (1855–63) and St. Thomas' Hospital Medical School (1865–71) where he was director of the laboratory of chemistry and pathology. By 1870 he was well established in the practice of his specialty, otolaryngology, and had to his credit some eighty scientific publications, including two important books (*A treatise on the pathology of urine*, in 1858, and *A treatise on gall stones*, in 1863, both published by Churchill, in London). He made important observations on urochrome (for which he was awarded the first Hastings gold medal of the British Medical Association in 1864[4]), discovered hematoporphyrin, which he called cruentine,[5] and the carotenoid pigments, which he called luteines.[6,7]

In 1864 Thudichum received his most important appointment: chemist to the Local Government Board. This represented an eighteen-year grant from the Medical Department of the Privy Council (now Medical Research Council) to conduct research on "the chemical identification of disease." Sir John Simon, the chief medical officer of the department was farsighted enough to obtain support for a group of such investigators.[8]

Thudichum's work on the chemical constitution of the brain began about 1869. Despite his evident interest in diseases generally[9] and those of the nervous system in particular,[10] he carefully refrained from attempting clinical or pathological correlations, asserting only about his findings "that all further developments in chemical neurology must start from them as a basis."[1(p. ix)] After five years of work and analyses on 1000 brains Thudichum made his first report,[11] but it was another ten years before he published his final results.[1] He can be credited with discovering in brain the cephalins, sphingomyelin, sphingosine, phrenosin (galactocerebroside), galactose ("cerebrose"), ethanolamine, glucose, inositol, lactic acid, cerebronic acid, sulfatides, phosphatidic acid, etc., and with the development of the first systematic classification of these products of analysis, including the group of "phosphorised principles," still called by his term, the phosphatides. Almost thirty years after Thudichum's death, Rosenheim discovered specimens of his preparations in the stable behind the family house at 11 Pembroke Gardens and reported on one of them: "Judged by modern standards this specimen of Thudichum's phrenosin is as pure as any prepared since. . . ."[12]

The excellence and accuracy of Thudichum's analyses can be attributed to his skill with the spectroscope (learned from Bunsen) and with the combustion train (his "most valued possession," a gift from Liebig); and to his insistence on the best reagents and equipment. He is reputed to have considered platinum vessels and retorts essential. His expenses for the first thirty months of research were £843 (about $4200), not including utilities supplied by St. Thomas' Hospital or the compounds he had synthesized himself. A further grant of £2000 (about $10,000) secured by Sir John Simon allowed completion of his studies.

Some influential contemporaries in England and abroad failed to appreciate Thudichum's work. Liebreich, a pupil of Hoppe-Seyler, had proposed in 1864 that the brain consisted almost entirely of a single substance, protagon, all others being decomposition products thereof.[13] Ten years later Thudichum showed that protagon was but a mixture of phosphatides and cerebrosides.[11] This angered Hoppe-Seyler (leading German biochemist and editor of the *Zeitschrift für physiologische Chemie*), who labelled Thudichum's results as "often patently false."[14] Richard Maly (leading Austrian chemist and editor of the *Jahresbericht*), evidently because Thudichum had disputed (correctly) about bile pigments with him, described Thudichum's work as "uncontrolled dilettantism" and "an epidemic plague for physiological chemistry."[15] Arthur Gamgee, another protagon proponent sneered at those "materials for a new formula" and "the excuse for a new name," with little or no gain to science.[16] "Throughout," wrote another critic, "impure smeary masses formed the basis for Thudichum's new substances. . . ."[15] Thudichum knew how to retort and had his supporters in Liebig, Virchow, Pflüger, and others. When upon Sir John Simon's retirement (in 1882) the Privy Council grant was terminated because of these criticisms, Thudichum had nearly completed his studies.

Thudichum died suddenly in 1901, cut off in midstream of a rich life. He had found time to write on wines[17] and on cookery,[18] keep dogs and horses (riding daily in Hyde Park), attend the West London Medical-Chirurgical Society (serving as president in 1883–84), and enjoy a concert of Beethoven quartets or a good cigar. He has left a legacy not only of analytical data but also of perspective.[1(p. xxi)]

"The brain is the most marvelous chemical laboratory of the animal economy; in it the albuminous, phosphorised, nitrogenised, oxygenated principles, which perform functions as acids, alcohols, alkaloids, or bases, or, as ethers, are brought into the most varied relations, for the production of power of the most refined nature. The inorganic ingredients are as varied and necessary as in any other part of the body and, in some portions of the brain at least, a selective faculty causes the potash-salts to prevail over the soda-salts, as they do in muscle. This brings about the same contrast between sodically alkaline blood and those parts of the brain, as exists between blood and muscle. The contrast is one which favours reaction."[10]

". . . I believe that the great diseases of the brain and spine . . . will all be shown to be connected with specific chemical changes in neuroplasm. . . . It is probable that by the aid of chemistry many derangements of the brain and mind, which are at present obscure, will become accurately definable and amenable to precise treatment, and what is now an object of anxious empiricism will become one for the proud exercise of exact science."[1] (p. 259-260)

BETHESDA, MARYLAND   DONALD B. TOWER

References and Notes

[1]A facsimile edition with introduction by D. L. Drabkin was issued in 1962 by Archon Books, Hamden, Conn.   [2]*Fiziologicheskaya khimiya go'ovnogo mozga* (transl. by Liona). Khar'kov, 1885.   [3]*Die chemische Konstitution des Gehirns des Menschen und der Tiere.* Tübingen, Pietzcker, 1901.   [4]Brit. Med. J., 1864, 2:509.   [5]*Rep. Med. Off. Privy Council* X (appendix 7), 1867, p. 227.   [6]*Ibid.,* XI (appendix 6), 1868, p. 184.   [7]Proc. Roy. Soc., London, 1868–69, 17:253 (communicated by J. Simon) .   [8]Letter from O. Rosenheim to D. L. Drabkin, quoted in reference to biography, p. 115.   [9]*Grundzüge der anatomischen und klinischen Chemie.* Berlin, Hirschwald, 1886, p. 24 (Thudichum).   [10]Brit. Med. J., 1883, 2:524.   [11]Rep. Med. Off. Privy Council, 1884, n.s. I (appendix 5):113–247.   [12]Chem. & Industry, Mar. 30, 1930 (Rosenheim).   [13]Ann. d. Chem. u. Pharm., 1865, 134:29.   [14]Virchows Jahrber. ü. d. Leistungen u. Fortschr. Ges. Med., 1868, 3(pt. 1):85.   [15]Jahrber., 1876, 5:203.   [16]Brit. & Foreign Med.-Chir. Rev., 1877, 60:1. The reference to Couërbe recalls the somewhat similar plight of J.-P. Couërbe, whose analyses of brain in 1834 were challenged before the French Académie des Sciences by Édmond

Frémy. Thudichum pointed out[3,11] that Couërbe was correct and Frémy wrong, but the controversy practically terminated Couërbe's promising career. (Cf. *Dictionnaire de biographie française*. Vol. 9. Paris Libr. Letonzey et Ané, 1961, p. 890.)   [17]*A treatise on the origin, nature and varieties of wine: being a complete manual of viticulture and oenology.* London, Macmillan, 1872 (with Dupré). (There was a second similar publication in 1894.)   [18]*The spirit of cookery.* London, Warne, 1895.

Reference to Biography and Works: Thudichum: Chemist of the brain. Philadelphia, U. of Pa., 1958 (Drabkin).

NICOLAS-LOUIS VAUQUELIN (1763–1829)

*T*HE impact of Vauquelin's report in 1811 on his *Analyse de la matière cérébrale de l'homme et de quelques animaux*[1] was prompt and widespread. The paper was reprinted in the leading French chemical journal[2] and translated within two years for the principal German[3] and English[4] scientific periodicals. Over several decades it was widely quoted and proved a major stimulus for subsequent investigations on cerebral lipids.

The author[5] was born at St. André d'Hébertot (near Pont l'Evêque, Calvados) in Normandy. His father was a farm laborer, the family large, their home a simple thatched cottage. Schooling was available through the generosity of the châtelain. When he was fourteen Vauquelin was apprenticed as "garçon de laboratoire" to a pharmacist in Rouen. His employer permitted him to attend the lectures on chemistry and pharmacy given to his paying pupils, but when he discovered Vauquelin recording the lectures, he destroyed the boy's notebooks and forbade his attendance. So Vauquelin journeyed to Paris, where after a severe illness with confinement in the Hôtel-Dieu, he was taken as a pupil by the pharmacist Chéradame in the rue St. Denis.

There he was treated like one of the family and spent two happy years learning Greek, Latin and the sciences. There also he met Chéradame's cousin, the illustrious chemist, Antoine François de Fourcroy, successor to Macquer and Lavoisier, leading revolu-

Portrait, courtesy of The Wellcome Trustees, London, England,

tionary, and councillor of state under Napoleon.[6] In 1785 Fourcroy invited Vauquelin to be his assistant at an annual salary of 300 livres (about $60). The two friends formed an excellent combination of talents resulting in over fifty joint publications. Vauquelin never married and for most of his career lodged with Fourcroy's two sisters. In his large laboratory Vauquelin taught many pupils and prepared chemicals for sale, the latter unprofitably.

Vauquelin scarcely participated in politics but was called upon to organize the supplying of saltpetre for the army's gunpowder. In 1795 he became Inspecteur des Mines, professor at the École des Mines, Maître en Pharmacie, even Membre de l'Institut.[7] The next year he was professor of chemistry at the École de Pharmacie, and at the Collège de France in 1801, but resigned three years later to become Professeur de Chimie appliquée aux Arts, at the Jardin des Plantes, with lodgings and laboratories at the Muséum d'Histoire naturelle. Even now one can walk down the beautiful long avenue of plane trees to the amphitheatre where Fourcroy and Vauquelin used to lecture. Vauquelin was also appointed Director of the École spéciale de Pharmacie and placed in charge of gold and silver assays at the Mint.

After Fourcroy's death in 1809, Vauquelin was the leading contender for the chair in chemistry at the Faculté de Médecine. The rules required that the incumbent hold a doctorate of medicine and be chosen by competitive examination. To conform, Vauquelin prepared a thesis dealing with the chemical composition of animal and human brains.[1] This earned him the doctorate of medicine as well as the chair (he was the only candidate). A decade later, many members of the Faculté, including Vauquelin, were dismissed for holding too liberal political views. Embittered, he retired to his boyhood home of St. André d'Hébertot, where he was provided with lodging at the local chateau. By then he was a member of the Académie de Médecine and the Royal Society (London), decorated with the orders of St. Michel, the Légion d'Honneur, and entitled Chevalier de l'Empire. He served in the Chambre des Députés for Calvados, but only briefly, for on 14 November 1829 he died at home after a short illness.

The turbulent times of the Revolution and First Empire were

an era when chemistry flourished in France. Vauquelin's intimate friends included not only Fourcroy but also Lavoisier, Berthollet, Guyton de Morveau, Haüy, Gay-Lussac, B. Pelletier, and Vicq d'Azyr, and he numbered among his many pupils Chevreul, Orfila, Robiquet and Thénard. The list should be supplemented with the many outstanding, contemporary English, Swedish and German scientists whose works were well known to and interwoven with those of the French group.

Vauquelin discovered chromium and beryllium, also allantoin and asparagine (the latter the first amino acid to be recognized), confirmed the existence of malic, quinic and other organic acids, investigated the cinchona and belladonna alkaloids and the comparative aspects of urea, uric acid and hippuric acid excretion. With Fourcroy he studied the respiration of invertebrates and confirmed Davy's observations on nitrous oxide.

Vauquelin's analyses ushered in the modern investigations of brain tissue composition. With the techniques available in 1811, he was able to report the following analysis for human brain [compared with present-day values given in brackets]:[1] water, about 80.00 per cent [77]; white fatty matter 4.53, red fatty matter 0.70 [total lipids 77.5];[8] albumin 7.00 [proteins 8.05]; phosphorus 1.50 [0.5]; osmazome,[9] salts (including phosphates of potash, lime and magnesia and some common salt), and sulfur 6.27 [3.45]. These data finally disposed of the longstanding opinions of brain substance as a kind of spermaceti or soap. More important, Vauquelin brought a realization of the presence of new and complex constituents exemplified by his description of a "matière grasse blanche." "While including it in the class of fatty substances, it must be considered a new a separate type. . ."; it "contains neither free phosphoric acid nor phosphate of ammonia, and . . . consequently the [phosphoric] acid which is developed by combustion has another origin."[1] According to Thudichum,[10] the "matière grasse blanche" of Vauquelin corresponded to the substances later described as *stéarine cérébrale* by Berzelius, as *myelokon* by Kuhn, as *cérébrote* by Couërbe: a mixture of educts containing phosphatides, cerebrosides, etc. "Vauquelin's data," Thudichum concludes, "are perfectly correct as far as they go; they furnished an excellent basis upon which the more perfect methods of later times might have built a complete analysis of brain matter. But the later analysts were all deficient in that appreciation of the totality of the subject which alone gives power for exhaustive research. With the one remarkable exception of Couërbe they were all men of detail, fishing for some chemical object of passing interest, and neglecting their predecessors as well as the physiological philosophy of the important organ upon which they undertook to operate." What a wonderful indictment of mediocrity and what a wonderful compliment to the genius of Vauquelin which most of his successors found so difficult to emulate.

BETHESDA, MARYLAND   DONALD B. TOWER

References and Notes

[1]Ann. Muséum d'Histoire naturelle, 1811, *18*:212–239.   [2]Ann. de Chimie, sér.1, 1812, *81*:37.   [3]Schweiggers Jour. f. Chem. u. Phys., 1813, *8*:430–460.   [4]Ann. Philos., 183, *1*:332.   [5]Vauquelin's given names are often cited as Louis-Nicolas; however, the birth record and contemporary works clearly show that Nicolas-Louis is the correct version.   [6]*Fourcroy, chemist and revolutionary, 1755–1809.* Cambridge, Heffer, 1962 (Smeaton).   [7]Successor to the Académie royale des Sciences (suppressed at the outbreak of the Revolution) and forerunner of the present Académie des Sciences de l'Institut de France. [8]Vauquelin was limited to alcohol extractions, so that he missed about half of the total lipids (extractable only with ether or other solvents which became available later).   [9]The name given by Thénard to an aqueous extract of tissues similar to a meat extract.   [10]In *Reports of the Medical Officer of the Privy Council and Local Government Board,* n.s., no. 1, appendix 5, London, Eyre & Spottiswoode, 1874, p. 212–215 (Thudichum).

References to Biography and Works: 1) J. de Chimie méd., 1850, sér.3, *6*:542–549 (Chevallier).   2) Rev. d'Hist. de la Pharmacie, 1963, *51*(no. 176):89–96 (Valette).   3) *Ibid.,* 1963, *51* (no. 176):78–88 (Delépine).   4) *Ibid.,* 1963, *51* (no. 176):17–25 (Bouvet).   5) Mém. Acad. Paris, 1833, sér.2, *12*:39–46 (Cuvier).   6) *A history of chemistry.* Vol. 2. London, Macmillan, 1962, p. 551–557 (Partington).

HANS WINTERSTEIN (1879–1963)

*A*T THE beginning of the twentieth century the emphasis in neurochemical investigations began to shift from the analytical approaches of Thudichum to the physiological approaches exemplified by the work of Hans Winterstein. The shift took place against a background of increasing knowledge of metabolism—the "Stoffwechsel" of Liebig—in terms of the recognition of enzymes, the elucidation of tissue respiration and the respiratory pigments, and the correlations between muscular contraction, lactic acid production, and oxygen requirements. Contributions were made by so many that it is difficult to single out individuals. Yet Winterstein's work on the mechanisms of narcosis, the chemical regulation of respiration, and especially on the metabolism of the nervous system was bridging the gap between the Thudichum era preoccupied with brain composition, and the more recent dynamic approaches to neurochemical mechanisms underlying normal and deranged cerebral functions.

Hans Winterstein was born in Prague, the son of well-to-do parents, in the old quarter of the city. He did well at the German classical Gymnasium despite an expressed aversion to its educational methods. From 1897 to 1903 he studied medicine at the universities of Prague and Jena, but was especially influenced, in Göttingen, by the ideas and infectious enthusiasm of the physiologist, Max Verworn, whose assistant he became after graduation in Prague in 1903. By this time he had already published four experimental studies on such problems as the action of CO_2 on the nervous system[1] and on the mechanism of narcosis.[2]

After three years Winterstein left for Rostock where he received his "Habilitation" under the physiologist, Oskar Langendorff. At the age of thirty-one, he was a very young full professor of physiology and Director of the Physiological Institute at Rostock, a small but stimulating Hanseatic city on the Baltic. In the modest "Eckhaus" of Rostock, as he brings out in later reminiscences,[3] one could find at that time the pharmacologist, Paul Trendelenburg, at work on the ground floor, the Physiological Institute with Win-

terstein on the first floor, and on the top floor the anatomist, Curt Elze.

During his tenure at Rostock and the numerous sojourns at the Naples zoological station, he added investigations on fatigue, muscle tetany, the respiration and blood gases of marine animals, and the heart. With regard to narcosis, he rejected the lipoid theory in

Portrait, courtesy of Universitätsdruckerei H. Stürtz AG, Würzburg, Germany.

favor of membrane blockade due to adsorption of the narcotic to cell membrane structures.[4] Winterstein quickly became recognized as an outstanding expert in the field of respiratory physiology and as the proponent of the "reaction theory" of regulation of respiration. In this theory the basic effect was attributable to H^+ ions derived from carbonic or other acids of metabolism. With subsequent modifications[5] this is still a major component of the current set of theories.[6] He was a prodigious worker, planning, editing and writing many of the pages of the 8-volume *Handbuch der vergleichenden Physiologie* (Jena, Fischer, 1910–1925), and translating with Baglioni into German the four-volume work by Luciani, *Physiologie des Menschen* (Jena, Fischer, 1905–1911), all in the same period.

In 1927 Winterstein left Rostock to accept the chair of Purkyně and Heidenhain at Breslau. There he had the misfortune, while conducting examinations, to find unqualified a young man who was district leader for the Nazi party in Silesia. The student threatened, to his face, that "when we got to the top, Winterstein will be kicked out in three hours." Not quite, but forbidden to lecture in 1933, he was altogether dismissed in 1934. Invited to be guest professor before, he now accepted the chair of physiology at the University of Istanbul where he remained until 1953. The move to Turkey separated him from his two sons studying and remaining in England, and eventually also from his wife, who joined them and divorced him in 1938. Two years later he was happily remarried.

At the age of seventy-seven, Hans Winterstein returned to Germany as guest professor in the Physiological Institute of the University of Munich, where he again collected a circle of students, resumed work in the laboratory, his literary output, and his visits to the mountains, often taxing the endurance of much younger companions. At age eighty a first heart attack put an end to his activities, and he eventually succumbed at eighty-five.

At the time of his death in 1963, Hans Winterstein was the dean of German physiologists and probably the last representative of the "classical" period of German physiology. He left over 200 publications, many distinguished pupils, and had received many honors: he was an Honorary M.D. at Heidelberg, Cologne, and

Munich; member of the Deutsche Akademie der Naturforscher (Leopoldina), at forty-three, five years later corresponding member of the Reale Accademia di Roma, honorary member of the Naturforschende Gesellschaft in Rostock, and honorary member of the Deutsche Physiologische Gesellschaft; in 1955 he received through the Federal German embassy in Turkey the grand cross for distinguished service. From Russia to the U.S.A. he was much sought after as a lecturer; at the age of seventy-six he delivered the Dunham lectures at Harvard.

There was much speculation at the turn of the century about a single mechanism being essential to all life phenomena. Because of its vital requirement by higher animals, oxygen played a vague but central role in most such theories. Winterstein investigated systematically the tolerance of living organisms and surviving organs to oxygen lack, and the effects of varying activity (elevated temperature, strychnine or tetanic stimulation versus narcosis, lowered temperature or fatigue). He insisted that not only tolerance to oxygen lack but also the oxygen requirements of these processes needed to be determined. As early as 1907 he had begun such measurements on his frog spinal cord-nerve-muscle preparation,[7] when methods became available to permit measurements of such small amounts of aerobic respiration.[8]

From these first determinations on respiration Winterstein went on to a systematic investigation of the metabolism of the central nervous system[9,10] and the peripheral nerves.[11] Abundant data resulted on the transformations of sugars,[12] nitrogenous substances,[13] and lipids.[14] He described his methods[15] and results,[16] culminating in the comprehensive review of 1929 in the *Handbuch der normalen und pathologischen Physiologie*.[16] This review represents a landmark in the development of neurochemistry as the first complete and authoritative coverage of brain metabolism, much of it Winterstein's own work, and the prologue to the modern upsurge to come twenty years later. With so much still unknown and techniques so relatively crude in his day, Hans Winterstein surely was one of the giants among the pioneers in the field of modern physiology and metabolism.

BETHESDA, MARYLAND   DONALD B. TOWER

References

[1]Arch. Anat. Physiol., Lpz., 1900, p. 177 (Winterstein's first scientific paper).   [2]Zschr. allg. Physiol., 1901, *1*:19.   [3]Hippokrates, Stuttg., 1962, *33*:79.   [4]*Die Narkose in ihrer Bedeutung für allgemeine Physiologie.* Berlin, Springer, 1919. (2nd ed., 1926.)   [5]Ergeb. Physiol., 1955, *48*:329–528.   [6]Mountcastle (ed.), *Medical physiology.* St. Louis, Mosby, 1968, 12th ed., vol. 1, p. 731–757 (Lambertson).   [7]Zbl. Physiol., Wien, 1908, *21*:869.   [8]Biochem. Zschr., 1912, *46*:440.   [9]Sitzber. Abh. naturforsch. Ges. Rostock, n.F., 1940, *6*.   [10]Biochem. Zschr., 1914, *61*:81.   [11]Zschr. physiol. Chem., 1919, *108*:21 (with Hirschberg).   [12]*Ibid.*, 1917, *100*:185 (with Hirschberg).   [13]*Ibid.*, 1918, *101*:212 (with Hirschberg).   [14]*Ibid.*, 1919, *105*:1 (with Hirschberg).   [15]Abderhalden (ed.), *Hdb. d. biol. Arbeitsmethoden.* Berlin, Urban u. Schwarzenberg, 1925, sect. V, pt. 5B, p. 427–462. (Republished in 1938.)   [16]Bethe *et al.* (eds.), *Hdb. d. norm. u. path. Physiologie.* Berlin, Springer, 1929, vol. 9, p. 365–412, 515–611.

References to Biography and Works: 1) Ergeb. Physiol., 1964, *55*:1–27 (Weber and Loeschke).   2) Hippokrates, Stuttg., 1962, *33*:79–83 (Winterstein).

V

NEUROPATHOLOGISTS

ALOIS ALZHEIMER (1864–1915)

*A*LZHEIMER will always be remembered for having demonstrated the unequivocal changes that occur in the brain in certain organic mental diseases. The leading psychiatrists of the late nineteenth century seriously doubted the value of histological study in such diseases, as psychological investigation of the "centers of thinking" dominated all else. Emil Kraepelin (1856–1926), "the Linnaeus of Psychiatry," was an exception, for in planning the institutes of psychiatry of which he was to be the Director, he provided unparalleled facilities for the study of pathological anatomy. To pursue this aspect he appointed the most promising men of the day, among them Alzheimer.

Kraepelin's conversion to patho-anatomical research occurred rather late in his career, after the turn of the century. Before that it was different. Oskar Vogt relates that he visited Kraepelin at Heidelberg in 1894, bringing him greetings from Forel. Kraepelin asked what he planned to do in the future. "Brain anatomy of the psychoses," replied Vogt. "Then I must give you a bad prognosis," said Kraepelin, "for anatomy can contribute nothing to psychiatry." Kraepelin had in mind certain studies which had contributed nothing to the understanding of psychic behavior: those by Forel on the subthalamic region in man and the experiments carried out by his teacher, von Gudden, on rabbits. In 1905 it was Kraepelin's turn to visit Oskar Vogt in Berlin. He had read Vogt's and Brodmann's papers on cortical cytoarchitectonics and now carefully studied the preparations. As a consequence, he became convinced of the importance of investigation of the brain in the psychoses. Nissl had all along been enthusiastic, but not Alzheimer, who felt that such studies had their limitations.

The characteristic of Alzheimer's work was to combine the clinical and pathological approach to brain disease. Having been a clinician before embarking on pathology, he saw with clarity the determining factors responsible for the clinical ensemble. Patiently, he observed the most characteristic cases of each disease group,

waiting sometimes for years before reporting his combined clinical and pathological findings. Thus emerged his classical descriptions of general paresis, arteriosclerosis, senility, and acute delirium.

Alzheimer established his reputation with a standard work on

Portrait, courtesy of Dr. F. H. Lewey, Philadephia, Pennsylvania.

the histopathology of general paresis, typical and atypical.[1] In arteriosclerosis he stressed the frequency of intracortical changes, which were inconspicuous, and he made the astute observation that arteriosclerotic and senile processes are unrelated. Finally, he described the pathological changes underlying senile dementia and its variants, among which he classified that form which Kraepelin called "Alzheimer's disease."[2] In other conditions, reactive changes in glia in the cortex in the absence of other pathological alterations were to him a particularly sensitive indicator of a disease process. His term, "Amöboidose," signifying disintegration of astrocytes, was later called "clasmatodendrosis" by Cajal.

The twenty seats in his laboratory in Munich were always filled by students from all over the world. None of them could forget the many hours which Alzheimer spent with each individually, his large head bent over the microscope, his pince-nez dangling on a long string. The indispensable cigar he forgot as soon as he sat down, only to light another as he moved to the next student; by the end of the day some twenty big stumps were found around the laboratory. He had little to beckon him home on time, as his wife had died.

Alzheimer was born in Marktbreit-am-Main (a small town in Bavaria), the son of a notary. He went to school in Aschaffenburg, and attended the medical schools of the Universities of Berlin, Würzburg and Tübingen from 1882 to 1887. He considered himself a pupil of von Kölliker, under whom he had worked as a young student in Würzburg. The atmosphere of this city he found congenial; he was no ascetic during his student days. Following an internship, he took a position at the Städtische Irrenanstalt in Frankfurt-am-Main (1888), where Nissl joined him one year later. Here began the close cooperation which lasted a lifetime. It was so perfect a companionship that it is impossible to decide which of the two owed more to the other. Nissl obtained his perspective from the laboratory bench, sitting there theorizing; Alzheimer's came from the clinic. Having known both of them, I would guess that the flood of startling ideas was Nissl's, but that it was Alzheimer who demonstrated their correctness histologically. Alzheimer had such a gift for describing what both had seen under the microscope, that the importance of their findings became immediately evident.

When Alzheimer's application for the position of director of a state institution had been turned down, Kraepelin, who had called Nissl to Heidelberg by 1895, added Alzheimer as well to his staff in 1902. In 1903 Alzheimer followed Kraepelin to Munich, where he worked in the Anatomisches Laboratorium der Psychiatrischen und Nervenklinik. Alzheimer habilitated himself as Privatdozent in 1904 and became Extraordinarius in 1908. These years—from 1903 to 1908—were Alzheimer's finest.

In Heidelberg, Alzheimer was also a close friend of Wilhelm Erb. The story goes that Erb, an authority on syphilis, was consulted by a banker who had contracted the disease. At the termination of the treatment (such as it was), the banker, to demonstrate his gratitude, offered to finance a scientific expedition to North Africa, provided that he and his wife could go along. Erb saw no contraindication. The expedition had hardly gotten underway when Erb received a frantic telegram from Algeria that the banker had had another mental breakdown. Erb prevailed upon Alzheimer to go to Algeria and bring home the banker and his party. The banker died, and Alzheimer married the widow.

In 1912 Alzheimer was appointed to the chair of psychiatry at the University of Breslau. He fell ill from a heart condition while on the train to Breslau. On arrival he was taken to a hospital and had to remain there for a time before taking on his responsibilities at the University. Onset of World War I left him without assistants. Years of strenuous work, day and night, and never a vacation, had sapped so much of his strength that little resistance was left, they say, when his rheumatic endocarditis recurred. He died at the age of fifty-two.

F. H. LEWEY

References

[1] *Histologische und histopathologische Arbeiten über die Grosshirnrinde* (Nissl-Alzheimer), Jena, 1904, *1*:315–494.   [2] Zschr. ges. Neur. Psychiat., 1911, *4*:356–385.

References to Biography and Works: 1) Kirchhoff (ed.), *Deutsche Irrenärzte*. Vol. 2. Berlin 1924, p. 299–307 (Kraepelin).   2) Münch.

med. Wschr., 1920, *67*:75–78 (Kraepelin).   3) Allg. Zschr. Psychiat.,
1949, *125*:63–76 (Scholz).   4) *A short history of psychiatric achievement. With a forecast for the future.* New York, Norton, 1941 (Lewis).
5) Kolle (Ed.): *Grosse Nervenärzte.* Vol. 2. Stuttgart, Thieme, 1959,
32–38 (Meyer).

MAX BIELSCHOWSKY (1869–1940)

*B*IELSCHOWSKY was born in Breslau, the son of a merchant. He received his medical education at the Universities of Breslau, Berlin and Munich, and the M.D. was conferred
on him at Munich in 1893. Three years later, at the invitation of
Ludwig Edinger, he joined the staff of the Senckenberg Pathologisches Institut at Frankfurt-am-Main. Here Weigert influenced
him the most. It was not until after he had gone to Berlin in 1896
to head Kurt Mendel's laboratory that he began to contribute to
neurological literature. In that year his first work with Paul Schuster on the histopathology of disseminated sclerosis appeared (additional publications in 1903, 1927 and 1932), and it was at about
this time that he commenced his fundamental studies on the silver
impregnation of nerve fibers, published in 1902[1] and 1903,[2] modified in 1908, and applied in intravital staining with Stanley Cobb
in 1924. His monograph on myelitis and inflammation of the optic
nerves was published in 1901,[3] and in the same year appeared his
initial study on brain tumors, which he continued in collaboration
with Ernst Unger, Henneberg, Simons, and Bruno Valentin.

A new period in his scientific work began when in 1904 he
joined Oskar Vogt at the Neurobiologisches Universitäts-Laboratorium in Berlin. Many publications in the *Journal für Psychologie und Neurologie* resulted from the stimulating partner-
ship with both the director and Cécile Vogt. After the Institute
had been moved to new quarters at Berlin-Buch (1931), Bielschowsky's work as Abteilungsleiter of the Institute continued un-
abated, but unfortunately his friendship with Vogt became
strained.

In the old laboratory originated the studies on the cytoarchitecture of the cerebral cortex and the striate body, in which he partic-

ipated with K. Brodmann (1901–10) and M. Rose (1921–25). Here, too, he worked on amaurotic family idiocy, describing a late infantile type,[4] and on tuberous sclerosis and its relation to von Recklinghausen's disease and gliosis. In his study on regeneration of fibers within the central nervous system (1909), he supported the idea then prevalent that such regeneration is possible. His important paper in 1918[5] on the occurrence of hemiplegia in two cases of encephalitis in which the pyramidal tracts were preserved, foreshadowed the discovery by Fulton and his associates[6] and Tower[7] that damage of transcortical association fibers and extrapyramidal cortical projections may cause many of the phenomena of spasticity. Following World War I, Bielschowsky studied the

Portrait, courtesy of Dr. Robert Wartenberg, San Francisco, California.

problem of trauma and surgery of peripheral nerves in association with Unger and Valentin.

During the years 1926–33 he published only four major papers: on von Recklinghausen's disease (1927, with M. Rose), on myotonia congenita (1929), on cerebellar progressive paralysis (1933, with R. Hirschfeld),[8] and on dystrophia myotonica (1933, with Maas and Ostertag). This period was the harvest time when from his wide knowledge he prepared contributions to standard textbooks on neurology. Major chapters to handbooks also appeared: general histology and histopathology of the central nervous system, in Lewandowsky's *Handbuch* in 1910 and herpes zoster in 1941; the status of the neuron theory, in von Möllendorff's *Handbuch* in 1928;[9] the histopathology of nerve cells and neuroblastic tumors of the sympathetic nervous system, in Penfield's three volumes;[10] and the general histology and histopathology of the nervous system, in Bumke and Foerster's *Handbuch* in 1935.[11] In these contributions his true nature as a scientist, astute observer, diligent worker, and excellent teacher was revealed, though he never was an aggressive fighter for new ideas. There is, strangely enough, little evidence in the literature that Bielschowsky was a clinician, though he conducted his own clinic in Berlin and was known to his colleagues as an excellent diagnostician.

Bielschowsky's most creative years (1900–25) were coincident with the zenith of European neurology and scientific life in general and its early decline after World War I. During the last decade of his life he was drawn into the whirlpool which destroyed all. In 1933 he lost his position at Berlin-Buch. An opening was soon created for him, however, in the Laboratorium of the Wilhelmina Gasthuis in Amsterdam. Here he found life a little grim. He moved in 1934 to Utrecht where, supported by a grant from the Rockefeller Foundation, he worked in the laboratory of the psychiatric clinic of the University. Here, Leendert Bouman was his staunch supporter.

In 1935 he spent some time at the Cajal Institute in Madrid. A year later he returned to Berlin under the threat that otherwise his old age pension would be withdrawn. In June of that year he suffered a stroke which put him to bed for three months. Shortly before the outbreak of World War II he and his family went to

London. For a time he worked in the Laboratory of Prof. Green of Sheffield. In August, 1940, Bielschowsky was the victim of another stroke. He died three days later. The urn containing his ashes was placed next to that of his friend Paul Schuster, in the chapel at Golders Green, as had been his wish.

ARTHUR WEIL

References

[1] Neur. Cbl., 1902, 21:579–584.   [2] Ibid., 1903, 22:997–1006.   [3] Myelitis und Sehnerventzündung. Berlin, Karger, 1901.   [4] J. Psychol. Neur., Lpz., 1920, 26:123–199.   [5] Ibid., 1918, 22:225–266.   [6] Brain, London, 1932, 55:524–536 (with Jacobsen and Kennard).   [7] Ibid., 1940, 63:36–90.   [8] J. Psychol. Neur., Lpz., 1933, 45:185–213. [9] von Möllendorff, W., Handbuch der mikroskopischen Anatomie des Menschen. Berlin, 1928, 4:1–201.   [10] Penfield (ed.), Cytology and cellular pathology of the nervous system. 3 vol. New York, Hoeber, 1932, 1:146–188; 3:1085–1094.   [11] Bumke, O., and Foerster, O., Handbuch der Neurologie. Berlin, 1935, 1:35–226.

References to Biography: 1) Bull. Acad. Med. Roum., 1937, 3:373–244 (Lewy).   2) Kolle (Ed.), Grosse Nervenärzte. Vol. 3. Stuttgart, Thieme, 1963, p. 3–8 (Ostertag).

JEAN CRUVEILHIER (1791–1874)

*I*N THE ancient Roman city of Limoges, France, Anno Domini 1791, there was born into the family of an army surgeon, a son who was destined to rise to fame, not only in his native country but also in the entire medical world. Inheriting a serious turn of mind from his mother, he decided while a student at the College of Limoges to enter the priesthood. But his mother's devotion was as practical as it was sincere, and she sent him off to Paris to study medicine, armed with letters to the famous Dupuytren. By the time Cruveilhier had passed the competitive examinations for interne in the hospitals of Paris (1811), Napoleon had already launched France on its imperial program. So the youthful

surgeon had the opportunity to serve his master Dupuytren in both the civil and military hospitals of Paris and its environs.

Meanwhile the interest of Cruveilhier had become directed to morbid anatomy, a new medical discipline, which gave promise of providing a solid foundation for medicine as a science. In 1816, when but a young man, he published his *Essai sur l'anatomie pathologique* (Paris; privately printed), a treatise based on his work as an interne under Dupuytren. But in spite of this introduction he purposed in his heart to practice medicine. He returned to Limoges, married, and settled down to the prosaic life of a small town doctor. Stung by his failure to secure an appointment as surgeon to the city hospital and stimulated by his father's overwhelming ambition for him, he returned to Paris, where he won a competitive examination for a professorship on the Faculté de Médecine. In the meantime, Dupuytren had secured for him an appointment to the chair of operative surgery at Montpellier, which he accepted; but the yearning for the haunts of his native city were stronger than the inducements of a scholastic career, so he returned again to Limoges and tried to establish himself in practice. Then the chair of anatomy at the University of Paris was suddenly vacated by the resignation of Béclard, and once again he returned to Paris to accept this appointment. His growing popularity enabled him to re-establish the Anatomical Society of Paris, a society organized in 1803 by Dupuytren and discontinued in 1808 while under the leadership of Laennec. Cruveilhier was to remain its president for over forty years.

His great opportunity came when he was made first appointee (at Dupuytren's request) to the professorship of pathology of the Faculté de Médecine, provision for which had been made in the will of Dupuytren, only recently deceased. The vast amount of material from the deadhouse of the Salpêtrière, the establishment of the Musée Dupuytren, and the lectureship in morbid anatomy, furnished both necessary material and incentive, and Cruveilhier continued to publish his folios of colored lithographs of his *Anatomie pathologique du corps humain* (Paris, Baillière, 1829–42), which was dedicated to the memory of Dupuytren. He escaped the siege of Paris by moving to his country estate at Succac, near his native city of Limoges, where he died at the age of eighty-three.

Cruveilhier's achievements were the result of inherent artistic and intellectual talents, his indefatigable industry, the inspiration of a deep and sincere humanitarianism, the friendship of noble minds, and the opportunities of a new science, coupled with a flood of pathologic material. His contributions to the science of neurology lay chiefly in the realm of the neoplasias. He is credited with the first description of an intracranial epidermoid (which he designated in 1829 as a *tumeur perlée*), and the portrayal of several anatomic types of meningioma (1856). His famed atlas also included many notable examples of infectious, vascular and degenerative lesions of the nervous system; here also can be found his classical description of disseminated sclerosis—the first on record (1835). Cruveilhier may, therefore, be considered as one in the long ancestry of the modern science of neuropathology.

CYRIL B. COURVILLE

References

References to Biography: 1) Biogr. méd., Paris, 1934, *8*:293–308 (Genty.)   2) Presse méd., 1926, *34*:1643–1644 (Roussy).   3) Med. Rec., N.Y., 1929, *130*:42–45 (not signed).   4) Arch gén. méd., 1874, *23*:594–599 (Lasègue).   5) Prog. méd., Paris, 1927, *42*:357–364 (Ménétrier).

CONSTANTIN von ECONOMO (1876–1931)

CONSTANTIN BARON ECONOMO von SAN SERFF was born of wealthy aristocratic Greek parentage in Braila (Romania) and was brought up in Austrian Trieste, where his family became established the year after his birth. At the age of fourteen he happened to read Lombroso's famous work, *Genius and insanity* (1864), which impressed him so deeply that he decided to study medicine. However, in 1893, after obtaining from the Trieste Gymnasium the certificate of maturity with highest honors, he had no other recourse than to follow the wish of his father that he study engineering. After two years in Vienna, which he later considered by no means wasted, he finally obtained his father's consent to study medicine. He became a student demonstrator at the Histological Institute of von Ebner in Vienna and during this time completed a paper on the avian hypophysis. Before obtaining his doctor's degree in 1901, he also worked as assistant in the Physiological Institute of Exner.

After graduation, Economo spent one year in medicine at the University Klinik under Nothnagel. He then went to Paris for

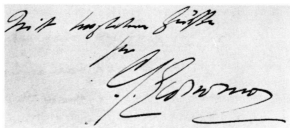

a year, where he worked in psychiatry under Magnan and in neurology under Pierre Marie. Following this he visited Bethe in
Strassburg, and Kraepelin in Munich, and published a paper on
the normal anatomy of nerve cells. In 1906 he returned to Vienna
as assistant at the psychiatric clinic of Wagner von Jauregg. Here
he was an enthusiastic aeronaut, becoming a balloon pilot and, in
1908, one of the first Austrian airplane pilots. He organized inter-

Portrait, courtesy of Prof. Dr. Hugo Spatz, Giessen, Germany.

national air meetings, promoted the building of the Vienna airports, and became president of the Austrain Aeroclub. During World War I he served for a time as pilot on the South Tyrol front.

His early neurological investigations, partly in collaboration with Karplus and Redlich, were concerned with physiology and anatomy of the midbrain.[1] He then worked on pons tumors and trigeminal pathways.[2] In 1916, during World War I and after being ordered back from his aviation activities to medical duties, he studied and treated brain injuries in the clinic of Wagner von Jauregg. In 1917 he began his outstanding studies on encephalitis lethargica,[3,4] which established his fame far beyond neurological circles. He did impressive work also on Wilson's disease[5] and on the nature of sleep.[6]

In 1920 he married a daughter of the Austrian general, Prince Alois von Schönburg-Hartenstein. About this time, assisted by Koskinas, of Athens, Greece, he turned his attention to studies on cortical architecture which he had begun in 1912, and in 1925 published his great text and atlas on the cytoarchitecture of the adult human cerebral cortex.[7] In 1928, on the retirement of Wagner von Jauregg, he was urged both by his chief and the Austrian government to assume the directorship of the psychiatric clinic and to take over the chair of psychiatry. He declined because he preferred to pursue his research work unhampered by administrative duties. In 1931 he became director of the newly organized brain research institute in connection with the psychiatric clinic. During his last years, he continued his cytoarchitectural studies and, in addition, published a monograph on encephalitis lethargica and its sequelae.[8] He was also much concerned with the problem of future human brain evolution, and postulated a general principle of "progressive cerebration."

Economo was a gentleman of independent means and a wide range of interests. He travelled extensively, and was very active in international scientific organizations. Shortly after his attendance at the First International Neurological Congress in Bern in 1931, he died suddenly of cardiac disease. He was one of the most brilliant and colorful of the Austrian neurologists.

PHILADELPHIA, PENNSYLVANIA   HARTWIG KUHLENBECK

References

[1] Arch. Psychiat., Berlin, 1909, *46*:377–429 (with Karplus).   [2] Jahrb. Psychiat. Neur., Wien, 1911, *32*:107–138.   [3] Wien. klin. Wschr., 1917, *30*:581–585.   [4] Neur. Cbl., 1917, *36*:866–868.   [5] Zschr. ges. Neur. Psychiat., 1918, *43*:173–209.   [6] J. Nerv. Ment. Dis., 1930, 71:249–259.   [7] *Die Cytoarchitektonik der Hirnrinde des erwachsenen Menschen*. Wien u. Berlin, Springer, 1925 (with Koskinas). [8] *Die Encephalitis lethargica, ihre Nachkrankheiten und ihre Behandlung*. Wien u. Berlin, Urban & Schwarzenberg, 1929.

References to Biography: 1) *Constantin Freiherr von Economo. Sein Leben und Wirken*. Wien, Mayer & Co., 1934 (contains bibliography; Freifrau von Economo and J. von Wagner-Jauregg). (Engl. trans. by Spillman: *Baron Constantin von Economo. His life and work*. Burlington, Free Press, 1937.)   2) Deut. Zschr. Nervenk., 1932, *123*:219–229 (Marburg).

GODWIN GREENFIELD (1884–1958)

*T*HE emergence of a great neuropathologist in twentieth century England comes as no surprise when one remembers the simple but seminal contributions—mainly to the anatomy of stroke —by Baillie, Abercrombie, and Carswell one hundred years earlier. British neuropathology, important in its beginnings, was overshadowed by the work done in France and Germany in the second half of the nineteenth century. By virtue of the same seminal simplicity, Greenfield revived a tradition. A son of a Professor of Pathology and Clinical Medicine in Edinburgh and a graduate from that school, growing up and rising to fame among the towering clinicians of the National Hospital, Queen Square, in London, Joseph Godwin Greenfield, the "backroom boy" behind the microscope, became their equal in stature.

As house physician at Edinburgh Royal Infirmary to Sir Byrom Bramwell and Alexander Bruce, he had to assemble, for the Wednesday clinical demonstrations, patients many of whom suffered from neurological disease; at the East London Hospital for Children he gained experience in the acute specific fevers with

Joseph Godwin Greenfield

which he was later to enrich neuropathology; and in 1910 he found his way to Queen Square.

After eighteen months there as house physician, however, his career took a new turn when he left to work with Matthew Stewart at Leeds, who was winning a reputation as the most distinguished morbid anatomist in the country. To earn a living in Leeds Greenfield obtained an assistantship in general practice. Meanwhile at Queen Square, Kinnier Wilson had decided not to reapply for the post of pathologist, hitherto held by one of the clinical neurologists in training. Thus the position fell to Greenfield in 1914 and remained his for the next thirty-five years. His original laboratory, adapted from the operating theatre where Sir Victor Horsley had carried out the first successful removal of a spinal cord tumour in 1887, hence large and with a high ceiling, was

Portrait, courtesy of Dr. Webb Haymaker, Moffett Field, California.

meagerly equipped and approached by a corridor lined with dusty pipes. To the ever-increasing stream of visitors, however, Greenfield's own room—small, dim, and with grimy windows—was brightly lit by his enthusiasm. Hardly any British neurologist of repute has failed to spend some of his training there.

When the new Queen Square hospital was being built in the thirties, rumor had it that Greenfield, not only an athletic golfer and tennis player but also a keen and accomplished carpenter, could be seen wielding a saw high up amongst the scaffolding. The story is typical for the man whose enjoyment in the use of his hands resulted in a widely accepted routine for histological investigation of the nervous system. For many years he had a single technician: Anderson, formerly a Yorkshire miner, later the author of that invaluable text with the startlingly direct title *How to stain the nervous system*. There is little doubt about Greenfield's major role in the book's modestly camouflaged joint authorship.

Greenfield's first visit in 1934 to the U.S.A. and Canada added to his international reputation. As the Dean at Queen Square, he represented the National Hospital at the opening of the Montreal Neurological Institute. Throughout the twenties and well into the thirties he was a wise friend to large numbers of American and Commonwealth graduates attracted to that neurological center. As he appeared humble rather than dramatic, his lectures were a little hesitant and, especially for the uninitiated, sometimes uninspiring and difficult to follow. He always sought the clinical relevance of his pathological findings, and his colleagues not infrequently invited him into the wards for his comments. A medical neuropathologist above all, he found little interest in placing cerebral tumours in their man-made pigeon holes and welcomed the integrative effect of the Kernohan grading system, which he defended hotly. Like Sir Charles Bell, he never carried out experimental work; this is why he decided not to apply for the chair of pathology at Guy's Hospital, where this would have been expected of him. Yet he always encouraged his pupils to perform any experiments that would throw light on human disease.

In 1925 he published a book on the cerebrospinal fluid with E. A. Carmichael,[1] a reminder that Greenfield was responsible for all the pathological services at his hospital; indeed during World War

II he organized the clinical pathology and carried out himself the Wasserman reactions at a large general hospital. Of his other books the first and the last were texts of neuropathology—the first, comparatively simple in 1921, with Sir Farquhar Buzzard[2]; the last in 1958, with Blackwood, McMenemey, Meyer and Norman,[3] to enshrine most of the new knowledge which he had seen acquired during his long professional life. That book he never saw in its final stage; his wife, Florence, prepared the index. She also saw through a second edition (1963) to which Dorothy Russell, their close friend, became the fifth contributor. It bore the title *Greenfield's Neuropathology* (Baltimore, Williams & Wilkins), a just tribute to the man. By unanimous wish of the other contributors, Ronald Melville Norman (1904–1968),[4] a modest, witty, forthright and distinguished man in Bristol, was editor-in-chief.

Greenfield's contributions were spread evenly over an enormous range of topics. He was particularly interested in encephalitis and did much to introduce order into a very confused subject.[5-9] He performed a similar service by clarifying the tangled classification of the spinocerebellar degenerations.[10] In 1938 he delivered the Oliver Sharpey Lecture to the Royal College of Physicians on the *Pathology of the neurone;* eleven years later, the Hughlings Jackson Lecture at the Royal Society of Medicine on encephalitis. In 1952 at the First International Congress of Neuropathology in Rome he brought order into another chaotic pathological state— diffuse sclerosis. As President of the Second International Congress of Neuropathology held in London in 1955, his opening address was on the pathology of involuntary movements, but the emphasis was on James Parkinson, the social protestor.

Greenfield worked in a period which saw the elaboration of numerous staining techniques to isolate and identify disease processes up to then grouped together, but there was only the most shadowy indication of their biochemical basis. As this and the quantitative assessment of morphological change had barely commenced by the end of his career, his many contributions were made without them. Among his descriptions of disease states none showed better his skillful use of staining techniques than late infantile metachromatic leucodystrophy,[11-13] rightly called Greenfield's disease.

One of the authors (A.L.W.), visiting Greenfield in late 1948 to inquire as to the possibility of training in neuropathology, remembers proceeding along the splendid wooden cabinets in the department Greenfield had designed, and facing a man of unusual distinction: his height—at that time the consultant staff at Queen Square were all over six feet tall—his snowy white hair, and above all, his manner. There was none of that cross examination as to past achievements; he simply assumed you had his own integrity and devotion until proved otherwise.

His even temperament allowed Greenfield to work with his door open; no student who knocked and walked in was turned away. He was very sensitive to the aesthetics of his brain sections; to a well-stained cell with unusually delicate features, he would react by exclaiming: "Isn't she a beauty!" Invariably he found something encouraging to say about the preparation he was shown and had suggestions for further consideration. His praise was never lavish and therefore all the more appreciated. The applause of his associates no doubt gave him pleasure, but no man went less out of his way to seek honours. It was a cause of some sadness amongst his friends that he was never given a chair and that only his old university should award him an honorary degree. He used to lunch with his pupils at a long table in the hospital refectory but rarely started the conversation or chose the subject. His wide knowledge of history and literature was by no means all highbrow, as when, with a rare blush on his pleasantly high-coloured cheeks, he commented on the subject of Yorkshire culinary compulsions: "Apple pie without cheese is like a kiss without a squeeze."

At the age of sixty-five Greenfield retired from the staff of the National Hospital but continued to work in his old room for four days a week. As he approached the seventies, a painful osteoarthritis of the hip eventually reduced him to walking with sticks, but characteristically he refrained from drawing anyone's attention to this.

In June 1954 and 1958 the Greenfields made extended working visits to Bethesda and nearby Washington. After a farewell dinner —delayed by a guest who was detained for hours at the White House (checking to see if the President had had a new stroke)— they arrived at their apartment late, and it was about two o'clock in the morning, while Greenfield was reading himself to sleep, that a heart attack brought his end. The memorial service was held in St. Martin's in the Fields, the church where he had been married.

SMETHWICK, ENGLAND   ANTHONY L. WOOLF
SAN FRANCISCO, CALIFORNIA   FRANCIS SCHILLER
MOFFETT FIELD, CALIFORNIA   WEBB HAYMAKER

References

[1] *Pathology of the nervous system.* London, Constable, 1921.   [2] *The cerebro-spinal fluid in clinical diagnosis.* London, Macmillan, 1925. [3] *Neuropathology.* London, Arnold, 1958.   [4] Acta neuropath., Berlin, 1969, *12*:I–II (biography of Norman, by Blackwood).   [5] Brain, London, 1919, *42*:305–338 (with Buzzard).   [6] Brit. Med. J., 1927, 2:535–537.   [7] Brain, London, 1929, *52*:171–195.   [8] *Ibid.,* 1948, 71:365–383 (with Brain and Russell).   [9] *Ibid.,* 1950, *73*:141–166. [10] *The spino-cerebellar degenerations.* Oxford, Blackwell, 1954. [11] Proc. Roy. Soc. Med., London, 1932–33, *26*:690–697.   [12] J. Neur. Psychopath., London, 1932–33, *13*:289–302.   [13] Brain, London, 1950, *73*:291–316.

References to Biography: 1) J. Path. Bact., London, 1959, *78*:577–585 (McMenemey).   2) *Ibid.,* 1959, *78*:585–586 (with bibliography; Walshe).   3) Arch. Neur. Psychiat., Chic., 1958, *80*:587–589 (Penfield).   4) *Ibid.,* 1958, *80*:590–592 (Haymaker).   5) Lancet, London, 1958, *1*:540–541 (Russell).   6) Brit. Med. J., 1958, *1*:583–586 (Carmichael, Symonds, Northfield).

SALOMON HENSCHEN (1847–1930)

$\mathcal{S}$ ALOMON EBERHARD HENSCHEN was born in Upsala, Sweden, of a family well known there for three hundred years. As a student he took trips to northern Norway, Lapland, and South America. His medical studies were pursued mostly in Stockholm, and among his teachers were Malmsten, Key and Retzius. He received the M.D. in Upsala in 1880. At intervals during the years that followed he had the advantage of working with Carl Ludwig and Cohnheim in Leipzig and with Ziemssen in Munich.

J. E. Henschen

He was called to Upsala in 1881 and one year later became professor of medicine and chief of the clinic for internal diseases. For some years he gave his attention to internal medicine, publishing papers on such varied subjects as cholera, typhus, neuritis, and pulmonary and intestinal diseases; but his greatest interest was in cardiovascular diseases. He was attracted to neurology by two of

Portrait, courtesy of Prof. Folke Henschen, Stockholm, Sweden.

his patients, one of whom had hemianopia, and the other aphasia; and soon he abandoned many of his other interests in an effort to track down the anatomical bases of these disorders. His work dealt with the gross features of the brains concerned; he did no fine microscopic studies and performed no experiments.

In 1888 appeared the first of a series of studies on the visual pathways[1] which was to bring him renown. Articles in 1893 and 1894[2,3] and volumes I and II of his *Klinische und anatomische Beiträge zur Pathologie des Gehirns* (Upsala, Almquist & Wiksell, 1890–1911) carried his basic observations concerning the projections of the retina on the calcarine cortex: it was he who first proved that hemianopia is due to a lesion involving nothing but the calcarine fissure.* When he had finished corralling the pertinent data on visual pathways as well as those on auditory[4] and gustatory and olfactory pathways[5] and on aphasia, amusia, agraphia, acalculia,[6-8] and color perception, there were eight large volumes of the *Beiträge* to show for his efforts.

In 1900 he was appointed professor of medicine in the Caroline Institute in Stockholm, and around him gathered a coterie of promising young men, such as Forsaner, Holmgren, Jacobaeus, Josefson and Tillgren. He served as a great stimulus to his pupil Carl Hammarberg (1865–93) in the latter's study of histology of the cerebral cortex and the pathology of idiocy.[9] At sixty-five he was made professor emeritus.

When Henschen first presented his discovery of the cortical visual center in London in 1892, its reception by Horsley, Beevor, Hitzig, and E. A. Schäfer was either circumspect or one of outright incredulity. To Paris and Rome he went on his crusade (1894, 1895), and later again to Paris (1900),[10] where in spirited discussions, von Monakow and Bernheimer opposed his theory of the significance of the parastriate areas 18 and 19. His travels took him to Madrid in 1903, where he found in Cajal a proponent of his views. Skepticism of his observations concerning the parastriate areas prevailed at a meeting in Budapest in 1909.[11] Oppenheim related to Oskar Vogt how Henschen, holding a pointer, one end in each hand, while demonstrating some lantern slides, referred to a

---

* Hermann Munk's localization had been less circumscribed.

statement of von Monakow, and exclaimed, "Eine neue Dumm-heit von Monakow" with such vigor and abandon that the pointer broke in the middle. "Henschen hat tatsächlich den Stab über Monakow gebrochen."

Henschen spoke at subsequent Congresses as a renowned scientist, but he remained embroiled in controversy over priorities during the closing years of his career, his "40-jähriger Kampf."[12] The pioneers in the field of the cortical representation of macular vision were Inouye,[13] and Holmes and Lister;[14] the final demonstration of the lateral geniculate body's role in vision was by Minkowski.[15]

Throughout his life, Henschen carried on a lively campaign against alcohol, crusaded against prostitution, and waged a war of his own on tuberculosis. He was a hard worker and was often heard to say: "The most attractive are the men who serve others." In his youth he had the voice of a professional singer, but in later years he had difficulty in keeping time. He was fond of music and would say, "My! I never have time to go to the opera," but when he did go he invariably fell asleep. Lively, outspoken, often excitable and argumentative, he became estranged from some of his friends, among them, Retzius.

Having failed to receive the Nobel Prize, Henschen registered his protest in a letter to the Nobel Committee, as follows: "My work on the brain was repeatedly proposed for the Nobel Prize by the most eminent neurologists in Scandinavia as well as some foreign authorities, one of whom was Paul Flechsig, the leading expert in our times in cerebral anatomy and physiology. All these recommendations by experts made no impression whatever on the committee members, who were not specialists themselves in this field. Because of the secrecy maintained by the Nobel jury . . . the candidate for a Prize stands completely helpless."[16]

His international reputation was such that in 1923 he was called to Moscow to see Lenin, then aged fifty-two, stricken with aphasia and other signs of cerebral disease. Foerster, Nonne and Bumke were also at his bedside and there was no disagreement in the diagnosis of arterial disease, but Henschen alone was correct that the disorder would be rapidly progressive. Henschen, the internist, based his opinion on the family history: Lenin's father and two sisters had died at about fifty of cerebral apoplexy and one brother had had his leg amputated because of arterial disease.

In Norway for a vacation when eighty-one, Henschen fell on the ice and broke his leg. After that he began to fail. Progressive cataracts plagued him. Gastric symptoms developed and cancer was suspected, but operation failed to reveal cancer. He continued to have pain in his abdomen and leg and received morphine until he needed it habitually. His physician abruptly stopped giving the morphine. Henschen died soon afterward. As an act of piety and devotion, Henschen's son, Prof. Folke Henschen, of Stockholm, presented his father's brain to Oskar Vogt, at that time in Berlin-Buch, so that it might be put to use for scientific purposes.

N. W. WINKELMAN

References

[1] Upsala läk. fören. förh., 1888, 27:507–601.   [2] Brain, London, 1893, 16:170–180.   [3] Upsala läk. fören. förh., 1893–94, 29:83–126.   [4] J. Psychol. Neur., Lpz., 1918, 22:319–474.   [5] Mschr. Psychiat., 1919, 45:121–165.   [6] Hygiea, Stockh., 1919, 81:721–747.   [7] Arch. Neur. Psychiat., Chic., 1925, 13:226–249.   [8] Klinische und anatomische Beiträge zur Patho'ogie des Gehirns. Upsala, Almquist & Wiksell, 1920, pt. 5.   [9] Studien über Klinik und Pathologie der Idiotie nebst . . . Akad. Buchdruckerei, Upsala, 1895 (trans. from the Swedish original, publ. 1893).   [10] XIIIᵉ Congr. Internat. Med., Paris, Sect. d'ophtal. Paris, Masson, 1900; p. 232–249.   [11] Med. Klin., Berlin, 1909, 5:1321–1323.   [12] Zschr. ges. Neur. Psychiat., 1923, 87:505–535.   [13] Die Sehstörungen bei Schussverletzungen der korticalen Sehsphäre. Leipzig, Engelmann, 1909.   [14] Brain, London, 1916, 39:34–73.   [15] Arb. hirnanat. Inst. Zürich, 1913, 1:255–362.   [16] Nobel; the man and his prizes. Norman, U. of Okla., 1951, p. 159 (Schück et al.).

References to Biography: 1) Acta med. scand., 1931, 74:325–333 (Ingvar).   2) Deut. Zschr. Nervenh., 1931, 120:111–116 (Friedrich Schultze).   3) Grote (ed.), Die Medizin der Gegenwart in Selbstdarstellungen. Vol. 5, Leipzig, Meiner, 1925 (contains autobiography and bibliography by Henschen).   4) Zschr. ges. Neur. Psychiat., 1924, 90:628–637 (Lenz).

ALFONS JAKOB (1884–1931)

*A*LFONS JAKOB was born in the Bavarian city of Aschaf-fenburg-am-Main, the son of a shopkeeper. Helping his father in the store was one of his chores. Being enterprising, Alfons raised the prices. Only rarely did they have to be lowered.

After receiving his medical training in Munich, Berlin, then Strassburg—where he graduated in 1909—Jakob returned to Munich, to join Kraepelin in the clinic, and Nissl and Alzheimer in the laboratory. Two years later he was called to Hamburg-Friedrichsberg as clinical assistant at the Staatskrankenanstalt, a "state hospital." He soon began working with Prosektor Dr. Josef Kaes, noted for his atlas, *Die Grosshirnrinde des Menschen in ihren Massen und ihrem Fasergehalt* (Jena, Fischer, 1907), in which he described the tangential myelinated fibers in cortical lamina III ("stria of Kaes-Bechterew"). Following the death of Kaes (1850–1930) Jakob received the post of Prosektor. Later, his modest laboratory grew to twenty rooms in the Neuropathological Department of the University's Nervenklinik, and he had a flourishing private neurological practice. In many ways he collaborated closely with the noted Hamburg neurologist Max Nonne (1861–1959).[1] After service at the front in World War I he returned to Hamburg. Here he became Privatdozent in 1918, ausserordentlicher Professor in 1924.

During his brief career (he died at forty-seven) Jakob published five monumental books and a host of articles. He had a prodigious memory and a remarkable bent in organizing what he saw and read; surrounded by all his sources he would dictate from beginning to end, and the typed manuscripts hardly needed any corrections. Among his most outstanding contributions were those on experimentally induced trauma and secondary degeneration in the central nervous system, both initiated back in Munich. He noted postconcussive degeneration of nerve fibers in the spinal cord,[2] confirming an observation made twenty two years earlier by Schmaus,[3] and thus became one in a long line cognizant of the significance of concussion, starting with Jean-Louis Petit, who distin-

Alfons Maria Jakob

guished concussion from compression (due to hemorrhage) (in 1715)[4] and proceeding through Benjamin Bell, who defined concussion (1787)[5] in terms still current. In a paper on secondary degeneration,[6] Jakob observed the successive changes occurring in nerve fibers (pyramidal, for instance) during the course of the degenerative process. Out of it grew a monograph on normal and pathological anatomy of the cerebrum,[7] which became a bible for neuropathologists. A volume on the normal histology of the cerebellum for von Möllendorff's *Handbuch der mikroskopischen Ana-*

Portrait, courtesy of Dr. K. Scharenberg, Ann Arbor, Michigan.

tomie des Menschen (1928) brought much praise from Cajal. His review of dystonia musculorum deformans[8] was also a significant contribution.

The enormous material on neurosyphilis at Jakob's disposal in Friedrichsberg—more than two hundred patients being on the wards at any one time—enabled him and his pupils to explore the pathology of virtually all forms of the disease—among them, atypical paresis (the galloping type and the Lissauer type), tabes psychosis, and syphilitic endarteritis.[9] His views on nodular inflammatory infiltrates in the vessel wall, miliary gumma, and strokes in general paresis brought bitter arguments, chiefly with Spielmeyer and Jahnel.

His monograph on extrapyramidal diseases[10] covered the field more comprehensively than many published since; it included the analysis of thirty-three cases of his own. In the Preface, Jakob acknowledges that the stimulus to undertake this gigantic task came from what he saw of the work of Alzheimer on Huntington's chorea in Munich, from Westphal and Strümpell's studies of pseudosclerosis, and from what he had learned from C. and O. Vogt's epoch-making contributions to striatal diseases that had opened up the whole field.

But the description of a new morbid condition really made his fame. In 1920 Hans Gerhardt Creutzfeldt[11] described a "peculiar nodule-forming disease of the nervous system," occurring in a young woman whom he had attended in Spielmeyer's institute in Munich, and a few months later (1921) Jakob[12] published three more cases, which he called "spastic pseudosclerosis," and two more subsequently. Long thought to be a rare form of presenile dementia (and nowadays considered to be due to a "slow virus"), the disorder was set apart as an entity on the basis of its distinctive pathological features: mental deterioration and disorders of the pyramidal and extrapyramidal systems.[13] Spielmeyer christened the condition "Creutzfeldt-Jakob's disease," but it was not long before it was rechristened "Jakob-Creutzfeldt's disease" in consideration of the magnitude of Jakob's contribution.

Glial reactions, which fascinated Jakob, were his lead in delineating other pathological states. The case histories of a sporadic form of a glial nodule type of encephalitis published from his Institut, won more interest in the following decades when it became known as the Pette-Döring form of encephalitis. Another development came from Jakob's recognition of a special glial reaction in "a strange cerebral disease involving particularly the gray matter," occurring in differing form in three infants. Accounts were published separately by his students Somza (Madrid), Freedom (Baltimore) and Alpers (Philadelphia), the latter describing (in 1931)[14] what has since been called "Alpers' disease."

In Hamburg, Jakob attracted innumerable scholars: from Japan came Onari, Kashida and Hayashi; from Russia, Kroll and Robustov; from Portugal, Almeida Diaz; from Turkey, Sükrü-Aksel; from Montevideo, Schröder; from the United States, Alpers, Leo Davidoff, Globus, Kernohan, Grinker, Hassin, Rabiner, Winkelman. Scharenburg was among his distinguished pupils. Mingazzini of Rome made frequent trips to study the rich material in Jakob's laboratory. They all came not only to his laboratory but also to his open house, and when the social, cultural and artistic life became too much he, his wife and three children would take off for their country home in the Bavarian mountains. To repay courtesies, he made a lecture tour in the United States (in 1924), and some years later (in 1928) went to Brazil, Argentina and Chile as visiting professor. Here, with customary intensity, he managed to complete a paper on the neuropathology of yellow fever.[15]

It is remarkable that Jakob could so successfully meet the immense responsibilities of his laboratory and his clinical practice if one considers that for seven years he had been ill with a streptococcic osteomyelitis in the right thigh. Complicated by retroperitoneal abscess and paralytic ileus, it proved fatal despite operation.

If three pupils of Nissl and Alzheimer were to be named as the most instrumental in upholding the traditions and interests of that school, they would be, in any order, Spielmeyer, Spatz, and Jakob.

MARBURG a.d. LAHN, GERMANY   HANS JACOB

References

[1] Kolle (ed.), *Grosse Nervenärzte*. Vol. 3. Stuttgart, Thieme, 1963, p. 164–173 (biography of Nonne, by Schaltenbrand).   [2] Histol. u. histopath. Arb. Grosshirnrinde (Nissl-Alzheimer), Jena, Fischer, 1912,

5:182–358.   [3] Virchows Arch. path. Anat., 1890, *122*:326–365, 470–495.   [4] *Oeuvres complètes de J. L. Petit. Maladies des os, maladies chirurgicales.* Paris, Prévost, 1944.   [5] *A system of surgery.* Edinburgh, Elliott, 1787.   [6] Histol. u. histopath. Arb. Grosshirnrinde (Nissl-Alzheimer), Jena, Fischer, 1912, *5*:1–181.   [7] *Normale und pathologische Anatomie und Histologie des Grosshirns.* 2 vol. Leipzig, Deuticke, 1927–29.   [8] Deut. Zschr. Nervenh., 1932, *124*:138–153. [9] Bumke, O. (ed.), *Handbuch der Geisteskrankheiten.* Berlin, Springer, 1930, *11*:349–416.   [10] *Die extrapyramidalen Erkrankungen.* Berlin, Springer, 1923.   [11] Zschr. ges. Neur. Psychiat., 1920, *57*:1–18. [12] *Ibid.,* 1921, *64*:147–228. Med. Klin., Berl., 1921, *17*:372–376. [13] Monogr. Neur. Psychiat., Berl., 1923, *37*:215–245.   [14] Arch. Neur. Psychiat., Chic., 1931, *25*:469–505.   [15] Deut. Zschr. Nervenh., 1929, *111*:111–116.

References to Biography and Works: 1) Deut. Zschr. Nervenh., 1931, *123*:I–IV (Weygandt).   2) Zschr. ges. Neur. Psychiat., 1932, *138*: 165–168 (Josephy).   3) Scholz (ed.), *50 Jahre Neuropathologie in Deutschland, 1885–1935.* Stuttgart, Thieme, 1961, p. 79–86 (Jacob). 4) Zschr. ges. Neur. Psychiat., 1930, *128*:172–178 (Jakob).   5) *Jakob-Creutzfeldt-disease.* New York, Elsevier, 1968 (Kirschbaum).   6) Acta neurol. scand., 1968, *44*:1–32 (May).

ETTORE MARCHIAFAVA (1847–1935)

*M*ARCHIAFAVA was born in Rome and throughout his long and distinguished career remained in that city. His ability was early recognized by the award of a gold medal at the completion of his medical course and by promotion to the rank of professor of pathological anatomy at the Royal University of Rome when he was only thirty-six. He held this position until he was appointed professor of clinical medicine in 1917.

Marchiafava, like Golgi, divided his research activities between malaria and the nervous system. Soon after assuming his professorship, Marchiafava began work on malaria, which culminated in the establishment of the life cycle of Plasmodium falciparum. His book *La infezione malarica* (Milano, Vallardi, 1902), based on his investigations, still remains an important source for malariologists. In fact, the reputation of Marchiafava today rests at least as much

Ettore Marchiafava

on these investigations as it does on his studies of the nervous system.

Throughout his career, however, Marchiafava maintained an intense interest in diseases of the nervous system, both infectious and degenerative. Among his early contributions to this field was the first description of syphilitic cerebral arteritis.[1] In 1897 he first observed primary degeneration of the corpus callosum in the brain of an alcoholic patient, and in 1903[2] published (with Bignami) a definitive account of the disorder. The recognition of this disease

Portrait, courtesy of Prof. Dott. Paolo Colombo, Verona, Italy.

throughout the world and the eponym, "Marchiafava's disease," have given prominence to this discovery. He and his associates did important research also on other pathologic changes in the brain in alcoholism.[3,4]

At the same time that these investigations were going on, Marchiafava was a busy and highly successful practitioner of internal medicine. Publications on such subjects as angina pectoris and myxedema found their way into his bibliography. He was the personal physician of three popes and of the House of Savoy. Of the many honors which Marchiafava received, he valued most his appointment as Senator of the Realm in 1913 and the award of the Manson Medal.

In spite of these great distinctions, Marchiafava remained a modest, kindly and cultured Roman, interested in the classics as well as in his contemporaries. One of his later publications dealt with a detailed study of Horace's references to wine. He remained aloof from the clamorings for credit which marred so much of the work of some of his contemporaries in malaria research.

It is with amazement that the specialist of the present day looks at the career of a man like Marchiafava—a career characterized by almost equal distinction in malariology, neurology and internal medicine.

CHICAGO, ILLINOIS   ORVILLE T. BAILEY

References

[1] Atti Accad. med. Roma, 1877, 3:101–140.   [2] Riv. pat. nerv., 1903, 8:544–549.   [3] Mschr. Psychiat., 1911, 29:181–215 *et seq.*   [4] Proc. Roy. Soc. Med., London, 1933, 26:1151–1158.

References to Biography: 1) Policlinico (Sez. Pratica), 1935, 42:2348–2349 (Mem. 47).   2) Arch. Ital. anat. pat., 1936, 7:207–225 (Sotti), 3) Bol. Accad. med. Roma, 1936, 62:119–127 (Bastianelli).

GEORGES MARINESCO (1864–1938)

*M*ARINESCO (or Marinescu) was born in Bucharest. After completing medical school he went to study with Charcot; at the Salpêtrière he was also associated with Pierre Marie, Babinski, and Raymond. Later he worked with Weigert at Frankfurt-am-Main and with du Bois-Reymond at Berlin.

Nine years' training behind him, most of it in Paris, Marinesco returned to his native city where he received his doctorate and an appointment to the staff of the Pantélimon Hospital. Shortly thereafter, in 1897, a chair of clinical neurology was created for him in the University of Bucharest. This was the beginning of Rumanian neurology; under his guiding genius and forty-one years' tenure it reached great heights.

Marinesco's contribution to Roumanian and international science was immense. About 250 articles and several books put on record his experience in the laboratory as well as on the wards of the Pantélimon and later the Colentina. Daily contact with scores of the infirm and his astuteness made him put to use every one of the latest methods as they became available: the roentgen ray, with which, as a pupil of Pierre Marie in the early days, he had investigated the bone changes in acromegaly, the film camera, for the study of body movements in health and disease. He studied normal nerve cells, and reparative processes following nerve section, by the method of Nissl,[1] and published a book on the subject.[2] He coined the term "chromatolysis" and proved by means of the ultramicroscope, that Nissl bodies in nerve cells are not artefacts.

Early in his career he published with the Roumanian bacteriologist Babès and the French physician Blocq a much needed atlas on the pathological histology of the nervous system.[3] His description with Blocq of a case of parkinsonian tremor due to tumor in the substantia nigra, in 1893,[4] was the basis of Brissaud's theory, announced the next year, that parkinsonism occurs as a consequence of damage of the substantia nigra. With Blocq he was the first to describe senile plaques (1892), and with Minea he confirmed Noguchi and Moore's discovery of treponema in the brain in general paresis. For years he was interested in hereditary and fa-

milial diseases: with Trétiakoff he published on Friedreich's ataxia[5] and with Draganesco and Stoicisco on a new form of familial
spasmodic paraplegia with extrapyramidal motor symptoms.[6] In
1928 his important paper with Nicolesco on clinical-anatomical
aspects of the thalamic syndrome[7] anticipated by several years

Portrait, courtesy of Prof. Ludo van Bogaert, Antwerp, Belgium. (Photographer:
Fayer.)

many of the data on thalamo-cortical projections which Dejerine and Roussy were to uncover. Marinesco also contributed much to our knowledge of the juvenile form of family amaurotic idiocy.[8] He was a leader in the study of the sites of degenerative changes in the anterior horns of the spinal cord following amputation.[9] In 1908 he demonstrated the presence of aberrant sympathetic ganglia in the upper lumbar nerve roots;[10] only four decades later was it clearly shown that the postganglionic fibers originating in these "intermediate ganglia" do not traverse the ganglionic chain, but proceed directly through the segmental nerves to the periphery.[11]

There was hardly a more distinguished exponent of the great French school than Marinesco. His pupils, many of whom have made their mark, included Goldstein, Minea, Radovici, Draganesco, Sager, Parhon, Kreindler, Grigoresco, Ionesco-Sisesti, and the Nicolescos. As a teacher, Marinesco was among the most eminent; in his lectures he emphasized ideas and gave perspective for further investigations. Recognition in the form of honors came to him from many countries. It was he above all others who was chosen to represent the students of Charcot when the centenary of the birth of that great master was celebrated.

ROCHESTER, MINNESOTA   JAMES W. KERNOHAN

References

[1] Rev. neur., Paris, 1905, *13*:5–16.   [2] *Le cellule nerveuse.* 2 vol. Paris, Doin, 1909.   [3] *Atlas der pathologischen Histologie des Nervensystems.* Berlin, Hirschwald, 1892.   [4] C. rend. Soc. biol., Paris, 1893, *5*:105–111.   [5] Rev. neur., Paris, 1920, *27*:113–131.   [6] Encéphale, 1925, *20*:645–654.   [7] Bull. Acad. Med. Roum., 1928, *11*:1–2.   [8] J. Psychol., Neur., Lpz., 1930, *41*:1–75.   [9] Neur. Cbl., 1892, *11*:463–467 et seq.   [10] Neur. Zbl., 1908, *27*:146–150 (with Minea.)   [11] J. Int. Coll. Surgeons, 1949, *12*:111–119 (Alexander, Kuntz, Henderson and Ehrlich).

References to Biography: 1) Bull. Acad. Med. Roum., 1937, *3*:373–385 (Parhon).   2) J. Nerv. Ment. Dis., 1938, *88*:730–731 (anonymous).   3) Presse méd., 1938, *46*:1547–1548 (Guillain).

GIOVANNI MINGAZZINI (1859–1929)

*M*INGAZZINI was born in Ancona, Italy. He received the M.D. in Rome in 1883. After studying under Mole-schott at the Istituto di Fisiologia in Rome, he spent several years with the anatomist Todaro and then a short period with von Gudden in Munich. During all this time he had acquired an immense clinical experience, especially in the hospitals in Rome. In 1895 he was appointed to the coveted position of professor of neurology and psychiatry to the University of Rome, a post keenly sought after by De Sanctis as well. For many years he was also director of the Ospedale Psichiatrico of Rome, and it was here that he founded the laboratory of pathological anatomy.

Mingazzini had an especial interest in the lenticular nucleus. He observed that connections exist between the third frontal convolution and the lenticular nucleus,[1] and on the basis mainly of a fronto-lenticulo-bulbar pathway he framed an hypothesis as to the neural mechanism concerned in motor aphasia.[2] (The region just in front of the left lenticular nucleus where the fibers from Broca's area of the two sides come together was later called "Mingazzini's field" by Henschen.) Another contribution was his establishment of the "acute syndrome of the putamen" (Mingazzini's lenticular hemiplegia),[3] a syndrome rediscovered in recent times, and called "striatal hemiplegia."[4] In regarding the hemiplegia as due to interruption of fibers from cortex to putamen he anticipated what is known today as "COEPS" (cortically originating extrapyramidal system). He is known also for his work on the components of the cerebellar peduncles[5,6] and the origin, course and destination of the nervus hypoglossus,[7] and for his treatise on applied anatomy of the nervous system.[8]

Although his study of aphasia was highly important, most neurologists would agree that his greatest contribution was his monograph on the corpus callosum. In this volume he collected a great fund of data, including their bibliography, which has made it the standard work on the subject. It appeared only in German[9] and was a rather poor product, as the translation of the manuscript had been entrusted to a Roman monk unacquainted with medical terminology.

Giovanni Mingazzini

Mingazzini's extraordinary personality rubbed off, as it were, on his professional surroundings. He was high-strung, easily upset, volatile. He also was usually liberal with his money and yet parsimonious in little things: at the café his assistants knew that they could accept the cup of coffee he graciously offered, but not the pastry. He was given to a hearty round of oaths when the occasion demanded. Decided in his dislikes, he was not on speaking terms with Sante De Sanctis (1862–1935)[10] or Ottorino Rossi (1877–1936)[11] in the later years of his life. In his private life he was a man of the world. Possessing the proverbial professor's absent-

Portrait, courtesy of the National Library of Medicine, Bethesda, Maryland.

mindedness he would go to the opera with his wife and return home alone, having forgotten that he had escorted her there.

The walls of Mingazzini's office were covered with certificates of honorary memberships and degrees, and he would say to admirers, "Oh, but you should see the many more I have in my study at home!" His was an open vanity, unlike, say, Cajal's, who on one page of his *Recuerdos* would state that he never really amounted to much, and on the next few pages describe and illustrate his medals and decorations.

Mingazzini, a liberal of the Garibaldi type, refused to sign the Fascist oath, and plans were on foot to have him transferred to Sardinia. Mussolini is said to have interceded: "Leave the professor alone, let him study his brains." Mingazzini's wife was German, and he was a Germanophile so far as science went. In Rome, stories about Mingazzini filtered down to the man in the street and his name became part of the vernacular. Altschul relates that he often heard the exclamation, "Go to Mingazzini!" in lieu of "Man, you are crazy."

He knew well the art of teaching; at his 7:00 A.M. lectures, always impromptu, very few students were tardy. He was beloved by his associates, which included Ayala, Altschul, Pisani and Fumarola—"the best figs in my basket," he called them. His formula for expressing dissatisfaction with a paper submitted to him by a staff member for publication was simple: he kept it in his desk.

While on a visit to Prague, after being honored in Germany, he was observed to stop in the streets, bent over with pain from what seemed to be abdominal angina. A few puffs from a cigarette, which otherwise he never used, would bring him relief.

Some time afterward he died. A pupil wrote a fitting epitaph: *Labor et gloria vita fuit, mors requies.*

HIALEAH, FLORIDA   ARMANDO FERRARO

References

[1] *Lezioni di anatomia clinica dei centri nervosi.* Torino, Unione Tipografico-editrice, 1908. (2nd ed., 1913).   [2] Deut. Zschr. Nervenh., 1922, *74*:189–193.   [3] Zschr. ges. Neur. Psychiat., 1911, *8*:85–106.
[4] J. Neurol. Neurosurg. Psychiat., 1967, *30*:134–139 (Oppenheimer).

[5] Riv. pat. nerv., 1908, *13*:433–452.   [6] von Möllendorff, W., *Handbuch der mikroskopischen Anatomie des Menschen*. Berlin, Springer, 1928, *4*:579–643.   [7] J. Psychol. Neur., Lpz., 1923, *29*:273–402. [8] *Trattato di anatomia clinica dei centri nervosi*. Torino, Unione Tipografico-editrice, 1913.   [9] *Der Balken. Ein anatomische, physiopathologische und klinische Studie*. Berlin, Springer, 1922.   [10] Haymaker (ed.), *The founders of neurology*. Springfield, Thomas, 1953, p. 379–382 (biography of De Sanctis, by Cazzullo).   [11] *Ibid.*, p. 370–373 (biography of Rossi, by Ferraro).

References to Biography: 1) Policlinico (Sez. Pratica), 1929, *36*:1900–1902 (Fumarola).   2) Arch. Psychiat., Berlin, 1930, *92*:1–7 (C. Frank).   3) *In memoria di Giovanni Mingazzini*. Roma, Sormani, 1931 (contains bibliography; articles by several authors).

FRANZ NISSL (1860–1919)

*B*ORN at Frankenthal in the Bavarian Palatinate, Franz Alexander Nissl's illustrious career began early. As a student in Munich, at the suggestion of von Gudden's assistant, Ganser, he wrote a prize essay in 1884 on the pathology of cortical cells.[1] By using alcohol as a fixative and staining with magenta red (which he soon replaced by methylene blue, then by toluidine blue) he demonstrated previously unknown constituents of nerve cells and thus opened up a new era in neurocytology and neuropathology. The essay contained an astonishing number of new aspects and discoveries.

As an M.D. in 1885 Nissl became assistant to von Gudden at the Münchener Kreisirrenanstalt, where he remained after his chief's tragic death in the following year. In 1889 Nissl was called to the Städtische Irrenanstalt at Frankfurt-am-Main as second physician under Sioli; here he found Alzheimer, who was to become his main disciple, collaborator, and friend.

In 1895, at Kraepelin's invitation, Nissl went to Heidelberg, where he became Privatdozent in 1896, Extraordinarius in 1901, successor to the chair of psychiatry and director of the clinic at Heidelberg, in 1904, when Kraepelin was called to Munich. In 1918, again at Kraepelin's invitation, Nissl moved to Munich to

take a research position of the newly founded Deutsche Forschungs-anstalt für Psychiatrie. But after one year spent with Spielmeyer and Brodmann, he died from an old kidney ailment at the age of fifty-eight.

Nissl's writings amount to 62 titles. In an elaborate classification of normal cells (1891–94),[2] and in reporting the selective action of poisons (1896), he made much of the stainable substances

Portrait, courtesy of Prof. Dr. W. Scholz, Munich, Germany.

brought out by basic aniline dyes ("Nissl granules"); but he also stressed the importance of a substance between nerve cells (Nissl's "nervöses Grau"). In the neuron controversy he sided with the advocates of the nerve-net theory,[3] and found in Cajal his greatest antagonist. By contrast, when Nissl pointed out in 1894 how nerve cell bodies react after the axon has been interrupted ("primäre Reizung") he started an entirely new line of thought. Thanks to his numerous contacts with Weigert, who was developing a neuroglial stain, Nissl added a great deal to our understanding of mental and nervous diseases by relating them to observable changes in glial cells, blood elements, blood vessels, and brain tissue in general.[4] To clinicians he became best known for his epic work, with Alzheimer, on general paresis.[5] He early and eagerly utilized spinal puncture (1902), devised a method for quantitative protein determination in spinal fluid: they called him "punctator maximus."

During the last ten years of his life he was intensively engaged in establishing connections between the cortex and certain thalamic nuclei. The thalamus is the key to the cortex, he would say. In the developing cortex of newborn rabbits he observed that the superficial strata undergo greater differentiation than the deeper strata. Death prevented completion of the task, but there were two important papers to show for his work.[6,7] Thus he had a hand in initiating the study of cytoarchitectonics not only by providing the most useful technical tool—his stain—but also by working out some of the corticothalamic projection systems.

Outwardly Nissl was a gnome of a man, with bad posture and a tilting of the head due perhaps to an effort to conceal the large birthmark on the left side of his face. He remained a bachelor. Behind glasses his dark eyes looked searchingly at a visitor—benevolently as a rule. For he was guileless and defenceless when confronted by a mean person. To patients he was a friend. When he became Geheimrat he passed the word that he preferred to be called "Professor." He was a genius, spilling over with ideas. Some seemed abstruse, for instance those on the neuron theory. He was critical of his own *Neuronenlehre* and joked about the many mistakes he found in Part I—written a considerable time before the manuscript had gone to the printer. To his friends he pointed out his bizarre statement that Betz cells were among the few which needed to be examined histologically for they mirrored the pathologic changes in the brain as a whole. When pitted against Forel in 1911 as an expert alienist, he fared none too well in Forel's opinion, but he won the case.

Work was his obsession. At Heidelberg the days belonged to his patients, the nights to his research; but time was always found for music. Hugo Spatz relates their first meeting to negotiate for a place in his laboratory. Nissl was busy that morning and asked the student to come to his home at twelve. Noon struck but Nissl was not at home. Finally his housekeeper said the professor must have meant midnight. At midnight, Spatz had to wait in the anteroom for half an hour until Nissl had finished the piano sonata he was playing. The conversation lasted till daybreak.

Many of Nissl's sayings have become legend, for instance, his instruction for getting the best results in staining the chromophil bodies of nerve cells. His advice of allowing the brain to stand half an hour before plunging it in alcohol, took this form: "Take the brain out. Put it on the desk. Spit on the floor. When the spit is dry, put the brain in alcohol." He made a great play on his pet word "Röhrchen" (barrel of a microscope, for example), twisting it into every kind of meaning. Students in Heidelberg could buy their "Nissl-Röhrchen" at cigar stores. Even today, tubes for collecting spinal fluid are called "Nissl-Röhrchen" in Germany. Nissl's quaint, good-humored mockery, extended particularly to his chief, Kraepelin, who seemed constantly distraught. Early one morning Nissl placed a row of empty beer bottles outside his own laboratory and made sure the rumor that he had been found intoxicated under his desk would reach Kraepelin, who was a fierce crusader against alcoholism.

But there was another side to this impish man. Although his discoveries brought him satisfaction, he always felt that things escaped him. Despair was not altogether a stranger to him. He was his own sharpest critic and labored over manuscripts that never went to press. Even on his death-bed Nissl, doubter of himself, deathless to the scientific world, kept complaining of what needed yet to be done.

A. T. RASMUSSEN

References

[1] *Resultate und Erfahrungen bei den Untersuchungen der pathologischen Veränderungen der Nervenzellen in der Grosshirnrinde.* 1884 (unpublished).   [2] Neur. Cbl., 1894, *13*:676–685 et seq.   [3] *Die Neuronenlehre und ihre Anhänger.* Jena, Fischer, 1903.   [4] *Beiträge zur Frage nach der Beziehung zwischen klinischem Verlauf und anatomischem Befund bei Nerven und Geisteskrankheiten.* Berlin, Springer, 1913–23.   [5] Histolog. histopath. Arb. (Nissl-Alzheimer), 1904, *1*:315–494.   [6] Sitzber. Heidelbg. Akad. Wissensch., Math.-naturw. Kl., *38.* Abh., 1911.   [7] Arch. Psychiat., Berlin, 1913, *52:* 1–87.

References to Biography: 1) Arch. Psychiat., Berlin, 1929, *87*:96–170 (contains bibliography; Schröder, Spatz, Steiner).   2) Münch. med. Wschr., 1919, *66*:1058–1060 (Kraepelin).   3) *Ibid.,* 1920, *67*:75–78 (Kraepelin).   4) *Ibid.,* 1929, *76*:1339–1340 (Spatz).   5) Berlin klin. Wschr., 1919, *56*:1006–1007 (Spatz).   6) Kolle (ed.), *Grosse Nervenärzte.* Vol. 2. Stuttgart, Thieme, 1959, p. 13–31 (Spatz).

HEINRICH OBERSTEINER (1847–1922)

OBERSTEINER was born in Vienna, the son and grandson of physicians. At the University of Vienna he studied medicine at the time (1865–70) that its medical school had reached its peak under Hyrtl, Brücke, Rokitansky, Skoda, Oppolzer and Billroth. While still an undergraduate, he started research in Brücke's laboratory. He became Privatdozent in anatomy and pathology of the nervous system in 1873, Extraordinarius in 1880, Ordinarius in 1898, and Hofrat in 1906.

In 1882 he founded the Neurologisches Institut at the University of Vienna, the first of its kind, and for years he supported it and ultimately gave it his unique library of about 40,000 volumes. Graduate students came to him from every corner of the earth. Well over four hundred of them were listed by Marburg in his historical account of the Institute on the occasion of the twenty-fifth anniversary of its founding.[1] During Obersteiner's directorship, twenty-two volumes of the *Arbeiten* of the Institute and about five hundred papers and monographs were published.

His versatile mind encompassed nearly every aspect of neurology and psychiatry. In his clinical studies he gave a classical description of the symptomatology of concussion of the spinal cord.[2] He was the first German neurologist to describe status epilepticus;[3] he discovered the peculiar symptom of allochiria;[4] he wrote an important monograph on general paresis;[5] he recognized not only that organic diseases often display a psychogenic component,

Portrait, courtesy of Mrs. Malvine Marburg, New York City.

but also that constitutional factors in nervous and mental disorders are important, as exemplified by his dictum about general paresis and tertiary syphilis: *Paralyticus nascitur atque fit*. Long before the "discovery" of psychosomatic medicine, he studied in psychotics the fluctuations of body weight and their prognostic significance, and observed that paralytic attacks were frequently preceded by a fall of body temperature. His interest in experimental and psychological research is illustrated by his studies in experimental epilepsy, by the construction (with S. Exner) of a "psychodometer" for measurement of the reaction time in psychic disorders, and by studies of the comparative psychology of the various senses.

Obersteiner's chief interest, however, centered on the morphology of the nervous system. His textbook on the anatomy of the central nervous system[6] was the bible for generations of budding neurologists and authors of anatomical texts; twice it was translated into English, twice into Russian, and into French and Italian. Virtually all of the text was based on his personal observations. His special studies dealt with the peripheral granular zone in the cerebellum of the newborn where he distinguished two zones, glial and neuroblastic; the significance of the spatial arrangement and interrelationship of Purkyně and granular cells in the cerebellum; the structure of the cerebral vessels, on which he was able to demonstrate nerve fibers; the variations in the course of neural pathways such as the pyramidal tract; Hellweg's bundle; an analysis of cerebral association systems (with Redlich); and the various types of pigment (lipoid and melanotic) in nerve cells.

One striking result of his studies (with Redlich) on pathology was the proposal that tabetic degeneration of the posterior columns begins in the posterior roots.[7,8] Their postulate that the initial site of involvement is at the place where the root becomes a central tract (the Obersteiner-Redlich zone) set off a controversy which is still not settled. As early as 1905 Obersteiner found that radium irradiation may produce hemorrhages and inflammatory reactions in the brain.[9] He also demonstrated the importance of vascular factors in the genesis of porencephaly, and the existence of internal microgyria.[10]

Until shortly before his last illness, which proved to be due to myocardial degeneration, he came every day to the laboratory, spending some time with each pupil, treating everyone with the same personal interest and unequaled charm, whether a famous foreign scientist or an undergraduate. He was exceedingly fond of classical music. A confirmed collector, he acquired not only antique clocks and rare books, but also such oddities as microtome sections of various sausages. Virtually every Viennese neurologist of importance spent some time in his laboratory—for instance, von Economo, von Frankl-Hochwart, Karplus, Redlich, Schlesinger and Spitzer. His outstanding and most devoted student and successor was Otto Marburg, who was director of the institute until 1938. Then followed Otto Gagel (1938–45), then Hans Hoff (1949–59), then Franz Seitelberger, who was appointed in 1959.

PHILADELPHIA, PENNSYLVANIA   ERNEST A. SPIEGEL

References

[1] Arb. Neur. Inst. Wien, 1907, *15:*VII-XXIII.   [2] Med. Jahrb., Wien, 1879, *3:*531–562.   [3] Wien. med. Wschr., 1873, *23:*544–547.   [4] Brain, London, 1884, *7:*289–309.   [5] *Die progressive allgemeine Paralyse.* ed. 2. Wien u. Leipzig, Hölder, 1908.   [6] *Anleitung beim Studium des Baues der nervösen Centralorgane im gesunden und kranken Zustande.* Leipzig u. Wien, Toeplitz u. Deuticke, 1888 (ed. 5, 1912).   [7] Arb. Neur. Inst. Wien, 1894, *2:*158–172.   [8] *Die Pathologie der tabischen Hinterstrangserkrankungen.* Jena, Fischer, 1897.   [9] Arb. Neur. Inst. Wien, 1905, *12:*87–104.   [10] *Ibid.*, 1902, *8:*1–66.

References to Biography and Works: 1) Arb. Neur. Inst. Wien, 1923, *24:*5–32 (contains bibliography; Marburg)   2) *Grosse Nervenärzte,* by K. Kolle (Ed.), vol. 3, p. 21–30, 1962 (Seitelberger).

ARNOLD PICK (1851–1924)

*P*ICK was born of German-Jewish parents in the small town of Velké Meziříčí, in Moravia. During his course in medicine at Vienna, he was student assistant to Meynert. After graduation in 1875, he became assistant to Westphal in Berlin. Wernicke, at the time, was also with Westphal. All three—

Arnold Pick

Meynert, Westphal and Wernicke—exerted an important influence on Pick's subsequent work on aphasia, that great meeting place of three painstaking methods: the verbatim psychiatric interview, the neurological, and the pathological examinations. In all three he excelled, as he brought to them his sophistication, his common sense, and his unending devotion to detail.

Arnold Pick became physician to the Landesirrenanstalt ("Kateřinky") in Prague in 1877, director of a newly opened hospital for mental diseases at Dobřan in 1880, and six years later pro-

Portrait, courtesy of Prof. Dr. F. Jahnel and Col. H. Sprinz, M.C., U. S. Army, Munich, Germany.

fessor of Psychiatry (hence Neurology) at the German University of Prague. There also was a Czech university; both claimed their descent from the institution founded by Charles IV in 1348, the first of its kind in Central Europe. As a cultural and medical center, Prague was second only to Vienna. But among the University's medical facilities the baroque psychiatric hospital, previously Saint Catherine's Convent, was particularly overcrowded and ill adapted to the maintenance of even the most primitive hygiene. It also belonged to the Kingdom (land, or province) of Bohemia, while the academic teaching in both medical schools was run by the state (the Austro-Hungarian empire). The province and the state were frequently at odds, especially as the Czechs, who made up the majority of the population of Bohemia, were engaged in a struggle to break loose from the old monarchy. Coupled with the political and administrative stresses was the fact that German professors taught German students in the German language, and in the "German" half of the madhouse, while the majority of the patients everywhere spoke only Czech. Finding German assistants who could speak Czech was one of Pick's problems. "The surgeon has an easy life," he would say. "All he has to ask is 'Does this hurt?' 'Bolí to?' To probe the patients' minds, the way we are supposed to, we need quite a bit more." Another problem was in getting neurological case material: for teaching purposes patients had to be "borrowed" from other departments.

Pick's contributions to medical literature numbered approximately 350. He is best known for his work on presenile dementia due to lobar atrophy, since called "Pick's disease." The first of a series of publications on this disorder, discovered in the course of studying a patient's aphasia, appeared in 1892.[1] No small part of his prodigious effort was devoted to the study of neuropathology, on which he wrote a textbook.[2] He was the first to put Wernicke's ideas on aphasia on a sound pathoanatomical basis, and his studies on this subject[3-5] and on apraxia[6] and agrammatism[7] remain classics in this field. They brought him recognition as one of the greatest contributors to the knowledge of the localization of cerebral function.

From his daughter, Dora Pick Fuchs, we learned of his lively correspondence with Dejerine, Marie, Head, Raymond, Strümpell,

Jolly, and above all, Hughlings Jackson. Pick, it is fair to say, discovered Jackson for Central European neurology; he particularly pursued the idea that aphasics not only lose part of their vocabulary but also the ability to construct their propositions according to logic and grammar. Otto Kahler was a close friend and associate. Together they had worked out what in 1880 became known as "Kahler-Pick's law." It concerned the respective arrangement of incoming posterior root fibers in the posterior columns of the spinal cord. An ingenious injection technique enabled them to demonstrate that the fibers at higher levels displace to progressively more medial planes those that enter at lower levels.[8] (Kahler also produced two classic descriptions: one on multiple myeloma—"Kahler's disease"[9]—and the other on syringomyelia.[10]) Pick's interdisciplinary interests are shown by the fact that many of his best friends were colleagues from outside the medical school; Ernst Mach, the famous physicist and experimental psychologist; the philosophers Friedrich Jodl and von Ehrenfels; the musicologist Guido Adler; the philologist Sauer; the biologist Steinach (of testicular rejuvenation fame); and Count Gleispach, the jurist. Pick was a great collector of books—German, French and English. At his home they reached to the ceiling and were piled on the floor. When he started on a vacation, some volumes of Goethe or Carlyle went into the large case full of medical books. He had a great love of music—Beethoven and the string quartet in particular.

Pick was a noble-minded, modest man—perhaps too modest—and the essence of calm serenity. His fearlessness in dealing single handed with the dangerously agitated psychotic—he was short and slender—was legendary, his skill in eliciting the delusional ideas from the most autistic and practically mute patients uncanny. The hurried stenograms were typed by a manic-depressive secretary—another inmate. Active to the end, Pick died from sepsis following the operation for a bladder calculus.

MADELAINE R. BROWN

References

[1] Prag. med. Wschr., 1892, *17*:165–167.   [2] *Beiträge zur Pathologie und pathologischen Anatomie des Centralnervensystems, mit Bemer-*

kungen zur normalen Anatomie desselben. Berlin, Karger, 1898.
[3] Arch. Psychiat., Berlin, 1892, *23*:896–918.   [4] *Über das Sprachver-
ständnis.* Leipzig, Barth, 1909.   [5] Zschr. ges. Neur. Psychiat., 1925,
95:231–247.   [6] *Studien über motorische Apraxie und ihr naheste-
hende Erscheinungen; ihre Bedeutung in der Symptomatologie psy-
chopathischer Symptomenkomplexe.* Leipzig, Deuticke, 1905.   [7] *Die
agrammatischen Sprachstörungen; Studien zur psychologischen Grund-
legung der Aphasielehre.* Berlin, Springer, 1913.   [8] *Nothnagel's
Specielle Pathologie* etc. Wien, Hölder, 1897, vol. 10, p. 19 (Leyden).
[9] Prag. med. Wschr., 1889, *14*:33–35; 44–49.   [10] *Ibid.* 1888, *13*:45–47;
63–65.

References to Biography: 1) Arch. Psychiat., Berl., 1925, *72*:1–20 (contains bibliography; Sittig).   2) Jahrb. Psychiat. Neur., Wien, 1925,
44:I–X (Sittig).

KÁROLY SCHAFFER (1864–1939)

*T*HE centenary celebration[1] held in Budapest honoring
Schaffer is not long past. All his energy had been harnessed
for science. He was reserved, austere, stern, had a deaf ear for
jokes and small talk. He kept social contacts to a minimum; his
closest associates would receive an invitation for dinner twice a
year—once in winter, to the family home in the center of Budapest, once in summer, to their small villa on the right bank of
the Danube. As to music, Schaffer's silver-stained sections were
his "visual concerts"; the spectacles of nature he appreciated only
under the microscope. In poetry, however, he found a deep interest; in Goethe's works he was particularly well oriented. Sketch-
ing and sculpture were household themes, his father having been
a sculptor whose work can still be admired in the Palais Károlyi
and the Serbian Church on Váci utca in Budapest.

Károly Schaffer (Karl in the German literature, Charles in the
West) was born in Vienna but spent his youth in Budapest. Here
he studied medicine, graduating in 1888. The faculty happened
to be neurologically oriented: Joseph von Lenhossék wrote mem-
orably on the microscopic anatomy of the medulla oblongata,
Victor von Mihálkovics on neuroembryology, Andreas Högyes

on the vestibular system. Four of their students, too, became known in neurology: Ernest Jendrassik for his work on reflexes and hereditary diseases, Michael von Lenhossék (Jr.)[2] as one of the pioneers of the neuron theory, Stephen von Apáthy as one of its most passionate opponents, and Schaffer. In the summer Schaffer would proceed to Vienna to attend Meynert's course, which undoubtedly influenced him in his approach to psychiatric matters through neuropathology.

Soon after Schaffer became assistant at the Psychiatric Clinic in Budapest he spent several months in Weigert's laboratory at Frankfurt-am-Main and came to know Edinger well. "Privatdozent" in 1893, and head of the neurological service and of an outpatient department from 1895, Schaffer was made ausserordent-

Portrait, courtesy of Prof. Stephen Környey, Pécs, Hungary.

licher Professor in 1901. With his hospital service he ran a histological laboratory, mainly on his private resources. In 1912 the University of Budapest created for him an Interacademic Brain Research Institute,[3] with a chapel-like stillness ideal for the investigator. He was sixty-one when his faculty colleagues urged him to become director of the Department of Neurology and Psychiatry. After much hesitation he accepted (in 1925). In 1935 he retired from his academic duties. Benedek was his successor.

In his first papers, on human rabies infection, Schaffer recognized that the most severe damage in the spinal cord was in the segments corresponding to the area of the skin that had been bitten, in accord with the animal experiments of Di Vestea and Zaggari; he so introduced the theory of virus propagation along nerves.[4] The structure of the hippocampus as brought out by the Golgi method, was tackled next.[5] "Schaffer's collaterals" (of the hippocampal pyramidal cells) is an expression currently used by neurophysiologists. Simultaneously with Simmarro, he established the morphological difference between neurite and dendrites.[6] Cajal's work had appeared during Schaffer's formative years; he followed the Cajal flag as it applied to neuropathology,[7] despite the bulwarks thrown up against the neuron theory by leading German neuropathologists, Nissl in particular. Schaffer's labors in the 1890's resulted in an important monograph[8] on cerebrospinal syphilis; it stressed the chronicity of the infiltrative, vascular, and meningeal changes in the tabetic root affection twenty years before Hugo Richter, in Schaffer's institute, produced a definitive study on root involvement in this disease.[9]

Schaffer's most important contribution came in 1905: the discovery that in infantile Tay-Sachs disease the enormous swelling of the nerve cells, originally described by Bernard Sachs, is due to accumulation of a lipid which he called "lecithinoid."[10] Schaffer demonstrated his findings at the same meeting where Spielmeyer reported on the juvenile form of familial amaurotic idiocy. A controversy arose, became a polemic, and now is in the graveyard of science: Schaffer maintained that the pathological process in the two forms was identical, Spielmeyer, that they were different; two years later Spielmeyer conceded. "Schafferscher Zellprozess," so called later by Bielschowsky, was a selective lesion of the ectodermal constituents of the nervous system, to be distinguished from visceral lipid storage.[11] He did not live to see his opinion supported by Klenk's[12] observation that the lipids encountered in nerve cells in familial amaurotic idiocy differ from those observed in visceral structures in Niemann-Pick disease, a condition in which, according to Klenk, the lipids are of a phosphatid nature. The more recent discovery of neurovisceral gangliosidoses, however, still clouds the issue.

According to Schaffer's doctrine, hereditary nervous system diseases exhibit a threefold selectivity: for a germ layer, for a region of the nervous system, and for a specific neuronal system.[13-15] "Neurocytogeny" is Schaffer's term to express his view that even where tract degeneration is the outstanding factor, the primarily affected part is the cell body. Schaffer grouped motoneuron disease, cerebellar degeneration, Huntington's chorea, and Pick's lobar atrophy under the term "systemic heredodegenerations"— later called "systemic atrophies" by Spatz.[16] One of Schaffer's greatest merits was his recognition that neuroglia could react independently from damage of the parenchyma ("Eigenerkrankung der Glia");[17] he set "neuroglial abiotrophies" up alongside "neuronal abiotrophies," after Scholz had demonstrated that leucodystrophies were based on a primary metabolic anomaly of the glia.

These and other original contributions (on the cortical localization of talent,[18] on hypnosis and reflex phenomena[19]) by no means exhaust the impact Schaffer had on his contemporaries. Citizen of a small country, lecturing and often writing in Hungarian, his influence was restricted. Brilliant as a clinician and a teacher, he also had his father's talent as a draftsman, published a comprehensive textbook on nervous and mental disease, and wrote on the psychic constitution of prominent Hungarians, e.g., the mathematicians Bolyai, father and son.[20] He had just put the final period to an essay on Semmelweiss[21] when, at seventy-five, he fell victim of an "abdominal catastrophe." His last request that his brain be subjected to study was honored.

PÉCS, HUNGARY   STEPHEN KÖRNYEY

References

[1] Acta med. Acad. Sci. Hung., 1965, *21*:361–495 (with bibliography).
[2] Sympos. Biol. Hung., 1965, *5*:15–18 (biography of Lenhossék).

[3] *Methods and problems of medical education.* Vol. 6. New York, Rockefeller Foundation, 1927, p. 221–227.   [4] Beitr. path. Anat., 1890, 7:191–244.   [5] Arch. mikr. Anat., 1892, 39:611–632. [6] Neur. Zbl., 1893, 12:849–851.   [7] Acta med. Szeged, 1938, 9:7–411 (with Miskolczy).   [8] *Anatomisch-klinische Vorträge aus dem Gebiete der Nervenpathologie. Über Tabes and Paralyse.* Jena, Fischer, 1901. [9] Zschr. ges. Neur. Psychiat., 1921, 67:1–189.   [10] Zschr. jugend. Schwachsinn, 1909, 3:19–73.   [11] Arch Neur. Psychiat., Chic., 1934, 24:765–775.   [12] Acta Neur. Psychiat. Belg. 1954, 54:586–596. [13] *Über das morphologische Wesen und die Histopathologie der hereditaersystematischen Nervenkrankheiten.* Berlin, Springer, 1926 (Monogr. Neur. 46).   [14] 3rd Internat. Neurol. Congr., Copenhagen, Munksgaard, 1939, p. 248–266.   [15] Arch. Neur. Psychiat., Chic., 1925, 14:731–741.   [16] Arch. Psychiat., Berl., 1938, 108:1–18. [17] Zschr. ges. Neur. Psychiat., 1918, 38:85–110.   [18] Arch. Psychiat., Berl., 1932, 96:683–699.   [19] *Suggestion und Reflex. Eine kritisch-experimentelle Studie über die Reflexphaenomene des Hypnotismus.* Jena, Fischer, 1895.   [20] Psychiat.-neur. Wschr., 1936, 38:489–498. [21] Zschr. ges. Neur. Psychiat., 1940, 169:246–249.

References to Biography: 1) Klin. Wschr., 1934, 13:1263 (Nonne). 2) *Ibid.,* 1940, 45:477–479 (Richter).   3) Zschr. ges. Neur. Psychiat., 1940, 168:36 (Scholz).   4) Deut. Zschr. Nervenh., 1940, 150:193–200 (Miskolczy).   5) Arch Psychiat., Berl., 1940, 110:615–618 (Környey).

PAUL SCHILDER (1886–1940)

S CHILDER was born in Vienna and attended the University there, graduating in medicine in 1909. He was influenced chiefly by the philosopher Laurenz Müller and the physiologist Exner. Although of strong philosophic bent, his first paper, published as a student, was in neuropathology, and while assistant to Gabriel Anton at Halle (1909–12) he carefully analyzed choreic and athetoid movements.[1,2] He noted, for instance, that athetosis complicating hemiplegia was caused probably by a lesion in the dentate nucleus of the cerebellum.[1] During this period he also made his first observations on encephalitis periaxialis diffusa,[3,4] since known as "Schilder's disease." His philosophic and psychologic interests found expression in the study of language, aphasia,

Paul Ferdinand Schilder

and states of consciousness, and while at Leipzig (1912–14) he published a paper on symbolism in schizophrenia[5] and a book, *Selbstbewusstsein und Persönlichkeitsbewusstsein* (Berlin, Springer, 1914).

At the outbreak of war he volunteered and saw active duty. However, he continued his studies and received the Ph.D. from Vienna *in absentia* in 1917. He was called to Vienna in 1918 by Wagner von Jauregg and was made Privatdozent in 1921 and Professor Extraordinarius in 1925. Having heard Freud's lectures as a student, he now developed closer personal ties with the master and became an active member of the Psychoanalytic Society, yet

Portrait, courtesy of Dr. Lauretta Bender, New York City.

never became a disciple. In fact he disagreed strongly with a number of the doctrines—particularly that of the death instinct—and elaborated his own theories of personality and techniques of therapy. He used not only his brilliant psychologic insight but also his broad knowledge of the mental symptoms of organic disease, particularly chronic epidemic encephalitis,[6,7] general paresis,[8] and Wernicke's polioencephalitis hemorrhagica superior.[9] His combined neurological and psychiatric thinking was presented in *Das Körperschema* (Berlin, Springer, 1923) (Schilder borrowed the term "body scheme" from Henry Head) and in the much enlarged English edition, *The image and the appearance of the human body; studies in constructive energies of the psyche* (London, Paul, Trench, Trubner, 1935), which he considered his most important contribution. Other significant neurological works were *Die Lagereflexe des Menschen* (with H. Hoff) (Wien, Springer, 1927) and an article, *Zur Lehre von den Sprachantrieben* (with E. Pollak).[10] He was an indefatigable writer. The story goes that when Schilder heard that Wagner von Jauregg was to receive the Nobel Prize in Medicine he was one of the first to congratulate him. Wagner von Jauregg remarked: "Don't worry; you will receive the Nobel Prize, too—but in literature."

In 1930 he came to New York as clinical director of the psychiatric division of Bellevue Hospital and research and associate professor of psychiatry at New York University Medical School. At the medical school he continued his diverse studies on consciousness, basing his conclusions not only on psychiatric observations but also on clinical and experimental neurological data dealing with vestibular functions, extrapyramidal motility, and postural reflexes. The psychiatric observations were carried out in large measure in work on children in conjunction with Lauretta Bender, his wife. This material was presented from the philosophical viewpoint of constructive action of the individual toward the outer world of reality. In a biography[11] written in 1940, he concluded, "The behavior of the child can only be understood as a continuous process of trial and error, which leads to construction and configuration as a basis for action. . . . Human beings drive into the future by trial and error and thereby find their happiness . . ."

Paul Schilder had a brilliant mind and a dynamic and colorful personality. He was a noted figure on the Vienna faculty, medium-sized, swarthy and handsome, his scholarly appearance accentuated by a dense, close-cropped beard. Intense and driving in his work, he still could relax and be composed and exhibit cheerfulness and humor. But in lectures and discussions he gesticulated in the grand manner, and his already high-pitched voice ascended out of range at climactic points.

His death, in 1940, came as a consequence of having been struck by an automobile: he had always been disdainful of traffic signals and was known to cross Times Square in the rush hour in spite of the red light, with books piled to eye level on one arm and the other held aloft motioning the speeding cars to come to a halt.

Schilder's research and teaching left an enduring impression not only on clinical neurology, but also on that more abstruse field of brain, mind and motivation.

ROCKVILLE, MARYLAND   DAVID McK. RIOCH

References

[1] Zschr. ges. Neur. Psychiat., 1911, 7:219–261.   [2] *Ibid.*, 1912, 9:35–42.   [3] *Ibid.*, 1912, 10:1–60.   [4] *Ibid.*, 1913, 15:359–376.   [5] *Ibid.*, 1914, 26:201–244.   [6] *Ibid.*, 1921, 68:299–340.   [7] *Ibid.*, 1929, 118:327–345.   [8] *Studien zur Psychologie und Symptomatologie der progressiven Paralyse.* Berlin, Karger, 1930.   [9] Arch. Neur. Psychiat., Chic., 1933, 29:990–1053 (with Bender).   [10] Zschr. ges. Neur. Psychiat., 1926, 104:480–502.   [11] J. Crim. Psychopath., 1940, 2:221–234.

Reference to Biography: Psychoanal. Q., 1941, 9:131–134 (Wittels).

HUGO SPATZ (1888–1969)

*A*S HIS FATHER was the editor of the *Münchener Medizinische Wochenschrift,* Hugo Spatz became exposed early to discussion of medical subjects. Not surprisingly, he entered upon a medical career, at Munich, then Heidelberg. The outbreak of World War I sent him, just graduated (1914), to the Western Front for the duration.

Already in Heidelberg his free time found him working in Nissl's laboratory. He was struck by the regressive glial changes during myelinogenesis—cells actually sacrificed for the benefit of normal growth! In his doctoral thesis, on histogenesis of the rabbit spinal cord,[1,2] he put the finger on "one of the characteristic reactions of the premature nervous system": the inability to produce scars, the rapid dissolution of tissue, so that an aplasia is simulated or a mere cyst left behind.[3]

It was at Kraepelin's Forschungsanstalt für Psychiatrie in Mu-

Portrait, courtesy of Prof. van Bogaert. Antwerp, Belgium.

nich, with Nissl, Brodmann and Spielmeyer—particularly the latter —where Spatz in 1919 found his place. Economo's description of encephalitis lethargica in 1918 and a monograph by the Vogts in 1920 were the background of his early interest in the basal ganglia; in 1922 he detected a relatively large iron concentration in the normal pallidum and reticulate zone of the substantia nigra,[4] a discovery which opened up a new field of neurochemistry. The striate system of the Vogts was expanded by Spatz to include the subthalamic nucleus, substantia nigra, red nucleus and dentate nucleus; this "extrapyramidal motor system in the narrower sense" was set off against "the extrapyramidal motor system in the broader sense" by his inclusion of lower lying nuclei. He at first believed in the genetic relation of the pallidum to the substantia nigra,[5] but further embryological analysis showed that the pallidum was derived from a hypothalamic anlage. The article in Bethe's *Handbuch* of 1927[6] on these and other aspects of the basal ganglia is one of his pioneering feats. The accumulation and transportation of hemosiderin and lipids[7] and the diagnostic value in general paresis of hemosiderin content[8] followed up his histochemical work.

In 1921 Spatz met Julius Hallervorden (1882–1965) at the Forschungsanstalt. Hallervorden, an East Prussian by birth, was prosector at a mental hospital in Landsberg on the Warthe (in Brandenburg) and came to spend his sabbatical year in Munich with Spielmeyer (1921–1922). He brought with him the brain of a girl who had suffered from progressive rigidity; pallidum and reticulate zone of the substantia nigra were a rusty brown from excessive iron: Hallervorden-Spatz's disease was born.[9]

In 1926 Spatz became Oberarzt to Bumke, Kraepelin's successor. Parkinsonism,[10] rabies,[11] Borna's disease (in horses),[12] studied with coworkers, became the subjects Spatz used for his chapter in Bumke's *Handbuch* on the encephalitides.[13] He classified them on a morphological basis, according to mode of spread rather than etiology.[14] Next, his attention was drawn to the cerebral swelling accompanying cerebral neoplasms. With Stroescu he described herniations into cisterns, and went on to explore cerebrospinal fluid flow, its obstruction (an extension of his work with vital dyes), and the blood-brain barrier.[15] With Hallervorden he postulated a "rhythmic" diffusion in the brain, suggesting that from a small focus next to a vessel, a myelinolytic substance might well spread, creating new lesions, particularly in the Baló form of demyelinative disease.[16]

In 1937, Spatz became Director of the Kaiser-Wilhelm-Institut für Hirnforschung at Berlin-Buch, succeeding Oskar Vogt. An ever-increasing material allowed him to investigate the systemic atrophies involving, among other structures, the basilar pontine nuclei and the inferior olivary nucleus,[17] also Pick's disease,[18] on which he worked in 1926 with Onari. A case of pubertas praecox occurring in association with hamartoma at the base of the hypothalamus, with cells characteristic of those of the tuber cinereum, prompted the idea of excessive local gonadotrophic neurosecretion.[19]

At the outbreak of World War II Spatz with his associate, Wilhelm Tönnis, the neurosurgeon (now in Cologne), and Richard Lindenberg, the neuropathologist (now in Baltimore, U.S.A.), were mobilized to the front by the Luftwaffe. Air attacks on Berlin in 1941 forced Spatz's return. In 1944 Hallervorden left with part of the Institute's collection for quiet Dillenburg (in the Westerwald, in Nassau). Spatz remained to the bitter end, trying to evacuate the rest of the collection to Munich. He reached Munich in the spring of 1945. Being a Director of a Kaiser Wilhelm Institut, he was put under arrest by the U.S. military police and interned in Garmisch-Partenkirchen, then invited to join the U.S. Aeromedical Center in Heidelberg. His chapter on brain trauma in *German aviation medicine, World War II* (Washington, D.C., U.S. Govt. Printing Office, 2 vol., 1950) was magnificent. Not until 1947 could Spatz reach Dillenburg to join his family and the Hallervordens in an old feudal castle overlooking the town, in which they had found shelter. The author, together with Webb Haymaker and Joseph Radermecker, visited them in their meditative atmosphere, sharing in the frugal communal meals, listening to madrigals sung by Spatz and his six children, with his wife at the organ—and discussing embryogenesis.

Through Otto Hahn, Planck's successor, Spatz and Hallervorden were, in 1949, allotted space at the Physiological Institute at Giessen. Here Spatz, together with a dozen young assistants, was able to complete an enormous work on the hypothalamus and pituitary, particularly of a tuberohypophysial secretory pathway,[20,21] and Hallervorden to ponder on the nature of the demyelinative diseases.

Rejoining, in 1952, the international neurological fraternity at the First Neuropathology Congress in Rome, Spatz gave a masterly report covering his work on the cerebral atrophies (prelude to a monograph published with Lüers[22]); and in that same year in Madrid (to celebrate the Cajal centenary), he lectured on "Neuronenlehre und Zellenlehre."[23] In 1955 he and Krücke were the mainstays of an Edinger centenary celebration in Frankfurt.

Emeritus in 1959, and later joined by Hallervorden (who died in 1965), he moved to a bright new institute in Frankfurt-Niederrad (Max-Planck-Institut für Hirnforschung). Here Spatz worked to the end, particularly on the brains of subhuman primates. Evolution of the human brain was his theme, and he dwelt especially on the basal (orbital) neocortex, phylogenetically and ontogenetically the latest to develop, and related, he found, to man's superior psychic activity.[24] Profound personality changes, preceding the intellectual deficit, would result from damage of this region. His concluding papers, logical yet wistful, were on the future of the human brain.[25,26]

Spatz was an inspired morphologist who combined vision with didactic talent such that, in his measured words, a living picture would emerge of whatever process in pathology or organogenesis any one wished to discuss with him. His clear and elegant style and the care he lavished on his writing, extended even to the manuscripts of assistants and to correspondents. Underneath the bearing of this dapper man, a little ceremonious on occasion, you soon detected his genuine sincerity. Where opinions differed he would ask questions, correct a detail, clarify your own thought with surprising tact and disarming kindness. If you had extensive professional dealings with him you could not help becoming friends, in an atmosphere almost of intimacy. In contrast to Hallervorden, who was blunt and seemingly lacking in sentimentality, Spatz was diplomatic and obviously a romantic. He had dreamy, yet penetrating, eyes; hair swept back and almost down to his shoulders; a voice, soft yet booming on occasion, and movements of an actor, which he continually was. An expert on medieval church architecture, he would draw a crowd of passers-by as he commented to companions on this or that aspect of an ancient façade. They also might smile at the proverbial professor sporting that letter stuck under his hat band he must not forget to mail! Unlike Hallervorden, who listened to symphonic music by the hour, Spatz preferred the brass band—"everyone is in some way a little feeble-minded," he used to say. Each Octoberfest in Munich he closed the laboratory for one afternoon, taking all as his guests to the fair grounds and the beer halls; he was the first to jump on the table and toast everyone from Diener to Professor. As director of the Institut in Berlin, he would take as much time ironing out the troubles of a scrub woman as in paying his respects to a dignitary.

In the wake of Hitler's war and the hatred it unleashed, Hallervorden and Spatz became objects of odious accusations. I was able to prove the integrity and good faith of both men after consulting the evidence of the Nuremberg trials. Under the German occupation Spatz had saved my country's scientific institutions from military depredation, and at personal risk had smuggled food to prisoners-of-war in German strongholds.

Hugo Spatz, and Julius Hallervorden with him—they are inseparable—as inseparable as is their work from international neuropathology and its lasting history.

BERCHEM-ANTWERP, BELGIUM   LUDO van BOGAERT

References

[1] Histolog. histopath. Arb. (Nissl-Alzheimer), 1918, 6:477–604. [2] Ibid., Ergbd., 1921, 49:264 et seq.   [3] Zschr. ges. Neur. Psychiat., 1920, 58:327–337.   [4] Ibid., 1922, 77:261–390.   [5] Deut. Zschr. Nervenh., 1924, 81:185–188.   [6] Bethe's Hdb. d. Physiologie, 10:318–417, 1927.   [7] Zschr. ges. Neurol., 1924, 89:138–170.   [8] Ibid., 1926, 100:428–449.   [9] Ibid., 1922, 79:254–302.   [10] Münch. med. Wschr., 1923, 70:1245 (with Lucksch).   [11] Zschr. ges. Neurol., 1925, 97:627–650.   [12] Ibid., 1930, 124:317–382.   [13] Bumke's Hdb. d. Geisteskrankheiten 11:157–288, 1930.   [14] Nervenarzt, 1931, 4:466–472, 531–542.   [15] Arch. Psychiat., Berlin, 1933, 101:267–358.   [16] Ibid., 1933, 98:457–461.   [17] Zschr. ges. Neurol., 1937, 158:208–232.   [18] Arch.

Psychiat., Berlin, 1938, *108*:1–18. [19] Virchows Arch., 1939, *305:* 567–592 (with Driggs). [20] Acta neuroveg., Berlin, 1952, *3*:5–49. [21] Möllendorff's *Hdb. d. mikr. Anat. d. Menschen, Nervensystem,* IV/7, 1962 (Diepen). [22] Henke-Lubarsch's *Hdb. spez. path. Anat.,* XIII/1A, 1957, p. 614–715 (with Lüers). [23] Münch. med. Wschr., 1952, *94*:1154–1164; 1209–1218; 1255–1262. [24] Zschr. ges. Neurol., 1937, *158*:208–232. [25] *Vergangenheit und Zukunft des Menschenhirns.* Akad d. Wissenschaften. Wiesbaden, Steiner, 1964. [26] Hassler and Stephen (eds.), *Evolution of the forebrain. Phylogenesis and ontogenesis of the forebrain.* Stuttgart, Thieme, 1966, p. 136–152 (Spatz).

References to Biography and Works of Spatz: 1) Mitteil. aus der Max-Planck-Gesellsch. 1958, Heft 6, p. 374–376 (Krücke). 2) Nervenarzt, 1963, *34*:416–418 (Hallervorden). 3) J. Hirnforsch., 1964, *6:* 257–268 (Hallervorden). 4) *Ibid.,* 1963, *6*:193–196 (van Bogaert). 5) Dtsch. Z. Nervenheilk., 1969, *195*:241–256 (with complete bibliography; Hassler). 6) Arch. Psychiat. Nervenkrankheit., 1969, *212:* 91–96 Scholz).

References to Biography and Works of Hallervorden: 1) Hessisches Ärzteblatt, März 1958 (Spatz). 2) Nervenarzt, 1966, *37*:477–482 (Spatz). 3) Electromedizin, 1966, *11*:109–110 (Spaar). 4) Acta neuropath., Berlin, 1966, *6*:113–116 (Krücke).

WALTHER SPIELMEYER (1879–1935)

S PIELMEYER was born in Dessau, the youngest of a large family. Living up to its name, which suggests "fiddling," Walther nearly failed grade school; to the threatened disgrace he had to sacrifice his piano lessons. Like other future scientists he thought of going into the ministry. Having decided in favor of medicine, he spent most of his student years in Halle, especially under the physiologists Hitzig and Heilbronner, and the pathologist Eberth. In 1906, as Privatdozent at Freiburg, he embarked on psychiatry under Hoche and typically established a laboratory of histopathology. Soon he was able to support the concept that amaurotic family idiocy is the result of disturbed lipoid metabolism,[1] and to demonstrate cerebral changes and primary degenera-

tion of the posterior columns in a brilliant monograph on experimental trypanosomiasis.[2] This did much for the understanding of the pathogenesis in general paresis and tabes dorsalis. In 1911 appeared the first edition of his *Technik der mikroskopischen Untersuchung des Nervensystems* (Berlin, Springer), which became a familiar manual to his many students. As a result Kraepelin called him to Munich. Here he was to head the Anatomisches Laborato-

Portrait, courtesy of Dr. Konrad Dobriner, New York City. (Photographer: Friedrichs, Munich.)

rium der Psychiatrischen- und Nervenklinik (as successor to Alzheimer), to become Extraordinarius in 1913, Director of the histopathology section of the newly founded Deutsche Forschungsanstalt für Psychiatrie in 1917, and Honorarprofessor in 1918. His
studies of peripheral nerve injuries during World War I culminated in monographs[3,4] rivaling those of Tinel,[5] Foerster,[6] Athan-
assio-Benisty,[7,8] and Purves Stewart and Evans.[9] When in 1918
Nissl came to Munich as chief of a second histopathology section
of the Forschungsanstalt, they had a period of close and happy collaboration, cut short by Nissl's death in 1919. In 1922 appeared his
superbly illustrated *Histopathologie des Nervensystems* (Berlin,
Springer), the first textbook on general histopathology. Special
histopathology was represented by his carefully documented chapter on microscopic changes in the psychoses.[10]

Chief among Spielmeyer's later investigations was the concept of
disordered cerebral function due to temporary circulatory disturbances. Gustav Ricker (of Magdeburg) had demonstrated the effect of reduced blood flow on a variety of severe tissue changes in
the thoracic and abdominal viscera. Spielmeyer extended this concept by showing that anoxia in general may cause incomplete necrosis in the brain, as in the sclerosis of Ammon's horn.[11] His vascular theory brought him into conflict with Oskar Vogt who favored
the topistic factor. They were both correct but could never harmo-
nize their views. Later Scholz was able to build on Spielmeyer's
framework the concept of elective neuronal necrosis resulting
from transient anoxia in convulsive seizures, with status marmoratus, ulegyria, lobar sclerosis, and even hemispheric atrophy the
outcome. Spielmeyer also did much original work by correlating
different types of lesions with clinical syndromes in
encephalitis.[10,12] He was largely responsible for reconciling the
conflict between Westphal-Strümpell's pseudosclerosis and Wilson's
disease, in showing that they belong to the same general category.[13]
His outline of the events in neuropathology from 1875 to 1925 was
an important contribution to historiography.[14]

Great hopes were raised for the advancement of psychiatry when
the new building of the Deutsche Forschungsanstalt für Psychiatrie
(Kaiser Wilhelm Institut), financed by the Rockefeller Foundation, was opened in 1928, with Spielmeyer as Director of its Hirn-

pathologisches Institut. Many of these hopes had already been realized when seven years later Spielmeyer's career was brought to an
end by pulmonary tuberculosis. His able assistant and friend, Wil-
libald Scholz (1899–   ), was appointed his successor.

Spielmeyer was unassuming, polished, and rather formal, but he
had a fine sense of humor and was highly musical. He would join
his daughter in singing Schubert, Brahms or Wolff to the piano accompaniment of his wife. Musicians and singers from the National
Theater in Munich would gather at his home after a performance.
He could be outspoken in his dislike of superficiality and affecta-
tion, but usually preferred quiet innuendo. He would castigate
ideas obviously elaborated in the armchair rather than at the microscope, such as A. Jakob's view that antiluetic therapy would
transform general paresis into some other form of cerebral syphilis, or Raecke's that all such problems were solved by the finding
of the spirochete in the brain. He all but exploded when Pette
proposed at a meeting that in encephalitis only mesenchymal reactions were caused by visible microorganisms, only glial changes by
viruses.

In his publications he never failed to give his disciples due
credit. He had perhaps not the genius of a Nissl or an Alzheimer,
but he was a perfectionist, and his knowledge of minute details in
neuropathology was amazing. He was tremendously helpful, but
declined to examine neoplasms ("davon verstehe ich nichts"), and
as a confirmed pupil of Nissl and Alzheimer, he rejected metallic
impregnation methods (there was nothing an aniline dye would
not show). An assistant (Harry M. Zimmerman) who had to purchase his gold chloride in a downtown Apotheke, once smuggled a
few impregnations into a set of orthodox slides he was showing to
Spielmeyer—against the imprecations of the technical assistant
Frau Grombach. Only after a loud argument did the chief, cooling
down, concede a little value in gold. Too many had joined the
Gold Rush to no avail. It was different with the Holzer crystal-
violet glial fiber method. As told by Scholz: One autumn morning
in 1920, an elderly and inconspicuous-looking man from Westphalia, a total stranger, entered his laboratory, nodded to him, and,
without further ado, unpacked glassware and vials of stains from
his briefcase; in an atmosphere rapidly becoming frosty he an-

nounced that he could stain glial fibers in frozen sections within a minute or two. What the astonished Scholz saw under the microscope caused him to beckon Spielmeyer. "Donnerwetter! . .," exclaimed Spielmeyer. After that, Holzer was always welcome in the laboratory.

Spielmeyer's accustomed optimism suffered a great setback when the Nazis seized power. His open denunciation of the Nazi system frequently brought him into great personal danger. The outside world knew little of his untiring efforts in helping many a scholar uprooted by the Third Reich. An unselfish readiness to help, it has been said, was indeed his outstanding trait.

STANLEY COBB
MOFFETT FIELD, CALIFORNIA   WEBB HAYMAKER

References

[1] *Histologische und histopathologische Arbeiten über die Grosshirnrinde* (Nissl-Alzheimer), Jena, 1908, *2*:193–251.   [2] *Die Trypanosomenkrankheiten und ihre Beziehungen zu den syphilogenen Nervenkrankheiten.* Jena, Fischer, 1908.   [3] *Zur Klinik und Anatomie der Nervenschussverletzungen.* Berlin, Springer, 1915.   [4] Bethe, A., Bergman, G., et al., *Handbuch der normalen und pathologischen Physiologie.* Berlin, 1929, *9*:285–333.   [5] *Les blessures des nerfs.* Paris, Masson, 1916.   [6] Lewandowsky, M. H., *Handbuch der Neurologie.* Ergänzungsband, 2.Teil. Berlin, 1929.   [7] *Formes cliniques des lésions des nerfs.* Paris, Masson, 1916.   [8] *Traitement et réstauration des lésions des nerfs.* Paris, Masson, 1917.   [9] *Nerve injuries and their treatment.* ed. 2. London, Oxford Univ. Press, 1919.   [10] Bumke, O., *Handbuch der Geisteskrankheiten.* Berlin, 1930, *11*:1–41.   [11] Mschr. Psychiat., 1928, *68*:605–620.   [12] Virchows Arch., 1928, *242*:479–499.   [13] Zschr. ges. Neur. Psychiat., 1920, *57*:312–351.   [14] Arch. Psychiat., Berlin, 1925, *76*:47–57.

References to Biography: 1) Zschr. ges. Neur. Psychiat., 1935, *153*: 1–36 (contains bibliography; Scholz).   2) Schweiz. Arch. Neur. Psychiat., 1935, *36*:191–196 (Walthard).   3) Arch. Psychiat., Berlin, 1935, *103*:455–470 (contains bibliography; Spatz).   4) *50 Jahre Neuropathologie in Deutschland 1885–1935.* Stuttgart, Thieme, 1961, pp. 87–107 (Scholz).

RUDOLF VIRCHOW (1821–1902)

*I*T IS the privilege of few men to share so greatly in the scientific, cultural, and political events of their time as did Rudolf Virchow. Born in the small Pomeranian town of Schievelbein, Virchow came to Berlin in 1839 to study at the University. Johannes Müller was then professor of physiology; among his students were the histologists Henle and Schwann and the physiologists du Bois-Reymond and Helmholtz. Certainly Virchow was indebted to these men, master and pupils alike, for his recognition that changes in the structure and function of the cell must play a prominent role in disease. Also to Wilhelm Griesinger (1817–1868), from Stuttgart, successor to Romberg (in 1865) at the Charité and founder of the *Berliner Gesellschaft für Psychiatrie und Nervenkrankheiten,* where Virchow often held forth. Besides, Griesinger was, in Germany, the champion of neuropathology as the basis of much mental illness, author of a distinguished treatise on pseudohypertrophic muscular dystrophy,[1] and the founder of the *Archiv für Psychiatrie.*

Virchow's doctoral thesis was on inflammation of a nonvascular organ, the cornea (*De rheumate praesertim corneae,* 1848). It is likely that this choice conditioned his later thinking on parenchymatous inflammation, on its cellular rather than its vascular basis. Upon graduation, he became assistant to the distinguished Froriep at the Charité and was delegated to perform all chemical and microscopic examinations for the hospital. The good use to which he put these studies is shown by the series of articles he published in early numbers of his *Archiv für pathologische Anatomie und Physiologie und für klinische Medizin.* He was only twenty-six years old when, jointly with Benno Reinhardt, and stung by having two of his papers rejected elsewhere, he founded this journal—called "Virchows Archiv" after his death.

Virchow had a tongue and a pen that sent chills into those espousing antiquated philosophical or social systems. At twenty-five, for the benefit of the Berlin Society for Scientific Medicine, he scathingly denounced dogmatism and asked that a pathological

Rudolf Ludwig Carl Virchow

physiology be developed, not by "a few heated brains," but by a core of patient investigators, with pathological anatomy and the clinic only the out-works. During the revolution of 1848 he was also explosive; for awhile he was at the barricades. Sent to Silesia to investigate and report on the cause of the typhoid epidemic that had been raging there, he returned, to the embarrassment of the Prussian Government, with a stinging denunciation of those responsible for the sanitary and social conditions. His alleged political agitation among the employees of the Charité brought him a reprimand from the Ministry of Education and dismissal from the University. Almost at once Bavaria offered him the professorship of pathology at Würzburg.

Here, Virchow laid the foundations for his concept of cellular pathology and made many of his contributions to normal as well as to pathological histology. In 1856 he was recalled to Berlin, and in the spring of 1858 gave the series of twenty lectures published as *Die Cellularpathologie* (Berlin, Hirschwald, 1858).[2] The almost equally epoch-making survey of neoplasms, *Die krankhaften Geschwülste,* appeared in 1863–67 (Berlin, Hirschwald).

When he laid down the principles of cellular pathology, Virchow already had a great feat in neuropathology behind him, that of establishing the major mechanisms of cerebral softening: embolism and thrombosis, putting in its place inflammation, the antiquated catch-all.[3] Virchow's contributions to neuropathology were many and varied—in all, thirty-five papers or more, including studies on pachymeningitis hemorrhagica interna; cerebral hemorrhage; meningitis; melanosis of the arachnoid; tumors of the central nervous system and peripheral nerves; and congenital anomalies of the skull, vertebrae, brain and spinal cord. Better known than any of these, however, were two discoveries he made in the field of neurohistology.

The first, in 1851, was the description of the perivascular space now associated with the names of Virchow and Robin. (The latter's contribution to the subject was made in 1859.[4]) This space was called to Virchow's attention by von Kölliker, who found it filled with blood in cases of subarachnoid hemorrhage and who thought that the hemorrhage in the perivascular space was from dissecting aneurysms. Virchow corrected this view, pointing out that no rupture existed in these vessels and that the blood had passed into the space from a hemorrhage in the arachnoid.[5]

In an appendix to a paper on corpora amylacea, which appeared in 1854, Virchow first described the cellular nature of the cerebral interstitial substance.[6] Two years later he named and defined this "connecting substance in the spinal cord and the higher sensory nerves" as "a sort of glue (*neuroglia*) sunk into which are the nervous elements."[7] On the basis of the word "Kitt," or glue, in this sentence, Virchow is frequently accused of having failed to recognize in the neuroglia any function other than that of a supporting structure. However, in an article published that same year he clearly described the phagocytic action of certain of these cells in an area of encephalomalacia.[8]

After 1870 Virchow's productivity in the field of pathology declined while he devoted increasing attention to politics and public health. For many years he sat in the Reichstag as an unrelenting liberal. F. H. Lewey could remember him emerging from the University portal, getting into a carriage with black tassels hanging from the top, and being driven off to the Reichstag with his eyes narrowed, concocting strategy as to how he would oppose Bismarck this time. In academic meetings he was a formidable power, even though he sat through them half asleep. In later years Virchow also devoted a great deal of effort to anthropology and is regarded by some as having achieved in this field an eminence almost equal to that assured him in pathology. He died from the complications of a traffic accident: this impetuous man had fractured his hip in jumping off a moving streetcar.

HANS G. SCHLUMBERGER

References

[1] Arch. Heilk., 1865, 6:1–13.   [2] *Cellular pathology*. London, Churchill, 1860 (transl. from the German by Chance).   [3] *Gesammelte Abh. wissensch. Med.* Frankfurt a.M., Meidlinger, 1856, p. 219–732. [4] J. Physiol., Paris, 1859, 2:536–548.   [5] Arch. path. Anat. (later Virchows Arch.), 1851, 3:428–462.   [6] *Ibid.*, 1854, 6:138.   [7] *Gesammelte Abh. wissensch. Med.* Frankfurt a.M., Meidlinger, 1856, p. 890. [8] Arch. path. Anat., 1856, 10:407–408.

References to Biography: 1) Virchows Arch., 1921, 235:1–452 (Memorial Volume) (Lubarsch).   2) Arch. Path., Chic., 1944, 37:396–407 (Schlumberger).   3) Abh. k. preuss. Akad. Wissensch., Berl., 1903, 1–52 (Waldeyer).   4) Virchows Arch., 1903, 121:2–7 (von Recklinghausen).   5) Johns Hopkins Univ. Circ., Balt., 1891, 11: 17–19 (Osler).   6) Science, 1902, n.s., 15:441–445 (Boas). *Rudolf Virchow und die deutschen Naturforscherversammlungen*. Leipzig, Akad. Verlagsgesellschaft, 1922 (Sudhoff).   7) *Rudolf Virchow, doctor, statesman, anthropologist*. Madison, Univ. of Wisconsin Press, 1953 (Ackerknecht).   8) *Young endeavour*. Springfield, Thomas, 1958, p. 156–159 (Gibson).   9) *Disease, life and man. Selected essays by Rudolf Virchow*. Stanford, Stanford U. P., 1958 (Rather). 10) *Utopien der Medizin*. Salzburg, Müller, 1968 (Schipperges).

CÉCILE MUGNIER VOGT (1875–1962)
OSKAR VOGT (1870–1959)

*T*HEY met in Paris. Mademoiselle Mugnier was studying with Pierre Marie at the Bicêtre; Dr. Vogt, fresh from anatomical studies at Jena and with Flechsig at Leipzig, had settled down at the Salpêtrière to learn clinical neurology under Dejerine (1898). She had the *savoir-vivre,* the even disposition, the quick perceptiveness and the ready wit, the logic and the smile in making a point that could brook no effective rebuttal, a rare graciousness that brought all into her confidence. He had an implacable will, a smoldering fire in his eyes, a nature in turn irascible and most engaging; great lung power, a vibrant voice in making a point, and no soft words where a breach of principle was involved; strong friendships, strong enmities—a gifted raconteur, a compelling speaker. Both had forebears who were of strong conviction and colorful. Cécile's mother, back in the Savoy Alps, having separated herself from her church, refrained from witnessing her daughter's confirmation, though she yielded to the extent of escorting the child as far as the portals of the cathedral. Oskar, half Danish, half German (Schleswig-Holstein), issued from a line that included liberal Lutheran ministers, sea captains, and a pirate. Cécile would quote Pierre Marie's warning to think twice before marrying Vogt.

They married in Berlin and in the same year (1899) founded a *Neurologische Zentralstation,* which they supported through private practice. Some thirty brains had been contributed by Pierre Marie; following a heated argument on some point in anatomy, Marie had announced "Monsieur Vogt, you need some brains to study!" In the years that followed, and as their contributions became recognized, they crusaded for the establishment of an institute. As a result their *Zentralstation* was renamed *Neurobiologisches Universitäts-Laboratorium* in 1915 and placed under the aegis of the *Kaiser Wilhelm-Gesellschaft zur Förderung der Wissenschaften;* in 1931 the imposing *Kaiser Wilhelm-Institut für Hirnforschung* was opened for them in Buch, a suburb of Berlin. Brodmann and Bielschowsky were on their staff,

and subsequently, Maximilian Rose. Their daughter, Marthe, held a post in chemistry and pharmacology.

Normal architectonics, pathoarchitectonics, cerebral fiber pathways, extrapyramidal diseases and varied pathological processes—these were the main fields in which the Vogts pioneered. "Allocortex" and "isocortex" were terms he fostered. A major paper on cytoarchitectonics came from both in 1919.[2] Later, they were sharply challenged for the extraordinarily large number of cortical fields and "topistic units" they described—by those who did not sit with them to review their evidence. Less well known is their physiological mapping of the simian cortex (e.g., of the functional boundary between area 4 and 6) which provided the groundwork for Otfrid Foerster's electrical stimulation of the human brain.

Their names, particularly Cécile's, are indelibly linked with the anatomy and disease states of the basal ganglia. Oskar Vogt was heard to exclaim: "It is marvelous! When my wife looks down the

Portraits, courtesy of the Vogts.

microscope she always finds something new." It was not long until
Cécile Vogt established herself as one of the first women in science, the others being her contemporaries, Mme. Curie, Mme.
Dejerine-Klumpke, and Mme. Nageotte. Her observation in 1909[3]
of a massive projection from the striatum to the ventral thalamic
nucleus went unnoticed until the 1930's, as did also their joint
work, published in 1941,[4] on the fiber systems from thalamus to
striatum. Much still lies hidden: for example, their observation
that the mamillothalamic tract, in its ascent, gives off collaterals in
the region of the nucleus campi Foreli.[5] Cécile Vogt's atlas on the
myeloarchitecture of the monkey's thalamus, based on Marchi
studies following destruction of the medial lemniscus and the brachium conjunctivum, revealed forty different grisea (1919[6]). Her
fundamental work on *athétose double* appeared in 1911; one of
the four communications was in collaboration with Oppenheim,[7]
who had clinically diagnosed that condition as "hereditary pseudobulbar palsy." Kinnier Wilson was quick to acknowledge her
contributions. *État marbré (status marmoratus)* she introduced as
a designation for the mottled appearance of the striatum in the
double athetosis commencing in childhood, a change which she
considered the substrate of uncomplicated double athetosis. *État
dysmyélinique (status dysmyelinisatus)* was the term she coined
for the selective myelin loss in the globus pallidus which was
thought by her to be the substrate of the rigid form of double athetosis. *État précriblé (status precribratus)* was the designation
she proposed for the early tissue loculation in the lenticular nucleus observed in extrapyramidal disorders. (In their publications
she used the French terms, he the Latin.) Their concept of *patho-
clisis*,[8,9] signifying selective brain damage in the face of exposure
to a noxious agent, was to follow. Tireless, more than anyone since,
they studied the brains of famous people. Lenin's was among them;
even prior to Lenin's death Oskar Vogt had journeyed to Moscow
as neurological consultant.

Because of his antagonism during the upsurgence of the Nazi
party, Oskar Vogt was forced to retire from the directorship of the
institute (1937). Anticipating the event, they had built a private
Institut für Hirnforschung und Allgemeine Biologie deep in the
Schwarzwald near Neustadt. The Krupps, long indebted to Oskar

Vogt for his defense of a family member in court, had helped in financing it. At first they stayed unmolested, but at the beginning of the war, Oskar Vogt, now sixty-nine, was drafted as a private and charged with organizing a military hospital in the area; before directing officers as to their duties he would cover his uniform with a white gown. After six weeks of this absurdity he was discharged.

Their institute flourished. Cytology came more and more into their sphere of interest. Nerve-cell aging, Oskar Vogt observed, is highly similar to the changes observed in transneuronal degeneration—as is brought out by Folke Henschen, in his review of the subject.[10] The Vogts turned also to genetic mutations, using as their specimens the bumblebees and beetles they had collected by the hundreds of thousands on their holiday trips to the Caucasus, the Balkans, North Africa, and the Balearic Islands. The Vogts' daughter Marguerite, a member of the staff, participated in this research for some ten years before departing to California. Jerzy Olszewski also made significant contributions here. Later he emigrated to Canada. Another pupil, Friedrich Sanides,[11] explored that obstacle-strewn wilderness, the substantia innominata of Reichert (Carl Bogislaus Reichert, 1811–1884), called such by some unknown wag in finding that Reichert had left it unnamed (in his Fig. 36) in his magnificent atlas of the brain published in 1859–1861.[12]

Honors too numerous to mention came. Cécile Vogt received honorary doctorates from the Universities of Freiburg and Jena. An honorary D.Sc. was conferred on Oskar Vogt by Oxford University; the Public Orator, referring to him as "Nestor of Neurology," was reminded of the poet Ennius who was declared to own three souls: "Dr. Vogt, I think has the same number—for *Jena* taught him his anatomy; a famous *Swiss* neurologist, Auguste Forel, was his next instructor, and his clinical neurology was learned from the *French*, who also gave him his wife . . ."

When Oskar Vogt died at the age of eighty-nine, Cécile moved to Cambridge to be with her daughter, Marthe. For the first time, and until the end, Cécile Vogt found it hard to cope with life.

MOFFETT FIELD, CALIFORNIA   WEBB HAYMAKER

References

[1] Congr. 20° des médecins alién. et neurol. de France le 8 août 1910, Brussels, 1911, p. 3–11.   [2] J. Psychol. Neur., Lpz., Erg. Heft 1, 1919, 25:279–462.   [3] *Ibid.*, Erg. Heft, 1919, 12:285–324.   [4] *Ibid.*, 1941, 50:31–154.   [5] Sitzber. Akad. Wiss. Wien, Math.-naturw. Cl. (Abt. B), 1919, 14:1–56.   [6] J. Psychol. Neur., Lpz., Erg. Heft, 1909, 12: 285–324.   [7] *Ibid.*, Erg. Heft, 1911, 18:293–308.   [8] *Ibid.*, Erg. Heft, 1922, 28:1–170.   [9] Neurology, 1951, 1:205–218.   [10] Thule Internat. Sympos. Cancer and Aging. Stockholm, Nord. Bokh. Förlag, 1968, p. 61–80.   [11] J. Hirnforsch., 1957, 3:243–273.   [12] *Der Bau des menschlichen Gehirns durch Abbildungen mit erläuterndem Text.* I. u. II. Abth. Leipzig, Engelmann, 1859–1861.

References to Biography and Works: 1) Nervenarzt, 1940, 13:145–154 (with partial bibliography; Spatz).   2) Arch. Psychiat., Berlin, u. Zschr. ges. Neur. Psychiat., 1951, 185:619–623 (Kleist).   3) Arch. Neur. Psychiat., Chic., 1950, 64:813–822 (Olszewski).   4) Neurology, 1951, 1:179–204 (with partial bibliography; Haymaker).   5) Amer. J. Psychiat., 1960, 116:958–960 (Bruetsch).   6) Arch. Neur. Psychiat., Chic., 1961, 4:675–684 (on O. Vogt) (with partial bibliography; Haymaker).   7) Kolle (ed.), *Grosse Nervenärzte.* Vol. 2. Stuttgart, Thieme, 1959, p. 45–64 (Hassler). 8) J. Hirnforsch., 1962, 5:246–248 (on C. Vogt) (Hopf).

CARL WEIGERT (1845–1904)

*C*ARL WEIGERT was born at Muensterberg, Silesia, Germany. He studied medicine in the Universities of Breslau, Berlin, and Vienna, and was influenced chiefly by the physiologist, Heidenhain and the anatomist, Waldeyer. After graduation in 1868, he was assistant to Waldeyer in Breslau. He saw active service during the Franco-Prussian War in 1870–71, then became assistant to the clinician and pathologist Lebert in Breslau (1871–73). In 1874, Cohnheim, attracted by Weigert's authoritative paper on the pathology of smallpox, made him first assistant at the Breslau Institute of Pathology, where his habilitation took place (1875). With Cohnheim, Weigert went to Leipzig in 1878 and was promoted to Extraordinarius of pathology in 1879. In 1885—after

Cohnheim's death—he moved to Frankfurt-am-Main to accept a post as chief of the pathology section at the Senckenbergisches Pathologisch-Anatomisches Institut. This "Institut" was an ill-equipped, old, private cottage, where, in the early 1900's, Ehrlich and Edinger were chiefs of the two other sections. Here the three of them—Weigert, the quiet introspective unremitting worker, Ehrlich, the fighter and the most ebullient, Edinger, the solid purveyor of constantly new ideas, with the genius to find rapidly the answers he was seeking—brought to Frankfurt a position equalling that of other German universities.

Portrait, courtesy of Prof. Dr. W. Krücke, Frankfurt-am-Main, Germany.

Weigert published about one hundred papers over a period of almost four decades.[1] Significantly, his first and his last papers dealt with the nervous system. The former was his doctor's thesis: *De nervorum lesionibus telorum ictu effectis;* the latter was on cerebellar changes in tabes. He was among the first to stain bacteria (1871). His research on inflammation, coagulation necrosis, pathogenesis of tuberculosis, Bright's disease, morphology of neuroglia,[2] and biology of the cell, resulted in signal contributions to our knowledge and clearly show that his interests encompassed the whole realm of pathology. It would be entirely wrong to call him only an inventor of technical methods, though it is said that he displayed a greater fondness for staining cells than for pursuing a study of their nature and functions. It is his methods, however, which have founded his reputation in neurology. Weigert introduced aniline dyes, and it may be more than coincidence in this connection that he was a cousin of Ehrlich. He also perfected the technique of celloidin embedding, which was introduced in 1882 by Schiefferdecker. His methods for the staining of fibrin, elastic fibers, myelin sheaths, and glia, and his modification of the hematoxylin-Van Gieson stain still are in use in laboratories of general and neural pathology everywhere. The technic for the staining of myelin sheaths, based on his observation that when brain tissue is mordanted in chromic salts the myelin sheaths stain selectively with acid fuchsin or hematoxylin,[3-5] opened new avenues to the understanding of many diseases of the spinal cord and brain. The glial method was Weigert's "child of sorrow"; he had experimented seven years before he published it in 1895. And for another nine years he tried to improve it. Weigert would say to his student Raubitschek from time to time, "That staining technic of mine just published took me ten years to work out, and I'd be surprised if someone didn't publish a modification within three weeks." Small wonder, then, that Alzheimer once remarked that Weigert was the master who created our tools. The significance of Weigert's studies of neuroglia was emphasized more recently by Krücke (1961).

Weigert's circle was small. Visitors to his laboratory were discouraged from staying; those who were accepted had to do their work in quiet. It was his custom to invite an assistant or two for dinner at a Gasthaus, where he assumed the role of attentive host. Despite his outward calm, Weigert was a disappointed man, for his hope to become Ordinarius was never fulfilled; this was not only because he was of Jewish extraction but also because he lacked the self-assurance needed to fill the role. He performed many autopsies for my father and my grandfather, both general practitioners in Frankfurt. They praised his ability in the elucidation of complicated cases, his modesty, balance and sincerity, his critical philosophical mind, and his keen, nonsatiric sense of humor.

One cannot cease to wonder at his unending patience in probing the mysteries of the affinities of different tissues for dyestuffs. Nor can one forget their array in little Liebig meat extract bottles on his desk (he preferred these to standard glassware) over which he used to hover; the solutions were filtering away at the time of his death, which came suddenly and unexpectedly from coronary thrombosis.

DENVER, COLORADO   KARL T. NEUBUERGER

References

[1] *Gesammelte Abhandlungen von Carl Weigert.* 2 vol. Berlin, Springer, 1906.   [2] *Beiträge zur Kenntnis der normalen menschlichen Neuroglia.* Festschr. zum 50-jährigen Jubil. d. ärztl. Vereins zu Frankfurt a.M., 1895.   [3] Cbl. med. Wissensch., 1882, *20*:753–757 *et seq.* [4] Deut. med. Wschr., 1891, *17*:1184–1186.   [5] Ciba Zschr., 1943, *8:* 3074–3109 (history of histological staining techniques; Hintzsche).

References to Biography and Works: 1) *Carl Weigert und seine Bedeutung für die medizinische Wissenschaft unserer Zeit. Eine biographische Skizze.* Berlin, Springer, 1906 (Rieder),   2) J.A.M.A., 1907, *48*:412–415 (contains bibliography; Dunham, Herter).   3) Ann. Med. Hist., New York, 1924, *6*:163–177 (Morrison).   4) *50 Jahre Neuropathologie in Deutschland 1885–1935,* by W. Scholz (Ed.). Stuttgart, Thieme, 1961 (Krücke).

OTTO IVAR WICKMAN (1872–1914)

W ICKMAN'S studies on poliomyelitis, coming midway between the pioneering work of Heine and the present, served to usher in the modern era of investigation of this disease. Jacob von Heine (1800–79), of Cannstatt, Germany, had indicated in 1840 that the essential lesion was in the spinal cord and that the disorder was an entity,[1] but his description did not surmount the then current belief that the muscle atrophy was due to inactivity. Credit for the recognition that the "primary" lesion is in the anterior horns goes to Duchenne, to Prévost, Charcot and Joffroy and to Cornil[2] and Clarke.[3] The epidemic in Sweden in 1887 provided Oscar Medin (1847–1928), of Stockholm, with the opportunity of studying the disorder on a large scale.

Wickman's principal publications, appearing in the remarkably short period between 1905 and 1911,[4-9] represented both a masterly extension of previous work and a comprehensive description and analysis of almost every phase of the disease. Wickman first formulated a clear concept of the mode of spread of the infection based on extensive evidence, and gave the first detailed description of the symptomatology. His picture of the alimentary portal of entry, of the spread of virus along nerves, and of the histopathologic manifestations has required little revision, even after experimental methods were brought to bear upon these difficult problems of pathogenesis. Since he himself considered his work essentially completed in 1907, it was fortuitous that there soon followed the transmission of the disease to monkeys by Landsteiner and Popper in 1908.[10] Since then his classical monographs on the natural history of the disease[8,9] have served as a durable source for both experimentalists and clinicians. In his publication in 1910,[7] in which a bibliography of the subject, including that on the "Landry form," is to be found, Wickman dealt with the story of the nomenclature of the disease: the prevalence of the use of the term "Heine-Medinsche Krankheit," the recommendation by P. Krause that it be named "akute epidemische Kinderlähmung," and his [Wickman's] reasons for calling it "Poliomyelitis acuta."

Wickman was born in Lund, Sweden, and received his medical

education in Stockholm. In 1907 he was made Docent in neurology there. Between 1899 and 1903 he served as teaching assistant in infectious diseases and in medicine, and between 1907 and 1909 as a district medical officer in Stockholm. These experiences gave

Portrait, courtesy of Prof. Folke Henschen, Stockholm, Sweden. (Taken in Strassburg, 1910.)

him the rare opportunity to deal with poliomyelitis as an infectious disease as well as a neurological one, and made possible the observations which gave overwhelming evidence in support of his theory of person-to-person spread of the disease. He confirmed Caverly's recognition in 1896[11] of abortive cases, and showed the role of healthy carriers as well.

Following his work on poliomyelitis, Wickman spent five years in Helsingfors, Berlin, Paris, Breslau and Strassburg, in studies intended to prepare him for the chair of pediatrics in Stockholm, soon to be relinquished by his teacher Medin. He returned to Sweden in 1914, but failed to be appointed. This was a blow which even the prospect of another professorship failed to cushion. A speech defect, which resisted all attempts at treatment, served to accentuate his unhappy position. He terminated a career of intense striving and great accomplishment by taking his own life at the age of forty-two.

BALTIMORE, MARYLAND   DAVID BODIAN

References

[1] *Beobachtungen über Lähmungszustände der untern Extremitäten und deren Behandlung.* Stuttgart, Köhler, 1840. (ed. 2: *Spinale Kinderlähmung.* Stuttgart, Cotta, 1860.)   [2] C. rend. Soc. biol., Paris, 1863, 3.sér., *5*:187–192.   [3] Med.-Chir. Trans., London, 1868, *51*:249–262 (with Johnson).   [4] *Studien über Poliomyelitis acuta, zugleich ein Beitrag zur Kenntnis der Myelitis acuta.* Berlin, Karger, 1905. [5] Arb. Path. Inst. Helsingfors, 1905, *1*:109–292.   [6] Zschr. ges. Neur. Psychiat., 1911, *4*:54–66.   [7] Deut. Zschr. Nervenh., 1910, *38*:396–437.   [8] *Beiträge zur Kenntnis der Heine-Medinschen Krankheit.* Berlin, Karger, 1907.   [9] Lewandowsky, M., *Handbuch der Neurologie.* Berlin, 1911, 2:807–910. (Engl. trans.: Nerv. Ment. Dis. Monogr., 1913, No. 16).   [10] Zschr. Immunforsch., 1909, *2*:377–390. [11] J.A.M.A., 1896, *26*:1–5.

References to Biography: 1) Hygiea, Stockh., 1914, *76*:479–484 (Josefson).   2) Zschr. ges. Neur. Psychiat., 1914, *26*:1–5 (Klotz).

VI

CLINICAL NEUROLOGISTS

JOSEPH FRANÇOIS FÉLIX BABINSKI (1857–1932)

*A*S political refugees, Babinski's parents fled in 1848 from Poland to Paris, where Joseph was born and grew up. He was graduated from the University of Paris in 1884. His thesis, of outstanding merit, dealt with multiple sclerosis. Under Charcot, he worked at the Salpêtrière, and from 1890 to 1927 headed the neurological clinic at the Hôpital de la Pitié. With Brissaud, Pierre Marie, Dejerine, Souques, and others, he founded the Société de Neurologie de Paris, to which he was profoundly devoted. The last years of his life were marred by paralysis agitans.

Babinski had a thorough training in general medicine before undertaking the study of neurology. His bibliography[1] contains 288 items, the first on typhoid fever (1882), the last on hysteria (1930). At a meeting of the Société de Biologie in 1896, he described his "cutaneous plantar reflex."[2] The report contained but twenty-eight lines. Although this sign had been reported three years before by E. Remak, it was Babinski who first realized its diagnostic significance. In its simplicity, clinical importance, and physiological implications, Babinski's sign has hardly an equal in medicine. The number of works devoted exclusively to "Babinski" runs into the hundreds, yet in 1900 its diagnostic importance was declared to be "minimal." His description of the associated fanning of the toes, subsequently referred to as the *signe de l'éventail,* was published in 1903.[3] Ranking among others of his important papers were those on combined flexion of thigh and trunk,[4] Argyll Robertson pupil in cerebrospinal syphilis,[5] cerebellar symptomatology, particularly asynergia[6,7] and adiadokokinesis,[8] deep and superficial reflexes,[9] and reflexes of defense.[10] In 1902, with Nageotte, he reported the syndrome of a unilateral bulbar lesion.[11] The syndrome of dystrophia adiposogenitalis was outlined by him in 1900,[12] a year before Fröhlich's description.

His concept of hysteria, which he called "pithiatisme" (curable by suggestion), was that its manifestations were produced by suggestion and abolished by countersuggestion. Once, in 1926, he

demonstrated this to me impressively. After a few words to a young hysteric he squeezed her right thumb, and a hysterical attack resulted; he squeezed her left thumb and it stopped abruptly. Babinski was among the first to note that much of the symptomatology vanished from the hysterics at the Salpêtrière after Charcot's death.

What Babinski may have lacked in heroic flourish in examining a patient, he more than made up for by his meticulous scrutiny, conscientiousness, and patience. He was a genius in searching for

Portrait, courtesy of Dr. Maurice Genty, Académie de Médecine, Paris, France.

defects, a man of inexorable logic. When, at a meeting of the Société de Neurologie de Paris, someone would present a case, Babinski's own examination of the patient would excite in the speaker both admiration and apprehension. Babinski's whole life work was charaterized by absolute honesty and scientific integrity. He worked for neurology, not for the glory of Babinski. He made little use of technical procedures; he was a clinical neurologist *par excellence,* guided by the maxim *observatio summa lex.* Some trends of modern neurology toward undue mechanization makes one think that a plea "Back to Babinski!" would not be without justification.

But Babinski was not solely a clinician. In the laboratory he was a discerning histologist and histopathologist. He recognized the muscle spindle for what it was, distinguished neuropathic from myopathic muscle lesions, recognized the hallmarks of the muscular dystrophies, and, in drawing attention to the hemiplegic form of multiple sclerosis, clarified the topography of the plaques through longitudinal sectioning of the cord.

Babinski's way of life allowed time to contemplate. He was spared the chore of systemic teaching (having failed in the highly competitive examination for the title *Professeur agrégé,* which, had he won, would have made him Charcot's successor). He thus could devote his mornings to clinical practice and research at the Pitié, and his afternoons in his private consulting room. At home his brother Henri, a distinguished engineer, was the housekeeper and his amanuensis. Evenings would frequently be spent in the theatre, especially at the opera or ballet. Another of his passions was gastronomy. He was known, on one occasion, to interrupt ward rounds and speed home in his carriage after a ward sister had whispered a telephone message in his ear that the soufflé was nearing perfection.

Babinski anticipated the approach of the neurosurgical era. In 1922, he localized the first spinal cord tumor to be removed in France.[13] Six days before his death he said that his best contribution was not his sign, but the fact that he had shown the way to de Martel and Vincent, the founders of French neurosurgery.

ROBERT WARTENBERG

References

[1]*Oeuvre scientifique: recueil des principaux travaux.* Publié par les soins de Barré, Chaillous, Charpentier, *et al.* Paris, Masson, 1934. [2]C. rend. Soc. biol., Paris, 1896, *3*:207–208.   [3]Rev. neur., Paris, 1903, *11*:728–729.   [4]Bull. Soc. méd. hôp. Paris, 1897, *14*:1098–1103. [5]Bull. Soc. fr. derm. syph., 1899, *10*:347–352.   [6]Rev. neur., Par., 1899, *7*:784–785.   [7]Tr. Internat. Congr. Med., London, 1913, sect., XI, Neuropath. pt. 1, p. 1–58.   [8]Rev. neur., Paris, 1902, *10*:1013.   [9]Bull. méd., Paris, 1912, *26*:929–936.   [10]Rev. neur., Paris, 1922, *38*:1049–1081. Brain, London, 1922, *45*:149–184.   [11]Rev. neur., Paris, 1902, *10*:358–365.   [12]*Ibid.,* 1900, *8*:531–533.   [13]*Ibid.,* 1912, *23*:1–4.

References to Biography and Works: 1) Arch. Neur. Psychiat., Chic., 1933, *29*:168–174 (contains partial bibliography; Fulton).   2) Bull. méd. (suppl.), 1934, *48*:1–8 (Charpentier).   3) J.A.M.A., 1947, *135:* 762–767 (Wartenberg).   4) Proc. Roy. Soc. Med., London, 1967, *60*:399–405 (Miller).

ROBERT BÁRÁNY (1876–1936)

*B*ÁRÁNY was born and brought up in Vienna, and it was there that he received his university training. After graduating in medicine in 1900, he became assistant in the medical clinic of von Noorden in Frankfurt-am-Main, worked in neurology with Kraepelin in Heidelberg, and then went to Paris. In 1903 he returned to Vienna. Among his teachers was Sigmund Freud, of whom he liked to tell this story: Freud maintained that dreams are an expression of desire (Wunschträume). He said to his students: "If you cannot explain your dreams then come and see me." Bárány did so and described for Freud a dream which had nothing to do with *desire.* Freud said, "That is very simple. You had the *desire* to contradict me."

It was when he found a place in the ear clinic of Adam Politzer (later under Urbantschitsch) in Vienna in 1905 that Bárány was able to devote himself to the work for which he is best known. He was impressed by the rhythmic nystagmus produced by syringing the ears, a phenomenon which, as he discovered, was related to the

Wien, April 1913

Dr Robert Bárány

temperature of the water. From his painstaking observations he was able to analyze the factors governing labyrinthine stimulation.[1-5] There was always a question in Vienna of priority in this field, for Bárány is said to have commenced working on the laby-

Portrait, courtesy of the National Library of Medicine, Bethesda, Maryland.

rinth after he had witnessed Spitzer's demonstration of labyrinthine nystagmus in experimental animals. The matter was even more discussed when, in 1914, Bárány received the Nobel Prize for his work on the physiology and pathology of the vestibular system.

Bárány was the first to arrive at a real understanding of recurrent labyrinthine vertigo, which previously had been confused with cerebellar disease, epilepsy, and a variety of other conditions. Recurrent labyrinthine vertigo was originally described by Prosper Menière (1799–1862) in 1861,[6] but his case was a symptomatic form of the disorder (due either to leukemic hemorrhage into the labyrinth or to acute purulent labyrinthitis), not Menière's disease as it is now known.

Bárány knew that altering the position of the head had a decided effect on labyrinthine stimulation, for he reported that the disagreeable sensations he had experienced while riding a scenic railway in a Vienna amusement park were alleviated by flexing his head 90°,[7] but it was Quix who was the first to observe that the effects of changing the position of the head were due to an alteration in the relation of the otolith organs to the plane of motion[8] and to demonstrate that 8th nerve section renders animals insensitive to motion.[9] Another of Bárány's important observations was that neck muscles send proprioceptor impulses to the extraocular nuclei for the reflex control of eye movements.[10] Because of his many contributions, Bárány may be regarded as a successor to such men as Purkyně, Goltz and Flourens, and, in the domain of motion sickness, a predecessor of Magnus and de Kleijn,[11] of Sjöberg (who, in a classical work, first demonstrated the indispensability of the labyrinths in the production of motion sickness),[12,13] of Spiegel,[14] and of Tyler and Bard.[9]

Following the suggestion of Bolk that the cerebellum must be organized on a plan of somatomotor localization, Bárány set to work to test this view. He believed that the vermis is concerned with coordinated movements of the trunk, and the hemispheres with those of the extremities,[15] and that the floccular cortex influences eye movements.[16]

Bárány was made Privatdozent at the University of Vienna in 1908. Shortly before World War I he was appointed Professor Extraordinarius. During the war he served in the Austrian army until his capture by the Russians. He was still a prisoner in the fortress of Przemysl when chosen for the highest honor of his career, the Nobel Prize for Physiology and Medicine in 1914. Prince Carl of Sweden at length prevailed upon the Czar to release Bárány, who then proceeded to Sweden for formal acceptance of the prize.

During this trip to Sweden, Bárány was invited to take the chair of otology in the University of Upsala, which he accepted in 1917, at first as Privatdozent and Titular Professor, and from 1926 as Ordinarius. He built up a great reputation as an aural surgeon, particularly in the surgical treatment of deafness, sinus disorders, and cerebral and cerebellar abscesses.

His explanation of the division of the granular layer of the visual cortex in mammals with binocular vision is well known.[17] Perhaps it will not be long before his explanation of the mechanism of hearing will become general in application. His interpretation of neuroses as being the result of closed chain activity foreshadowed later utilizations of this theory by Kuhlenbeck,[18] Kubie, Hinsey and Ranson, de Nó, and Rosenblueth.

Bárány adapted himself well to his new country, Sweden, where his activities as philanthropist, pacifist and humanist brought him further prominence. It was upon his instigation that the International Academy of Politics and Social Science for the Promotion of World Peace was founded in Sweden in 1929. Besides being a prolific writer (his papers number almost 200), he found time to edit scientific journals.

Bárány was essentially a man of theory. He would develop a theory and then put it to the experimental test. A victim of insomnia, he would lie in bed until the early hours thinking, thinking, thinking. His dependence on theory is illustrated by the following story. While he was in Berlin in Oskar and Cécile Vogt's laboratory he and the Vogts were performing an experiment on a monkey. Oskar Vogt syringed cold water in one ear and simultaneously stimulated the cortex of the same side while Cécile Vogt and Bárány watched the direction in which nystagmus occurred. On cessation of the ocular movements Bárány declared that they were to the left, whereas Cécile argued that they were to the right. The argument grew more and more heated for the ensuing five minutes. The next day Bárány came into the laboratory and stated that during the night he had reconsidered the matter. He conceded that Cécile was right. He had allowed himself to be so influenced by theory that he failed in the observation. The same happened to Bárány several times in the Vogts' laboratory. His unreliable memory for observed facts might well serve as an explanation for his forgetfulness of the work of Spitzer, referred to in the foregoing; there was no question but that he was most honest and upright.

Bárány died after having been afflicted with thalamic pain for a year and a half. Had he survived two weeks longer he would have witnessed an appropriate celebration of the anniversary of his sixtieth birthday. His death occurred one-hundred years after the birth of his teacher, Adam Politzer, of whom Bárány was a worthy successor.

NEW YORK CITY   FRED A. METTLER

References

[1]Arch. Ohr. &c. Heilk., 1906, *68*:1–30.   [2]*Untersuchungen über den vom Vestibularapparat des Ohres reflektorisch ausgelösten rhythmischen Nystagmus und sein Begleiterscheinungen.* Berlin, Coblenz, 1906. [3]*Physiologie und Pathologie (Funktionsprüfung) des Bogengang-Apparates beim Menschen.* Leipzig, Deuticke, 1907.   [4]Verh. Deut. otolog. Ges., 1911, *20*:37–168 *et seq.* (with Wittmaack).   [5]Verh. Ges. deut. Naturforsch., 1913, *85* (I.Teil):241–250.   [6]Gaz. méd. Paris, 1861, 3.sér., *16*:29.   [7]Lewandowsky, M. H., *Handbuch der Neurologie*, Berlin, 1912, Vol. 3, Specielle Neurologie.   [8]Arch. internat. laryng., Paris, 1922, *28*:16–25.   [9]Physiol. Rev., 1949, *29*:311–369 (Tyler and Bard).   [10]Acta otolar., Stockh., 1918, *1*:97–102.   [11]*Körperstellung.* Berlin, Springer 1924 (Magnus).   [12]Acta otolar., Stockh., 1929, *13*:343–347.   [13]*Ibid.,* suppl. 14, 1931.   [14]War Med., Chic., 1944, *6*:283–290 (with Oppenheimer, Henny and Wycis).   [15]Wien. klin. Wschr., 1913, *26*:277.   [16]Jahrb. Psychiat. Neur., Wien, 1941, *36*:631–651.   [17]Riv. otoneuroft., 1927, *4*:141–149.   [18]*Vorlesungen über das Zentralnervensystem der Wirbeltiere.* Jena, Fischer, 1927, p. 249.

References to Biography: 1) Hygiea, Stockh., 1936, *98*:241–248 (Nylén). 2) Hospitalstidende, 1916, *58*:1171–1174 (Schmiegelow).   3) *Das medizinische Wien. Geschichte. Werden Würdigung.* ed. 2. Jena, Urban & Schwarzenberg, 1947, p. 420–421 (Schönbauer).

HENRY CHARLTON BASTIAN (1837–1915)

*B*ASTIAN was born at Truro, Cornwall. He studied at University College, graduated from London University in 1861, and received the M.D. in 1866. The next year, when only thirty years of age, he became professor of pathologic anatomy at University College where at the time the distinguished Sir J. Russell Reynolds held sway in the teaching of neurology. Gowers, eight years Bastian's junior, was also at the University College, just having qualified in medicine by taking his M.R.C.S. (1867). Bastian later held the chair in medicine, with neurology his special interest. For many years (1884–98) he was referee for the Crown in cases of questionable insanity.

Bastian's activities and interests centered around two entirely different fields, in both of which he indulged frequently in philosophical conjecture. In his earlier years and again after his retirement, he was concerned with the controversy as to the origin of life and heterogenesis.[1,2] His other chief interest was clinical neurology, which at that time was emerging as an exact science. As a teacher in this discipline, he gained international recognition for his methods of diagnosis and the sharpness of his intellect. He was also a neuroanatomist of note, describing in 1867 a degenerating tract in the spinal cord, which from 1880 on, however, became known as "Gowers' tract." Gowers did not appreciate this distinction for he was averse to eponymic designations. Bastian's volume on *The brain as an organ of mind* (New York, Appleton, 1880), translated into French and German, was an outstanding contribution; he himself felt it to be his greatest. This was followed by other books, all based on his studies and lectures at the University Hospital and at the National Hospital, Queen Square. He was much interested in the terms "hysterical" and "functional," and condemned the practice of using them synonymously. He maintained that if hysteria were defined as a neurosis in accordance with the views of Charcot and Briquet, then all the cases of functional spinal paralysis should be placed in some other category. In 1887 appeared his important paper on *The "muscular sense"; its nature and cortical localization,*[3] discussed vigorously and on some

points heatedly by Ferrier, Ross, Hughlings Jackson, Horsley, Crichton-Browne, and others. In crossing swords with Ferrier he was "compelled to point out" that Ferrier's doctrines "did not hang together at all well" and were "even made up of contradictory statements." Bastian also contended that "neither on physiological nor on psychological grounds was it needful to postulate the existence of motor centers in the cortex."

In 1897 Bastian delivered the Lumleian Lectures on aphasia and other speech defects, which formed the basis of a classical treatise on the subject.[4] He held that aphasia depends either on damage of one or the other of the four centers in the cerebral cortex

Portrait, courtesy of Dr. Maurice Genty, Académie de Médecine, Paris, France.

which are concerned in the production of spoken and written language, or on interruption of the neural pathways connecting them. In 1869 he clearly delineated speech impairment[5] of the type described five years later by Wernicke as sensory aphasia, since known as "Wernicke's aphasia." His lectures and studies on aphasia were published in book form in 1898[4]; had he accomplished nothing else, these would have established him as a pioneer in neurology.

He was the first to show that in total transverse lesions of the upper spinal cord the reflexes below the level of the lesion are abolished and muscle tonus lost (Bastian's Law).[6] He was very critical of the excessive emphasis given by physicians of that day to "inflammation," and effectively opposed the practice of diagnosing as "myelitis" all kinds of transverse lesions of the cord.

Shortly after Bastian retired from University College (1897) he gave up the practice of neurology in order to resume his studies on biology. Contrary to the views of Pasteur and Tyndall, he denied that life always develops from pre-existing life, prepounding as an alternative the doctrine of abiogenesis. His painstaking experiments formed the basis of many articles and books, some of which were illustrated by his own photomicrographs. The firm beliefs he held in this realm were, however, not shared by others. He deeply resented the indifference, and even ridicule, with which his ideas were received, but he continued to hold fast to his faith until his death, which occurred at Chesham Bois, Bucks, when he was seventy-five.

NEW YORK CITY LOTHAR B. KALINOWSKY

References

[1]*The evolution of life*. London, Methuen, 1907. [2]*Studies in heterogenesis*. 2 vol. London, William & Norgate, 1901. [3]Brain, London, 1888, *10*:1-137, p. 119-120. [4]*A treatise on aphasia and other speech defects*. London, Lewis, 1898. [5]Brit. & For. M.-Chir. Rev., London, 1869, *43*:209–236. [6]Med.-Chir. Tr., London, 1890, *73*:151–217.

References to Biography: 1) Lancet, London, 1915, 2:1220–1224 (contains bibliography; not signed). 2) Brit. Med., J., 1915, 2:795–796 (not signed).

MORITZ BENEDIKT (1835–1920)

*M*ORITZ BENEDIKT was born in Eisenstadt, Hungary, which at that time was part of the Austro-Hungarian Empire. He lived all his life in Vienna where he obtained his medical education under such celebrities as Hyrtl, Brücke, Skoda and Oppolzer. After graduation, Benedikt joined the army and participated in the military campaigns of 1859–61. On his return to Vienna, he was appointed Dozent to the University. In 1868 he became Extraordinarius, and in 1899 Ordinarius of Electrotherapy—a chair just created; "Neurology," a province of Psychiatry, had not yet achieved equal and independent status.

Throughout his long life, Benedikt exhibited extraordinary activity as a teacher, author, medicolegal expert, lecturer, clinician, traveler, and critic of art and drama. He was one of the founders of the General Poliklinik of Vienna and was greatly interested in sociological problems in connection with crime, tuberculosis and alcoholism. His work in criminology antedated that of Lombroso, for he had been interested in the criminal phases of anthropology (termed by Benedikt "criminal anthropology") from 1858 onwards. He boldly and ably maintained that a criminal is a sick person, a degenerate possessing abnormal anatomical and physiological traits. He based his views on extensive personal observations of inmates of prisons in various countries and on examinations of their skulls and brains.[1,2]

The contributions of Benedikt were varied and numerous in many other fields of neurology. Electrotherapy, for instance, was effectively popularized by him. In recognition of his activities in this field, the results of which are embodied in his two books on the subject,[3,4] he was promoted to Ordinarius. His work on the innervation of the choroid plexus[5] is of some historical interest; he described a nerve in the floor of the fourth ventricle which, according to him, originated in a special nucleus and supplied the blood vessels and the villi of the choroid plexus. This nerve, which he termed the 13th cranial nerve, was said to influence the circulation of various areas in the brain. Still widely quoted are his classic observations on the occupational neuroses, in which he distin-

guished three types: spastic, tremulous, and paralytic.[3] He was the first to describe the syndrome of midbrain disease characterized by ipsilateral oculomotor nerve palsy and contralateral involuntary movements, sometimes preceded by hemiplegia,[6] also one of the first to link hemichorea to this area. Thus his name became an eponym alongside that of Sir Hermann David Weber (1823–1918), of London, who, in 1863, had set his stamp on the midbrain syndrome characterized by oculomotor nerve palsy on one side and hemiplegia on the other.[7] For an account of the many brain-stem syndromes the reader is referred to the monumental

Portrait, courtesy of the National Library of Medicine, Bethesda, Maryland.

works by Claude and Lévy-Valensi.[8-10] Benedikt lived in times of economic, political and scientific upheavals, when men of exceptional ability and energy were needed to carry on the fight for progressive ideas and to keep them alive. He was such a man. His eloquent dissertations at local, national and international gatherings, where he was a familiar figure, exerted a leavening power not only on the medical profession but on human welfare as well.

GEORGE B. HASSIN

References

[1]*Anatomische Studien an Verbrecher-Gehirnen für Anthropologen, Mediciner, Juristen und Psychologen bearbeitet.* Wien, Braumüller, 1879. (Engl. transl. by Fowler: *Anatomical studies upon brains of criminals.* New York, Wood, 1881.) [2]*Kraniometrie und Kephalometrie. Vorlesungen gehalten an der Wiener Poliklinik.* Wien u. Leipzig, Urban & Schwarzenberg, 1888. [3]*Electrotherapie.* Wien, Tendler, 1868. [4]*Nervenpathologie und Elektrotherapie.* Leipzig, Fues, 1874–76. [5]Virchows Arch., 1874, *59*:395–400. [6]Bull. méd., Par., 1889, *3*:547–548. [7]Med.-Chir. Tr., Lond., 1863, *46*:121–139. [8]*Maladies du cervelet et de l'isthme de l'encéphale (pédoncule, protubérance, bulbe).* Paris, Baillière, 1922. [9]Arch. Psychiat., Berlin, 1875, *6*:1–56. [10]Arch. Heilk., 1865, *6*:1–13.

Reference to Biography: Aus meinem Leben. Erinnerungen und Erörterungen. Wien, Konegen, 1906 (Benedikt).

DÉSIRÉ MAGLOIRE BOURNEVILLE (1840–1909)

*B*OURNEVILLE was the son of a small Normandy landowner in the little village of Garancières (Eure). He studied medicine in Paris. During a severe cholera epidemic in Amiens, in 1866, he volunteered his services and worked so tirelessly that at the end of the siege he was presented with a gold watch which bore an inscription expressing the city's gratitude. This was his first official recognition.

During the Franco-Prussian War he volunteered as surgeon in the 160th Bataillon of the Garde Nationale. Later he became assis-

Désiré Magloire Bourneville

tant medical officer at the field hospital of the Jardin des Plantes and finally—even though he was a well-established physician—resumed his internship at the Pitié which then was covered by fire from German artillery. When Paris was under the Commune in 1871, the violent revolutionaries wanted to execute their wounded political enemies, but Bourneville, by virtue of his authority and with great courage effectively resisted their demands.

Bourneville's medical schooling and lines of thought were influenced by his close association with other leading physicians of his time, among them Noël Pascal, Claude Bernard, and the psychiatrist Delasiauve, who was his teacher. He began in 1872 the editing of Charcot's *Leçons sur les maladies du système nerveux faites à la Salpêtrière* (Paris, Delahaye, 1872–73). He founded *La progrès médical* in 1873, and, under the patronage of Charcot, the *Archives de neurologie* in 1880. Most of Bourneville's papers were published in the *Recherches cliniques et thérapeutiques sur l'épilepsie, l'hystérie et l'idiotie.*

Portrait from *Nos grands médecins d'aujourd'hui*, Paris, 1891; by H. Bianchon.

Bourneville's name is linked with our knowledge of tuberous sclerosis (Bourneville's disease), which he established as a morbid entity.[1,2] Almost simultaneously the disorder was described by Hartdegen,[3] who called it "glioma gangliocellulare cerebri congenitum." Bourneville also made a number of significant clinical contributions to the problems of myxedema and cretinism.[4,5] Stimulated by English work on mongolism, Bourneville, at the turn of the century, contributed a series of articles on this subject.[6] He was physician to the pediatric service of the Bicêtre from 1879 to 1905; after reaching the legal retirement age he remained in charge of the Foundation Vallée at the Bicêtre. He founded the first day school for special instruction of defective children in Paris, a movement which later took hold in many countries. On Saturdays he held open-house at the Bicêtre in which his charges performed exercises and dances to the accompaniment of a band composed of idiots, epileptics, and spastics; the trombonist had wooden legs.

No wonder that Bourneville was celebrated as the leading continental authority on all that concerned mentally abnormal children and was acknowledged as a great psychiatrist and scholar, whose modesty and brilliance commanded both love and respect.

Among French physicians Bourneville stands out as embodying fully the French ideal of un homme de pensées et d'actions. He combined the rare virtues of a thinker who adhered unswervingly to his convictions and a man who never hesitated to put his thoughts into action. He was councilman at Paris in 1876 and deputy in 1883. It is readily understandable that his reforming zeal involved him frequently in differences with his colleagues and exposed him to attacks by the clerical party. But when he died at the age of sixty-nine, his funeral was an occasion in which the profession, the Government and the people participated with equal mourning.

WAVERLEY, MASSACHUSETTS   CLEMENS E. BENDA

References

[1]Arch. neurol., Paris, 1880, 7:69–91.   [2]Recherch. clin. thérap. sur l'épileps. [etc.]. Paris, 1882, 2:3–16 with Bonnaire).   [3]Arch. Psychiat., Berlin, 1880, 11:117–131.   [4]Recherch. clin. thérap. sur l'épileps. [etc.],

Paris, 1901, *21*:123–129.   [5]*Ibid.,* 1897, *17*:144–178.   [6]*Ibid.,* 1902, *22*:136–147.

References to Biography: 1) Rev. philanthrop., Paris, 1909, *25*:174–180 (Thulié).   2) Progr. méd., Paris, 1909, 3.sér., *25*:293–295 (Noir).

BYROM BRAMWELL (1847–1931)

*B*YROM BRAMWELL was born at North Shields, Northumberland, where his father and grandfather were engaged in general practice. Educated at Cheltenham College and Edinburgh University, he took his degree in 1869. The eminent neurologist, Laycock, then professor of medicine in Edinburgh (also Jackson's mentor), thought so highly of him that he awarded him the Medal in Medicine, and invited him, upon graduation, to become his University assistant. Bramwell felt it his duty to return to North Shields and help his father with his busy practice. Strenuously he gathered the experience which he frequently referred to as most valuable and which was essentially the basis of his reputation.

Appointed in 1874, at the early age of twenty-seven, honorary physician and pathologist to the Newcastle Royal Infirmary and lecturer on clinical medicine in the Durham University School of Medicine (where three years previously, he had lectured on medical jurisprudence), he left North Shields and commenced practice as a consulting physician in Newcastle-upon-Tyne. The *Transactions of the Durham and Northumberland Medical Society* of this time contain many of his early contributions.

Ambitious for a larger sphere for his activities, and probably tempted by the opening of the new Royal Infirmary that year, he settled as a consultant in Edinburgh in 1879. A course of a hundred lectures on medicine, which he gave each winter, and short courses on medical diagnosis, which he instituted, made him a favorite with the students. In 1882 he was appointed pathologist and in 1855, assistant physician to the Royal Infirmary. One morning a week he taught in the out-patient department—the only opportunity the assistant physicians then had of teaching clinically—and had to obtain the unique privilege to hold his clinic in one of the

Sir Byrom Bramwell

Portrait, courtesy of Dr. Edwin Bramwell, Edinburgh, Scotland. (Photographer: Swan Watson, Edinburgh.)

large clinical theatres. In 1897, he became a full physician to the Royal Infirmary, but to his chagrin, he was not appointed to the chair of medicine on Sir Thomas Grainger Stewart's death in 1900.

Bramwell's name is not attached to any disease, syndrome, physical sign or symptom. Yet no one was more aware of Bramwell's greatness as a clinical neurologist than Harvey Cushing, who in his Lister Memorial Lecture in 1730[1] made this comment: "It has been said that if some unusual clinical condition turns up concerning which one seeks information, an account of it is likely to be found in Jonathan Hutchinson's Archives. To this I would like to add, particularly for the benefit of neurologists, that if Hutchinson fails, then try Byrom Bramwell."

Much of this information for neurologists is contained in his two classics, one on diseases of the spinal cord (1882),[2] the other on intracranial tumors (1888).[3] In the latter, Bramwell observed: "Tumours of the pituitary body are in many instances attended by an excessive development of the subcutaneous fat, and in some cases with the presence of sugar in the urine, or with simple polyuria (diabetes insipidus)." And he went on to remark, "Whether these symptoms are due to the fact that the pituitary body itself is diseased, or whether, as seems more likely, to the secondary results which tumours in this situation produce in the surrounding cerebral tissue, has not yet been decided. . . ." The story takes up again a quarter of a century later: Goldzieher (1910, 1913)[4] and Simmonds (1914)[5] found the infundibulum and/or posterior lobe of the pituitary destroyed in cases of diabetes insipidus, and Farini (1913)[6] and von den Velden (1913)[7] discovered that diabetes insipidus could be successfully treated with posterior pituitary extract. Despite all this, Bailey and Bremer concluded in 1921[8] that the pars nervosa is normally nothing more than an atrophied nervous lobe, having nothing to do with diabetes insipidus, and that pituitrin is merely a pharmacologically very interesting extract. In later publications, Bramwell seems not to have become entangled in the arguments that ensued.

Bramwell's further contributions included a monumental three-volume atlas of clinical medicine[9] and a monograph on diseases of the blood-forming organs and endocrine glands.[10] Eight volumes of the quarterly publication *Clinical studies* (1903–11) carry a record of his teaching at the bedside and in the clinic, characterized by exact observation, logical inference, careful recording, and clarity of expression.

A man of robust physique, boundless energy and great powers of concentration, an untiring and thorough worker, every moment of his day from early morning to bedtime was, in his earlier years, fully occupied. Bramwell's activities were at their height at a time when attention was focused upon the application of morbid anatomy to symptomatology, the differentiation of clinical entities, and the significance of signs and symptoms. A profuse note-taker and coordinator, he was able to summarize and review his personal experience upon the topic of the moment. He had no use for "the textbook clinician" nor for the man whose thoughts were always "in the air"; but for a great scientific thinker, such as his older contemporary Hughlings Jackson, he had an admiration amounting almost to reverence. He took little interest in medical politics, and committee work did not appeal to him.

In 1925 he received a knighthood, and in 1927 an invitation to deliver the Seventh Hughlings Jackson Lecture—the previous lecturers had been Hughlings Jackson (1897), Hitzig (1900), Broadbent (1903), Horsley (1906), Gowers (1909), and Henry Head (1920)—but for reasons of health he was obliged to decline the invitation.

EDINBURGH, SCOTLAND   EDWIN BRAMWELL

References

[1]Lancet, Lond., 1930, 2:119–175.   [2]The diseases of the spinal cord. Edinburgh, Maclachlan & Stewart, 1882. 2nd ed., Edinburgh, Pentland, 1884. Lectures on diseases of the spinal cord. Edinburgh, Pentland, 1895.   [3]Intracranial tumours. Edinburgh, Pentland, 1888.   [4]Verh. Deut. path. Ges., 1913, 16:281–287.   [5]Münch. med. Wschr., 1914, 61: 180–181.   [6]Gazz. osp. (Milano), 1913, 34. Cited by A. D. Rolleston, in The Endocrine Organs. London, Oxford U. P., 1936, p. 36.   [7]Klin. Wschr., 1913, 50:2083–2086.   [8]Arch. Int. Med., 1921, 28:773–803. [9]Atlas of clinical medicine. Edinburgh, Constable, 1892–96.   [10]Anemia and some of the diseases of the blood-forming organs and ductless glands. Edinburgh, Oliver & Boyd, 1899.

References to Biography: 1) Brit. Med. J., 1931, 1:822–826 (Drummond, Hutchison, Kinnier Wilson *et al.*).   2) Lancet, London, 1931, *1*:1108 (Gulland).   3) Edinburgh Med. J., 1931, n.s., *38*:444–447 (R.W.P.).

ÉDOUARD BRISSAUD (1852–1909)

*B*RISSAUD was a neurologist's neurologist. He grew up in the school of Charcot and Lasègue, wrote his thesis on the permanent contractures in hemiplegia, in which he showed that hemiplegia due to pontile lesions may occasionally be of the spasmodic type[1]; he rose steadily in the ranks from interne to agrégé, taking the chair of medicine in 1899 and of internal medicine the following year.

His interest in neurology and neuropathology was early excited by his work at the Salpêtrière, and both in the clinic and in the laboratory he toiled to cultivate the fields which Charcot planted. He described in detail the double innervation of the face, the dissociation between voluntary and mimetic expression, and the analogy between the facies of pseudobulbar palsy and that of parkinsonism.[2] Referring to the tremor of the tongue, mandible and lips in a patient with paralysis agitans, Brissaud used the unforgettable expression: He "murmurs an interminable litany."[3] He had, in 1894, the astuteness to conclude that "the localization of Parkinson's disease must be subthalamic or peduncular," and to reject the current notions that the disease was either muscular or a neurosis, in favor of his cerebral hypothesis, seeing the essential morbid feature as a central disorder of muscle tone. Based on a postmortem case where a tuberculoma destroying the substantia nigra had given rise to the Parkinson syndrome, he concluded that "the *locus niger* might well be its anatomical substratum."[2] A decade or so afterward more lesions were found at this and at the basal ganglion levels by Manschot,[4] Jelgersma,[5] and Lewy.[6,7] Subsequently the pathological study of paralysis agitans was rounded out by such authorities as C. and O. Vogt,[8] Bielschowsky[9] and Lotmar.[15]

Brissaud also described tics, spasms and torticollis, but rather on clinical than anatomical lines.[3,10-11] Tic without characteristic

Édouard Brissaud

march, he said, consists of a series of fleeting movements without uniformity—a step, a shrug, frown, sigh, crack of the fingers, exclamation.[3] Brissaud also found time to publish a text on the anatomy of the human brain, illustrated by his own hand.[12] One of his major contributions to French neurology was the founding, with Pierre Marie, of the *Revue neurologique*.

Brissaud ventured into other fields: psychiatry, at the instigation of Lasègue; folklore in medicine[13]; hygiene for asthmatics.[14] In his

Portrait, courtesy of Dr. Maurice Genty, Académie de Médecine, Paris, France.

medicolegal work he became known as the national expert on injuries in relation to conversion hysteria. Breaking with Charcot on the organic nature of hysteria, he aligned himself with Babinski, saying that one could always differentiate between organic and functional disorders, but that the distinction between conversion hysteria and simulation was sometimes impossible. "A symptom that cannot be simulated is not a symptom of hysteria." Brissaud had a wide field for his expert testimony following passage of a compensation law in 1898.

Brissaud brought informality to the classroom and the laboratory. He even gave up the top hat, that symbol of professorial majesty. His verbal sallies brought delight to students. At the same time he emphasized honesty and ethics. " 'Hypothesis,' " he said in a lecture apropos the substantia nigra, "is an honest euphemism for 'ignorance'—the sort of ignorance that knows itself . . . surely the sort we may on occasion be permitted to brag about?" Work, for him, seemed altogether effortless. He was a target for the cartoonist, who embellished his generous paunch to overflowing. It was not hard to see that culinary art was one of his chief diversions.

Brissaud died of a brain tumor at the early age of fifty-seven. Horsley operated on him in Paris but it was too late. One of his last wishes, that he be buried without benefit of the church—for he considered himself a freethinker—was not granted.

SAN FRANCISCO, CALIFORNIA   WALTER FREEMAN

References

[1]*Recherches anatomo-pathologiques et physiologiques sur la contracture permanente des hémiplégiques.* Thèse de Paris, 1880.   [2]*Leçons sur les maladies nerveuses.* Paris, Masson, 1895, p. 469–501.   [3]*Ibid.,* vol. 2, 1899. (Trans. of phrase by Wilson in his *Neurology,* 1940.) [4]Psychiat. Neur. Bl., Amst., 1904, *8:*597–775.   [5]Neur. Cbl., 1908, *27:* 995–996.   [6]Lewandowsky, M. H., *Handbuch der Neurologie.* Berlin, 1902, *3:*920–933.   [7]Deut. Zschr. Nervenh., 1913, *50:*50–55.   [8]J. Psychol. Neur., 1920, *25,* Erg. Heft *3:*279–462.   [9]*Ibid.,* 1922, *27:*233–288.   [10]Rev. neur., Paris, 1896, *4:*417–431.   [11]Presse méd., 1908, *16:*234–236 (with Sicard).   [12]*Anatomie du cerveau de l'homme; morphologie des hémisphères cérébraux, ou cerveau proprement dit.* Paris,

Masson, 1893.   [13]*Histoire des expressions populaires relatives à l'anatomie . . . la médecine.* Paris, Chamerot, 1888.   [14]*L'hygiène des asthmatiques.* Paris, 1896.   [15]*Die Stammganglien und die extrapyramidalmotorischen Syndrome.* Berlin, Springer, 1926.

References to Biography: 1) Rev. méd., Paris, 1910, *24*:1–3 (Ballet). 2) *Ibid.*, 1910, *24*:195–200 (Dupré).   3) Rev. neur., Paris, 1910, *18*:1–4 (Souques).

JEAN MARTIN CHARCOT (1825–1893)

A MONG the multitude of names that illumine the pages of neurology none shines with greater brilliance than that of Charcot. Charcot typified French medical genius. There was much of the artist in him. Few possessed more *éclat.*

He was born in Paris, the son of a carriage-maker. For a time he wavered in his choice between medicine and art—he was a talented caricaturist—but decided on a medical career. This began and closed at the Salpêtrière. Here he became an interne at the age of twenty-three (1848). For nine years he worked elsewhere in pathology and medicine under Rayer, and wrote on diseases of the heart, lungs, and kidneys, on rheumatism and gout. When thirty-seven he won his agrégation and was appointed medical superintendent to the Hospice de la Salpêtrière. This provided him with the opportunity he was quick to exploit.

When Charcot re-entered the Salpêtrière—so named because the buildings were at one time Louis the XIIIth's gunpowder store—he found, among the five to eight thousand welfare inmates, innumerable unclassified conditions which were a challenge to his curiosity. He observed, studied, described, classified—and soon made inroads in bringing order out of chaos. In his association with Vulpian, Charcot became a distinguished neuropathologist, and he succeeded Vulpian to the chair of pathological anatomy in 1872. As a clinician Charcot was even more renowned. His masterly *Leçons sur les maladies du système nerveux faites à la Salpêtrière* (Paris, Delahaye, 1872–73) saw repeated translations in English.[1] Charcot established clinical neurology as an autonomous disci-

Portrait, courtesy of Dr. Maurice Genty, Académie de Médecine, Paris, France.

pline, and in 1882 he was the first professor ever to occupy a Chair of Diseases of the Nervous System. He wrote on cerebral localization, the while crossing swords with Brown-Séquard over the problem of localization in Jacksonian epilepsy. His description of disseminated sclerosis embodied the triad which goes by his name.[2,3] Not only that, but together with his friend Vulpian he firmly established disseminated sclerosis as an entity, where previously it had been confused with parkinsonism.

Charcot also put his stamp on tabes dorsalis and described the arthropathies now called "Charcot joints," though he might have erred in attributing the disorder to a trophic disturbance. Amyotrophic lateral sclerosis was first described and named by him in 1865.[4] (Progressive bulbar palsy was recognized by Duchenne de Boulogne in 1861 as a "primary labioglossolaryngeal paralysis," and it was Dejerine who, in 1883,[5] connected the disorder with amyotrophic lateral sclerosis.) In one of the neuropathies (peroneal muscular atrophy), Charcot's name is linked with that of Pierre Marie, in a paper which appeared in 1886[6]; later the disorder came to be known as Charcot-Marie-Tooth's disease, from the latter's description of the disorder in his Cambridge M.D. thesis that same year. With Joffroy, Charcot formulated the concept that in poliomyelitis an "irritation" suddenly seizes nerve cells of the anterior horns and causes them promptly to lose their function, and he expressed the opinion that the interstitial inflammatory reaction was a secondary phenomenon.[7] Atrophy of anterior horns and disappearance of their nerve cells in poliomyelitis had been noted previously by Vulpian's student Prévost,[8] but he did not comment on pathogenesis. Moreover, together with Vulpian, Charcot first described ankle clonus (1862). With his pupil Bouchard, he uncovered ruptured miliary aneurysm as a cause of intracerebral hemorrhage (1868). No man, before or since, had made more contributions to nosology. Toward the end of his career, and especially outside neurological circles, Charcot became identified with his studies on hysteria. No matter what our reservations in this matter, we all admit that he laid much of the groundwork for Janet and Freud, both his pupils. He made hypnotism respectable, though there is still the question whether he ever personally hypnotized anyone.[9] There was artistry, if not histrionics, in his Tuesday and Friday morning lectures. The medical world rang with them, and enemies had opportunity to criticize. Disinclined to animal experimentation, he had inscribed over his door, "Vous ne trouverez pas une clinique des chiens chez moi." Charcot the artist is at his best in two graphic volumes, one on *Les démoniaques dans l'art* (Paris, Delahaye & Lecrosnier, 1897) and the other on *Les difformes et les malades dans l'art* (Paris, Lecrosnier & Babe, 1889), both written in collaboration with P. Richer. An impressive article on the artistic achievements of Charcot is that by Meige in the *Nouvelle Iconographie de la Salpêtrière,*[10] a journal which Charcot founded.

So great a teacher could not fail to inspire great pupils. It must have been an exciting give-and-take. Marie, Babinski, Bekhterev, Bourneville, Marinesco, Brissaud, Souques, and a host of others had their start with him. Altogether, the teamwork which he directed with such wisdom, authority and success—that creation and example of a neurological institute in 19th century France—was perhaps his greatest achievement. Austere, rather cold and haughty in public, Charcot was gracious in his palatial neo-Gothic home, open to literateurs and pupils alike, every Tuesday evening. Gifted also as a linguist, he had command of English, German, Spanish and Italian. While away on a vacation he died suddenly at the age of sixty-eight of pulmonary edema, probably the consequence of myocardial disease. His son, Dr. Jean Baptiste Charcot, became the dean of Antarctic explorers, and led the search for the lost Amundsen.

It may be said that Charcot entered neurology in its infancy and left it at its coming-of-age, largely nourished by his contributions and personal magic.

ISRAEL S. WECHSLER

References

[1]*Lectures on the diseases of the nervous system.* Philadelphia, Lea, 1879 (transl. by G. Sigerson). *Lectures on the nervous system.* London, New Sydenham Soc., 1881. [2]Gaz. hôp., 1865, *38*:93. [3]C. rend. Soc. biol. Paris, 1863, *20*:13–14. [4]Gaz. hôp., 1868, *41*:554–555 *et seq.* [5]Arch. Physiol., Paris, 1883, *2*:180–227. [6]Rev. méd., Paris, 1886, *6*:97–138

(with Marie). ⁷Arch. physiol. norm. path., 1869, 2:354–373 *et seq.*, p. 756. ⁸C. rend. Soc. Biol. Paris, 1865, 4. sér., 2:215–218. ⁹J. Hist. M., New York, 1961, 16:297–305 (Schneck). ¹⁰Nouv. Iconogr. Salpêtrière, 1898, 11:489–546.

References to Biography: 1) Bull. N. Y. Acad. Med., 1926, ser.2 (suppl.), 2:1–32 (Garrison *et al.*) 2) Ann. Med. Hist., 1928, 10:126–132 (Beeson). 3) J. Neuropath., 1950, 9:1–17 (Hassin). 4) Bull. Acad. méd., Paris, 1925, 3. sér., 43:573–603 (Marie, Marinesco, Christiansen). 5) Bull. méd., Paris, 1900, 14:1389–1394 (Debove). 6) *J.-M. Charcot 1825–1893 his life, his work.* New York, Hoeber, 1959 (Guillain; edit. and transl. by Pearce Bailey). 7) Proc. Roy. Soc. Med., London, 1967, 60:399–405 (Miller).

JAMES STANSFIELD COLLIER (1870–1935)

*J*AMES COLLIER, whose vivid personality is a pleasant memory to many neurologists of the present day, was born in Cranford, near London, the son of a medical practitioner. His elder brother was a surgeon whose brilliant career ended prematurely. James was educated in London, and graduated Bachelor of Medicine in 1894, completing his M.D. in 1896. After house appointments at the National Hospital, Queen Square, he became pathologist to the hospital in 1901. He was appointed to the visiting staff of the National Hospital in 1902, and physician (in general medicine) to St. George's Hospital in 1903. The calls of hospital and private practice soon made it necessary for him to give up his appointment as pathologist, but he continued to show a lively interest in neuropathology throughout his career.

Apart from his profound influence as a teacher, the major contribution of Collier was undoubtedly his part in the first comprehensive description of subacute combined degeneration of the spinal cord and its relation to pernicious anemia, which was written in collaboration with J. S. R. Russell and F. E. Batten.¹ Ludwig Lichtheim (1845–1915), of Bern, had already noted this association in 1887, and Gowers had provided a clinical description of the disorder in 1886² under the designation "ataxic paraplegia," but the classical description by Collier and his associates in 1900

James Stansfield Collier

was the first complete one, which has hardly been improved upon. His other contributions covered a wide range of subjects, chiefly clinical, of which his views on cerebral diplegia,[3,4] Babinski's sign,[5] amyotonia congenita,[6,7] epilepsy,[8] aphasia, apraxia and agnosia,[9,10] intracranial aneurysm,[11] and peripheral neuritis,[12] are the best known.

In the English school of neurology the memory of Collier is cherished as the last of the tradition of dramatic teachers in the manner of Charcot and Trousseau. The elegant phrases, falling to a whisper, as with the air and mannerisms of a magician he dis-

Portrait, courtesy of Dr. D. Denny-Brown, Southborough, Massachusetts.

closed the climax to the clinical story, fascinated the large audiences which unfailingly crowded his Wednesday afternoon clinics. Inherent in such teaching is a dogmatism and overemphasis which occasionally crept into his writing. Few would accept his generalizations regarding the constant defect in maturation of the pyramidal system in all cerebral diplegias, or his insistence upon the absence of infectivity of poliomyelitis after the onset of the paralytic phase. Yet by such categorical statements he continually stimulated further thought and investigation. There was some subtle quality by which he could demolish false dogma without setting up another equally false.

Without doubt Collier did more to mold medical opinion and contributed more to the betterment of clinical neurological ability of internists in general than any other man of his time.

SOUTHBOROUGH, MASSACHUSETTS   D. DENNY-BROWN

References

[1]Brain, London, 1900, 23:39–110.   [2]Lancet, London, 1886, 2:1–3 et seq.   [3]Brain, London, 1899, 22:374–441.   [4]Ibid., 1924, 47:1–21. [5]Ibid., 1899, 22:71–99.   [6]Ibid., 1908, 31:1–44 (with Wilson). [7]Ibid., 1909. 32:269–284 (with Holmes).   [8]Lancet, London, 1928, 1: 587–592 et seq.   [9]Allbutt, T. C., and Rolleston, H. D., A system of medicine. London, Macmillan, 1910, 8:385–446; Ibid., p. 447–451. [10]Price, F. W., A textbook of the practice of medicine, ed. 1 to 3. London, Oxford U. P. 1922–29.   [11]Brit. Med. J., 1939, 2:519–521. [12]Edinburgh, M. J., 1932, 39:601–607 et seq.

Reference to Biography: Lancet, London, 1935, 1:403–404 (not signed).

JOSEPH JULES DEJERINE (1849–1917)

"*O*N PARIS, you always can advance yourself by work and enthusiasm. You don't need any 'strings.' You are the product of your work." These words of Jules Dejerine* were borne out by his own career.

*According to Dejerine's daughter (Mme. le Dr. Sorrel-Dejerine), the name is not Déjerine or Déjérine.

Joseph Jules Dejerine

This young Frenchman was born and raised in the provincial atmosphere of Geneva, Switzerland, where his father was a carriage proprietor. In school in earlier years Joseph Jules was better known as a boxer and swimmer, and for his fishing on Lake Léman, than for his academic accomplishments, but all this changed when he became attracted to biology and comparative anatomy. In 1871, when twenty-two years old, he decided that he should pursue his clinical studies in Paris. He set out for that great metropolis in a third-class compartment, with no more than a

Portrait, courtesy of Mme. le Docteur Sorrel-Dejerine, Paris, France.

brief introduction to Vulpian given him by Prévost, and arrived in the midst of the turmoil created by war and revolution. Unswervingly he set out to reach his goal and was to prove Vulpian's most distinguished pupil.

His career was punctuated by appointments to high position and a succession of brilliant works, connected both with the Salpêtrière and the Bicêtre. As a climax he was elected, in 1910, Professeur de clinique des maladies du système nerveux à la Faculté de Médicine.

Dejerine's masterpieces include his studies on *nervotabès périphérique*,[1] progressive muscular dystrophy (with Landouzy),[2] Friedreich's disease (with André-Thomas),[3] progressive hypertrophic interstitial neuritis (with Sottas and André-Thomas),[4,5] olivopontocerebellar atrophy (with André-Thomas),[6] and the thalamic syndrome (with Roussy—it was, above all, Dejerine who discovered the role of the thalamus in hemianesthetic syndromes).[7] Perhaps the most lasting achievements were his *Anatomie des centres nerveux* (Paris, Rueff, 1890–1901) and *Sémiologie des affections du système nerveux* (Paris, Masson, 1914). He was as modern as many today in his view that the mesencephalic reticular formation continues forward in the diencephalon to the septal region. Further, Dejerine was one of the pioneers in the study of localization of function in the brain, having first shown, with Vialet, that word blindness may occur as the result of lesions of the supramarginal and angular gyri.[8–11] Among his pupils were Roussy, Bernheim, André-Thomas and Alajouanine.

Although Dejerine is best known for his contributions in the field of organic neurology, his interest in functional disorders of the nervous system was also keen, and was greatly stimulated by his friendship with Paul Dubois of Bern. His vacations always brought him back to the land of his birth, to his place at Thalgut, near Bern, where his simple tastes and fondness for the rustic life found complete satisfaction. Robert Bing (1878–1956),[12,13] in his warm-hearted tribute to Dejerine, tells that during this period Dejerine developed many of his ideas of psychotherapy which were applied by him with such remarkable success. Later on, Dubois's and Dejerine's views began to diverge, the latter insisting that the personality of the therapist was of extreme importance.

He told his students: "It is rare that you will be able to use subtle logic; it is your heart that carries you along—if I may express myself thus—and much more than your reason. In man, emotion is almost everything and reason very little."

In the wards made famous by Charcot, it was inspiring to me as to the others who were in his service in 1900–01 to note the earnest, simple, direct way in which Dejerine explained the basis of symptoms and the encouragement that he gave his patients. In the out-patient department he was equally effective. On one occasion, a young woman was being examined and her maladjustment to life was discussed with great frankness. The question arose of her relations with her lover, who was present with her. She described one of her dreams in which a phallic symbol played a prominent part. A certain slang word she used brought forth a hearty laugh from the audience. The professor informed the audience that they were not here to be amused.

Life with Dejerine was always stimulating. At the meetings of the Société Neurologique of Paris the presentations were terse and the discussion at times tinged with biting sarcasm. Speakers had their gloves off.

Dejerine owed much to his wife, Augusta Marie Klumpke (1859–1927), one of the brilliant sisters of a famous San Francisco family, whom he married in 1888. She had studied medicine in Paris, and through intellect, courage and persistence, became the first woman to receive the title of "interne des hôpitaux" (1887), in the face of great opposition, finally overcome by Paul Bert, then Minister of Public Instruction. The Dejerine marriage presented the spectacle of two intellectual giants collaborating and inspiring each other. Only the Curies and the Vogts could boast of comparable achievements. When Dejerine died during the dark hours of World War I, having spent himself in the exhausting service of an army hospital, it was his wife who carried on the bulk of his work both in practice and in research.

It was most fitting for the members of the Fourth International Neurological Congress (Paris, 1949) to celebrate the centennial of Dejerine's birth, to hear at the Sorbonne a discourse on Dejerine by André-Thomas,[14] to wear the medallion struck off in his honor, and to join with his daughter, Mme. le Dr. Sorrel-Dejerine, in laying a wreath on his grave.

EDWIN G. ZABRISKIE

References

[1]C. rend. Acad. sci., Paris, 1883, 97:914–916.   [2]Mém. Soc. biol., Paris, 1886, 38:478–481.   [3]Rev. neur., Paris, 1907, 15:41–54.   [4]C. rend. Soc. biol., Paris, 1893, 5:63–96.   [5]Nouv. Iconogr. Salpêtrière, 1906, 19:477–509.   [6]Ibid., 1900, 13:330–370.   [7]Rev. neur., Paris, 1906, 14:521–532.   [8]C. rend. Soc. biol., Paris, 1891, 43:167–173 (Dejerine). [9]Ibid., 1892, 44:61–90 (Dejerine).   [10]Ibid., 1893, 45:790–791 (Dejerine and Vialet).   [11]Les centres cérébraux de la vision et l'appareil nerveux visuel intracérébral. Paris, Alcan, 1893 (Vialet).   [12]Schweiz. Arch. Neur. Psychiat., 1957, 79:138–154 (biography of Bing, by Georgi; with biliography).   [13]Arch. Neur. Psychiat., Chic., 1956, 76:508–510 (biography of Bing, by Haymaker; with selected bibliography).   [14]C. rend. IVᵉ Congrès Neurologique International, Paris, 1949. Vol. 3. Paris, Masson, 1951, pp. 450–469.

References to Biography: 1) Schweiz. Arch. Neur. Psychiat., 1918, 2: 314–315 (Bing).   2) Encéphale, 1928, 23:75–88 (André-Thomas). 3) Le Professeur J. Dejerine 1849–1917. Paris, Masson, 1922 (contains bibliography; Gauckler).   4) Éloge de Madame Dejerine-Klumpke, 1859–1917. Paris, Lahure, 1927 (Roussy).   5) Paris méd., 1917, 24: 90–91 (Camus).   6) Proc. Roy. Soc. Med., London, 1967, 60:399–405 (Miller).   7) J.A.M.A., 1969, 207:359–360 (anon.).

AMAND DUCHENNE (1806–1875)

*D*UCHENNE "DE BOULOGNE" (to distinguish him from Duchesne de Paris) was one of the greatest clinicians of the nineteenth century. No better proof of this exists than Charcot's statement that Duchenne was his master.

Duchenne was descended from a family of fishermen, traders and sea captains who had resided in Boulogne-sur-Mer since the beginning of the eighteenth century; his character, mind, and physical features were said to bear the stamp of the Boulognese.

Guillaume Benjamin Amand Duchenne

According to Lasègue and Straus[1] he was "of medium height, thickset, active in movement and slow in speech," with a faint provincial accent, and he closely resembled his father who had received the Croix de la Légion d'Honneur from Napoleon for valor as a sea captain in the French-English wars.

Duchenne was educated at a local collège, at Douai, before moving on to Paris for his medical education when he was twenty-one.

Portrait, courtesy of Dr. Maurice Genty, Académie de Médecine, Paris, France.

Upon returning to Boulogne five years later he entered the practice of his profession; but after eleven years of insufficient scope for his interests he removed himself again to Paris, where, from the age of thirty-six, he lived for the remainder of his life.

Having lost his wife in childbirth a few years after his marriage and being alienated from his only son by his wife's family, he arrived in Paris alone, without funds, and set to work in charity clinics and hospitals. He gained his livelihood from private practice, which presumably became adequate to supply his limited needs. He seemed to live only for his patients and his scholarship. At no time was he offered, nor did he ever seek, an official hospital or university appointment. At first he had to endure humiliations and even contempt by some of the established physicians—the "monarchs" of the wards, as he called them. But as the years passed, his extraordinary skill in analyzing clinical problems became recognized, and his fame was spread by two famous friends: Trousseau and Charcot.

Duchenne's habitual routine was to visit each morning one or two hospitals, "avec sa pile et sa bobine," as they apostrophied his electrical gadget. Nothing escaped his searching eye; he sought ways of testing every nervous function; his patience was extreme. If any students or staff members were interested he gave freely of his own technical experience and was ready to offer his interpretation of the case. Through his entire career he went his own way, persevering in the face of obstacles, single-minded in seeking discovery of new facts about nervous disease, never satisfied with his own knowledge. His profuse descriptions seem a little tedious now, but his utterances were said to have had a sharp emphasis; their quaint delivery was always appealing, and the final explosive "bon!" became a byword. Later in life he turned from the clinic to pathological anatomy after he had gained some familiarity with the microscope under the guidance of Charcot.

In taking stock of Duchenne's major achievements, it may be said that he more than any other person of his day was responsible for developing the technique of the meticulous neurological examination. He had discovered that electrical stimulation[2,3] would cause muscles to reveal their individual role in willed movement, and although he first seized upon this as a therapeutic method, he later used it as a diagnostic tool for studying the natural motion of every muscle. Diseases were divided into two categories: those in which the muscle had degenerated and did not respond at all, or only in proportion to the residual muscle fibers, and those in which they still did because the innervation was recently interrupted. Duchenne's detailed methodology attracted the attention of men like Charcot, who sought reliable clinical observations and related anatomical data. No doubt Duchenne's lack of official attachment to any hospital gave him time to pursue his clinical studies. Part of his vast number of clinical observations went into the analysis of muscle action in health and disease, published as those two masterpieces, *De l'électrisation localisée* . . .[2,3] (which went through three editions) and *La physiologie des mouvements.*

These painstaking observations enabled Duchenne to discover new diseases and provide the first accurate descriptions of others still poorly understood. (For the English reader these are condensed in an excellent translation by Poore.[4]) His delineation of tabetic locomotor ataxia, which he clearly distinguished from the Friedreich form of locomotor ataxia,[5] was the first clear account of this late complication of syphilis. By a series of observations and deductions he proved that acute poliomyelitis[6] (previously called "paralysie essentielle de l'enfance," localization unknown) was a disease of motor nerve cells in the spinal cord. He also clarified the various forms of lead poisoning and revealed their electrical reactions. A new entity known as progressive muscular atrophy,[7] examples of which François Amilcar Aran published in 1850[8] with full acknowledgement of Duchenne's help, was another major contribution. It was but a further step for him to identify progressive bulbar paralysis to which he led Louis Duménil and Wachsmuth.[9-12] The latter made it known as Duchenne's disease. Pseudohypertrophic muscle dystrophy[13] was identified as a primary muscle disease. Lacking postmortem material, his inventive mind hit upon the "tissue punch," or "histological harpoon." This biopsy procedure, possibly the first, excited a heated polemic in the lay press as to the morality of examining the living tissues of the body. In the laboratory he developed an improved technique for the sectioning of tissues, well in advance of the microtome.

Although Duchenne was given no official recognition by the

Académie de Médicine and the Institut de France, he was made honorary or corresponding member of academies in Rome, Madrid, Stockholm, St. Petersburg, Geneva and Leipzig, to his great satisfaction. The reunion with his estranged son, who took up neurology in Paris in 1862, was a joy soon to be snatched from him when in 1871 the young man's promising career was cut short by death from typhoid fever; the famous monograph on poliomyelitis his son wrote was incorporated in the third edition of *De l'électrisation*. . . .[14] Alone once more, with failing health, he courageously pursued his studies until a cerebral hemorrhage claimed him in 1875.

In the Salpêtrière an unpretentious bas-relief depicts a doctor leaning over a patient to whom he applies the electrodes of a simple electrical generator. Above it, the monument bears a plaque saying

1806–1875
A. Duchenne (de Boulogne)
Electrisation Localisée

Physiologie des Mouvements   *Neuropathologie*

BOSTON, MASSACHUSETTS   RAYMOND D. ADAMS

References

[1]Arch. gén. méd., Paris, 1875, 6.sér., *26*:687–715.   [2]*De l'électrisation localisée, et de son application à la pathologie et à la thérapeutique.* Paris, Baillière, 1855. (2nd ed., 1861.)   [3]*Ibid.*, 3rd ed., 1872.   [4]*Selections from the clinical works of Duchenne.* London, New Sydenham Society, 1883.   [5]Arch. gén. méd., Paris, 1858, 5.sér., *12*:641–652 *et seq.* [6]*Ibid.*, 1864, 6.sér., *2*:28–50 *et seq.*   [7]C. rend. Acad. sci., Paris, 1894, *29*:667–670.   [8]Arch. gén. méd., Paris, 1850, 4.sér., *24*:1–35 *et seq.* [9]*Ibid.*, 1860, 5.sér., *2*:283–296 *et seq.*   [10]*Ibid.*, 1870, 6.sér., *15*:539–547.   [11]Gaz. hebd. de méd., 1859, *6*:390–392.   [12]*Über progressive Bulbärparalyse (Bulbus medullae) und die Diplegia facialis.* Dorpat, Gläser, 1864.   [13]Arch. gén. méd., Paris, 1868, 6.sér., *11*:5–25 *et seq.* [14]*De l'électrisation.* . . ., 3rd ed. Footnotes, p. 384, also p. 395–397 *et seq.*, p. 381–437.

References to Biography: 1) Bull. Acad. méd., Paris, 1946, *130*:745–755 (Lhermitte).   2) Bull. N. Y. Acad. Med., 1948, *24*:772–783 (Viets).

3) *Duchenne de Boulogne.* Thèse de Paris, 1936 (contains bibliography; Guilly).   4) Med. Rec., N. Y., 1908, *73*:50–54 (Collins).   5) Kagan (ed.): *Victor Robinson memorial volume. Essays on history of medicine.* New York, Froben, 1948 (Kaplan), p. 177–192.   6) Med. Rev. of Rev., 1931, *37*:641–656 (Robinson).

HEINRICH ERB (1840–1921)

*F*OR HALF A century Wilhelm Heinrich Erb ruled over German Neurology with an imperial hand; internationally, his example made him one of its most distinguished elder statesmen and "political founders."

He was born in Winweiler, in the Bavarian Palatinate, studied medicine in Heidelberg, Erlangen, and finally Munich, where he received his doctorate in 1864. With the exception of the three years in the 80's, when he was called to Leipzig as Ordinarius for special pathology and therapy and director of the medical polyclinic, his career began and ended in Heidelberg, the site of Germany's oldest university.

As Privatdozent for internal medicine at Heidelberg from 1865 (one year after graduation), and Ordinarius from 1883, he was in every way the successor of his chief, Nikolaus Friedreich. It was Friedreich who stimulated Erb's interest in neurology, then an almost virgin territory, providing unparalleled scope for a clinician's eye coupled with a pathologist's acumen. Adolf Kussmaul (1822–1902) (of Strassburg), had gone through the same school, rivalled at the time only by those of Berlin and Vienna, later also Leipzig, Munich, and Breslau.

Friedreich's views were uppermost in the scientific work of Erb, first on peripheral nerves and later on diseases of the spinal cord and medulla oblongata–273 publications altogether. To Erb we owe the delineation, in part, of progressive muscular dystrophy,[1,2] spastic spinal paralysis (Erb-Charcot disease),[3] upper brachial-plexus palsy (Duchenne-Erb paralysis),[4] and myasthenia gravis[5] (called Erb-Goldflam-Oppenheim disease, though Thomas Willis first described it in 1672[6] and Gowers reported the features of a typical case in his *Manual* in 1886–88). The most dramatic develop-

ment in this field was the discovery in 1934 by M. B. Walker[7,8] that neostigmine constitutes an effective treatment.

After C. F. O. Westphal (1833–1890), of Berlin, had demonstrated the association between general paresis and tabes "dorsualis" in the 1860's, Erb confirmed by statistics the syphilitic ori-

Portrait, courtesy of the Library, Northwestern University School of Medicine, Chicago, Illinois.

gin of tabes in 1892[9] (following Alfred Fournier's [1832–1913] similar work). This was some fourteen years before the relationship became established by Schaudinn and Wassermann, and twenty-one years before Noguchi found the spirochete in the brain. In theory and practice tabes was the number one neurological disease. Stimulated by the studies of Duchenne, Erb also took up electrodiagnosis and therapy; the test of reaction of degeneration significantly bears his name,[10] and so does increased electrical irritability of motor nerves in tetany (Erb's phenomenon).[11] He held high hopes for electrotherapy in mental disease as well, only to be bitterly disappointed when his efforts failed.

Of great importance were his contributions to the teaching of neurology. He developed the systematic examination and evaluation of signs and symptoms, including that *sine qua non,* the "tendon" reflex,[12] discovered by him simultaneously with Westphal;[13] both accounts appeared in the same issue of the *Archiv für Psychiatrie.* Erb appears to have been the first neurologist to wield a reflex hammer. Against vigorous opposition, he established a course in neurology as an integral part of the undergraduate curriculum at Heidelberg. With Fr. Schultze he founded the *Deutsche Zeitschrift für Nervenheilkunde* in 1891, as a rival to Westphal's (originally also Griesinger's) *Archiv für Psychiatrie und Nervenkrankheiten,* established in 1868.

Although Westphal ranked as the first titular Professor of Neurology, Erb was to Germany what Charcot was to France, and Gowers to England—her leading neurologist. He may well be called a Father of Neurology, for at many professional meetings he threw his weight into the struggle for recognition of this branch of medicine as an acceptable specialty. Of his many students, which included E. Remak, Fisher, Eisenlohr and Fr. Schultze, the most outstanding was Nonne, who carried the Erb tradition a long way into the twentieth century.

Erb had the appearance of a cultured gentleman; he was always immaculately dressed and kept his professorial beard trimmed to the last hair. There was an air of detachment about him: neither he nor anyone else in that rigid hierarchy forgot that he was the Herr Geheimrat. He was punctual to the minute, and always on the alert; he would say to the students: "Pray every morning before you get out of bed, 'Oh, Lord, let me not idle away my life today.' " He could lose his temper and often did; on such occasions his language was not that customarily heard in academic circles—a holdover from his rugged youth while helping his father, a forester. Yet he also was noted for his benevolence, as reflected, considering the period, in the equal care he gave to all patients— peasant or aristocrat—in his large international practice. The title Seine Excellenz was conferred on him by the local reigning prince, the Grand Duke of Baden. His 70th birthday was an occasion for a special town and gown celebration in Heidelberg, where fighting fraternities in full fig and torch parades for academic worthies presented nothing unusual. His statue in bronze was unveiled in the park near the Akademisches Krankenhaus, and a street named after him,

In his latter years Erb was a broken man; two of his four sons had died, and a third was killed at the front on the first day of World War I. Erb's end came quietly. On the way home from listening to Beethoven's *Eroica* he caught a cold, and a few days later, bronchopneumonia claimed him.

HENRY R. VIETS

References

[1]Arch. Psychiat., Berlin, 1879, *9:*369–388 (with Fr. Schultze).   [2]Deut. Arch. klin. Med., 1884, *34:*467–519.   [3]Berlin klin. Wschr., 1875, *12:* 357–359.   [4]Verh. naturhist. med. Verein. Heidelberg, 1877, *1:*130– 136.   [5]Arch. Psychiat., Berlin, 1879, *9:*336–350.   [6]J.A.M.A., 1953, *153:*1273–1280 (Viets).   [7]Lancet, London, 1934, *1:*1200–1201. [8]Proc. Roy. Soc. Med., London, 1935, *28:*759–761.   [9]Samml. klin. Vortr., n.F., 1892, No. 53 (Inn. Med., No. 18); p. 515–542.   [10]Deut. Arch. klin. Med, 1868, *4:*535–578 *et seq.*   [11]Arch. Psychiat., Berlin, 1872, *4:*271–316.   [12]*Ibid.,* 1875, *6:*792–802.   [13]*Ibid.,* 1875, *6:*803– 834 (Westphal).

References to Biography: 1) Deut. Zschr. Nervenh., 1922, *73:*i–xvii (Fr. Schultze).   2) Zschr. ges. Neur. Psychiat., 1922, *47:*i–x (Nonne). 3) Penfield (Ed.), *Neurological biographies and addresses.* London, Oxford U. P., 1936 (Torkildsen and Erickson), p. 115–119.   4) Deut. Zschr. Nervenh., 1911, *41:*169–171 (Oppenheim).   5) Kolle (Ed.): *Grosse Nervenärzte.* Vol. 1. Stuttgart, Thieme, 1956, p. 68–70 (Nonne).

NIKOLAUS FRIEDREICH (1825–1882)

*F*RIEDREICH was born in Würzburg, and it was there that
he had most of his undergraduate and medical training. At
the age of thirty-one he succeeded Virchow, as Extraordinarius, in
the chair of pathological anatomy at Würzburg, where his father
and grandfather had been on the medical faculty before him. The
following year he accepted a call to Heidelberg as chief of the
medical clinic, where he worked until his death twenty-five years
later from aortic aneurysm. His entire tenure at Heidelberg was in
the rank of Professor Ordinarius of Pathology and Therapy. He
may have died too young to be a *Geheimrat,* but all about him
conforms with the idea of that title.

Early in his career, Friedreich had profited by his contacts with
von Kölliker, and had served as first assistant under the blind clinician Marcus, but the prime molding influence on his life was Virchow. His particular strength lay in his broad grasp of pathology
as applied to clinical problems. His first work of importance
(1853), a Habilitationsschrift dealing with intracranial tumors,
demonstrated the great capacity he had for supporting original
clinical observations by means of exact pathological descriptions.

Adept in pathology though he was, Friedreich's foremost talent
lay in clinical medicine, with an especial flair for physical diagnosis. All his work was remarkable for its volume, excellence and versatility. He was an authority in almost all branches of internal
medicine, and wrote extensively on diseases of the heart and blood
vessels. His main interest, however, was in neurology.

The most elaborate of his writings was a monograph on
progressive muscular atrophy.[1] This publication, dedicated to
Virchow, contributed much to the early understanding of muscular dystrophy; but Friedreich fell into the error of regarding all
muscular atrophy as myopathic, and this marred the value of the
work. His studies of hereditary spinal ataxia, however, are justly
regarded as classics.[2,3] They were pioneer achievements which laid
the groundwork for all subsequent knowledge of hereditary degenerations of the spinal cord, brain stem, and cerebellum. Details
have been added or changed and some of the physiologic interpre-

tations proposed by Friedreich are no longer tenable, but the main clinical and pathologic observations and ideas are sound and enduring. From a clinical-pathological point of view, Friedreich's ataxia is still exactly as he saw it. Among Friedreich's gifts to neurological lore, his original description of paramyoclonus multiplex,[4] so named by him, also remains standard.

Friedreich was not only an investigator but also an assiduous

Portrait, courtesy of Yale Medical Library, New Haven, Connecticut. (Photographer: Lange, Heidelberg.)

teacher, and not the least of his contributions was the training he gave to his many gifted pupils and assistants, among whom were Adolf Kussmaul, Fr. Schultze, and especially, Wilhelm Erb.

The rest of his busy life was occupied by much attention to the administration of his clinic, to university affairs, and to one of the largest consulting practices in Europe. There was not time for other interests: for him, medicine was everything. His only diversion came from the joys of his family life. Though loyal to his friends, of whom he had many, he was inclined to be sensitive and even mistrustful of others, and was bitterly vindictive to his open enemies. His drive for work was tremendous. The whole direction of that work is best expressed in his own words, written in a prefatory dedication to Virchow: "To me as a clinician the principles of cellular pathology have become the cynosure in the labyrinth of pathological processes."

CHICAGO, ILLINOIS   RICHARD B. RICHTER

References

[1]*Über progressive Muskelatrophie, über wahre und falsche Muskelhypertrophie.* Berlin, Hirschwald, 1873.   [2]Virchows Arch., 1863, *36:* 391–419 *et seq.*   [3]*Ibid.,* 1876, *68:*145–245; 1877, *70:*140–152.   [4]*Ibid.,* 1881, *86:*421–430.

References to Biography: 1) *Heidelberger Professoren aus dem 19 Jahrhundert.* Vol. 2. Heidelberg, Winter, 1903 (Erb).   2) *Verdienste deutscher Ärtzte um die Erkenntnis der Neuro-Pathologie.* Inaug.-Diss., Düsseldorf, 1936 (Kleinjohann).

WILLIAM GOWERS (1845–1915)

*W*ILLIAM RICHARD GOWERS, to become "Sir William" in 1897, was one of a brilliant group who, in the latter part of the past century, were the glory of British neurology and indeed of British medicine. Hughlings Jackson, David Ferrier, Victor Horsley, and William Gowers led knowledge and the meth-

Portrait, courtesy of Dr. Foster Kennedy, New York City.

ods of knowledge to new heights and into unexplored territory. Their pupils, who often became their colleagues, have maintained the march they led. Of these four, Gowers, the clinician, deepened the foundations of neural medicine; Ferrier and Horsley, experimental investigators, physician and surgeon, raised its pillars strongly; and Jackson, the neurological philosopher, erected flying buttresses for its perpetual strength.

Gowers' life was spent in London, at University College and especially at "Queen Square." It was spent with a diversity of interest and a thoroughness of energy which brought to him all honour and to all of us, education. We should be better doctors, better teachers, better writers, if we from time to time read Gowers' *Clinical lectures on diseases of the nervous system* (Philadelphia, Blakiston, 1895), his *The borderland of epilepsy* (London, Churchill, 1907), his occasional papers such as that *On special sense cortical discharges from organic disease,*[1] and *On syringal haemorrhage into the spinal cord,*[2] and thereby learn some of the art of perfect observation and perfect precise description, written in easy simple prose. His textbook,[3] which wore his health, was written when he was around forty. It used to be called "The Bible of Neurology," and can still give light on diagnostic problems, difficult for us. He illustrated it himself. His drawing was as clear and simple as was his writing and vastly better in instruction than our photographs which embarrass by their views of the unessential. Such was his gift in paint, draughtsmanship and imagination that his pictures were "hung" regularly by the Royal Academy of Arts. This gift allowed him to publish in 1904 his famous *Manual and atlas of medical ophthalmoscopy* (London, Churchill, 1904) which has not since been bettered even through the craft of retinal photography.

Once at dinner he said to me—"I'm not sure what I shall do this summer. Last year I studied—British grasses, so perhaps this year I'll study—clouds." This zest in diversity made him, as it must make all wise physicians, a philosopher with a view of life,—and of life universal. Some quotations from one of his lectures show the modern quality of his thought: "The energy of the Universe is only perpetual motion"; "Atomic motion along nerve fibrils," when discussing neural impulse transmission; "We must accept

the fact of discontinuity of structure and continuity of function,"
—this in *The dynamics of life* in 1894 (Philadelphia; Blakiston)
when most of us elders were small boys, or as unborn as were then
wireless transmission and radar! He added here the warning that
"words have a strong tendency to cause opacity if they be numerous," and made a half-apology for his speculative thoughts: "Who
is there that does not feel that an earnest effort to perceive that
which is unseen leaves him on a higher level,—and that if he be
still at his old standpoint he has a better view?"

He was a passionate man in his beliefs and zests. He thought
obsessionally about shorthand and to the last day would tuck up
the skirts of his frock coat, and sit on the edge of the bed taking
shorthand notes of the case,—it was a life habit. He was once seen,
—and it probably happened often,—to stop his coachman in
crowded Southampton Row, having fastened his eye on a likely-
looking young man hurrying on his lawful occasions along the
pavement. Gowers climbed out of his carriage, white beard wav-
ing, stumbled up to him,—his gait was unsteady,—clutched him by
the arm, and glaring at him with his frightening flaming fierce
blue eyes said, "Young man, do you write shorthand?" To which
the shocked man answered, "No, I don't." Whereupon Gowers
dropped his arm, saying bitterly, "You're a fool, and will fail in
life." He then clambered abruptly back into his carriage.

However, no picture of Gowers can be appreciated without at
the same time having in the mind's eye his look of being a combination of one of the Wise Men of the East and the Ancient Mari-
ner, and hearing too his harsh loud staccato voice speaking in sardonic humorous invective against the errors of the world.

Such were the "Original" spirits who led our Profession half a
century ago. The Gods have departed. "Leadership" now lies with
the "Deans' Executive Committees" compounded of medical medi-
ocrities or with the lay bureaucrats of Socialized Medicine! Having lost Men to lead us, we shall surely dwindle into a necessary
"City Service,"—like the Department of Sanitation. We shall cease
to be a learned profession and shall become instead a Union of
Slick Gadgeteers,—of proletarian proclivities and level!

FOSTER KENNEDY

References

[1]Brain, London, 1909, *32*:303–326 (Hughlings–Jackson Lecture). [2]Lancet, London, 1903, 2:993–997. [3]*A manual of diseases of the nervous system.* 2 vol. London, Churchill, 1886–88.

Reference to Biography: Sir William Gowers, 1845–1915. A biographical appreciation. London Heineman, 1949 (contains complete bibliography) (Critchley).

WILLIAM ALEXANDER HAMMOND (1828–1900)

*H*AMMOND, a native of Maryland and the son of a physician, entered the U.S. Army Medical Department as assistant surgeon early in his career (1849). His first tour of duty was in the Southwest, where he took part in campaigns against the Sioux Indians. After a few years an illness brought him extended sick leave which he spent in Europe making an intensive study of military hospitals. On his return, a friendship with Weir Mitchell was kindled by their mutual interest in arrow and ordeal poisons and snake venoms, on the latter of which they published their first account in 1859 in the *American Journal of Medicine*. Being of the same age, they were on equal terms. Both were looking for antidotes for snakebite. One day Hammond mentioned to Weir Mitchell that while in Texas he had successfully used a certain antidote for rattlesnake poison. Mitchell then purchased a half dozen of these snakes, only to prove to his satisfaction that the antidote was of no value.

Hammond's academic interests were the cause of his resignation from the army in 1860 to accept the chair of anatomy and physiology at the University of Maryland. However, at the outbreak of the War between the States he re-entered the army as assistant surgeon. Regarding promotion, he was at the bottom of the list, but his accomplishments as inspector of hospitals, where he introduced humane management, were such that despite his youth—he was thirty-four—President Lincoln appointed him Surgeon General (1862). His tenure was distinguished by many achievements,

William Alexander Hammond

among them the founding in 1862 of the Army Medical Museum, more recently (1949) the Armed Forces Institute of Pathology. In the same year he began with J. H. Brinton, J. J. Woodward and G. A. Otis the work of compiling the *Medical and surgical history of the War of the Rebellion*,[1] those weighty tomes of which Ru-

Portrait, courtesy of the National Library of Medicine, Bethesda, Maryland.

dolf Virchow stated (1874): "Whoever takes in hand and examines these comprehensive publications will continually have his astonishment excited anew by the riches of the experience, purchased at so dear a price, which is there recorded . . ."[10]

Constant friction between General Hammond and Secretary of War Stanton—the former keen of intellect, indomitable in spirit and, to some, pompous and arrogant; the latter autocratic, irascible and unrelenting in his prejudices—came to a climax in 1863 when General Hammond was ordered on an extended, obviously permanent, inspection tour. This caused Hammond to demand restoration of the prerogatives of his office or trial by court-martial. Tried in 1864 by a "packed court" on the charge of irregularities incident to the purchase of medical supplies, General Hammond received a verdict of guilty and was dismissed from the Army. After more than a decade (1878) he was vindicated by Act of Congress. It was some years later that he donned the resplendent dress uniform (of a Brigadier General) to sit for the portrait shown herewith.

Shortly after the trial, penniless and in debt, Hammond moved to New York and succeeded in establishing a practice of neurology. This not only brought him prominence but also made him exceedingly wealthy. He became professor at the University of the City of New York in 1874, and at Bellevue Hospital Medical College in 1876, the year his *Spiritualism* . . . (New York, Putnam) appeared: a book of fantastic tales, such as that of a girl abstaining from food and drink for years, raising in her doctor's mind the question: "Why does the body grow when nothing goes into it?" Hammond was among the seven who founded the American Neurological Association. In 1888 he returned to Washington, where some years later he died of a cardiac ailment.

Hammond shares with Weir Mitchell the distinction of having secured for neurology its place in American medicine. What raised Hammond most above the rank and file was his observation, reported in 1871 (in his textbook, *A treatise on diseases of the nervous system;* Appleton, New York), of a bizarre muscular affliction involving the hand and foot of one side, for which he coined the term "athetosis" ("without fixed position"). In his assessment of the two cases, this percipient observer found reason to remark: "the analogies of the affection are with chorea and cere-bro-spinal sclerosis, but it is neither of these diseases. One prob-able seat of the morbid process is in the corpus striatum."

Abduction of the fingers, extension and pronation or supination of the hand, and "agitation" of the limbs by irregular movements, all occurring in association with spastic hemiplegia, had been de-scribed by Cazauvielh[2] as early as 1827 in a study of varied cortical hemiatrophic states, but he brought no substance into his evalua-tion. In a case of hemiathetosis Gowers (1876)[3] found a puckered scar in the contralateral thalamus. Hammond's term was adopted neither by Weir Mitchell (1874),[4] who referred to the disorder (posthemiplegic) as "hemichorea," nor by Gowers,[3] who spoke of "mobile spasm." Charcot (1879),[5] too, was critical, and remarked that athetosis is nothing else but a variety of chorea. Congeni-tal *"double* athetosis" was so designated in 1873 by Shaw,[6] as a dis-ease "most closely resembling chorea, but the distinction is, on careful examination, well marked." Greidenberg (1886),[7] assert-ing that he was the first in Russia to publish on this subject (in 1881), suggested that the disorder be called "the disease of Ham-mond." Credit for the finding of lesions in the putamen of the two sides in congenital cases of *double* athetosis goes to Anton (1896),[8] though he acknowledged earlier descriptions to this effect. Anton found patches of "hypermyelinated" nerve fibers in the putamen, but it was Freund and Cécile Vogt[9] who, in 1911, emphasized this feature, referring to the abnormality as état marbré ("status mar-moratus").

Hammond was an uncommonly tall and large man with a voice so powerful that it could be heard up-wind in a hurricane. He had a penchant for theatrical action, which he exercised as playwright, lecturer and novelist. Moreover, there was a substantial dash of Paracelsus in him. He was not only an outstanding leader and tal-ented organizer but also an aristocrat among the laborers in the neurological field. Tough-fibered to begin with, and toughened further by exposure in Kansas while on duty in the Indian coun-try, he was, above all, a "brave figure out of the past, a reminder of the days when words were plain and men were men" (Duncan).

MOFFETT FIELD, CALIFORNIA   WEBB HAYMAKER

References

[1]By Woodward and Otis, under direction of the U.S. Surgeon General. Washington, D.C., Govt. Printing Office, 1870–80.   [2]Arch. Gen. Med., Paris, 1827, *14*:5–23, 347–366.   [3]Med.-Chir. Soc. Tr., 1876, *59*: 271–326.   [4]Amer. J. Med. Sci., 1874, *68*:342–352.   [5]*Lectures on the diseases of the nervous system.* Philadelphia, Lea, 1879 (trans. by Sigerson), p. 390.   [6]S. Barth. Hosp. Rep., London, 1873, *9*:130–140. [7]Arch. Psychiat., Berlin, 1886, *17*:131–216.   [8]Jahrb. Psychiat. Neur., Wien, 1896, *14*:141–182.   [9]J. Psychol. Neur., Lpz., Heft 4, 1911, *18*: 489–500.   [10]*Die Fortschritte der Kriegsheilkunde, besonders im Gebiet der Infectionskrankheiten.* Berlin, Hirschwald, 1874, p. 7.

References to Biography and Works: 1) Mil. Surgeon, 1929, *64*:98–110, 252–262 (Duncan).   2) Army Med. Bull., 1940, *52*:42–46 (Phalen). 3) *Chiefs of the Medical Department, United States Army, 1775–1940. Biographical sketches.* Washington, D.C., privately printed, 1940 (Phalen).   4) *Diseases of the basal ganglia and subthalamic nuclei.* New York, Oxford U. P., 1946, p. 272–273 (Denny-Brown).   5) Arch. Neur. Psychiat., Chic., 1950, *63*:875–901 (Carpenter).   6) Neurology, 1951, *1*:1–17 (Pearce Bailey).   7) Bull. Hist. Med., 1967, *41*:515–538 (Schiller).

HENRY HEAD (1861–1940)

*H*ENRY HEAD came of an old Quaker family of Stamford Hill in England. In 1880 he was elected to a scholarship at Trinity College, Cambridge, where, with Langley and Sherrington, he was strongly influenced by the physiologists Gaskell and Michael Foster. After graduating B.A. with honors in natural science he spent two years in the German University of Prague and the University of Halle. He is reputed to have introduced association football to Prague where it has ever since been a popular national pastime.

Head's first paper was on the action potential of nerve. Next, from Hering's laboratory in Halle in 1889, he published a masterly treatise on the respiratory effects of the vagus nerve. Following study in University College Hospital, London, he graduated in

Portrait, courtesy of the National Library of Medicine, Bethesda, Maryland.

1892. His thesis for the M.D., *On disturbance of sensation, with special reference to the pain of visceral disease*,[1] was of outstanding merit. At the instigation of Hitzig, Head's studies in this field were brought out as a book in German.[2]

Referral of pain from deep structures led him to study herpes zoster; from this his investigation of the dermatomes naturally evolved.[3] It was typical of his enthusiasm that he lived in a mental hospital for two years in order to obtain firsthand information on the herpes that was then common in paretics. Foerster called attention to the remarkable accuracy of Head's observations when compared with the method of section of nerve roots. In 1898 Head was elected assistant physician to the London Hospital and was occupied in hospital and private practice to the time of his retirement in 1925.

Following his study on dermatomes, Head's investigations were devoted almost wholly to the sensory system, where he brought order out of chaos at every level by his vivid thought and refined clinical method. In 1903, with Rivers' assistance, he made many observations on himself after sectioning the superficial ramus of his own radial nerve. He undertook this auto-experiment because of his annoyance when patients became weary after an hour's testing of a restricted skin area. Two years before beginning the experiment, he further states in the account of it, he gave up smoking, and abstained from alcohol, except on holidays!

Pre-eminent was his paper with Gordon Holmes in 1911 on sensory disturbances from cerebral lesions.[4] Collected papers on sensation appeared in 1920.[5] His postulate of two separate sensory systems—protopathic and epicritic—to explain the different susceptibilities of sensation, was severely criticized, and for many years was considered disproven. Recent recording from single sensory neurones has reaffirmed much in Head's separation of highly differentiated sensations from other types.[6] Head did indeed provide the first rational explanation of the nature of sensory dissociation. The clinical facts which he and his collaborators established remain the basis for most clinical investigations of sensation today; in order to realize the magnitude of his contribution one has only to review the knowledge of sensory disorders before Head's investigations. His extensive study of spinal reflex functions also brought new light and abundant stimulus to that problem. No less monumental was his contribution to aphasia.[7] Here his originality brought new definition to the more complex aspects of these disorders. Describing "semantic aphasia," he provided a link between the linguistic and the intellectual aspects of speech forecast by Pierre Marie. The full implications of this work are even yet not generally recognized. Head's remaining writings include a volume of attractive verse.[8]

Head was editor of *Brain* from 1910 to 1925, and the honor of knighthood was conferred on him in 1927. He became fluent in German and French, to the point of confusing the customs officials as to his nationality. A man of great patience, humility, and profound learning, he was fated to endure, for the last twenty years of his life, the prolonged physical discomfort and incapacity brought about by paralysis agitans. Even in this period his lively mind and indomitable enthusiasm immensely stimulated the fortunate few who were privileged to enjoy his conversation.

SOUTHBOROUGH, MASSACHUSETTS   D. DENNY-BROWN

References

[1]Brain, London, 1893, *16*:1–133; 1894, *17*:339–480; 1896, *19*:153–276.
[2]*Die Sensibilitätsstörungen der Haut bei Visceralerkrankungen* (trans. by Seiffer, with foreword by Hitzig). Berlin, Hirschwald, 1898.
[3]Brain, London, 1900, *23*:353–523.   [4]*Ibid.*, 1911, *34*:102–271.
[5]*Studies in neurology.* 2 vol. London, Oxford U. P., 1920.   [6]Brain, London, 1965, *88*:725–738 (Denny-Brown).   [7]*Aphasia and kindred disorders of speech.* 2 vol. Cambridge U. P., 1926.   [8]*Destroyers, and other verses. London,* Oxford U. P., 1919.

References to Biography: 1) Brit. Med. J., 1940, *2*:539–541 (anon.).
2) Brain, London, 1940, *63*:205–208 (contains bibliography; anon.).
3) Arch. Neur. Psychiat., Chic., 1941, *45*:698–702 (Kennedy).

GEORGE HUNTINGTON (1850–1916)

*G*EORGE SUMNER HUNTINGTON was born in East Hampton, Long Island, New York. His grandfather, Dr. Abel Huntington, had settled in East Hampton in 1797, and his father, Dr. George Lee Huntington, spent many years in the practice of medicine in that locality.

After receiving preliminary training from his father, Huntington attended the College of Physicians and Surgeons of Columbia University, graduating in 1871. He returned to East Hampton to assist his father in practice, and was able to observe further the cases of hereditary chorea which he had first seen with his grandfather and father. It was here that in all probability he began his paper on chorea, as his father's correctional marks have been found on the original manuscript. Later in the same year he moved to Pomeroy, Ohio, and on February 15, 1872, he read his paper, *On chorea*,[1] before the Meigs and Mason Academy of Medicine in Middleport, Ohio. He was only twenty-two years old at the time. In 1874 he moved to New York, and aside from two years in North Carolina, spent the remainder of his life in the practice of medicine in Dutchess County. He retired in 1915.

Huntington's one major scientific contribution dealt with the subject of chorea in general, but it included his description of the hereditary form which he had observed in East Hampton. He stressed as marked peculiarities of the disease its hereditary nature, its occurrence only in adult life, and the tendency for patients so afflicted to become insane and sometimes suicidal. Speaking before the New York Neurological Society on December 7, 1909, he stated that without the facts and observations imparted to him by his grandfather and father he could never have formulated a picture of the salient characteristics of the disease. From personal memories he recounted: "Over fifty years ago, in riding with my father on his professional rounds, I saw my first case of 'that disorder,' which was the way in which the natives always referred to the dreaded disease. It made a most enduring impression upon my boyish mind, an impression every detail of which I recall today, an

impression which was the very first impulse to my choosing chorea
as my virgin contribution to medical lore. We suddenly came
upon two women, mother and daughter, both tall, thin, almost ca-
daverous, both bowing, twisting, grimacing. I stared in wonder-
ment, almost fear. What could it mean? My father paused to speak
with them and we passed on. Then my Gamaliel-like instruction
began; my medical instruction had its inception. From this point
on my interest in the disease has never wholly ceased."

Portrait, courtesy of Dr. Edwin G. Zabriskie, New York City.

Even though it has since been shown that previous workers had described the same condition, Huntington, by his lucid, concise and accurate account of the disease, deserves the credit of having been the discoverer of the disorder which bears his name. But the study of this family did not rest with Huntington's description of it. Jelliffe[2] and Tilney[3] took up the task of tracing the ancestry of the families concerned, a study concluded some years later by Vessie (1932),[4] who found that they stemmed from two brothers and their families who left Bures (in Essex) for Suffolk, England, and then sailed to Boston Bay in 1630. During the intervening three centuries about 1,000 descendents of the original settlers were known to have come down with the disease. Not a few of these unfortunate persons were tried for witchcraft in the Colonial courts, and in other ways, too, they were persecuted because their involuntary movements were interpreted as "a derisive pantomine of the sufferings of the Saviour during crucifixion." Among the pioneers in the study of the pathological changes in the basal ganglia in this disease were Jelgersma,[5] Alzheimer,[6] Pfeiffer,[7] Marie and Lhermitte,[8] and C. and O. Vogt.[9]

Huntington was a general practitioner of medicine; his major interests were his patients and their problems. No faculty appointments came his way, nor did he perform any significant research. Because of his attractive personality, keen intellect, ready wit, and sense of humor, he was widely admired and respected. He had a great fondness for music and often played the flute to his wife's accompaniment. Moreover, he was an ardent student of nature and a devotee of the rod and gun. Drawing was one of his lifetime interests and he often made sketches of game birds during his trips through the woods. Here, then, was a man who enjoyed life to the full, and who, because of his insight and imagination, gained a place in neurological history.

ANN ARBOR, MICHIGAN   RUSSELL N. DeJONG

References

[1]Med. & Surg. Reporter, Phila., 1872, 26:317–321.   [2]Neurographs, 1908, 1:116–124.   [3]Ibid., p. 124–127.   [4]J. Nerv. Ment. Dis., 1932, 76:553–573.   [5]Verh. Ges. Deut. Naturf., 1908, 80, 2. Teil, 2. Hälfte, p. 383–388.   [6]Neur. Cbl., 1911, 30:891–892.   [7]Brain, London, 1913,

35:276–291.   [8]Ann. méd., Paris, 1914, *1:18–47*.   [9]J. Psychol. Neur., Lpz., 1920, *25,* Erg. Heft: 627–846.

References to Biography and Works: 1) Ann. Med. Hist., 1937, n.s., *9*:201–210 (DeJong).   2) *Diseases of the basal ganglia and subthalmic nuclei.* New York, Oxford U. P., 1946 (Denny-Brown).   3) *Historical introduction: the basal ganglia and their diseases.* In *The diseases of the basal ganglia.* Ass. Research Nerv. & Ment. Dis., Proc., 1942, *21:* 1–20 (Lewy).

HUGHLINGS JACKSON (1835–1911)

*O*NE of five children, John Hughlings Jackson was born of a farmer father at Providence Green, Hammerton, Yorkshire, England. He had only a grammar school education and his medical training was not impressive. After qualifying for medicine at the age of twenty-one, he worked at the York Dispensary under Thomas Laycock, a doctor deeply concerned, in word and print, with consciousness and the brain. Inspired, like Darwin, by the writings of Herbert Spencer, Jackson on his return to London in 1859 was ready to abandon medicine in favor of philosophy. Sir Jonathan Hutchinson, himself a York man, took credit for dissuading Jackson from this course in favor of medicine. Given an appointment at Moorfields Eye Hospital, Jackson's interest in the nervous system was stimulated by his peephole view of it through the ophthalmoscope, invented by Helmholtz ten years before. In 1860 the National Hospital, Queen Square, London, was founded, with Brown-Séquard as physician-in-chief, and in 1862 Jackson became a member of the staff of this hospital where he worked for the next forty-five years. His early interest in seizures was doubtless sustained by the fact that his cousin wife experienced what we now call Jacksonian epilepsy.

W. Russell Brain[1] makes this cogent observation: "The discoverer of a substantial thing, such as a bacillus, an extract or a disease, achieves more certain immortality than one who discovers a principle, for permanently valid principles soon become part of current thought and in time appear so obvious as to have needed

no discovery." The name of Jackson is embedded in our everyday medical vocabulary, for at the suggestion of Charcot, seizures that on anatomical grounds might have been termed rolandic, are called Jacksonian. "Uncinate seizures" was Jackson's own coinage. However, the man's importance does not rest on his description of a certain seizure pattern but on his formulation of concepts or

Portrait, courtesy of the National Library of Medicine, Bethesda, Maryland.

principles that explain paroxysmal seizures of all sorts. "Epilepsy is the name for occasional, sudden, excessive, rapid and local discharge of the gray matter." Far-reaching conclusions regarding neurophysiology were based on meticulous study of a few selected patients, supplemented whenever possible by gross examination of the brain, but without the aid of animal experimentation or the microscope.[2-7] The manifestations of epilepsy formed the key to the workings of the nervous system. We owe to him the dynamic concept of balancing forces that control a gradation of movement "from the most voluntary to the most involuntary."

Jackson postulated three evolutionary levels of the sensorimotor mechanism: the lowest, cord, medulla and pons; the middle, the rolandic region; the highest level, the prefrontal lobes.[8] He described an evolution from automatic to purposive movements and a dissolution from the purposive to the automatic. Excessive discharge of grey matter is followed by its exhaustion. Discharges from a lower center might result from a loss of inhibition from the highest center. An excessive discharge of the "epileptogenous focus" is a consequence of instability of nerve cells, due in turn to their malnutrition, possibly the result of a defective blood supply.

Many of Jackson's approximately three-hundred publications appeared in obscure journals. Because of his meager education or his philosophic and meticulous cast of mind, his writing is involved and repetitious, its continuity broken by qualifying statements. "His papers," a critic wrote, "resembled the love of God which passeth all understanding." He made no use of illustrations, diagrams or statistical data. He shirked writing a book. "If I did," he once remarked, "my enemies would find me out." But this deficit has been made good in part by the volume of *Selected writings* (London, Hodder & Stoughton, 1931), edited by James Taylor. Although Jackson carried on an active practice, his writings reflect no interest in the patient as a person or in his treatment.

Jackson was quiet, unassuming, serious, inordinately shy, hobbyless. Exercise he abhorred. He was easily fatigued, restless, could not endure boredom. He would seldom sit a dinner out, would leave a theatre at the end of the first act, and he took care not to reach a medical meeting until the discussion following the paper had begun. To relax he would read the latest novels and even penny thrillers. (He often said that he was happy not to be over-educated.) Great books, too, he would read. They were not for adornment: he would buy a book, rip off the cover, tear the book down the middle, stuff one-half into each pocket, then leave the store; the clerk thought him mad.

He suffered from vertigo and migraine. Sir Hugh Cairns tells the story that on one occasion Sir Henry Head emerged from "Queen Square" jubilant over a new observation he had made, and spying Jackson standing quietly on the corner, came up to him to relate his find. Jackson interrupted him with the remark: "Don't bother me now, Head. I'm making some observations on my own migraine." Childless, he lived alone for thirty-five years after the early death of his wife from cerebral thrombosis. He died of pneumonia at the age of seventy-six. He joined Ferrier, Bucknill and Crichton-Browne as editors of *Brain* when that great periodical was established in 1878. "Father of British Neurology," he appears to us as having been foremost on the brilliant staff that made "Queen Square" a center of world neurology. Yet partially eclipsed during life by some more mundane contemporaries Jackson's light acquired ever greater brilliance in the afterglow. Perhaps best of all, he subjected the ancient ill of epilepsy to the genius of his scrutiny, and thereby opened a door of hope on this hitherto hopeless disease.

WILLIAM G. LENNOX

References

[1]Postgrad. Med. J., London, 1935, *11*:145–149.   [2]Med. Times Gaz., 1864, *50*:166–167.   [3]*Ibid.*, 1864, *50*:167.   [4]Trans. St. Andrew's Med. Grad. Assn., 1870, *3*:162–207.   [5]Brit. Med. J., 1875, *1*:773–774. [6]Brain, London, 1888, *11*:179–207 *et seq.*   [7]Brit. Med. J., 1890, *1:* 703–707 *et seq.*   [8]Lancet, London, 1898, *1*:79–87.

References to Biography: 1) Postgrad. Med. J., London, 1935, *11*:145–149 (Brain).   2) Bull. N. Y. Acad. Med., 1935, *11*:479–480 (Kennedy).   3) Brit. Med. J., 1911, *2*:950–954 *et seq.* (Hutchinson). 4) *Ibid.*, 1912, *1*:85 (Mercier).   5) Brain, London, 1903, *26*:305–366 (Broadbent).   6) *Ibid.*, 1915, *28*:1–190 (Head).

SERGEI KORSAKOV (1853–1900)

*J*HE first great psychiatrist of Russia, Sergei Sergeivich Korsakov ranks high among the *Founders of Neurology* through his many contributions to the knowledge of organic psychoses. He was born on the Gus estate (Vladimir Province), a locality known for its glass factory, of which his father was the manager. He studied medicine at the University of Moscow, and upon graduating in 1875 became physician to Preobrazhenskii Hospital. From 1876 to 1879 he was on Kozhevnikov's staff in the clinic for nervous diseases. His thesis on "alcoholic paralysis"[1] won him the M.D. in 1887. In the following year he received the title of Privatdozent, and in 1892 he became superintendent to the newly opened University Psychiatric Clinic and Professor Extraordinarius. During this time he visited Vienna where he was a pupil of Meynert.

The general recognition of Korsakov as an original thinker is largely due to his description of the disorder which bears his name. In 1887[2] and again in 1890[3] he drew attention to several cases of alcoholic polyneuritis with distinctive mental symptoms: faulty retention of impressions, amnesia, disorientation in time and place, and confabulation. "This mental disorder," he said, "appears at times in the form of sharply delineated irritable weakness in the mental sphere, at times in the form of confusion with characteristic mistakes in orientation for place, time and situation, and at times as an almost pure form of acute anmesia, where the recent memory is most severely involved, while the remote memory is well preserved. . . . Some have suffered so widespread a memory loss that they literally forget everything immediately."[4] In another paper in 1890[5] he emphasized, as he had in his previous publications, that this amnestic-confabulatory syndrome, which he called "cerebropathia psychica toxaemica" could occur in a great variety of disorders other than alcoholism and even without neuritis. In time it became customary to apply the term "Korsakov's psychosis" only when the mental disorder was accompanied by neuritic symptoms. Jolly[6] introduced that eponymic term and full credit for this contribution was given Korsakov by others as well,[7] though he himself[5] accorded priority to Magnus Huss.

But Korsakov's reputation was not based on a single observation; he struck out into the whole field of psychiatry with telling effect, orienting psychiatry to medicine, and bringing his efforts to bear on the social factors in psychiatry. He is credited with establishing the concept of paranoia ("paranoia hyperphantastica," as he called it)[8]; his textbook on psychiatry[9] compared favorably with the best contemporary works in other languages; his classification of mental diseases[8] offered distinct advantages over that of Krafft-Ebing, which was more generally accepted; and his elaboration of memory disturbance in alcoholism, described in Bumke's *Handbuch*,[10] added further to his fame. He was responsible for freeing

Portrait, courtesy of Dr. Maurice Genty, Académie de Médecine, Paris, France.

mental patients from straitjackets and other restraints. The "no restraint" principle was not popular with the hospital personnel for,
as Korsakov remarked, "The less restraint for the patient, the
more restraint for the doctor," that is, he must give "more attention, affection and devotion to the patient."⁸ Another new therapeutic measure advocated and practiced by Korsakov was the family care of psychotic patients—transferring them from psychiatric
institutions to families on farms, under close hospital supervision.
He raised the question "whether rest cure, indiscriminately used
might not be apt to inhibit the energies and the guiding forces of
the intellect," and in regard to narcotics, he warned that their use
should be solely for the purpose of calming the patient.⁷

Korsakov was deeply respected by his colleagues and students.
His humanitarianism may be traced to his boyhood: when only
eleven he wrote, "Help others. When the occasion presents itself
to do good deeds, do them. Withdraw from evil." To this principle he remained true. He deplored the fact that students had to
waste their energies obtaining the bare necessities of life when
they should be concentrating on their studies, and as chairman of
"The Society for Aid to Needy Students," he did much to alleviate
their financial difficulties. But he also clearly indicated what he expected of students: "First of all I wish that all students recognize
the absolute necessity of education; that they deeply love science
and knowledge, and that they despise ignorance . . . For the great
privilege of being educated, students must be ready to sacrifice,
even to pay with their lives if necessary, for the good of the Country and for the ideals of mankind." One of Korsakov's pupils was
Serbskii, who at a meeting of Russian psychiatrists in 1911,
achieved fame for his attack on the government for its disregard of
the social services. Reforms soon followed.

An able organizer, Korsakov was instrumental in founding in
1890 the Moscow Society of Neuropathologists and Psychiatrists.
In his opening address, he laid down as the basic principle for
each member, "to further scientific knowledge without being concerned who will be first to reach a scientific achievement."

A high point in his career was the organization of the 12th International Medical Congress, which was held in Moscow in 1897.
He then set out to achieve a lifelong ambition: namely, to establish a Russian Association of Psychiatrists and Neurologists which

would have national scope. He worked out the constitution in all details, but worn by the intensity of his striving he died, at the age of forty-six, just before the Association came into being. The warmth of his heart and his many contributions left an indelible mark on the scientists of his time. By acclamation the *Zhurnal nevropatologii i psikhiatrii* was named after him. He is to be counted among such "moral geniuses" as Pinel and Charcot.

BETHESDA, MARYLAND   S. KATZENELBOGEN

References

[1]*Ob alkogolnom paralichie.* Moskva, Kushnerev, 1887.   [2]Arkh. Psikhiat. Nevrol., 1887, *9*, No. 2:16–38; No. 3:1–14.   [3]Arch. Psychiat., Berlin, 1890, *21*:669–704.   [4]Trans. from Bull. Johns Hopkins Hosp., 1942, *70*:467–487 (Gantt and Muncie).   [5]Allg. Zschr. Psychiat., 1890, *46*:475–485.   [6]Charité Ann., Berlin, 1897, *22*:580–612.   [7]Sovremennaia psikhiat., 1911, *5*:16–51 (Geiner).   [8]Vopr. filosof. psikhol., 1901, *12*:XIII–XXXVIII (Serbskii).   [9]*Kurs psikhiatri.* Moskva, Kushnerev, 1893. (2nd ed., Moskva, Rikhter, 1901.)   [10]Bumke, O., *Handbuch der Geisteskrankheiten,* Berlin, 1928, 7 (Spez. Teil III):271–285 (in chapter by Meggendorfer).

References to Biography and Works: 1) Med. obozrenie, 1900, *53*:948–951.   2) Zh. nevropat. psikhol. imeni Korsakova, 1900, *1*:1–40 (Rot).   3) Vopr. filosof. psikhol., 1901, *12*:I–XII (Rot).   4) Sovremennaia psikhiat., 1911, *5*:1–10 (Melnikov-Razvendenskov).   5) *Ibid.,* p. 10–15 (Ferkhmin).   6) Vopr. filosof. psikhol., 1900, *11*:V–XIX (Lopatin *et al.*).   7) Amer. J. Psychiat., 1939, *95*:887–899 (Tarachow).

ALEKSEI KOZHEVNIKOV (1836–1902)

*A*LEKSEI YAKOVLEVICH KOZHEVNIKOV was born in Ryazan, where he early proved himself a brilliant student. He entered the University of Moscow in 1853 and received the M.D. in 1860. His doctoral dissertation, presented in 1865, was on progressive locomotor ataxia.

The interest that Kozhevnikov had shown in nervous diseases prompted the state to send him abroad, in 1866, for further study, principally to Germany, and also to England, Switzerland and

Aleksei Yakovlevich Kozhevnikov

France. In Charcot's laboratory in Paris he showed that in amyotrophic lateral sclerosis the nerve degeneration in the form of *corps granuleux* could be followed up to the motor cortex, a most important contribution to the pathology of this morbid condition.

Upon his return to Russia he was named Dozent in nervous and mental diseases at the Novo-Ekaterininskii Hospital. He became the first neuropathologist and the first alienist of the Moscow faculty. For three years, starting in 1871, he had charge of a course in general pathology and therapeutics. Later he was invested with the newly created chair in nervous and mental diseases in Moscow. He initiated improvements in the psychiatric clinic, which his brilliant young pupil Korsakov, who later was Kozhevnikov's assistant, built into the Moscow school of psychiatry. His interest in psychia-

Portrait, courtesy of the Armed Forces Institute of Pathology, Washington, D. C. (Portrait in *Méd. mod., Paris, Suppl., 8:*357, 1895, redrawn by Van Cott.)

try went much further than the scientific aspects: he was also motivated by a great humanitarian interest in championing the protection of the insane throughout the Russian empire. Kozhevnikov also founded the neurological clinic in Moscow, establishing in the latter a neurological museum, financed largely by himself. In conjunction with his students, he also founded the Moscow Society of Neurology and Psychiatry, over which he presided for several years.

Kozhevnikov's earlier work was mainly in the field of neuroanatomy, in which he was concerned especially with the nerve fiber connections in the cerebellar and cerebral cortices.[1,2] He is perhaps best known for his description of an atypical form of convulsive seizure[3,4] of cortical origin, which has generally been referred to as *epilepsia partialis continua* (Kozhevnikov's epilepsy). When he reported the condition to the Moscow Society of Neurology and Psychiatry, Nil Filatov, the famous Russian pediatrician, commented that this was an observation ranking in importance with that made by Hughlings Jackson on another seizure pattern called cortical epilepsy. His work on lathyrism[5] is regarded as a classic. He described progressive familial spastic diplegia[6] and wrote on the neuropathology of nuclear ophthalmoplegia,[7] myasthenia, and bulbar paralysis. His textbook on nervous diseases[8] was a popular manual because of its brevity and lucidity. He was an editor of *Korsakov's Zhurnal nevropatologii i psikhiatrii*.

Kozhevnikov was a man whom nature favored with a kindly spirit, great industry, and a high degree of intelligence. His ability as a speaker, his critical judgment and his quiet dignity won for him a position of leadership in all his endeavors. On the occasion of the twenty-fifth anniversary of the completion of his doctoral thesis, his friends and pupils, as a mark of devotion, published in book form his many papers.[9] Although a Russian patriot, Kozhevnikov was not a chauvinist: he had a profound respect for the advances made in other countries, giving credit where it was due. Minor, in referring to him, said that in his passing—he died of cancer after a long illness—Russian science had lost a creator, and western Europe an earnest, forceful and true friend.

NEW YORK CITY   DOROTHY GOODENOW
NEW YORK CITY   FRED A. METTLER

References

[1]Arch. neur., Paris, 1883, *6:*356–376.   [2]Arch. mikr. Anat., 1869, *5:* 332–333.   [3]Tr. Obshch. nevropat. Mosk., 1893–94, p. 30.   [4]Neur. Cbl., 1895, *14:*47–48.   [5]*Latirizm-boliezn obuslovlennaya upotreblen-iem v pishtshu gorokha; lathyrus.* St. Petersburg, Stasyulevich, 1894. [6]Med. obozr., Moskva, 1895, *43:*329–366.   [7]*Ibid.,* 1887, *27:*148–159. [8]*Kurs nervnikh bolieznei; lekstsii.* Moskva, Volchaninov, 1892. [9]*Sbornik stateĭ po nevropatologiĭ i psikhiatrii.* Moskva, Kushner, 1890.

References to Biography: 1) Med. obozr., Moskva, 1902, *57:*342–352 (contains bibliography; Pribytkov).   2) Arch. Psychiat., Berlin, 1902, *35:*874–875 (Minor).   3) Méd. mod., Paris, 1895, suppl., *6:*357–358 (not signed).

OCTAVE LANDRY (1826–1865)

*J*EAN BAPTISTE OCTAVE LANDRY DE THÉZILLAT was born and brought up in Limoges. His uncle, Dr. de Thézillat, a neurologist and psychiatrist, did much to influence him in his decision to study medicine. In 1850 Landry became externe des hôpitaux in Paris. When cholera swept into the Département de l'Oise, decimating its population, Landry distinguished himself as a volunteer. A medal commemorating the gratitude of the people of the Oise was struck for him on his return to Paris.

He became interne under Sandras and Gubler at the Hôtel-Dieu and Hôpital Beaujon. In 1852, while still an interne, he brought forward evidence that movements, both passive and active, are dependent on afferent impulses from muscles—"sens de l'activité," he called it.[1] Thus his work anticipated the similar studies by Duchenne by three years, of Bellion's[2] by two, as has been brought out so well by Bastian.[3] His independent description in 1855[4] of ataxia in posterior column disease was as graphic and true as Romberg's in 1851.

Landry's celebrated memoir on ascending paralysis appeared in 1859,[5] simultaneously with the first volume of his *Traité complet des paralysies* (Paris, Masson). The memoir, his greatest literary

legacy to medicine, dealt with ten cases of this mysterious malady, five of which had been under his care. The greatness of Landry's report consists not only in the precision of his observations and the clarity with which he set them down, but in his contention that the disorder could manifest itself in three ways: as an ascending paralysis without sensory signs or symptoms, as an ascending paralysis with concomitant ascending anesthesia and analgesia, and as a progressive generalized disorder characterized by paralysis and sen-

Portrait, courtesy of Charles Martin de Thézillat, Paris.

sory disturbances. Landry's concept was lost sight of in the subsequent heated controversy on the pathogenesis of the disorder. Gradually Landry's name came to be associated solely with the ascending form.

Although Landry made no attempt to ascertain the nature of the pathological changes in this disorder, mentioning only that the spinal cord was free from change macroscopically, his contribution helped to set the stage for the brilliant work on neuritis by Louis Duménil (1823–1890)[6] a few years later (1864 and 1866). It was also the forerunner of the famous report in 1916[7] on polyradiculoneuritis by Guillain and Barré, together with Strohl who performed the electrical reactions. Significantly, the spinal fluid of those two French soldiers contained an immense amount of protein without the expected increase in cells. When some thirty years later the term "Landry-Guillain-Barré syndrome" was introduced to encompass all aspects of this pleomorphic disorder,[8] Guillain (1876–1961[9]) irately contended that since lumbar puncture was not practiced at Landry's time, the linking of Landry's name with theirs spelled "une confusion nosographique absolue."[10] Barré (1880–1967[11]), back in Strassburg by that time, had other problems to occupy his mind.

Although Landry had opened the door on a new vista, he went no further. His circumstances perhaps account for this. In 1857 he had married Claire Giustigniani (1832–1901)—"d'une grande beauté, d'une distinction suprême, mais beaucoup plus riche de noblesse que d'argent"—and his father's death had left his own family in equally straitened circumstances. To make an adequate livelihood he took charge of the Établissement hydrothérapeutique at Auteuil for the treatment of nervous diseases; his unbounding energy brought him financial success and considerable prominence.

Landry's career was interrupted a second time by an epidemic of cholera which reached the environs of Paris. He attended the destitute victims unceasingly until he contracted the infection himself and died a few days later. Charcot was at his bedside.

Landry had the mark of gentility. Affable, unusually generous and possessed of *une grande simplicité,* he lived a very full life; a distinguished violoncellist like his father, he also had the voice of a professional singer and was an expert dancer—in fact, his elegance was the talk of the salons. He moved in the circle of artists and sat for E. Corbet in 1864. No city slicker, he also was a fervent alpinist, an accomplished horseman and hunter, a geologist and crystallographer *passioné*. He had spent his thirty-nine years generously. The common people would remember him, but he left no impression on his professional colleagues. The *Gazette des hôpitaux* and the *Gazette médicale de Paris* devoted a few perfunctory lines in their obituary notices, and the *Gazette hebdomadaire,* in whose pages his now famous work had appeared six years earlier, even fewer. None of the obituary writers seemed aware of the accolade given Landry a few months earlier by Pellegrino-Lévi[12] in an important paper on descending paralysis.

MOFFETT FIELD, CALIFORNIA   WEBB HAYMAKER

References

[1]Arch. gén. méd., 1852, *29:*257–275 *et seq.*   [2]Thèse de Paris, 1853. [3]Brain, London, 1888, *10:*1–137.   [4]Gaz. hôp., 1855, *28:*262.   [5]Gaz. hebd. méd., Paris, 1859, *6:*472–474 *et seq.*   [6]Rev. méd. Normandie, 1900, *1:*195–198 (Halipré).   [7]Bull. Soc. méd. hôp. Paris, 1916, *40:* 1462–1470.   [8]Medicine, Balt., 1949, *28:*59–141 (Haymaker and Kernohan).   [9]Presse méd., 1961, *69:*1695–1696 (obituary by Mollaret). [10]Ann. méd., Paris, 1953, *54:*81–149.   [11]J. neurol. Sci., Amst., 1968, *6:*381–382 (obituary by Thiebaut).   [12]Arch. gén. méd., Paris, 1865, 6.sér., *5:*129–147.

Reference to Biography: Presse méd., Paris, 1933, *41:*227–229 (Remlinger).

CHARLES LASÈGUE (1816–1883)

*E*RNEST CHARLES LASÈGUE was born in Paris. During his student days he and Claude Bernard roomed together in the Latin Quarter, and often so many of their francs went for the purchase of guinea pigs and rabbits with which to experiment that they did not have enough left to pay their rent. Lasègue had embarked on the study of philosophy, but on listening one day to a lecture by Trousseau at the Hôpital Necker, decided in favor of

clinical medicine. Subsequently he became Trousseau's favorite pupil and frequent collaborator, and on the occasion of Trousseau's death in 1867, he delivered a eulogy which remains to this day one of the finest orations in the French language.

He registered at the Faculté de Médecine in 1839. On obtaining the M.D. in 1847 he was sent by the French government to study the cholera epidemic than raging in southern Russia. In 1853 he won his agrégation on the basis of a thesis on general pa-

Portrait, courtesy of the Library of the College of Physicians and Surgeons, Philadelphia, Pennsylvania.

ralysis,[1] which dealt with a large group of chronic cerebral disorders, comprising several pathological entities. In the same year—he was then thirty-seven—he was made, with Valleix and Follin, co-editor of the *Archives générales de médecine*. He became physician to many hospitals in Paris, among them the Salpêtrière, the Necker, and the Pitié. From 1852 to 1854 he was Trousseau's *chef de clinique*.

Lasègue published 115 works. Although he wrote on a wide variety of subjects, psychiatry was his forte. In this field he is best known for his studies on hysteria,[2] dipsomania,[3] delusions of persecution, "folie à deux," catalepsy, and exhibitionism. He was forever after malingerers, varying his tests and traps; and when confronted by a psychotic individual he would give to his listeners the following advice: "Go back in the history of the patient, and if you search carefully you will find the 'ictus' which suddenly destroyed his mental balance. From then on, the brain is like a piano from which certain keys have been removed and which, therefore, produces only imperfect and dissonant chords."

His joust with Virchow was a classic. He had criticized Virchow's *Cellularpathologie* (1858), stating that the disease of cells was only a fragment of pathology. Virchow replied that the only critics he worried about were competent ones and that thus far he had not heard from them, whereupon Lasègue answered ironically that innovators such as Virchow are like knights who feel that they are fast in the saddle just because they have sharp spurs.

Among his publications in neurology was his classic work on *Les cérébraux,* dealing with vascular disorders of the brain, in which he said that those who have lost their "cerebral virginity" are thereby predisposed to future accidents. Astruc has related in his inimitable way the story of Lasègue's discovery of the sign which bears his name: "On one Sunday morning he thinks of the question which he had been asked by Inspector General Dujardin-Baumetz: how to discover the malingerer simulating sciatica. He promised to study the question; it is ever present in his thoughts. While smoking his pipe, he sees Mme. Lasègue seated at the piano while his son-in-law, Cesbron, is tuning his violin. Is not the string stretched over the bridge like the sciatic nerve which is made taut on the ischium when the lower extremity is elevated?

Undoubtedly as he listens to the classical music he has formulated the answer to the Inspector General's question. Tomorrow he will look for the sign in his clinic . . ." In his widely quoted *Considérations sur la sciatique*[4] a description of his sign does not, however, appear. Detective work by Wartenberg[5] revealed that it was only years later that his pupil Forst[6] put the sign on record. Lazarevič, Serbian neurologist, described the sign fully and accurately in 1884,[7] independently of Forst.

Versatile in almost every field of medicine, Lasègue was indeed a "universal specialist." His work in neurology which made his name an eponym was but a minor phase of his remarkable career. He was a friend of the arts and a man free from all outward formalities, who in his speech could pass readily from Gallic witticisms to the highest form of eloquence. In defending a broad education based on the humanities, he stated that the time given to these studies is like that which the soldier spends on making his armor shine. Ritti described him at the Infirmerie Spéciale, in a dreary room where daylight hardly ever entered, as "urging, begging, ironical, good-natured, even endearing, permitting the patient to express himself freely or on other occasions asking him innumerable questions, but never tiring until he was sure to have obtained all possible information." When he died of diabetes at the age of sixty-seven, France lost one of an illustrious group of physicians which had raised French medicine to its pinnacle.

SAN FRANCISCO, CALIFORNIA   ROBERT AIRD

References

[1]*De la paralysie générale progressive.* Thèse de Paris, 1853.   [2]Arch. gén. méd., Paris, 1864, 6.sér., *1*:385–402.   [3]*Ibid.,* 1882, 7.sér., *10*:257–271.   [4]*Ibid.,* 1864, 6.sér., *2*:558–580.   [5]Arch. Neur. Psychiat., Chic., 1951, *66*:58–60.   [6]Thèse de Paris, 1881.   [7]Allg. Wien. med. Ztg., 1884, *29*:425–426 *et seq.*

References to Biography and Works: 1) *Essai sur Ch. Lasègue, 1816–1883.* Thèse de Paris, 1908 (Streletski).   2) Biogr. méd., Paris, 1934, *8*:33–64 *et seq.* (Astruc).   3) Ann. médico-psychol., Paris, 1885, 7.sér., *2*:88–121 (Ritti).   4) *Études médicales du Professeur Ch. Lasègue.* 2 vol. Paris, Asselin, 1884 (contains complete works).

HUGO KARL LIEPMANN (1863–1925)

$\mathcal{H}$ UGO LIEPMANN was born in Berlin, the son of a Jewish family of culture and wealth. He first studied philosophy and acquired his Ph.D. with a thesis on the atomistic doctrine of Leucippus and Democritus. Later he published a paper on Schopenhauer. He had a deep interest in philosophical problems, but the solutions which he found did not satisfy him. He was looking, as one of his friends wrote, for the real and certain things and, as a consequence, shifted to natural science and medicine. It has been told that he literally threw the work of a famous Neo-Kantian philosopher into the corner and went to the great anatomist Waldeyer to ask him for an anatomical specimen. But the ardor for philosophy never left him. It later became apparent in his deep interest in the psycho-physical problem of the classification of the processes of thinking and the role ideation plays in action, which found its special reflection in his concept of apraxia.

Liepmann passed his medical examination in 1894, was for a short time assistant of the psychiatrist Jolly, and studied anatomy with Weigert. Then he went to Breslau and came under the influence of Wernicke. He considered himself primarily a pupil of his highly admired teacher though he later deviated from his teachings, even opposing him on essential points.

He returned in 1899 to Berlin as psychiatrist of the municipal mental institution of Dalldorf. Here he did the work on apraxia which made his name famous. In 1901 he became Privatdozent at the University of Berlin. He was never appointed Ordinarius. According to Oskar Vogt, he was told by faculty members of the University of Berlin that if he would change his name and adopt Protestantism a place for him was assured. Although he had no strong religious convictions in regard to the Jewish faith he decided not to accept the suggestion. As he was an excellent teacher he greatly regretted losing this opportunity to exercise his pedagogic skill to the full. Later he was director of the mental institution at Herzberge, a position which he was forced to relinquish because of paralysis agitans. When he could no longer endure the hardships of this disease, he ended his life by taking an overdose of poison. He

Hugo Karl Liepmann

had the reputation of being a man of the highest ethical standards, as exemplified during the blockade of Germany in 1915–16, when he voluntarily underwent starvation (he lost sixty pounds), refusing to eat more food than his patients.

Liepmann's earliest paper dealt with alcoholic delirium.[1] In it he showed for the first time that hallucinations may be evoked artificially. Then followed studies on word deafness, visual agnosia, and echolalia—all of which showed his excellent capacity to combine clinical observation and scientific interpretation. His paper, *Das Krankheitsbild der Apraxie,* which appeared in 1900,[2] secured for him at once a place among the eminent men of his profession. The great merit of this paper was the clarification of the structure of human action ("Bewegungsformel") and of the relation of its

Portrait, courtesy of the Armed Forces Institute of Pathology, Washington, D. C. (from *Mschr. Psychiat. Neur., 54:* frontispiece, 1923, redrawn by Van Cott.)

single parts to psychological processes. He distinguished the learned motor automatisms from the processes which bring them into action, the ideation. The problem of ideation led him to become preoccupied with the phenomena of will and recognition. His psychological analysis of the thinking process in a book entitled *Ideenflucht* (Halle a.S., Marhold, 1904) is one of the finest representations of this topic in the literature. He tried to bring all phenomena into relation with physiological processes. This made possible the separation of different forms of disturbance of action, the recognition of various types of apraxia, which he illustrated by clinical observations. He followed, in general, Wernicke's ideas, but went much further and deeper into psychological and physiological analysis. From his careful clinical observations came the important confirmation of the dominance of the left hemisphere,[3,4] and it was he who found that isolated apraxia of the left side of the body is a sign of involvement of the corpus callosum.[5] He was a theoretical neuroanatomist. One does not find any pathoanatomical contributions in his papers. The brains from his patients were sent to his friend, Oskar Vogt, in Berlin-Buch, who examined them in detail. The Liepmann collection, consisting of about twenty-six brains and histories, is now at the Vogts' *Institut für Hirnforschung* in Neustadt/Schwarzwald.

Liepmann's work will remain one of the landmarks in the progress of our knowledge of the function of the brain. He is a worthy representative of a great creative epoch in neurology.

KURT GOLDSTEIN

References

[1]Arch. Psychiat., Berlin, 1895, 27:172–232.   [2]Mschr. Psychiat., 1900, 8:15–44 et seq.   [3]Münch. med. Wschr., 1905, 52:2322–2326 et seq. [4]Über Störungen des Handelns bei Gehirnkranken. Berlin, Karger, 1905.   [5]Med. Klin., Berlin, 1907, 3:725–729 et seq.

References to Biography: 1) Psychol. & Med., Stuttg., 1925 26, 1:257 277 (Niessl von Mayendorf).   2) Mschr. Psychiat., 1925, 59:225–232 (Kramer).   3) Zschr. ges. Neur. Psychiat., 1923, 83:1–16 (Isserlin). 4) Ibid., 1925, 99:635–650 (Isserlin; contains bibliography).

PIERRE MARIE (1853–1940)

*P*IERRE MARIE was born into a wealthy bourgeois family of Paris. He first studied law but soon turned to medicine. At the age of twenty-five (1878) he became interne in the hospitals of Paris. In this role he profited particularly from his contact with Charcot, then at the height of his career. Marie's thesis for the M.D. (1883) carried a graphic description of the tremor observed in the extended arms and fingers in persons with Graves' disease—a phenomenon he had begun to study while a medical student. He was appointed chef de clinique and chef de laboratoire under Charcot, and in 1889 became médecin des hôpitaux and professeur agrégé. During this period he gave his famous lectures on diseases of the spinal cord.[1] Eruptive fevers (measles, scarlatina, smallpox), he stated in these lectures, commonly have sequelae of neural origin. Smallpox may, during the convalescent period, give rise to symptoms of "insular sclerosis" (multiple sclerosis): "tremor in the limbs with more or less paresis, disorder of the speech which becomes slow and scanning, nystagmus and in short all the characteristic symptoms of insular sclerosis may exist. . . . The symptoms may continue, and confirmed insular sclerosis occurs." Marie's observations thus fall in line with a current concept that multiple sclerosis may be due to the action of a "slow" virus.

Marie published numerous classical descriptions of new clinical entities which he not only isolated but christened: progressive muscular atrophy (with Charcot) in 1886,[2] acromegaly in 1886,[3] hypertrophic osteoarthropathy in 1890,[4] cerebellar heredoataxia in 1893,[5] spondylose rhizomélique in 1898.[6] This period of sustained creative activity gave him an international reputation.

In 1897 he transferred his activities to the Hospice de Bicêtre and established there a neurological service which attracted pupils from all over the world. During the ten years he remained there he became interested in the problems of aphasia, and his documentation of the subject (reported in detail in the thesis of Moutier) was the basis of a devastating critique on the previous work.[7] Not only did he attack the ideas of Broca, using as the provocative title for his paper "The third left frontal convolution has no spe-

cial role in the function of language," but he even examined Broca's original specimen to prove how erroneous was his observation,
and in the process swept away many old prejudices. In his fondness for controversy, Marie drew in Babinski and the Dejerines,
setting neurologists at each other's doctrines so that they took sides
and debated vigorously. Marie's work on aphasia was extended
later by his pupil, Charles Foix. In 1907, in the midst of the controversy over aphasia, Marie took the chair of pathological anat-

Portrait, courtesy of Dr. Percival Bailey, Chicago, Illinois.

omy in the faculty. Here he did much to improve the teaching but added little to the subject itself. Again his work was continued by a brilliant pupil, Gustave Roussy, when the latter succeeded Dejerine to the chair of clinical neurology at the Salpêtrière.

At sixty-five years Marie finally assumed the chair of neurology which had been created for Charcot and occupied since his tenure by Raymond, Brissaud and Dejerine. This was in 1918 toward the end of a destructive war. There were no longer the facilities or the means to continue the painstaking laboratory studies of the Dejerine school, nor did Marie's interests incline him in that direction. In collaboration with Meige, Foix, Chatelin and Bouttier he published interesting studies of the neurological lesions caused by the war,[8] but his great productive period was over.

In October 1921, I entered his clinic as foreign assistant, too late to feel the full impact of his creative personality. I remember him as a dignified old gentleman, who came regularly about 10:00 A.M. to the little building called the Pavillon de la Grille where patients were brought to him for examination. Only rarely did he enter the wards and never the laboratory, for he was very sensitive to formalin and would look at fixed brains only through a window, and there dictate his description. He was at his best in clinical consultation, in which his discussions were short and pithy. His teaching seems always to have been simple, clear, plain exposition. He was very kind to me and courteous to everyone, including the patients. His agrégé at that time was Foix, a brilliant lecturer, whose early death was a great loss to French neurology.

By 1925 Marie withdrew from his professorship and retired to his estate on the Côte d'Azur, taking his leisure seriously. He returned to Paris rarely except to attend meetings of the Comité de Direction of the *Revue neurologique,* which he and Brissaud had founded in 1893 and of which he was very proud. His later years were saddened by the loss of his daughter, wife and only son from infectious diseases. After several months of painful illness—from an abdominal condition for which de Martel had operated—he, too, died.

Pierre Marie's influence in the Parisian medical world was immense. His great wealth made him independent; his honesty made him respected; his innate courtesy and dignity made him friends and disarmed his opponents; and his creative intelligence spread his reputation throughout the world. He is a good example of the best in French medicine.

CHICAGO, ILLINOIS   PERCIVAL BAILEY

References

[1]*Leçons sur les maladies de la moëlle.* Paris, Masson, 1892.   [2]Rev. méd., Paris, 1886, *6*:97–138.   [3]*Ibid.*, 1886, *6*:297–333.   [4]*Ibid.*, 1890, *10*:1–36.   [5]Sem. méd., Paris, 1893, *13*:444–447.   [6]Rev. méd., Paris, 1898, *18*:285–315.   [7]Sem. méd., Paris, 1906, *26*:241–247. [8]*Travaux et mémoires.* 2 vol. Paris, Masson, 1926–28.

References to Biography: 1) Rev. neur., Paris, 1939–40, *72*:533–543 ("Le Comité").   2) *Ibid.*, 1928, *35*(1):691–694 (Guillain).   3) *Young endeavour.* Springfield, Thomas, 1958, p. 127–129 (Gibson).

WEIR MITCHELL (1829–1914)

*I*N HIS PRIME, Silas Weir Mitchell, of Scottish origin, was a tall, slim, alert man with deeply chiselled features and an expression denoting clear aims. All this and his long, narrow face, abundant grey forelocks, chin whiskers, and moustache, caused some people of the day to liken him to "Uncle Sam." The grey cap he wore and the long grey cape which hung from his shoulders made him a familiar figure. His erudition and versatility brought him friends by the score, among them William Osler, Oliver Wendell Holmes, William James, Walt Whitman, and Andrew Carnegie. He made a point of cultivating younger men in whom he sensed the spark of brilliance: John Shaw Billings and Hideyo Noguchi, to mention only two. W. W. Keen wrote of Mitchell, "Never have I known so original, suggestive, and fertile a mind. I often called him a yeasty man. . . . An hour in his office set my own mind in a turmoil so that I could hardly sleep." Yet this "most versatile American since Franklin" was never in a hurry.

Weir Mitchell was born in Philadelphia in surroundings of culture, the seventh physician in three generations. He was required

Portrait, courtesy of Dr. Loyal Davis, Chicago, Illinois. (Painted by Frank Hall, engraved by T. Johnson.)

to learn a daily Bible text and to attend church twice on Sundays, but he made the service less boring by smuggling in a copy of *Midshipman Easy*, which he read in a dark corner of the pew. During his early years as a student at the University of Pennsylvania, which he entered when he was fifteen, his record was a poor one, for he had an aversion to such subjects as mathematics. He preferred to daydream, write poetry, play billiards, steal peaches and melons from Jersey farmers, and make a general nuisance of himself in the classroom. "You are wanting in nearly all the qualities that go to make a success in medicine," his father, the distinguished Dr. John Kearsley Mitchell, remarked. Weir was enrolled at Jefferson Medical College in 1848, received the M.D. in 1851, and forthwith boarded a clipper ship for Europe. In Paris he did not permit the legendary distractions to encroach on his scholarship, though after his Montmartre ramblings he could not help reminisce that the *can-can* resembled a "witches' sabbath." The person who influenced him most in Paris was Claude Bernard. "Why think?" Claude Bernard inquired of Mitchell on one occasion. "Exhaust experiment, then think."

On returning to Philadelphia he plunged into research. One of his interests was snake venoms, on which he worked with Hammond and later with W. W. Keen and Simon Flexner. A six-foot rattler once got loose, climbed up the back of the chair on which Mitchell was reading and put its swaying head over his shoulder. Only when the snake touched the hot lamp and drew back in anger could Mitchell leap up and escape.

Soon after the outbreak of the War between the States, Weir Mitchell became "contract surgeon" to a 400-bed hospital in Philadelphia, created for him and Dr. George R. Morehouse by Surgeon General Hammond. This experience was to transform his life. W. W. Keen became an associate. They would go to Gettysburg and bring back carloads of wounded. Together they collected thousands of pages of notes on wounded soldiers, which culminated in a masterpiece on nerve and related injuries (1864)[1] in which the entity known as "causalgia" was given its place in medicine (and more firmly established in a volume in 1872[2]). A soldier in continuous pain, he remarked, becomes a coward, and the strongest man is scarcely less nervous than the most hysterical girl.

Mitchell's eminence in this field stands secure, though priority goes to Denmark for his description, in 1813, of the excruciating sequelae suffered by a soldier who had been wounded in the arm at the storming of Badajoz; the article was entitled: "An example of symptoms resembling tic douloureux produced by a wound in the radial nerve."[3]

Another great work by Mitchell, Morehouse and Keen was on *Reflex paralysis* . . . (1864).[4] This was the term given to the sudden motor loss resulting from wounds of the brain, especially the forebrain where motor centers, Mitchell and his collaborators reasoned, surely must control muscles of the opposite side, an observation anticipating Fritsch and Hitzig's announcement by about five years.

Other important contributions followed: on erythromelalgia ("Weir Mitchell's disease"),[5] postparalytic chorea,[6] and the functions of the cerebellum, in which he supported the view that the cerebellum augments and reinforces movements.[7] His "rest cure" for psychoneurosis[8] was the standard therapy for decades, especially in England. Also in France: On a visit to Paris in his later years, Mitchell sought out the great Charcot for help without revealing his name. Where was he from? "Philadelphia?" Then, said Charcot: "You should consult Weir Mitchell; he is the best man in America for your kind of trouble." Some of Mitchell's ideas strike knowledgeable psychiatrists today as very sound. But sometimes he resorted to strange diagnostic measures in functional illnesses, and he sometimes performed "miracles." As consultant to a lady considered sick unto death, he once sent all assistants and attendants out of the room, then soon emerged himself. Asked whether she had any chance for survival, he remarked: "Yes, she will be running out of the door inside of two minutes; I set her sheet on fire. A case of hysteria." His prediction proved correct.

His failure to receive the vacated chair of physiology at Jefferson Medical College (1863 and 1868) and at the University of Pennsylvania, caused Hammond to write: "I am disgusted with everything and can only say that it is an honor to be rejected by such a set of apes!" Mitchell concluded that his Republican beliefs had cost him the post at Jefferson; the trustees were violently Democratic.

From the early 1880's Mitchell turned his major efforts to literary pursuits: novel, short story, essay, drama and verse.[9,10] His *Ode on a Lycian tomb* is said to be the finest elegiac poem written in America. *Hugh Wynn: free Quaker* (New York, Century, 1879) was by far his most successful novel, but by no means his best. To a friend he admitted that "Hugh" was only fair, but stood up for his *Constance Trescott* which he thought contained the fullest report of a medical consultation in all literature. *Westways,* a novel written when he was past eighty, reflects "a most horrible memory" left upon him shortly after the battle of Gettysburg.

As "the sage," he continued to enjoy the company of brilliant men. "He was vain, but he had much to be vain about," wrote Harvey Cushing, after a long evening of Madeira and strong cigars with him. At eighty-four Mitchell bombarded Osler with questions about some rare books he was after and some letters of William Harvey. Not long afterward he was stricken with influenza, but took the occasion to read the proof of his dramatic poem, *Barabbas,* when he lapsed into a terminal delirium and found himself again at Gettysburg, operating on the wounded.

MOFFETT FIELD, CALIFORNIA   WEBB HAYMAKER

References

[1]*Gunshot wounds and other injuries of nerves.* Philadelphia, Lippincott, 1864 (Mitchell, Morehouse and Keen).   [2]*Injuries of nerves and their consequences.* Philadelphia, Lippincott, 1872, p. 318–321 (Mitchell).   [3]Med.-Chir. Tr., 1913, *4*:48–52.   [4]*Reflex paralysis, the result of gunshot wounds, and other injuries of nerves, founded chiefly upon cases observed in the United States General Hospital, Christian Street, Philadelphia.* Philadelphia, Lippincott, 1864.   [5]Amer. J. Med. Sci., 1878, *76*:17–36.   [6]*Ibid.,* 1874, *68*:342–352.   [7]*Ibid.,* 1869, *57*: 320–338.   [8]*Fat and blood, and how to make them.* Philadelphia, Lippincott, 1877.   [9]*Selections from the poems of S. Weir Mitchell.* London, Macmillan, 1901.   [10]*Hephzibah Guinness.* Philadelphia, Lippincott, 1880.

References to Biography and Works: 1) Brit. Med. J., 1914, *1*:119–121 (Osler).   2) Nature, London, 1914, *92*:534–535 (Brunton).   3) Boston Med. Sci. J., 1914, *170*:821–825 (Putnam).   4) J. Nerv. Ment. Dis., 1914, *41*:65–74 (Mills).   5) *History of the American Physiologi-*

cal Society semicentennial 1887–1937. Baltimore, 1938 (Howell, Greene), p. 1–128.   6) *Amid masters of twentieth century medicine*. Springfield, Thomas, 1958, p. 405–410 (Rowntree).   7) *S. Weir Mitchell, novelist and physician*. Philadelphia, Univ. Pennsylvania Press, 1950 (Earnest).   8) *Nerves and nerve injuries*. Edinburgh, Livingstone, 1968 (Sunderland).

CONSTANTIN von MONAKOW (1853–1930)

*V*ON MONAKOW was born on the family estate Brobret-zovo, in Vologda, north of Moscow. His Polish mother died when he was four years old. His father, Ivan Monakow, a wealthy, well-educated nobleman, was censor of the political press during the reigns of Nicolas I and Alexander II. In 1863 he sold his estates with some dispatch and emigrated with his two sons and daughter to Dresden. Three years later the Austro-Prussian war caused the family to move to Paris. After a year in Paris, then in the glittering period of the Second Empire, the forebodings of the Franco-Prussian war which was to come in 1870 must have influenced the elder Monakow to look for a more peaceful place in which to rear his family. They moved to Zürich, where in 1869 they became naturalized.

According to von Monakow's autobiographical notes, as retold by Minkowski, it appears that he was mediocre as a student and frequently at odds with his teachers. His father became more and more annoyed with him, until finally he bade him—he was then seventeen—to leave the paternal home. Against his father's wishes he took up medicine. In 1876, while still a candidate for the M.D., the search for work led him to the famed Hitzig, then director of Burghölzli Asylum near Zürich. Hitzig sent him to survey the administration of asylums in Germany. This brought him to von Gudden in Munich. Von Gudden showed him the microtome—his invention—and sections of the brain of an adult rabbit in which the superior colliculus had undergone atrophy after removal of the contralateral eye at birth. Von Monakow was impressed. In 1877 he returned to Munich, and then went to Würzburg for further study, but a pressing need for money forced him to look for a job.

After a trip to Brazil as ship's doctor, he obtained the position of ward physician in the Cantonal Asylum St. Pirminsberg, near Ragaz. It was here, in 1879, that von Monakow removed the occipital lobes in two newborn rabbits and, after keeping them alive for

Portrait, courtesy of Dr. Paul I. Yakovlev, Boston, Massachusetts.

more than a year, he found that the lateral geniculate nuclei were completely degenerated, while the rest of the thalami was intact. This was a significant discovery and the beginning of his *exegi monumentum*. In 1885, after a three-month sojourn in Berlin, where he attended the clinics and lectures of Westphal, Oppenheim, Virchow, du Bois-Reymond, and especially Munk, he returned to Zürich, where he set up a private research laboratory and became an active practitioner. In 1894 his Hirnanatomisches Institut was incorporated with the University of Zürich, and he was appointed Extraordinarius.

Judging by the picaresque stories told about him, he must have been an eccentric figure. A huge man, his high-pitched voice contrasted oddly with his monumental stature and heavily bearded countenance. To his more gracile Swiss compatriots he represented the generalized prototype of that forensic abstraction—a Russian—*ein russischer Mensch*.[1] To him, however, Switzerland was the mother country or, as he put it, his "cradle."[2] In his younger days he is said to have been a boisterous *bon vivant* and a devotee of the *Bierstube*. In his maturity he became and remained an abstemious man devoted to family life. Many of his students remember the pleasure of weekly *soirées musicales,* during which his friends and pupils gathered at his home to hear concerts played by members of his family and some musically adept guests.[3] He was a prodigious worker, a copious writer, and an omnivorous reader. His *Gehirnpathologie* contains over 3,000 references, compiled by himself. He was an impetuous and at times an irascible man: there is a certain door in the laboratory of his Institute which once he attempted to open, unaware that it was locked—he pulled the handle and the door yielded with the frame.[3] Faculty affairs did not seem to interest him. It is said that he is known to have attended only one faculty meeting during the many years he was its member, and then it was to sponsor the candidature of his son for a faculty appointment. There are those who can remember the Russian-style blouse and the great long boots he wore on that unique occasion.[4]

The War of 1914–18 and the Russian Revolution of 1917 made a deep impression on him. He reread Russian classics avidly.[3] During the later years of his life he became deeply absorbed in problems of philosophy, religion and biological sources of the forces of ethics and morality (the values) in human affairs.[5]

His was one of the most forceful and original personalities in neurology at the turn of the century. The qualification *eccentric* may not accurately describe the temper of his character, but its picturesque uncommonnness made him a fit subject for a biography in the form of a novel, *Begegnung am Abend* (Stuttgart, Deutsche Verlagsanstalt, 1933), written by the poetess Maria Waser.

He retired in 1928 at the age of seventy-five. His health began rapidly to decline. He was a recalcitrant patient and refused medical care. An enlarged prostate, which caused retention-uremia, was established at autopsy as the cause of his death.[4] Had he been in a position to be present, the old man would probably have frowned into his beard upon learning that his spinal cord had been lost, for in his will he had requested that the pathologist search a certain level for the alterations responsible for the long-standing atrophy of his thenar eminence.[4]

With the work of his younger and living contemporary, Kurt Goldstein, that of von Monakow will remain an outstanding contribution to the empirically founded theory of neurology. Von Monakow's scientific life and work may be divided into three over-lapping periods, one rising above the other like tiers of a pyramid: the first from 1880 to the publication of his *Gehirnpathologie* (Wien; Hölder) in 1897; the second from about 1900 to the publication in 1914 of his greatest work, *Die Lokalisation im Grosshirn und der Abbau der Funktion durch kortikale Herde* (Wiesbaden; Bergmann); and the third period, deeply philosophical, from World War I to his death in 1930. This last period in the development of his thought is epitomized in his book with Raoul Mourgue, *Introduction biologique à l'étude de la neurologie et de la psychopathologie* (Paris; Alcan), published in 1928.

During the first period, inaugurated with the classical studies of visual and acoustic pathways, von Monakow laid the foundation upon which the present knowledge of developmental and functional unity of the thalamus and cortex securely rests. During the second period he elaborated the concept of *diaschisis,* and brought forth the fundamental distinction between the *geometric* localization of symptoms (e.g., paralysis, aphasia) and the *chronogenic* localization of functions (e.g., locomotion, language). He thus introduced concepts which make clinical neurology a truly biological science of organismal dynamics in human behavior. In this orientation of thought, von Monakow's work reveals many interesting parallels with the contemporary work in this country of the Herrick brothers and of Coghill, which made so meaningful the comparative neurobiology of vertebrate behavior. In the last period of his life he made a sublime effort to delineate ethical and moral values in terms of the neurobiological frame of reference which he had created. His three lectures on *Emotions, morality and the brain* were published in this country in English, but unfortunately the translation was grossly inadequate. In the orginal German text,[5] involved as it is, these lectures are a noteworthy example of penetrating empirical generalization. Von Monakow's Promethean thoughts have not yet been fully appraised.

On October 19, 1930, at the age of seventy-seven, as he was preparing a manuscript on *The value of life,* he put down his pen and lay on the couch to rest. A peaceful end came. The last words jotted on the sheaf of manuscript were "Angemessenes Handeln..." The context which was to follow is not given us to know, but the words are a fitting epitaph for the pyramid of his life and work. Indeed, from the relevant foundation of the measurable truth, his understanding rose above the misty clouds which veil the vision of lesser minds, and from that lonely pinnacle he reached for the immense.

BOSTON, MASSACHUSETTS   PAUL I. YAKOVLEV

References

[1]Erich Katzenstein (personal communication to P.I.Y.).   [2]Schweiz. Arch. Neur. Psychiat., 1931, *27*:1–63 (Minkowski).   [3]Eugen Frey (personal communication to P.I.Y.).   [4]E. A. Uehlinger (personal communication to Webb Haymaker).   [5]*Gefühl, Gesittung und Gehirn.* Arb. Hirnanat. Inst., Zürich, 1916, Heft X, p. 115–213.

Additional Reference to Biography: Arch. Neur. Psychiat., Chic., 1931, *25*:389–390 (Adolf Meyer).

EGAS MONIZ (Antonio Caetano deAbreu Freire) (1875–1955)

*J*HIS man's genius became evident in his second career, which began when most people are thinking of retirement. Antonio Caetano deAbreu Freire was born in Northern Portugal on a farm which had been in his family for centuries. The name Egas Moniz—a hero of the Portuguese resistance against the Moors —Antonio's godfather added at the christening. As a student with political interests, Moniz used this as a pen name to adopt it for good in his professional career. He received his medical education at the University of Coimbra from which he graduated in 1899. After studying neurology at Bordeaux and Paris, he returned to the University of Coimbra where he was appointed to the chair of Neurology. However, when the University of Lisbon was reorganized with an expanded faculty of medicine, Moniz was invited to be the Professor of Neurology. This position gave him an opportunity to exploit his interests in politics. He shortly became Minister of Foreign Affairs and then Ambassador to Spain after the overthrow of the monarchy in Portugal. It is noteworthy that at the end of World War I he signed the Versailles Treaty for Portugal. During this time, in fact, until he was almost fifty years of age, he had written little on medical themes. True, early in his career he published small monographs on the physiology and pathology of sex, and after World War I, a treatise on neurology in war, but these did not reveal his genius.[1]

It was not until after his party was deposed and Egas Moniz returned to his University post as Professor of Neurology that he began to develop the ideas which brought him world acclaim. At the age of fifty-two, he conceived of visualizing the cerebral vessels by roentgenography. He experimented with a number of iodine compounds which diffused into the tissues, producing convulsions and paralyses in animals, and with oily suspensions that caused embolic phenomena. However, the concept was valid and in 1927 he reported the first carotid angiograms for which he used sodium iodide as a medium.[2] Shortly thereafter, German investigators introduced the use of colloidal thorium dioxide for visualization of ab-

1950   *Egas Moniz*

dominal organs. Moniz followed up this lead for cerebral angiography, to visualize intracranial tumors, aneurysms, vascular anomalies, etc.,[3] and he wrote more than a hundred papers on the subject.
The technique did not gain universal acceptance because of the
carcinogenic nature of thorium. The development of better nonirri-
tating radiopaque substances, again based on iodine, enabled
Swedish radiologists to popularize the technique.

The development of frontal leucotomy was the second brain-
child of Egas Moniz to bring him world renown. Previous workers

Portrait, courtesy of Dr. A. Earl Walker, Baltimore, Maryland.

had suggested the possibility of modifying behavior by lesions of the brain, indeed had actually carried out operations for this purpose. However, Moniz' work rested on the sound physiological principles enunciated by Fulton and Jacobsen at the 2nd International Neurological Congress in London in 1935: their bilaterally lobectomized chimpanzees did not become disturbed and angry in frustrating situations. At that meeting, Dr. Moniz discussed his own idea of intervening on the frontal lobe to relieve anxiety states in man. Upon his return to Lisbon, he persuaded his surgical associate Almeida Lima to devise a leucotome which could be inserted into the white matter of the frontal lobe to cut a core of fibers.[4] The results were startling, and in more ways than one. For whereas the quieting effect upon certain restless, aggressive, psychotic patients was astonishing, the response of certain physicians to the suggestion that the psyche of man be so altered was catastrophic. Editorials in medical journals of many parts of the world assailed this technique at the very time Moniz was being awarded the Nobel Prize for its introduction. Because of the opposition even in his own University, Moniz never acquired a large service, and while psychotherapeutic operations were being carried out by the thousands in many other countries, Moniz' series came to only about one hundred patients.

Although at first Egas Moniz' fame was largely based upon his pioneering in psychosurgery, cerebral angiography proved to be of more lasting importance. Nonetheless, the concept of modifying mental disease—so often considered to be unrelated to brain structure by organic means—was an essential step toward the introduction of psychopharmacological drugs which later displaced psychosurgery.

In 1944 Moniz retired from the Professorship of Neurology and devoted himself to literary and artistic pursuits. He wrote a number of biographical sketches, critical essays on politics, art and literature, and a full-length autobiography.

Of broad physique and sanguine temperament, Moniz was an ardent and subtle card player; genial and convivial, he was a gourmet plagued by gout. Well aware of the significance of his discoveries which he defended and promoted in domestic and foreign journals, he nevertheless remained good-natured and dignified in his numerous controversies. At sixty-five he was critically wounded in his office by one of his patients, a gun-toting schizophrenic. He recovered fully.

In his later life Egas Moniz was recognized throughout the medical world. He was president of the Section of Medicine of the Academia das Ciencias de Lisboa; in 1948, the year before he received the Nobel Prize, an International Congress on Psychosurgery was held in his honor in Lisbon where also a Centro dos Estudos Egas Moniz was founded.

On 18 December 1955 he died where he was born, on his family estate in Avanca.

BALTIMORE, MARYLAND   A. EARL WALKER

References

[1]*A neurologia na guerra.* Lisboa, Livr. Ferreira, 1917.   [2]Rev. neur., Paris, 1927, 2:72–90.   [3]*Diagnostic des tumeurs cérébrales et épreuve de l'encéphalographie artérielle.* Paris, Masson, 1931.   [4]*Tentatives opératoires dans le traitement de certaines psychoses.* Paris, Masson, 1936.

References to Biography: 1) *Confideñcias de un investigador cientifico.* Lisboa, Ed. Atica, 1949 (Moniz).   2) Kolle (Ed.), *Grosse Nervenärzte.* Vol. 1. Stuttgart, Thieme, 1966, p. 187–199 (Barahona Fernandes). 3) J.A.M.A., 1967, 206:368–369 (anon.).

HERMANN OPPENHEIM (1858–1919)

(O)PPENHEIM was born at Warburg, Westphalia. After graduation from the Gymnasium in 1876 he studied medicine at the Universities of Göttingen, Berlin, and Bonn. During the years 1880–82 he was especially interested in physiology and, under the guidance of Zuntz, published three papers on the metabolism of urea, which formed the basis of his doctoral dissertation in 1881. Shortly afterward he became assistant at the psychiatric clinic Maison de Santé in Berlin, and later (1883) at the neurological and psychiatric clinic of the Charité, a part of the University of Berlin. Here he soon became the favorite assistant of

Westphal, whose support enabled him to become established as Privatdozent in 1886 and as Titular Professor in 1893.

His first publications dealt with tabes dorsalis, bulbar paralysis, and neuritis associated with lead intoxication and with alcoholism. During 1887–88 there followed studies on syphilis, disseminated sclerosis, and chronic anterior poliomyelitis. The first publication of his monograph on traumatic neuroses, which appeared in 1889,[1]

Portrait, courtesy of Library of Northwestern University School of Medicine, Chicago, Illinois.

started a never ending flow of acrimonious debate. Oppenheim's contention was that the psychic disturbances following trauma originate in an actual organic disturbance of the brain (molecular changes), and that the altered psyche continued to perpetuate the neurosis. His theory was vigorously opposed by Charcot, Mendel, Nonne and others, who did not accept the idea of organic changes, and especially during World War I this debate, which concerned also hysteria and malingering, became very heated.[2] Oppenheim seems to have been very sensitive to such opposition and considered it a personal affront. His sensibility may have been conditioned by a previous experience: During Westphal's protracted illness prior to his death in 1890, Oppenheim conducted his clinic, and despite being unanimously nominated by the Berlin medical faculty as Professor Extraordinarius to succeed Westphal, the nomination was not confirmed by the Prussian Secretary of Education, who acted in the spirit of intolerance of that period. As a consequence, Oppenheim had to leave the Charité.

In 1890 he opened his own private clinic, which later was to become the international center of clinical neurology in Berlin. This year marked the beginning of a veritable flood of publications which inspired neurologists the world over. The last decade of the nineteenth century was a fertile period for clinical neurology. Charcot, Westphal, Erb and others had done the primary investigation and left it to their successors to collect cases, analyze the findings, and classify them. One can hardly understand now the enthusiasm with which Oppenheim, together with his associates, R. Koehler, M. Borchardt and F. Krause, reported single cases of successfully diagnosed and verified brain tumor. Oppenheim's neurosurgical experiences on brain tumors were collected in book form in 1896[3] and again in 1907.[4] It was on the basis of Oppenheim's diagnosis that the first surgical removal of a brain tumor was performed by Koehler.[5] Important monographs which he published included those on syphilitic diseases of the brain[6] and encephalitis.[7] He provided the term "dystonia musculorum deformans" in his paper on the subject in 1911[8]; four cases were described and the characteristic "dromedary gait" emphasized. Other pioneers in this particular field were Schwalbe[9] and Ziehen.[10] The disorder has been called "Oppenheim-Ziehen's disease," but

Schwalbe deserves credit for the original description if not interpretation.

Although primarily an expert clinical diagnostician, Oppenheim did not neglect therapy—surgical, pharmacologic and psychic —limited though it was at that time. The volumes on brain surgery have been mentioned. He was one of the first to try Ehrlich's salvarsan in the treatment of syphilis of the nervous system (1910). A monograph on peripheral nerve lesions appeared in 1917, *Die ersten Zeichen der Nervosität im Kindesalter* (Berlin; Karger) in 1904, and *Psychotherapeutische Briefe (Berlin; Karger) in 1906*. The latter had three editions. Oppenheim attacked therapeutic charlatanry in his article, *Zum Nil Nocere in der Neurologie*.[11]

Lasting monuments to the fame of this veteran neurologist were his description of amyotonia congenita,[12] called "Oppenheim's disease," and the seven German editions of his *Lehrbuch der Nervenkrankheiten* (Berlin, Karger, 1894), which was translated into English (3 editions), and into Russian, Spanish and Italian.

ARTHUR WEIL

References

[1]*Die traumatischen Neurosen nach den in der Nervenklinik der Charité in den letzten 5 Jahren gesammelten Beobachtungen.* Berlin, Hirschwald, 1889.   (2nd ed., 1892; 3rd ed., 1918.)   [2]See Bumke in Arch. Psychiat., Berlin, 1925, *76*:58–67.   [3]*Die Geschwülste des Gehirns.* Wien, Hölder, 1896. (2nd ed., 1902.) (Also in Nothnagel, H., *Specielle Pathologie und Therapie. Wien,* 1896. 9.Bd., 1.Theil, 3.Abth., 1.Lfg.) [4]*Beiträge zur Diagnostik und Therapie der Geschwülste im Bereich des zentralen Nervensystems.* Berlin, Karger, 1907.   [5]Berl. klin. Wschr., 1890, *27*:677–681.   [6]Nothnagel, H., *Specielle Pathologie und Therapie.* Wien, 1897, 9.Bd., 1.Theil, 3.Abth., 2.Lfg.   [7]*Ibid.,* 1897, 9.Bd., 2.Theil.   [8]Neur. Cbl., 1911, *30*:1090–1107.   [9]*Eine eigentümliche tonische Krampfform mit hysterischen Symptomen.* Inaug. Dissert., Berlin, 1907.   [10]Neur. Cbl., 1911, *30*:109–110.   [11]Berlin. klin. Wschr., 1910, *47*:198–201.   [12]Mschr. Psychiat., 1900, *8*:232–233.

Reference to Biography: Berl. klin. Wschr., 1919, *52*:669–671 (Cassirer).

JAMES PARKINSON (1755–1828)

$\mathcal{J}$O SPEAK of Parkinson's disease is a tradition that originated in 1862 with Charcot and Vulpian.[1] "Paralysis agitans," Parkinson's own latinized subtitle to his *Essay on the shaking palsy*,[2] has lately almost gone out of use. The description he gave in 1817 had little impact for nearly half a century; his name was almost forgotten. In 1850, without anyone in the Paris Académie de Médecine objecting, he was quoted as "Patterson" by Germain Sée[3] who linked rheumatic heart disease to Sydenham's chorea and distinguished this from paralysis agitans. French, Austrian and German physicians began to make an even more basic distinction: that between the tremor of multiple sclerosis, and of "the very little known *maladie de Parkinson*."[1] Parkinson was naturally unaware of multiple sclerosis. He would quote van Swieten on Galen's "subtle distinction" between *palmos,* the "tremor in parts not in motion and even when supported" (Parkinson's own definition), and *tremos,* our "intention tremor."[2]

The good doctor knew the literature well, although he was just a suburban physician-surgeon-apothecary near London, practicing at a period when suburbs such as his Shoreditch were pleasant resort towns, not yet swallowed up by a grimy metropolis and an industrial revolution. He was naturally familiar with François Boissier de Sauvages who in his standard *Nosologia methodica* of 1763 had classified some 2400 clinical entities. Among them was *skelotyrbe festinans* (the "running disturbance of the limbs") alias *festinia,* as the "second species" of the "genus" for "involuntary tremulous motion," chorea being the first such species.[2] The botanical trend went back to Sydenham holding up botany as an example for medicine[4]; Sauvages had in turn inspired his friend Linné, that other taxonomist-physician. Among other forerunners, likewise quoted by Parkinson, there had been the *tremor coactus* ("forced") of Sylvius de le Boë, and the *tremor paralytoides* of Juncker,[2] both of Sydenham's day. Mere straws in the wind those, not the detailed, life-like portrait of a disease, lovingly drawn as though by an Audubon or Redouté that put Parkinson in a class with Addison, Graves, Bright, Hodgkin, the great eponyms of the

AN

ESSAY

ON THE

SHAKING PALSY.

BY

JAMES PARKINSON,
MEMBER OF THE ROYAL COLLEGE OF SURGEONS.

LONDON:
PRINTED BY WHITTINGHAM AND ROWLAND,
Goswell Street,

FOR SHERWOOD, NEELY, AND JONES,
PATERNOSTER ROW.

1817.

following generation. He displayed more of that *akribeia,* that meticulous care, than Sydenham himself who had prescribed and mastered it so admirably.[4]

There is no evidence that the doctor suffered from his disease although he was the right ripe age of sixty-two when he published those famous six case histories. None of his patients had died; he

Title page. No portrait of Parkinson seems to exist.

apologized for being unable to indicate the site of the lesion—cervical cord or oblongata, he guessed.[2] And although Sauvages had already noticed that in *festinia* the muscles "lack flexibility,"[5] it was not until 1868 that Charcot mentioned "rigidity . . . overlooked, we believe, by Parkinson as well as by most of his successors."[1a] Given "paralysis," rigidity had perhaps been taken for granted. But even motor power, as Charcot further commented, is "retarded rather than actually enfeebled."[1a] "Spastic rigidity" was the term J. W. Little, the orthopedist, used in 1861 to characterize his disease.[6] Jackson also, as late as 1899, made no distinction between rigidity of hemiplegia and that of paralysis agitans,[7] although the helpful tendon reflexes had been introduced nearly a quarter of a century earlier. But as Parkinson intended and predicted, his entity came fully into its own "through the benevolent labours . . . of those who humanely employ anatomical examination," when toward the end of his century and during ours the basal ganglia were reassessed, the concept of an extrapyramidal system born, and finally "appropriate modes of relief, or even of cure, pointed out"; all this even before "its real nature may be ascertained."[2] We too, on the threshold, are still hoping.

The humble Shoreditch practitioner started his publishing career with a most irreverent criticism of an old fogey whose lectures were being widely acclaimed.[8] He also wrote a progressive humanitarian tract against cruelty to the insane[9] and produced the first clinico-pathological description of a ruptured appendix, in collaboration with his son.[10] He may have been a cofounder of the London Medical and Chirurgical Society; certainly he was one of the Geological Society, for his main interest in later years was fossils. *Organic remains of a former world,* a two-volume work, shows him in the forefront of scientific progress. Nor must we forget the social reformer. As a young member of the hot-headed London Corresponding Society, in numerous pamphlets under the pen-name "Old Hubert," he had attacked the government of Pitt; his ardent sympathy was with the underprivileged and the revolution raging across the Channel. This perhaps is at least one of the reasons why the medical Establishment of his own country failed to remember him, to the point of leaving neither obituary nor portrait of so worthy a man. It was an American, Leonard G. Rowntree, in England on vacation, who rescued Parkinson, the man, from oblivion; his article, in 1912, entitled "English born, English bred, forgotten by the English and by the world at large, such was the fate of James Parkinson,"[11] brought a congratulatory letter in 1955 from Critchley, Walshe, Greenfield, and McMenemey on the occasion of Parkinson's bicentennial birthday ceremonial.[12]

SAN FRANCISCO, CALIFORNIA   FRANCIS SCHILLER

References

[1]Gaz. hebd., 1861, *8:*765, 816. *Ibid.,* 1862, *9:*54.   [1a]Gaz. hôp., 1869: 189–190, 229–239, 445–446. *Oeuvres complètes.* Vol. 1, Paris, 1886, p. 155–186.   [2]*An essay on the shaking palsy.* London, 1817, p. 1, 19–32.   [3]Mem. Acad. Med., 1850/51, *15:*373.   [4]*Works.* London, Sydenham Soc., 1848, vol. 1, p. 13 *et seq.;* vol. 2, p. 198 (on chorea). [5]Quoted by R. Wallenberg in Nothnagel's *Specielle Pathologie u. Therapie,* Wien, 1897, vol. 12, pt. II, p. 119.   [6]Trans. Obstet. Soc. London, 1861, *3:*293.   [7]*Selected writings of Hughlings Jackson.* New York, Basic Books, 1958, vol. 2, 452.   [8]*Observations on Dr. Hugh Smith's philosophy of physic.* London, 1780(?) (Anon.).   [9]*Observations on the act for regulating madhouses.* London, 1811.   [10]Med. Chir. Trans. 1816, *3:*57.   [11]Bull. Johns Hopkins Hosp., 1912, *23:*33–45. [12]*Amid masters of twentieth century medicine. A panorama of persons and pictures.* Springfield, Thomas, 1958, p. 145–147 (Rowntree).

References to Biography: 1) Bull. Johns Hopkins Hosp., 1912, *23:*33 (Rowntree). 2) Critchley (ed.): *James Parkinson, 1755–1824, bicentenary volume.* London, 1955 (McMenemey).   3) Proc. 2d Internat. Congr. Neuropathology. Amsterdam, Exc. Med. Foundation, 1955, pt. 1, p. 3–8 (Greenfield).

HEINRICH QUINCKE (1842–1922)

QUINCKE would deserve a place in the history of medicine even if his only achievement had been the introduction of spinal puncture. No other single clinical method has done so much to clarify the understanding of diseases of the central nervous system.

Heinrich Irenaeus Quincke was born at Frankfurt-an-der-Oder, the son of a distinguished physician who, with his family, later moved to Berlin. Here he could be seen riding every morning into the forest, impeccably dressed, ramrod straight in the saddle, accompanied by his properly liveried groom. Impressions of him

Portrait, courtesy of Dr. Frederick Hiller, Chicago, Illinois.

were that he was a fine gentleman but a pedant: fussy, obstreperous when pressed, and most "dangerous" to get into an argument with.

After studying medicine at Berlin, Würzburg and Heidelberg under such celebrated men as Virchow, von Kölliker and Helmholtz, Quincke in 1867 became assistant to the great Frerichs. He must have considerably impressed his fellow scientists, for in no other way can one account for his call to the chair of internal medicine at Bern only three years after obtaining his *venia legendi* in Berlin. In 1878 he went to Kiel where he remained for thirty years, retiring in 1908, only to continue his scientific work in the stimulating atmosphere of Frankfurt-am-Main. Here his discussions at the autopsy table were, as before, "an oasis in the wastes of every-day work." In his country home, still standing today, this distinguished physician, teacher, and scientist died at the age of eighty, sitting quietly among his books.

Quincke's numerous contributions to medical literature covered an amazing variety of subjects, among them his classic description of angioneurotic edema,[1] a clinical syndrome which bears his name. Early in his career, Quincke became fascinated by the functions and dysfunctions of the nervous system. As far back as 1869 he began the studies of the mechanisms of body temperature that later led him to postulate the existence of a caloric center.[2] He recognized the syndrome of meningitis serosa,[3] described anosmia in traumatic brain lesions, and noted hyperthermia in the agonal states of lesions of the upper cervical cord.[4]

Quincke's idea of spinal puncture for the withdrawal of fluid occurred neither by intuition nor by accident, and it is interesting to reconstruct the steps that led him to it. Searching for a simple and harmless way to relieve the increasing tension in hydrocephalus in children and thus save their lives, he reasoned that removal of the spinal fluid would break the vicious circle of the over-production and under-resorption of liquor caused by compression of the pacchionian granulations. As Frerichs' assistant, he had studied in 1872 the anatomy and physiology related to the cerebrospinal fluid in dogs by injecting red sulphide of mercury into the spinal subarachnoid space.[5] The knowledge gained thereby encouraged him to insert a fine needle with a stylet into the lumbar interspace of an infant, a procedure which he thought might cause slight injury to a root fiber of the cauda but would not cause paralysis. It is to Quincke's credit that from the beginning he utilized his puncture for diagnostic (1891[6]) as well as for therapeutic purposes (1895[7]). He insisted on accurate manometric pressure readings both at the beginning and at the end of the puncture, he studied the cells and measured the total protein, found tubercle bacilli in the fibrinous pedicle, noticed diminution of liquor sugar in purulent meningitis, identified bacteria, and gave consideration to the basis for the presence of blood. Of special neurological interest is the fact that in one of his very first patients, an infant, Quincke described the occurrence of a transient bilateral abducens paralysis following repeated removal of a considerable amount of fluid. Quincke was also the first to withdraw fluid from the lateral ventricle; this he did in two infants with hydrocephalus.

Quincke announced his technique for spinal puncture at the Wiesbaden Congress in 1891,[6] but there was little response from the audience, and no echo from the press. Reports on spinal puncture trickled into the literature for five years before the magnitude of Quincke's contribution became recognized. He then had the satisfaction of witnessing what followed: Froin[8] described the syndrome of compression or obstruction of the liquor in 1903, and Nonne[9] in 1907; Lange[10] announced his discovery of the colloidal-gold reaction in 1912, and its application in 1913[11]; Mestrezat's[12] great monograph on the composition of the spinal fluid in health and disease appeared in 1912, and the announcement of the test by Queckenstedt[13,14] in 1916. Across the Atlantic not long afterward, Cushing, Weed and Dandy were to carry out their notable physiological studies in the field, and Dandy to puncture the ventricle (twenty-five years after Quincke) for the purpose of pneumoencephalography.

FREDERICK HILLER

References

[1]Mschr. prakt. Derm., Hamb. u. Lpz., 1882, 1:129–131.   [2]Arch. Anat. Physiol., Lpz., 1869, p. 174–198 (with Naunyn).   [3]Deut. Zschr. Nervenh., 1896, 9:149–163.   [4]Arch. exp. Path., 1881, 15:1–21.

[5]Arch. Anat. Physiol., Lpz., 1872, p. 153–177.   [6]Verhandl. Cong. innere Med., Wiesb., 1891, *10*:321–331.   [7]Berl. klin. Wschr., 1895, *32*:861–862 *et seq.*   [8]Gaz. hôp., 1903, *76*:1005–1006.   [9]Arch. Psychiat., Berlin, 1907, *43*:433–460.   [10]Berlin klin. Wschr., 1912, *49*:897–901.   [11]Zschr. Chemotherap., 1913, *1*:44–78.   [12]*Le liquide céphalorachidien normal et pathologique. Valeur clinique et l'examen chimique. Syndromes humoraux dans diverses affections.* Paris, Maloine, 1912.   [13]Deut. Zschr. Nervenh., 1916, *55*:325–333.   [14]*The founders of neurology.* 1st ed. Springfield, Thomas, 1953, p. 353–359 (Haymaker).

References to Biography: 1) Arch. exp. Path., Lpz., 1922, *93*:1–3 (Naunyn).   2) Zschr. klin. Med., 1923, *96*:1–21 (G. von Bergmann). 3) *Classic descriptions of disease. With biographical sketches of the authors.* Springfield, Thomas, 1932 (Major). (3rd ed., 3rd printing, 1948.)   4) Kolle (Ed.): *Grosse Nervenärzte.* Vol. 2. Stuttgart, Thieme, 1959, p. 78–84 (Kolle).

DOUGLAS ARGYLL ROBERTSON (1837–1909)

A MONG those who added much to the medical ferment of Edinburgh was Douglas Argyll Robertson, the son of Doctor John Argyll Robertson, President of the College of Surgeons of Edinburgh in 1848. After preliminary medical training in Edinburgh, he received the M.D. from St. Andrews in 1857 and was appointed house surgeon to the Royal Infirmary. He then studied in Berlin under Albrecht von Graefe (1828–70), who was establishing ophthalmology as a definite medical specialty. Returning to Edinburgh, Argyll Robertson slowly developed a distinguished ophthalmologic practice. Meanwhile he taught the first laboratory class in physiology organized by the University of Edinburgh. In 1886 he became president of the College of Surgeons, and in 1894 was president of the International Ophthalmological Congress in Edinburgh. From 1867 to 1896 he was ophthalmic surgeon to the Royal Infirmary.

It is not difficult to trace the factors influencing the major contributions of Argyll Robertson. His father had taught materia medica. His friend, Thomas R. Fraser (1841–1919), made a sys-

Douglas Moray Cooper Lamb Argyll Robertson

tematic study of African arrow poisons while collecting them for
the materia medica museum. Robertson was searching for an agent
which would stimulate the sphincter pupillae in a manner opposite to the dilating effect produced by belladonna or atropine.
Fraser suggested an extract of the ordeal bean of Calabar, which

Portrait by permission of the President and Council of the Royal College of
Surgeons of Edinburgh.

he had observed to cause pupillary constriction. Robertson's experiments were conducted on himself. He demonstrated that an active agent, later isolated as the alkaloid eserine or physostigmine, contracts the ciliary muscle of accommodation and the sphincter pupillae. Since both are supplied by the ciliary nerves, he concluded that the action is due to their stimulation.[1] The early study of Robertson on the Calabar bean (physostigma venenosa) began a significant chain of chemical discoveries of great importance in neurology.

The pupillary condition to which Argyll Robertson's name is given was thoroughly described in two brilliant reports (in 1869) dealing with five tabetic patients[2,3]—reports in which he drew attention to some other cases shown him by Remak in Berlin and in which he acknowledged the description by Romberg (in 1839), by Trousseau, and by Stellwag. Robertson's discussion was significant. He emphasized miosis as a characteristic of the pupil, the peculiar reactions of the pupil to extracts of belladonna and of the Calabar bean, the associated color blindness, and the condition of the retinal vessels. He went on to describe the reduced dilatation of the pupil from belladonna, and further contraction from Calabar bean; and he elucidated fully the action of belladonna in paralyzing the circular fibers of the sphincter pupillae, and of Calabar bean in stimulating them. He concluded from the five cases that "for contraction of the pupil under light it is necessary that the ciliospinal nerves remain intact and, as in these cases of miosis the ciliospinal nerves are paralyzed, light does not influence the pupil." In two of the five cases some locomotor ataxia was present, while in the others the form of spinal affection was doubtful. The "tonic pupil" had a longer history. The London ophthalmologist of the day, James Ware (1756–1815), described some of its features in 1813,[4] and while accounts continued to appear (for example, by Srassburger[5] and by Saenger[6] in 1902), the disorder came to be known as the Holmes[7]-Adie[8] syndrome through their independent descriptions in 1931, of cases in which tonic pupils were combined with absent patellar and other deep reflexes (1932); Hughlings Jackson, however, described this syndrome fully in 1881,[9] and Oloff (1914)[10] appears to have been the first to show that the disorder is not syphilitic in origin.

Argyll Robertson, in his grey frock coat and top hat, was a classical figure in the days when such garments were *de rigueur* for the dignity of the doctor. His tall, athletic figure, his handsome features, his air of distinction, and his old-world courtesy made him a conspicuous figure in any professional assembly, and endeared him to students and colleagues alike. A great golfer, he won many medals in tournaments. He and his wife travelled around the world in 1894 and became close friends of the Thakar of Gondal in India. Before retiring to a farm in Jersey in 1900, and again in 1909, they went to India to see their regal friend, and it was there that Argyll Robertson died.

SAN FRANCISCO, CALIFORNIA   CHAUNCEY D. LEAKE

References

[1]Edinburgh Med. J., 1863, *8:*815–820.   [2]*Ibid.*, 1969, *14:*696–708. [3]*Ibid.*, 1869, *15:*487–493.   [4]Philos. Tr. Roy. Soc. London, 1813:31– 50. Brit. J. Ophth., 1917, *1:*401–410 (biography of Ware, by Dunn). [5]Neur. Cbl., 1902, *21:*738–740 *et seq.*   [6]*Ibid.*, 1902, *21:*837–839 *et seq.* [7]Tr. Ophth. Soc. U. K., 1931, *51:*209–228.   [8]Brit. Med. J., 1931, *1:* 928–930. Haymaker (ed.), *The founders of neurology.* Springfield, Thomas, 1953, p. 231–233 (biography of Adie, by Caughey).   [9]Tr. Ophth. Soc. U. K., 1881, *1:*139–154.   [10]Klin. Monatsbl. Augenh., 1914, *53:*493–502.

References to Biography: 1) Edinburgh Med. J., 1909, n.s., *2:*159–162 (Lundy). 2) J. Lancet, Minneap., 1929, *49:*173–174 (Woltman). 3) Brit. Med. J., 1909, *1:*191–193 (anon.).

MORITZ HEINRICH ROMBERG (1795–1873)

*R*OMBERG was a native of Meiningen, Thuringia, a part of Saxony. His medical studies were pursued at Berlin where, at the age of twenty-two, he received the M.D. on the basis of a thesis in which he gave his classic description of achondroplasia ("congenital rickets").[1] He soon devoted himself to the study of nervous disease, the first physician in history to give particular attention to altered structure related to clinical manifestations—the neurology as we know it today.

Moritz Heinrich Romberg

A trip to Vienna in 1820 gained him the friendship of Johann
Peter Frank, who was not only a pioneer in the study of diseases of
the spinal cord (1792), but also a founder of modern public hy-

Portrait, courtesy of the National Library of Medicine, Bethesda, Maryland.

giene, and a humanitarian; his influence on Romberg was considerable and lasting.

Romberg derived much of his background from contemporary English neuroanatomy and neuropathology in translating Andrew Marshall's *The morbid anatomy of the brain, in mania and hydrophobia* (London, Longman & Co., 1815) into German in 1820, and, more significant still, Sir Charles Bell's *The nervous system of the human body* (London, Longman & Co., 1830) in 1832. He was conscious of the importance of having brought Bell's great landmark in neurology to the German-speaking world, for he stated: "The researches of Sir Charles Bell fill me with enthusiasm, and in 1831 I translated his great work and made known to my professional brethren in Germany his investigations which will ever serve as models of scientific inquiry."

At the University of Berlin he was appointed Privatdozent for special pathology and therapy (1830), then Extraordinarius (1838), and finally Director of the University Hospital (1840), where he began his study of patients, promptly recording his observations for inclusion in his textbook, which was published in parts from 1840 to 1846.[2] Three editions were called for before 1857. This, the first systematic book on neurology, well documented with full references to the literature, deals in admirable fashion with such disorders as neuritis, causalgia, ciliary neuralgia, facial neuralgia, sciatica, neuromas, chorea, tetany, epilepsy and facial paralysis. Romberg's discussion of tabes dorsalis, lucid in clinical details and brilliant in his surmise as to the site of the initial pathological changes, contains the classic remark that ataxics cannot stand with their eyes shut (Romberg's sign): "Lässt man ihn in aufrechter Stellung die Augen schliessen, so fängt er sofort an zu schwanken und zu taumeln . . ." (ed. 1, 1846, p. 795). His description of progressive facial hemiatrophy (Parry-Romberg's syndrome) appeared in 1846.[3] Romberg was also a neuropathologist of note, and was made Ordinarius in special pathology and therapy in 1845.

Romberg collected and incorporated into his precise clinical pictures of neurological diseases the scattered reports of experimental investigations from many sources. He was acutely aware of the physiological work of Sir Charles Bell and of Magendie, and the acceptance of the difference between sensory and motor nerves led to a division of his textbook into two sections, one on sensation and the other on motion. The German text was translated into English in 1853[4] and the volumes had a wide influence not only in Great Britain but also in America. Although Romberg's nosology, which included many kinds of "neuroses," was slowly abandoned as specific neurological and neuromuscular entities were recognized and pathogenesis revealed,[5] Romberg deserves enduring fame for his success at bringing some order into neurological thought.

Romberg excelled as a teacher, and he was always intent on closest personal relations with his students. He was particularly self-effacing during the Berlin cholera epidemic, when in 1831 and 1837 he was in charge of cholera hospitals.[6] He died of heart disease at the age of seventy-eight.

HENRY R. VIETS

References

[1]*De rachitide congenita.* Berlin, Platen, 1817.   [2]*Lehrbuch der Nervenkrankheiten des Menschen.* Berlin, Duncker, 1840–46. (2nd ed., 1851.)   [3]*Klinische Ergebnisse.* Berlin, Förstner, 1846.   [4]*A manual of the nervous diseases of man.* 2 vol. London, Sydenham Society, 1853 (trans. and ed. by Sieveking).   [5]J.A.M.A., 1965, *193*:1119–1120 (anon.).   [6]Wschr. ges. Heilk., Berlin, 1838, *6*:33–39 *et seq.*

References to Biography: 1) Bull. N. Y. Acad. Med., 1948, *24*:772–782 (Viets).   2) Berlin klin. Wschr., 1873, *10*:289–290 (Waldenburg). 3) Deut. Klinik, 1867, *19*:109–110 *et seq.;* 1873, *25*:245 (Göschen).   4) *Verdienste deutscher Ärzte um die Erkenntnis der Neuro-Pathologie.* Inaug.-Diss.-Düsseldorf, 1936 (Kleinjohann).   5) Dana, *Textbook of nervous diseases.* 10th ed., New York, Wood, 1925, p. XV–LVI. (Garrison, on the history of neurology).   6) *Garrison's history of neurology.* Springfield, Thomas, 1969, p. 274–278 (McHenry).

GUSTAVE ROUSSY (1874–1948)

G USTAVE ROUSSY was born at Vevey, in Switzerland. He pursued his undergraduate studies at Lausanne, and spent his first three years in medicine at the University of Geneva; in 1897 he continued his studies at the Faculté de Médecine in Paris.

From then on he advanced steadily in the academic hierarchy. In 1902 he became interne des hôpitaux de Paris. He was Chef de travaux de physiologie pathologique in François-Franck's laboratory at the Collège de France from 1906 to 1908, Chef de travaux d'anatomie pathologique at the Faculté de Médecine in 1908, and Médecin en chef of the Hôpital Paul Brousse in 1913. His exceptional gifts were rewarded by appointments to positions of high place: successively he became Professeur d'anatomie pathologique at the Faculté de Médecine de Paris (1925); Director of the Institut du Cancer (1930); Dean of the Faculté de Médecine (1933); and Rector of the Université de Paris (1937). On November 11, 1940, during the German occupation, he was dismissed from the university without any given reason. But in 1944, after the liberation of Paris, he was fully reinstated and again served the university with rare distinction.

Roussy was a Member of the Académie des Sciences and Secrétaire Général of the Académie de Médecine, besides belonging to numerous other French and foreign learned societies. The Universities of Geneva, Lausanne, Athens, and Budapest bestowed upon him the Doctor's degree, *honoris causa*.

During the early part of his career, Roussy served as an intern under two eminent neurologists, Pierre Marie and Jules Dejerine, both of whom stimulated Roussy in his intense pursuit of neurology. With Dejerine he brought to light the thalamic syndrome (1906),[1] and a year later, in his doctoral dissertation,[2] he explored the anatomy, physiology and pathology of the thalamus. A more detailed paper on the thalamic syndrome appeared in 1909.[3] Altogether it was shown that the lesion responsible for the syndrome was situated in the "external" thalamic nucleus, in its lateral and posterior parts, and extended through the "internal" and median

nuclei, involving some of the fibers of the posterior limb of the internal capsule. Foix, Masson and Hillemand[4,5] were to show some years later that the syndrome could result from occlusion of the thalamogeniculate branches of the posterior cerebral artery.

There was brilliance also in Roussy's papers on the degeneration of the cerebral cortex in amyotrophic lateral sclerosis; the experimental induction of a syrinx in the spinal cord of the dog and cat; the pathology of the conus terminalis, a work in which he demonstrated the location in the spinal cord of the parasympathetic centers for micturition and defecation, and the abdominalpelvic sympathetic mechanism for the functional regulation and automatic activity of the bladder and rectum.

During World War I, Roussy wrote two important books in col-

Portrait, courtesy of the National Library of Medicine, Bethesda, Maryland.

laboration with J. Lhermitte, one on injuries of the spinal cord and cauda equina[6] and the other on the psychoneuroses engendered by war[7]; and with J. Boisseau and M. d'Oelsnitz he published a volume on the treatment of the psychoneuroses of war.[8]

The pituitary and tuber cinereum engaged Roussy's attention during the years 1912 to 1924. He and his distinguished collaborator, J. Camus, were the first to demonstrate that damage to the hypothalamus without removal of the pituitary could cause polyuria, gonadal atrophy, obesity and transient glycosuria; the conclusions reached were that gonadal atrophy was more likely due to a hypothalamic than a pituitary lesion and that the obesity was not necessarily dependent upon the existence of gonadal atrophy.[9,10] Subsequently, with M. Mosinger, he undertook the systematic study of the nuclei and fiber pathways of the hypothalamus and the diencephalic excito-secretory centers of the hypophysis, and insisted that the elaboration of endocrine secretions, such as pituitary colloid, occurred through the mediation of a process which they termed *neurocrinie*. All these studies culminated in 1946 in a *Traité de neuroendocrinologie* (Paris; Masson), an important volume of 1100 pages.

Besides neurology, Roussy was particularly interested in the problem of cancer. Not only did many papers on experimental aspects of the subject come from his pen, but also a remarkable book,[11] written in collaboration with R. Leroux and M. Wolf.

Roussy was pre-eminent as a man of science, but he was also a great organizer and a leader in the battle against social injustices. He was highly cultured, the personification of sincerity, distinguished in his bearing, a gentleman down to his very finger tips. He was a stimulus to those with whom he came in contact; and at all times he was ready to help and welcome those who came from France or the outside world to acquaint themselves with his work. He was greatly admired not only by his colleagues and his students in France, but also by the international élite.

GEORGES GUILLAIN

References

[1]Rev. neur., Paris, 1906, *14*:521–532.   [2]*La couche optique; étude anatomique, physiologique et clinique.* Thèse de Paris, 1907.   [3]Rev.

neur., Paris, 1909, *1*:301–317.   [4]Presse méd., *31*:361–365 (Foix and Masson).   [5]*Ibid.*, 1925, *33*:113–117 (Foix and Hillemand).   [6]*Blessures de la moëlle et da la queue de cheval.* Paris, Masson, 1918. [7]*Les psychonévroses de guerre.* Paris, Masson, 1917.   [8]*Traitement des psychonévroses de guerre.* Paris, Masson, 1919.   [9]C. rend. Soc. biol., Paris, 1913, *75*:483–486.   [10]Endocrinology, 1920, *4*:507–522. [11]*Le Cancer.* Paris, Masson, 1929.

References to Biography: 1) Rev. neur., Paris, 1948, *2*:729–734 (Guillain).   2) Bull. Acad. Nat. Méd., 1949, 3.sér., *133*:450–459 (Lhermitte).

BERNARD SACHS (1858–1944)

*B*ARNEY SACHS—he was thus christened—was a product of both the old world and the new. His father, a prominent teacher, was born and raised amidst the humblest surroundings in a small Bavarian town near Schweinfurt. While pursuing studies in Würzburg, he became romantically involved. Protests in the air, the pair eloped to Hamburg in 1847, were soon aboard a sailing ship, and finally reached Baltimore. They could be counted among the promising young Germans whom American historians later called the "Forty-eighters." Barney was born at the time Lincoln was campaigning for a seat in the Senate. This was the name he clung to until years later when he began signing his name "Bernard."

A two-year sojourn in Germany with the family when Barney was in his early teens stood him in good stead at Harvard (1874–1878). William James, who was having trouble with his eyes, sought a volunteer from the class who would read to him each day a chapter from Wundt's *Psychologie.* Barney volunteered. This experience had a determining influence on the young man's subsequent career. His dissertation on *A comparison of the fore and hind limb in vertebrates* won him the Bowdoin Prize and fifty dollars; twenty-five went for the purchase of Darwin's *Works,* the rest to host a dinner for four of his friends. (The outstanding dish, he recalled, was fried bananas!)

Receiving a B.A. from Harvard in 1878, he was off to Europe. He

chose Strasbourg for its vigorous medical faculty. Waldeyer, he was soon to find, frowned on all textbooks of anatomy, except, perhaps, Josef Hyrtl's for "it contains anecdotes; you will remember the anecdotes and promptly forget the anatomy." Sachs found von Recklinghausen a vivacious and inspiring little man; Kussmaul, he idolized; under Goltz he wrote his first paper: *Über den Einfluss des Rückenmarks auf die Harnsekretion* (his thesis for the M.D.); it appeared in Virchows Archiv in 1882. Westphal and Virchow in Berlin, Meynert and Freud in Vienna, Charcot in Paris, and

Portrait, courtesy of Dr. Joseph H. Globus, New York City.

Hughlings Jackson in London: these were the men he worked with or got to know before sailing for New York (in 1884), where his parents had settled.

The year 1887 was his *annus mirabilis*. He became happily married and was soon to have a family. He now had his translation of Meynert's *Psychiatrie* behind him, and was getting along well as Instructor at the New York Polyclinic. His article, *On arrested cerebral development, with special reference to its cortical pathology* appeared.[1] "Cherry red" maculae had been noted clinically in the infant (by his associate Knapp), and on histological examination Sachs discovered ballooned nerve cells in the cortex. "We have here an agenetic condition pure and simple," he wrote. Ira Van Gieson (1865–1913)[2] oversaw the processing of the brain sections (his picric acid stain was originally devised to show up nervous tissue), and he also made the drawings for Sachs' paper. Later, upon recognizing the familial nature of the condition from studies of other cases, Sachs coined the term, "amaurotic family idiocy."[3-5] (Some were quick to point out that these infants had dementia, not idiocy.) Unbeknown to Sachs, Waren Tay (1843–1927), an English ophthalmologist, had, in 1881, published an account of "a brownish-red, rairly circular spot" in each macula, surrounded by a white halo, which he had observed in an infant.[6] The change was comparable, Tay had remarked, to the picture of embolism of the central artery of the retina. Hughlings Jackson, called in as consultant, had been unable to find any clinical evidence of a cerebral affection. Kingdon (in 1892) recognized that Tay and Sachs were seeing different facets of the same condition. There are those who say that Ennals Martin (1758–1834), of Eastland, Maryland, published (in 1817) the first paper on the juvenile form of amaurotic idiocy, under the title, *Remarkable account of hereditary blindness, affecting several branches of an extensive family*,[7] but although "during the decline of sight [those afflicted] seemed melancholy and dejected . . . after total blindness they became as cheerful and sprightly as most people."

Papers on progressive muscular dystrophy, infantile cerebral palsy, cerebral hemorrhage in the young, syphilis of the spinal cord, and others, brought his publications to a total of 194. A central personality in all phases of American Neurology, he belonged with

Charles Loomis Dana (1852–1935)[8] and Moses Allen Starr (1854–
1932)[9] to "the New York triumvirate." Dana had the idea that
Sachs should write a book on nervous diseases of children; it was
the first of its kind in America.[10] Sachs' principle affiliations at the
time were with Mt. Sinai, Montefiori, and Bellevue Hospitals.

Recognition came as a flood. The peak was his election as President of the First International Congress of Neurology, held in
Bern in 1931. When proffered the presidency of the New York
Academy of Medicine he accepted, despite the time it took from
his practice. (Almost all his life's savings had been swept away during the great depression. "This is important public work; I'll sell
my car and economize," he told the family.) It was natural that a
special issue of the *Journal of the Mount Sinai Hospital* should be
prepared in his honor.[11]

Sachs had a dignified bearing and, as he himself remarked, a
Puritan conscience. He was also ambitious and unabashedly held
himself in high esteem. "I had the will to succeed," he would remark. At Harvard: "I came to College just an average decent young
fellow and a burning desire to prepare for a successful life's career."
He said what he thought; he could be sharp in his replies. Stub after
stub in his checkbook showed his deep sense of civic duty: contributions to philanthropic organizations and seldom any entry for
his own pleasure. An expert in the arts, he could commonly be
seen entering galleries along Fifth Avenue, and was consultant to
Altman on numerous paintings and porcelains now on display at
the Metropolitan Museum of Art. An alienist expert, he once testified that a certain old lady was suffering from senile dementia when
she left most of her money to the lawyer who drew up her will. "I
suppose," queried the cross-examining lawyer, "that it is very easy
for you, Dr. Sachs, to tell whether a person is sane or insane. I pre-
sume you can tell by *looking* at me whether I am sane or insane.
Very promptly I answered: Not by *looking*, but possibly by listening to you. That settled him." This was the last entry in Sachs' autobiography, commenced when he was eighty. Death came at the age
of eighty-seven. The mayor of New York, Fiorello La Guardia,
who had often turned to Sachs for advice on medical problems,
was among the public mourners.

MOFFETT FIELD, CALIFORNIA   WEBB HAYMAKER

References

[1]J. Nerv. Ment. Dis., 1887, *14*:541–553.   [2]Boston Med. Surg. J., 1913, *168*:634–635 (biography, anon.).   [3]J. Nerv. Ment. Dis., 1892, *19*:603–607.   [4]*Ibid.*, 1896, *23*:475–479.   [5]*Ibid.*, 1903, *30*:1–13. [6]Trans. Ophth. Soc. U.K., 1881, *1*:55–57.   [7]Med. Repository, N.S., 1817, *3*:75–79.   [8]Trans. Amer. Neur. Assn., 1936, *62*:187–193 (biography, by Jelliffe). J. Nerv. Ment. Dis., 1936, *83*:622–637 (biography with bibliography, by Tilney).   [9]Haymaker (Ed.), *The founders of neurology*, 1st. ed. Springfield, Thomas, 1953, p. 392–395 (biography, by Pearce Bailey).   [10]*A treatise on the nervous diseases of children.* New York, Wood, 1895. 2nd ed., 1905.   [11]J. Mt. Sinai Hosp., 1942, *9*:213–271 (contains Sachs' bibliography).

Reference to Biography: Barney Sachs, 1858–1944. An autobiography. New York, privately printed, 1949 (with biographic notes by Nathan Strauss and Foster Kennedy).

JEAN ATHANASE SICARD (1872–1929)

*S*ICARD was born and brought up in Marseilles, and it was here that he began the study of medicine. Subsequently he completed his medical training in Paris, where he spent the remainder of his life.

In Paris he was associated with many of the leaders of French medicine. Widal was one of his first teachers, and it was with him that Sicard pursued some of his immunological investigations. In 1894 he was externe to Raymond, and a year later became interne to Danlos, Widal, Troisier, Brissaud and Raymond. He owed most to his friend, Brissaud. He passed his thesis requirement in 1899, became chef de clinique in 1901, médecin des hôpitaux in 1903, agrégé in 1907, chef de service at the Hôpital Necker in 1910, and professeur de pathologie interne in 1923. During World War I he was director of the Neurological Center of the 15th Region.

Sicard was always preoccupied with what could be accomplished with the needle, both in diagnosis and in treatment. Numerous papers dealing with injections of many types came from his pen: alcohol for the relief of trigeminal neuralgia and other painful

Jean Athanase Sicard

afflictions[1,2]; blood for the treatment of acute anterior poliomyelitis and other diseases; sera for direct intracranial therapy; bicarbonate of soda in the alleviation of tetany; milk in the treatment of migraine[3]; and sclerosing solutions for varicose veins, the last a procedure which he introduced.

He was one of the first to be interested in pneumoencephalography. His many papers on various manifestations and sequelae of lethargic encephalitis,[4,5] and on the clinical manifestations and treatment of syphilis of the central nervous system were all significant contributions. He recognized that peripheral neuri-

Portrait, courtesy of Dr. Paul Bucy, Chicago, Illinois. (Photographer: P. Simonet, Paris.)

tis may develop as a consequence of injection of immunological sera and following the injection of quinine in the treatment of malaria. He took up where Ramsay Hunt had left off, by describing herpes zoster in the realms of the trigeminal and facial nerves.[6] In 1917 he put on record a case of traumatic injury of the neck in which the IXth, Xth, XIth and XIIth cranial nerves were damaged,[7,8] and as a consequence his name became linked with that of Collet, who in 1915[9] had described a similar case. Thus Sicard and Collet joined the long list of those—some obscure, some distinguished—whose names became eponyms in connection with syndromes of involvement of the bulbar cranial nerves: Avellis (X),[10] Schmidt and Hughlings Jackson (X, XI, XII),[11,12] Tapia (X, XII, and sometimes IX and the sympathetic),[13] Vernet (IX, X, XI),[14] and Villaret (X, XII and sympathetic).[15]

Sicard's fame rests, however, largely upon his introduction, with his pupil Jacques Forestier, of radio-opaque iodized oil (lipiodol).[16-18] This was unquestionably his greatest contribution to medicine and particularly to neurology. In the neurological field, lipiodol is usually thought of in connection with the diagnosis and localization of intraspinal neoplasms. But Sicard and his associates were well aware of the much wider application of this substance. They advocated its use in the diagnosis of intraspinal adhesions and inflammatory processes, urethral disorders, the outlining of sinus tracts, the demonstration of intra-arterial thromboses, the diagnosis of pulmonary disease, and even the diagnosis of intracranial tumors (through intraspinal injection of the lipiodol which ascended into the intracranial cavity). These and many other observations on the use of lipiodol were published with Forestier in book form[19] the year before Sicard died. Since 1944 lipiodol has been supplanted by Pantopaque, introduced by Steinhausen and his associates.[20]

The day before his death, Sicard had invited friends to dinner and with unaccustomed joie-de-vivre related the experiences he had had while on a trip to Cairo to attend the Congrès de médecine tropicale et d'hygiène. The next morning angina pectoris developed. He himself suggested the appropriate therapy, which consisted of injection of sympathetic ganglia with novocaine. The operation was to have been performed by his close friend, the surgeon Robineau. But before the needle for which he had become famous could be used, death supervened.

CHICAGO, ILLINOIS   PAUL C. BUCY

References

[1]Presse méd., Paris, 1908, *16*:289–292.   [2]Lancet, London, 1918, *1:* 213–214.   [3]Rev. neur., Paris, 1925, *1*:944 (with Haguenau).   [4]Bull. Soc. méd. hôp. Paris, 1920, 3.sér., *44*:390–391 (with Kudelski).   [5]J. méd. Franç., 1923, *12*:140–142.   [6]Rev. neur., Paris, 1919, *26*:15–19 (with Roger and Vernet).   [7]Marseille méd., 1917, n.s., *1*:385–397. [8]*Ibid.*, 1918, *55*:886 (with Roger).   [9]Lyon méd., 1915, *124*:121–129. [10]Berlin Klin., 1891, *40*:1–26.   [11]*Die Krankheiten der oberen Luftwege.* 2nd ed., Berlin, Springer, 1897, p. 48.   [12]Lancet, London, 1872, *2*:770–773.   [13]Arch. internat. laryng., 1906, *22*:780–785.   [14]Bull. Soc. méd. hôp. Paris, 1916, *40*:210–223.   [15]Rev. neur., Paris, 1916, *1:* 188–190.   [16]Rev. neur., Paris, 1921, *28*:1264–1266.   [17]Bull. Soc. méd. hôp. Paris, 1922, 3.sér., *46*:462–469.   [18]Presse méd., Paris, 1923, *31*:885–887.   [19]*Diagnostic et thérapeutique par le lipiodol.* Paris, Masson, 1928.   [20]Radiology, 1944, *43*:230–235.

References to Biography: Rev. neur., Paris, 1929, *1*:161–164 (Babonniex).

WILLIAM GIBSON SPILLER (1863–1940)

*S*PILLER was the most distinguished American clinical neurologist of his time. He was born in Baltimore. After receiving an M.D. from the University of Pennsylvania in 1892, he spent four years abroad in specialized studies, at first in internal medicine and later in neurology, with such savants as Obersteiner, Oppenheim, Edinger, Dejerine and Gowers. He often spoke of the clinical thoroughness of these men, especially Obersteiner and Oppenheim, and when in later years it was repeatedly suggested that he write a textbook on neurology, his favorite retort was: "When I can write a better book than Oppenheim's, I'll do so."

On his return to Philadelphia he entered into neuropatholog-

ical research in the William Pepper Laboratory of the University of Pennsylvania, a connection which was maintained until 1910. At the turn of the century he became head of the neurological department of the Philadelphia Polyclinic Hospital. It was at about this time that he came to know Charles Karsner Mills (1845–1931), regarded as "the dean of American neurologists."[1] To both of them the winning of prestige for the department of neurology was the great object of their lives, and when Spiller would drop into Mills' office every few days, his customary salutation, "What's

Portrait, courtesy of Dr. A. M. Ornsteen, Philadelphia, Pennsylvania.

new?" always meant "What's new in neurology?" Sometimes Mills would launch into an account of some of his experiences, such as those on the battlefield of Gettysburg; or Spiller, to save Mills's failing vision, would read to him. In 1915 Spiller succeeded Mills as professor of neurology to the University of Pennsylvania, and retained the chair until 1932, when he retired as professor emeritus.

Spiller's publications numbered almost 250, and all were important. The subject matter for his remarkably varied output was furnished by an enormous collection of specimens, many of them from the Philadelphia General Hospital. Like Mills, who was the first to describe the syndrome of occlusion of the superior cerebellar artery[2,3] (Spiller did the pathologic study of this case[4]), Spiller became a pioneer in the field of vascular occlusions of the brain stem.[5-7] He was the first to postulate the medullary syndrome resulting from anterior spinal artery occlusion.[6] Equally impressive were his many papers on disorders of conjugate extraocular muscle movements,[8-12] in which he took up where Henri Parinaud (1844–1905)[13] had left off on the subject of paralysis of upward conjugate movements and provided a better understanding of the internuclear paralyses of Lhermitte.[14] His articles on cordotomy,[15] perhaps the most dramatic of all, showed the keen Spillerian instinct for research. The lion's share of his interest was centered for a time round trigeminal neuralgia, and his ten papers on this subject (the two most important being those on surgical intervention[16,17]) were regarded by him as his most important practical offering. Not least was his discovery that deep sensibility of the face is conveyed centrally by way of the facial nerve,[18] an observation confirmed subsequently by Souques and Hartmann[19] and many others. Mills, too, had made contributions to the clinical aspects of the facial nerve, and this may not have been a coincidence, for he himself suffered from Bell's palsy complicated by facial spasm. Patients would occasionally say to him: "Stop winking at me."

As editor of the *Journal of Nervous and Mental Disease,* Spiller's daily pabulum was the current scientific literature, which was shared with students and associates. His command of the neurological literature—old and new—was phenomenal. Hours were spent every day in the out-patient neurological service of the Hospital of the University of Pennsylvania. His associates included McConnell, Cadwalader, Weisenburg, Camp, Wilson, Winkelman, Ornsteen, and Hadden.

Spiller was of serious demeanor, a little stooped, rather quiet and contained, and wholly lacking in sartorial splendor. The story goes that he, delighting in an argument, would carry a spinal cord or some other specimen in his coat pocket, and whip it out on almost any occasion in the hope that his discourse on it would bring some divergence of opinion. His office was as bare of decoration as that of an ascetic. No doubt he was very far from extravagant. He and a friend were strolling down the boardwalk at Atlantic City one morning when the friend hailed a newsboy and gave him a quarter for a paper. "But you did not get your change back," said Spiller. "No," said the friend, "I wanted the boy to have it," to which Spiller replied, "That's wasting money; you could have borrowed the paper I bought last evening."

For years Spiller refused to enter the private practice of neurology, and when in 1910 he finally yielded to the pleas of those of us who were his confreres, he seemed to feel that he had somehow been duped. In the sickroom he appeared doleful and was regarded by some as coldly scientific—a case being a problem to be solved—but those who knew him well were aware of his capacity for great depth of feeling. His lectures were always crowded, and famous for the quotations from Shakespeare that punctuated his solutions of neurological mysteries—all produced in his rather soft voice.

In the years which have passed since death, Spiller has not been eclipsed on the American neurological scene.

PHILADELPHIA, PENNSYLVANIA   A. M. ORNSTEEN

References

[1]Arch. Neur. Psychiat., Chic., 1932, *28*:1390–1410 (Frazier, Spiller, Burr, McConnell, Cadwalader).   [2]J. Nerv. Ment. Dis., 1908, *35*:331–332.   [3]*Ibid.*, 1912, *39*:73–76.   [4]Arch. Neur. Psychiat., Chic., 1931, *25*:1003–1010 (Russel).   [5]J. Nerv. Ment. Dis., 1908, *35*:365–387.   [6]*Ibid.*, 1908, *35*:775–778.   [7]*Ibid.*, 1909, *36*:601–613.   [8]Univ. Pennsylvania M. Bull., 1903, *16*:362–366 (Potts).   [9]J. Nerv. Ment. Dis.,

1905, *32*:417–426 *et seq.*   [10]Amer. J. Med. Sci., 1919, *157*:695–699. [11]Brain, London, 1924, *47*:345–357.   [12]Arch. Neur. Psychiat., Chic., 1932, *28*:251–271.   [13]Arch. Neur., Paris, 1883, *5*:145–172.   [14]*L'encéphalite léthargique. Questions neurologiques d'actualité.* Paris, Masson, 1922.   [15]Arch. Neur. Psychiat., Chic., 1923, *9*:1–21. [16]Amer. J. Med. Sci., 1898, n.s., *116*:503–532 (with Keen).   [17]Univ. Pennsylvania M. Bull., 1901, *14*:341–352 (with Frazier).   [18]*Ibid.,* 1907, *20*:35–38 (R. H. Ivy and L. W. Johnson).   [19]Rev. neur., Paris, 1924, *31*:86–87.

Reference to Biography: Arch. Neur. Psychiat., Chic., 1940, *44*:175–179 (McConnell).

ADOLF STRÜMPELL (1853–1925)

E RNST ADOLF GUSTAV GOTTFRIED von STRÜMPELL was born in Neu-Autz, Kurland (a part of the Baltic Provinces of Russia), but spent his youth in nearby Dorpat (now Estonia), where his father was professor of philosophy. The high intellectual level of his family and the way of thought and life among the German minority of the Baltic Provinces were important elements in von Strümpell's development, character and career. Already at the age of six he showed much promise as a violinist. While still a "Gymnasiast," he played chamber music and on one occasion took part in a performance of Mozart's *Entführung.* In his autobiography he tells of his embarrassment when during the overture he heard the orchestra play along in prestissimo while he still held the half notes of the first measures.

After a semester in Prague, where he studied philosophy and psychology, he turned to medicine, first in the German university of Dorpat under L. Stieda and E. von Bergmann. Later he went to Leipzig, following his father who had been called to the University there. His teachers included Wunderlich, Thiersch, Credé and Carl Ludwig. After graduation in 1875 he was appointed assistant in Wunderlich's clinic of internal diseases. The winter of 1877–78 was spent in Vienna where he was impressed by Meynert and Benedikt, and where he met Johannes Brahms. In 1878 he was appointed Privatdozent and came into close scientific and personal

Portrait from frontispiece in von Strümpell's *Aus dem Leben eines deutschen Klinikers.* Leipzig, Vogel, 1925.

contact with Wagner, Cohnheim, Weigert and Erb. His first course of lectures at the University on acute infectious diseases attracted just one student, who fled, however, at the teacher's approach, evidently frightened by the lonely atmosphere of the classroom. But what he published in this field[1] brought considerable attention. Even today we notice, for example, his observation of a cobbler's apprentice who, following an attack of encephalitis, had been deprived of sensitivity and had only one intact eye and ear; whenever the eye was covered and the ear blocked, he would promptly fall into deep sleep.

When Erb was appointed Ordinarius at Heidelberg in 1883, von Strümpell moved to that city to become Director of the Medizinische Poliklinik and Professor extraordinarius, with the brilliant P. J. Möbius as his assistant. Von Strümpell was later the chief of internal medicine in Erlangen (1886–1903), then in Breslau (1903–1909). After a short intermezzo in Vienna he was, after thirty years, back in Leipzig (in 1910) as successor to Heinrich Curschmann.

Von Strümpell won much of his fame and international reputation through his textbook of internal medicine, which first appeared in 1883; he worked on subsequent editions until the day he died. There were more than thirty editions, many translated into foreign languages. Being written almost entirely on the basis of personal observation, it was, indeed, a one-man performance. His lasting achievements were due to most careful observation and a critical and constructive analysis of the functional disorders resulting from lesions of the nervous system. He described several disease entities, among them hereditary spinal spastic paralysis[2] (later described in greater detail by Lorrain[3]—hence called Strümpell-Lorrain's disease). His name is linked with Westphal's as a pioneer in the study of pseudosclerosis. Alexander Karl Otto Westphal (1833–90), of Berlin, well known for his observation that patellar reflexes are lost in tabes dorsalis (1875),[4] proposed in 1883 the term "pseudosclerosis" for a condition characterized by tremor, difficulty in speech, and poverty of movement, but without nystagmus (hence not multiple sclerosis); he could find no changes in the brain and did not mention hepatic cirrhosis.[5] Similar cases were reported by von Strümpell in 1898[6] and 1899[7]; in the latter paper he coined the term "amyostatic symptom-complex" to include pseudosclerosis, paralysis agitans, etc. The term pseudosclerosis, born under an inauspicious star, took hold, however, as more cases were assembled, and finally the condition was established as an entity by Hösslin and Alzheimer.[8] In time, the gap that separated this disorder from Wilson's disease (1912) was bridged, mainly through the writings of W. Spielmeyer,[9] H. C. Hall,[10] and F. Lüthy.[11] Several reflexes bear his name.[12,13] Not only his clinical sense, but also his intense preoccupation with human affairs generally, enabled him to detect and describe the psychogenic element in nervous symptoms at a time when the organic approach was all-powerful among neurologists. Such was the background of his numerous contributions to the study of mental hygiene, alcoholism, education and, above all, traumatic neurosis, a term coined by him.

His personality as reflected in his autobiography and the testimony of his pupils, was that of a modest, kind, serene and optimistic person, a devoted physician, a faithful friend and colleague. In his search for knowledge, he had an undeniable trend toward the general; his analysis of neurotic behavior, for instance, seems cursory. In all matters of science and life he was a liberal with a healthy respect for tradition. His devotion to music brought him into personal contact with outstanding artists of his time. He believed teaching to be the most precious contribution man can make to his time.

GLEN ALLEN, VIRGINIA   WALTHER RIESE

References

[1]Deut. Arch. klin. Med., 1878, 22:321–361.   [2]Arch. Psychiat., Berlin, 1880, 10:676–717.   Ibid., 1886, 17:217–238. Deut. Zschr. Nervenh., 1893, 4:173–188.   [3]Contribution à l'étude de la paraplégie spasmodique familiale. Thèse, Steinheil, Paris, 1898.   [4]Arch. Psychiat., Berlin, 1875, 5:803–834.   [5]Ibid., 1883, 14:87–134 et seq.   [6]Deut. Zschr. Nervenh., 1898, 12:115–149.   [7]Ibid., 1899, 14:348–355. [8]Zschr. ges. Neur. Psychiat., 1912, 8:183–209.   [9]Ibid., 1920, 57:312–351.   [10]La dégénérescence hépatolenticulaire. Paris, Masson, 1921. [11]Deut. Zschr. Nervenh., 1931, 123:101–181.   [12]Neur. Cbl., 1899, 18:617–619.   [13]Deut. Zschr. Nervenh., 1899, 15:254–273.

References to Biography and Works: 1) *Aus dem Leben eines deutschen Klinikers. Erinnerungen und Beobachtungen.* Leipzig, Vogel, 1925 (von Strümpell). 2) Klin. Wschr., 1925, *4*:382–383 (His). 3) *Diseases of the basal ganglia and subthalamic nuclei.* New York, Oxford U. P., 1946 (Denny-Brown).

JULIUS WAGNER von JAUREGG (1857–1940)

*W*AGNER von JAUREGG was born in Wels, Austria. His father, a native of Austrian Silesia and state official, was born "Wagner," but on being ennobled in 1883 he added the name Ritter von Jauregg, an adaptation of his mother's maiden name, Jauernigg. Since the ennobling took place rather late in his father's life some of the early publications of young Julius were under the name "Julius Wagner." On the termination of World War I, ennobled Austrians were deprived by law of their titles, but Julius was granted permission to use the name Wagner-Jauregg.

Wagner von Jauregg, as we shall call him, studied medicine at the University of Vienna, where he received his doctorate in 1880. As a student, and after graduation, he worked in Stricker's Institute of Pathology in Vienna (1876–82). Being unsuccessful in his effort to obtain a position at one of the clinics of internal medicine, he accepted a post at the psychiatric clinic in Vienna with Leidesdorf even though, as he later confessed, he knew nothing about the subject. In 1885 he became Privatdozent. He moved to Graz in 1889 to head the department of psychiatry of the University, but upon Meynert's death in 1892 he returned to Vienna, taking charge of the Psychiatric Clinic of the Allgemeine Krankenhaus. In 1902 he succeeded Krafft-Ebing as professor of neurology and psychiatry.

One of his first publications dealt with cerebral symptoms following the resuscitation of strangulated individuals.[1] In this paper he expressed ideas which could easily have become the basis of "shock therapy": the use of large amounts of chemical and physical agents for the induction of violent metabolic changes in the brain in the treatment of psychoses.

Wagner von Jauregg's best-known contribution to medical science was the introduction of malarial fever for the treatment of

Portrait, courtesy of Prof. Dr. F. Jahnel, Munich, Germany.

general paresis. He conceived the idea that fever might be of therapeutic value in 1887, when he observed that "not rarely psychoses were healed through intercurrent infectious diseases," and he proposed that "one should intentionally imitate this experiment of nature."[2,3] He first attempted to induce fever with erysipelas, tuberculin, and typhoid vaccines. In 1917 he resorted to the inoculation of tertian malarial organisms into paretics, blood containing the organisms being taken by syringe from the cubital vein of a wounded and shell-shocked malarious soldier who had been admitted to Wagner von Jauregg's clinic. Of the nine patients thus treated, six were definitely benefited and three of them were still at their occupations four years later. For his discovery of the therapeutic value of malaria inoculation in the treatment of dementia paralytica, Wagner von Jauregg was awarded the Nobel Prize for Physiology and Medicine in 1927. He was the first psychiatrist to be thus honored, and to date the only one. Although malaria therapy is not used any longer, all the current modifications of nonspecific or stress therapy (including metrazol, insulin, and electroshock) are based upon Wagner von Jauregg's idea of fever therapy.

Wagner von Jauregg was also a pioneer in the prevention of cretinism, being the first to suggest obligatory addition of iodide to table salt for protection of the population in endemic goiter areas.[4] Many of his papers convey the concept that mental diseases are caused by somatic rather than by psychic disorders.[5] The effects of heredity in the field of neurology and psychiatry also commanded his most careful attention.[6] His last monograph, published posthumously by his son, Dr. Theodor Wagner-Jauregg, dealt with the duration of life as determined by heredity.[7] He was also a well-known figure as psychiatric expert in numerous famous forensic cases, and for many years played an important part in shaping legislation concerned with psychiatry. Many of his ideas have been worked out with the assistance of his pupils von Economo, Pilcz, Stransky, Bonvicini, Gerstmann, Kauders, and Poetzl, the last named of whom became his successor.

After recovering from typhoid fever in his childhood he became exceptionally strong of body, an athlete every inch of his five-foot-seven frame. During his student days he was stricken with tuberculosis, and not having the means to go to a sanatorium and being a person of great determination, he continued his studies, relaxing between classes in a nearby park until his hemoptyses ceased. Soon his health and strength were restored. His son, Theodor told us that the Professor had outperformed the champion weight lifter Jagendorfer by raising with his foot a 30 kilogram iron dumbbell from the floor to the seat of a chair. Like Cajal, he conquered tuberculosis, developed superb biceps, was addicted to chess. When the nights in Vienna were wintry he would often play chess with a friend by telephone, and when he had insomnia—he seldom slept more than five or six hours at night but always had a twenty-minute nap after lunch—he would usually get up and play a game with an imaginary opponent.

Wagner von Jauregg was a conservative. The style of his clothes never changed. It was because of his appearance and personal characteristics, his athletic body, his bushy eyebrows, his deep voice, his imperturbable calm, and his dry humor that Vienna society recognized him as one of its most conspicuous figures. On retirement from the University in 1928, he remained at his home in Vienna, continually putting his pen to its accustomed use. His almost completed autobiography was at his bedside when death came to him at the ripe age of eighty-three. Much of it has been used by Schönbauer and Jantsch in their book on Wagner von Jauregg and other celebrities of Vienna.

BERNHARD DATTNER

References

[1] Jahrb. Psychiat. Neur., Wien, 1889, *8:*313–332. [2] *Fieber und Infektionstherapie. Ausgewählte Beiträge 1887–1935.* Wien, Weidmann, 1936. [3] J. Nerv. Ment. Dis., 1922, *55:*369–375. [4] Jahrb. Psychiat. Neur., Wien, 1894, *12:*102–137 *et seq.* [5] *Ibid.,* 1892, *10:*180–198. [6] Wien. klin. Wschr., 1929, *42:*925–927 *et seq.* [7] *Über die menschliche Lebensdauer.* Innsbruck, Deut. Alpenverl., 1941.

References to Biography: 1) *Die medizinische Welt.* Wien, Urban & Schwarzenberg, 1944 (Schönbauer). 2) Wien. med. Wschr., 1928, *78:*892–894 (contains bibliography; Pilcz). 3) Arch. Neur. Psychiat., Chic., 1940, *44:*1319–1322 (Bruetsch). 4) *Julius Wagner-Jauregg. Lebenserinnerungen.* Wien, Springer, 1950 (Schönbauer and Jantsch).

CARL WERNICKE (1848–1904)

*W*ERNICKE was the son of a civil servant in Tarnowitz, a small town in Upper Silesia which at that time was German. After graduating in medicine at Breslau, he worked as assistant of Neumann in Breslau and of Westphal at the Charité in Berlin. Neumann gave him the chance to go to Vienna for six months, where he studied under Meynert. Years later, Meynert's

Portrait from *Mschr. Psychiat., 18:* i, 1905.

portrait was the only one which hung on the walls of the auditorium in Wernicke's clinic, and his name was one of the few ever mentioned by Wernicke in his lectures. From 1878–85 Wernicke carried on a private practice in nervous diseases in Berlin, and then gladly accepted a call to his alma mater at Breslau as Extraordinarius. In 1890 he received the Ordinariat in psychiatry. Years later (1904) he moved on to Halle in the same capacity, but had barely become well settled when he met with a fatal accident while riding a bicycle in the Thuringian forest.

Wernicke, in the current tradition of psychiatry (and neurology), began his scientific career in anatomy, in which he was influenced particularly by Meynert. An interesting product of his studies was his emphasis on Leuret and Gratiolet's three primordial convolutions ("Urwindungen"), forming concentric crescents around the Sylvian fissure in lower mammals; the first of them, already pointed out by Foville in 1844 as *circonvolution d'enceinte,* turned out to be, in man, the joined convolutions of Broca and Wernicke. The three-volume *Lehrbuch der Gehirnkrankheiten* (Kassel u. Berlin, Fischer) that came later (1881–83) is an astounding accomplishment for so young a man. It was the first comprehensive account of the achievements in cerebral localization up to that time. Particularly interesting was his postulation of the symptomatology resulting from thrombosis of the posterior inferior cerebellar artery, based on his anatomical investigations of the arterial supply of the medulla oblongata—an assumption confirmed in 1895 by Wallenberg.[1] Also he was the first to predict the occurrence of pseudo-ophthalmoplegia,[2] that rare apraxic disorder sometimes accompanying pseudobulbar palsy in which the patient is unable to move his eyes voluntarily on command or to fix his gaze on an object in the peripheral visual field, but can follow slowly moving objects; he reads a line by letting his eyes wander aimlessly until finally all the words are perceived. In his *Lehrbuch* (vol. 2, p. 229), too, he brought to light the clinical syndrome of "polio-encephalitis superior haemorrhagica," which has become "Wernicke's encephalopathy." Although he was aware of a "toxic" factor as etiological, years passed before it was realized that the basis of the disorder was a nutritional deficiency. Reported earlier than any of these was his observation in 1877 that lesions more or

less limited to the abducens nucleus result in paralysis of conjugate gaze to the side of the lesion.[3] He was thus the first to postulate a "center for conjugate gaze" in the dorsal pontile tegmentum.

The work for which Wernicke became internationally famous
earlier was a small book on aphasia,[4] published when he was twenty-six. In it he stressed the influence of Meynert and Broca. The
originality of this and subsequent works lies not in precise patho-
anatomical analysis so much as in his attempt to interpret the various aphasic symptom-complexes as consequences of impairment of
various elementary psychic processes which he localized in different parts of the cerebral cortex and their subcortical connections
(e.g., "Leitungsaphasie"). Yet in the course of these studies he did
describe, for the first time, sensory aphasia and its localization in
the posterior part of the first temporal convolution. The simple
graphic presentation of his ideas on the structure of language in
relation to the cerebral cortex was based on the reflex concept. It
became the mainspring of the many brain "diagrams" so characteristic of this era until they were criticized by Freud, Marie, Head
and Lashley[5] in a return to "holistic" views. On the other hand,
his ideas have been recently revived by Geschwind.[6]

For Wernicke, mental disorders were diseases of the brain, making the separation of psychiatry and neurology appear artificial:
"Geisteskrankheiten sind Gehirnkrankheiten." After he had had
the chance to observe psychiatric patients in greater number, he
published a system of psychiatry in three parts (1894). In this he
tried to apply the principles which had proved so successful in his
study of aphasia: the breakdown of, or *Sejunction* (dysjunction)
between, a man's concepts regarding his environment, his body, or
his self.[7] But it would be unfair to criticize him for having "localized" these concepts to bits of a cortical mosaic. Today one may
have a critical attitude toward his physiological concepts as the
basis for an understanding of the various psychiatric syndromes,
but he nevertheless will find them a source of stimulation; his
Krankenvorstellungen[8] is a good example. One may miss descriptions of clinical entities in Wernicke's psychiatry. This is not acci-
dental. Wernicke considered the time not yet ripe for distinction
of separate psychiatric diseases. Thus he was and remained always

an ardent adversary of Kraepelin, whose method he considered not sufficiently scientific.

Wernicke was a taciturn and reserved man, not easy to deal with. He was close to his older co-workers, particularly Ernst Storch, whom he held in high esteem. He had not much contact with his younger pupils, but his way of examining patients and his demonstrations were so lucid and stimulating that we who had the good fortune to attend his clinics were deeply influenced in our further consideration of neurological and psychiatric problems. We could never forget him. His influence can be seen in the work of a whole generation of German psychiatrists, and of aphasiologists generally.

KURT GOLDSTEIN

References

[1]Arch. Psychiat., Berlin, 1895, 27:504–540.   [2]Ibid., 1889, 20:243–275. [3]Ibid., 1877, 7:513–538.   [4]Der aphasische Symptomenkomplex. Breslau, Cohn, Weigert, 1874.   [5]Physiol. Rev., 1933, 13:1–42.   [6]Brain, 1965, 88:237–294, 585–644.   [7]Grundrisse der Psychiatrie, etc. Leipzig, Thieme, 1894.   [8]Krankenvorstellungen aus der psychiatrischen Klinik in Breslau. Breslau, Schletter, 1899–1900. (Also in Psychiat. Abh., Heft 10, p. 13–15.)

References to Biography: 1) Arch. Psychiat., Berlin, 1905, 40:1016– 1019 (Siemerling).   2) Med. Klin., 1905, 1:735–736 (Rothmann). 3) Mschr. Psychiat., 1905, 18:i–iv (Ziehen).   4) Münch. med. Wschr., 1905, 52:1402–1404 (Kleist).   5) Zschr. ges. Neur. Psychiat., 1939, 165:38–47 (Schröder).

KINNIER WILSON (1878–1937)

*K*INNIER WILSON was born at Cedarville, New Jersey. His father, the Rev. James Kinnier Wilson, was a native of Ireland. In Kinnier's early youth the Wilsons left for Scotland. Here he was brought up and educated. At the University of Edinburgh he obtained the B.M. in 1902, and in 1903 was awarded the

Samuel Alexander Kinnier Wilson

B.Sc. in physiology with honors. Shortly thereafter he was house physician at the Royal Edinburgh Infirmary under Byrom Bramwell, through whose influence he was directed toward neurology. He then studied in France for about a year under Pierre Marie and Babinski. Afterward, following a brief visit to Leipzig, he re-

Portrait, courtesy of Dr. Foster Kennedy, New York City.

turned to London. Here, in 1904, he began work as house physician at the National Hospital, Queen Square, then became registrar and pathologist, and on up to honorary physician until his death, by cancer, which occurred at the height of his powers. Most of his professional life was spent in London as one of the group of brilliant neurologists at the National Hospital, which included Gowers, Hughlings Jackson, Bastian, and Horsley.

Kinnier Wilson's written contributions were many, and all of them had remarkable distinction. He became established as a master in the field in 1912—he was then thirty-three—when he published, as his M.D. thesis, a monograph entitled, *Progressive lenticular degeneration: A familial nervous disease associated with cirrhosis of the liver*.[1,2] It earned him a gold medal from the University of Edinburgh. This work was the beginning of the modern study of the anatomy, functions and disorders of the "extrapyramidal system," as he called it. In this publication, Wilson made only passing reference to Westphal-Strümpell's pseudosclerosis, and when in later years, during lectures at "Queen Square," the matter would be brought up by a listener, this large man with "ham-like" hands would slowly roll up the the collar of his white coat, with infinite grace bringing the lapels together beneath his chin, cross his arms on his expansive chest—this series of movements was a mannerism of his—and with his resonant voice and penetrating eye would transfix his audience by telling them the story of the disorder, putting each character into proper perspective. Westphal and von Strümpell never fared too well! Nor did they in his *Neurology* (vol. 2, p. 807, 808), in which he pointed out that the essential aspects of *hepato,* as well as *lenticular,* were missed by these two writers. On occasion he also looked with disdain on the expression "abdominal Wilson" applied by certain clinicians to patients having liver cirrhosis as the only sign of Wilson's disease. Denny-Brown once asked Kinnier Wilson his opinion on the essential aspects of "hepatolenticular degeneration," whereupon Wilson eyed him with some circumspection, and, starting to walk away, asked, "Do you mean Kinnier Wilson's disease?" Wilson may not have looked kindly on subsequent developments: use of the term "Wilson-pseudosclerosis" as synonymous with "hepatolenticular degen-

eration"; hepatolenticular degeneration as having two components, "Wilson's disease," occurring in younger persons, "Westphal's pseudosclerosis" in the older.[3]

Kinnier Wilson's account of hepatolenticular degeneration was
only the beginning. The paper on *The old motor system and the
new*[4] was an example of his analytical powers; his Croonian Lectures in 1925 on *Disorders of motility and muscle tone* and his
Harveian Lecture in 1926 on *The epilepsies* had the same quality,
and his volume on *Modern problems in neurology* (London, Arnold, 1928) showed remarkable insight. However, his unfinished
two-volume *Neurology* (London, Arnold, 1940) with a style remi-
niscent of that of Samuel Johnson, was his magnum opus: it was
the greatest since Oppenheim's.

Other subjects were clarified by Kinnier Wilson: apraxia,[5]
aphasia,[6] epidemic encephalitis,[7,8] and tics and allied conditions.[9]
He reopened the field of pathological laughing and crying and
their counterpart, paralysis of emotional facial movements, suggesting that the supranuclear pathways for emotional facial movements ran in the part of the brain supplied by the posterior communicating artery.[10] Gowers[11] recognized the dissociation between
emotional and voluntary innervation in cerebral facial paresis,[11]
an observation expanded by Monrad-Krohn,[12] but it was Wilson
who set down the problem of expression in its then anatomical en-
tirety. Any syndrome originating from a lesion of the brain stem
fascinated him, and only exceptionally was he thwarted. At Bellevue Hospital in New York, while making rounds with Foster Kennedy, he spent three frustrating hours examining a patient with a
lateral medullary syndrome, in which the signs were inconsistent
with the anatomy of the region; to Kennedy's embarrassment, he
abruptly asked the patient, "Will you see to it that I get your
brain when you die?" No one dared deny the overpowering Kinnier Wilson a request, even this.

Kinnier Wilson will remain an important figure in science because of his original work on hepatolenticular degeneration and
because of the great textbook of neurology he wrote. By his hundreds of students he will be remembered as a great teacher in the
period between the wars, one who enriched "Queen Square's" fine
tradition with ingredients brought over from the Bicêtre and the

Salpêtrière. His commanding physique, his rich voice, his keen, quick analysis of a situation, his ironical humor, and his skill at histrionics, made of him a figure of Olympian stature.

MOFFETT FIELD, CALIFORNIA   WEBB HAYMAKER

References

[1]Brain, London, 1912, *34*:295–509.   [2]Lewandowsky, M. H., *Handbuch der Neurologie*. Berlin, 1910–19, *5*:951–990.   [3]N. Engl. J. Med., 1964, *270*:1149–1156 (Denny-Brown).   [4]Arch. Neur. Psychiat., Chic., 1924, *11*:385–404.   [5]Brain, London, 1908, *31*:164–216.   [6]*Aphasia*. London, Paul, Trench, Trubner, 1926.   [7]Lancet, London, 1931, *2*: 1143–1147.   [8]*Ibid.*, 1918, *2*:7–12 *et seq.*   [9]J. Neur. Psychiat., London, 1927, *8*:93–109.   [10]*Ibid.*, 1924, *4*:299–333.   [11]*A manual of diseases of the nervous system*. Vol. 2. London, Churchill, 1888, p. 72. [12]Brain, London, 1924, *47*:22–35.

References to Biography: 1) Arch. Neur. Psychiat., Chic., 1937, *38*:388–389 (Kennedy).   2) *Dictionary of national biography*. London, Oxford U. P., 1931–1940, p. 914–915 (Critchley).   3) J.A.M.A., 1968, *205*:871–872 (anon.).

VII
NEUROSURGEONS

HARVEY CUSHING (1869-1939)

*A*S IN his younger days he vowed he would, Cushing, perhaps more than anyone else, guided neurosurgery through its formative years and established it as one of the great specialties. In those early days the mortality rate in operated brain tumor was such that his colleagues at Johns Hopkins urged him to limit his efforts to the relief of intracranial pressure and not attempt removal. The turning point came in 1910, when Cushing was called upon to operate on Major General Leonard Wood, Chief of Staff of the U. S. Army, to remove a large meningioma; the General returned to his official duties within a month, served throughout World War I, and finally became Governor of the Philippines.

Harvey William Cushing was born in Cleveland, Ohio, a century ago, the fourth in line of pioneering doctors. His father was a stern Puritan, almost too stern toward his sons; his mother was even-tempered, kindly, gay, forceful. Living a few blocks away from the Cushings was Katharine Crowell, an attractive girl with a ready wit who seemed to understand Harvey better than he did himself. They were married in 1902 and had three daughters and two sons.

Harvey Cushing went through Yale College, Harvard Medical School, and an internship at Massachusetts General Hospital in Boston. During the next four years (1896–1900) he was resident, assistant, and finally associate, in surgery, under William Halsted at the Johns Hopkins Hospital. Baltimore, he wrote home soon after arrival, is "architecturally most monotonous. Rows of unbroken brick fronts are as alike as Streptococci. . . . The Hospital is a very sloppy place and the work of everyone most unsystematic, i.e., on the surgical side. Dr. Halsted has only operated once this month and rarely appears. Hope things clear up or I can't stand it." Cushing's relationship with Halsted had none of the warmth and affection that came to exist between Cushing and Osler. This friendship began during Cushing's bachelor days at Hopkins when

543

Portrait, courtesy of Yale University Art Gallery, gift of Mrs. Cushing; by John S. Sargent.

he lived next door to the Osler menage and enjoyed a "latch-key relationship" with the Osler family.

After four years of surgical training, Cushing set off for a *Wanderjahr* in England and the Continent (1900–01). In Berne he experimented on the interrelation between intracranial pressure and systolic blood pressure, under the supervision of Theodor Kocher, whose interests were then turning to neurological surgery. During a month in Liverpool, Cushing's surgical skills were utilized in Sherrington's celebrated experiments (with A. S. F. Grünbaum, later with Leyton) on the anthropoid motor cortex.

A self-assured and somewhat provincial young American when he arrived in Europe, Cushing returned to Johns Hopkins in 1901 with a deep respect for European culture and tradition and better equipped to pursue his course in neurological surgery. In his earlier Hopkins days he had devised an approach to the Gasserian ganglion, and he now began to develop technical procedures for minimizing hemorrhage in all operations involving the brain and spinal cord. But his chief interest during these years at Johns Hopkins was the surgical treatment of patients with pituitary tumor; his famous monograph, *The pituitary body and its disorders* (Philadelphia, Lippincott), was published during his closing days at Hopkins (1912).

In Boston, Cushing, then forty-three, became Moseley Professor of Surgery at Harvard and Surgeon-in-Chief at Peter Bent Brigham Hospital. Here he held sway for twenty years, retiring in 1932. His last seven years were spent at Yale as Sterling Professor of Neurology (1933–37) and Director of Studies in the History of Medicine. Death came in 1939 from coronary thrombosis.

At Harvard, Cushing's flow of scientific contributions brought him awards, honorary degrees, membership in foreign societies. Any one of several of his publications was a model of medical writing, each having been rewritten at least ten times, to the exasperation of his secretaries. His *Tumors of the nervus acusticus and syndromes of the cerebello-pontile angle* (Philadelphia, Saunders, 1917) can be considered a classic. *Meningiomas* (Springfield, Thomas, 1938) was the product of twenty-five years' work, with Louise Eisenhardt as collaborator. Whatever Cushing published in the area of neurosurgery of brain tumors was epoch-making, most of all his *Intracranial tumors* (Springfield, Thomas, 1932). Equally important were the histological studies on gliomas carried out largely by his assistant Percival Bailey—the first serious attempt to classify gliomatous tumors,[1] based on histogenesis of the central nervous system. The rigidity of their classification became loosened in 1949 through a paper by Kernohan and his colleagues at Mayo Clinic, who introduced the grading system.[2]

Less distinguished were Cushing's contributions in the area of endocrinology, particularly in regard to posterior pituitary secretion, and it is no secret that much of his pharmacological work was of the "Alice in Wonderland" kind. He drew certain unwarranted conclusions from his own experiments and allowed himself to be biased by reports in the literature that the posterior pituitary hormone entered the circulation only by way of the cerebrospinal fluid. Another stumbling block was his persistent belief that obesity following hypophysectomy was due to a deficiency of posterior pituitary hormone. When his assistants, Bailey and Bremer, showed in 1921[3] that a puncture wound of the hypothalamus of dogs, without injury to the pituitary, resulted in obesity, diabetes insipidus and genital atrophy, Cushing would not accept the interpretation that these disturbances were primarily hypothalamic and opposed publication; nor would he be swayed by Roussy and Camus' authoritative previous demonstration that hypothalamic injury led to these disturbances. Ten years later in his Lister Lectures he formally bowed to the Bailey-Bremer view, remarking that the discovery had produced "a veritable bouleversement of our cherished preconceptions."

Cushing's name has become the familiar eponym for an endocrine disease caused by an overfunctioning adrenal cortex. Cushing had originally called the condition "pituitary basophilism,"[4] believing that it was due to increased function of basophil tumor cells. Failure to establish an etiological role of the basophil cells in this condition made his term obsolete. "Cushing's disease" came to be the term used for his brilliant delineation of the clinical syndrome.

There were many facets to this man. He was slightly taller than average, handsome, wiry, animated, with sharply chiseled features and a compelling voice. There was a cigarette almost constantly between his fingers. As a gesture of his esteem he bestowed a plaster cast of his hands to the Royal College of Surgeons which is still on display there. To some he was the soul of kindness, a man of personal charm, an inspiring friend. He was a great favorite with his patients, gentle, very sympathetic, never in a hurry with them. To the student nurses in the operating room he could be a tyrant, often reducing them to tears; sometimes he apologized afterwards. To his house officers he was an irascible chief, a holy terror at the operating table, demanding perfection, exacting the best. Percival Bailey (1892–   )[5] reminisced at a party given him on the occasion of his own sixty-fifth birthday, at which a portrait of him was unveiled: "Whether it looks like me, you must judge. I look at myself only when shaving in the morning. I shall not be too much astonished because I remember the time when Mrs. Cushing took me to see Sargent's portrait of my master. I was speechless, stuttered something about its being a remarkable work of art and ducked out. Sargent had caught the mean look in the eyes and the distainful sneer on the lips which his pupils had seen so often when they had fallen short of his fastidious expectations. When he first saw it he is said to have remarked, 'Looks like I'd been weaned on a pickle.' "[6]

Cushing's stormy temperament often visited itself on journal editors, accusations flying that they had changed his English, his spelling, his punctuation, and generally wrecked his manuscript. When *Brain* published his Cavendish Lecture in 1922, a number of the figures were omitted and, according to Cushing, the others reproduced badly. Cushing chose to have the lecture privately reprinted in Boston. On another occasion it was Cushing who suffered a rebuff from an editor. He had accepted an invitation by the Medical Research Society of University College, London, to inaugurate a new Lectureship. Sir Thomas Lewis, editor of the journal in which the lecture (Hyperactivation of the neurohypophysis as the pathological basis of eclampsia and other hypertensive states) was to be published, turned it down. Eventually it found its way into the *American Journal of Pathology*. Cushing also had his troubles with the military. During World War I, when a Colonel with the Harvard Unit serving with the British Expeditional Forces, he offered harsh criticism of a British surgeon (in a letter to his wife intercepted by French censors and sent to the British government) and was kept in suspense by threat of court-martial. The matter was smoothed over by transferral from the offended British to an American command. Later the War Department awarded him the Distinguished Service Medal.

Only occasionally could this man meet his match. In the early Hopkins days while exchanging stories on Paris with William MacCallum, Cushing casually remarked: "Let us meet at the top of the Eiffel Tower ten years from now on July the fourth at 2:00 in the afternoon and continue this conversation." Without ever alluding again to their agreement, MacCallum went to Paris, reached the top of the Tower at the appointed time, to find no trace of Cushing. A guide suggested going up the iron staircase to the very top. A hundred rickety steps later, on reaching the small look-out he was greeted with: "Well, Willy, I had almost despaired of your getting here."

Cushing's gifts extended to his writing of medical history. *The life of Sir William Osler* (2 vol., Oxford, Clarendon, 1926) won for him a Pulitzer Prize. His short biographies of Vesalius and Galvani can also be considered masterpieces. To the Yale Medical Library he bequeathed his collection of rare medical historical books together with the royalties from his publications, to be used toward the maintenance of this library.

A high point in Cushing's career was his nomination to deliver the Cameron Prize Lectures in 1924. An account of the Lectures appearing in the London Hospital Gazette (1926) had this closing remark: "Here is the right kind of specialist fit to join such former Cameron Prizeman as Pasteur, Lister, Horsley. *Si sic omnes!*"

MOFFETT FIELD, CALIFORNIA   EVELYN ANDERSON
MOFFETT FIELD, CALIFORNIA   WEBB HAYMAKER

References

[1]*A classification of the tumors of the glioma group on a histogenetic basis with a correlated study of prognosis.* Philadelphia, Lippincott, 1926 (with Cushing).   [2]Proc. Staff Meeting, Mayo Clin., 1949, *24:* 71–75 (with Mahon, Svien and Adson).   [3]Arch. Int. Med., 1921, *28:* 773–803.   [4]Bull. Johns Hopkins Hosp., 1932, *50:*137–195.   [5]*Perspectives in biology and medicine.* Chicago, U. of Chicago P., 1967,

p. 540–558 (autobiography by Bailey).   [6]*The unveiling of the portrait of Dr. Percival Bailey.* Presented as a keepsake of the ceremony on October 5, 1957 (privately printed).

References to Biography and Works: 1) *Harvey Cushing: A biography.* Springfield, Thomas, 1946 (Fulton).   2) *Harvey Cushing: surgeon, author, artist.* New York, Schuman, 1950 (Thomson).   3) *Harvey Cushing's seventieth birthday party April 8, 1939.* Publ. by The Harvey Cushing Society. Springfield, Thomas, 1939 (Viets and others). 4) *Amid masters of twentieth century medicine. A panorama of persons and pictures.* Springfield, Thomas, 1958 (Rowntree).   5) *Neurosurgical classics.* New York, Johnson Reprint Corp., 1965; p. 28–60 et seq. (Wilkins).   6) *A bibliography of the writings of Harvey Cushing.* 2nd printing. Springfield, Thomas, 1940 (Harvey Cushing Society).   7) J. Neurosurg., 1969, *30*:365–376 (Cushing anecdotes, collected and edited by Heyl).   8) Canad. J. Surg., 1969, *12*:269–274 (Clein).

WALTER DANDY (1886–1946)

W ALTER EDWARD DANDY, who by his exemplary teaching did more to advance the technique of neurosurgery than any other pioneer in this specialty, was born in Sedalia, Missouri. After receiving the B.A. at the University of Missouri, he studied medicine at The Johns Hopkins School of Medicine, graduating in 1910. For the next few years he served as house officer in surgery at The Johns Hopkins Hospital. During this period he was a prolific writer, his most important articles being on the production and absorption of spinal fluid and the pathogenesis of hydrocephalus, written in collaboration with Blackfan.[1]

Dandy's greatest contribution to neurosurgery came in 1918, when he introduced diagnostic ventriculography and pneumoencephalography.[2]

Following these experimental studies, Dandy's interest turned more and more toward the development and perfection of neurosurgical techniques. In 1925 he described a posterior approach for the section of the trigeminal root to relieve tic douloureux. In his skillful hands this operation was easier, simpler, safer, and less likely to be complicated by keratitis and facial paralysis, than the

retrogasserian neurectomy introduced a quarter of a century earlier by Frazier and Spiller. In 1928 Dandy devised an operation for
the relief of Menière's syndrome,[3-5] a procedure suggested by Mills
twenty years previously,[6] i.e., differential section of the vestibular
portion of the 8th nerve.

    With his amazing skill he was able to perform difficult feats of
surgery with a relatively low mortality. Thus, he demonstrated
that intraventricular tumors could be safely removed without pro-

Portrait, courtesy of Dr. A. Earl Walker, Baltimore, Maryland.

ducing serious neurological deficits. He advocated the complete extirpation of acoustic tumors—a radical procedure previously considered entirely too hazardous. Then he showed that cerebral aneurysms were amenable to surgical attack. In the preface to his scholarly monograph on the subject,[7] he stated: "Intracranial arterial aneurysms, always considered rare and almost impossible both of diagnosis and of treatment, are now added to the lengthening line of lesions that are curable by surgery. This is another example of the results that can be attained from intensive cultivation of a seemingly barren field . . . they are now known to be quite common, and many at least are amenable to cure with a surprisingly low mortality."

Dandy's contributions to medical literature were diverse and many. Besides the numerous papers on hydrocephalus, trigeminal neuralgia, glossopharyngeal neuralgia, Menière's disease, and his monographs on intraventricular tumors, orbital tumors and vascular abnormalities of the brain, he wrote the section on the brain for Lewis's *System of surgery*.[8] This treatise on neurological surgery, beautifully illustrated as were all his papers, was a classical volume on technique in brain surgery.

Visiting surgeons and students from all parts of the world came to watch Dandy operate. In his intense preoccupation with his work he seemed to stand aloof from the rank and file of the growing specialty of neurosurgery. But the privileged friends who knew Dandy intimately were aware of his congenial home life, his personal interest in his pupils and associates, and his generous nature. His greatness, which did not make him lose the common touch, is well described in an editorial on his death in the *Baltimore Sun:* "The imaginative genius to conceive of new and startling techniques, courage to try them and skill—superb skill—to make them successful."

BALTIMORE, MARYLAND   A. EARL WALKER

References

[1]Am. J. Dis. Child., 1914, *8:*406–482.   [2]Ann. Surg., 1918, *68:*5–11.
[3]Arch. Surg., 1928, *16:*1127–1152.   [4]Arch. Otolar., Chic., 1934, *20:*1–30.   [5]J.A.M.A., *1937, 108:*931–937.   [6]Arch. Neur. Psychiat., Chic.,

1932, 28:1390–1394 (Frazier).   7*Intracranial arterial aneurysms.* Ithaca, N.Y., Comstock, 1944.   8Lewis (ed.), *System of surgery,* Hagerstown, Prior, 1945, 12:1–671.

References to Biography and Works: 1) Surgery, 1946, 19:577–579 et seq. (Blalock).   2) Ann. Surg., 1947, 126:113–115 (Firor).   3) Klin. Wschr., 1928, 7:169–173 et seq. (Wartenberg).   4) J. Neurosurg., 1951, 8:249–262 (Campbell).

CHARLES ELSBERG (1871–1948)

*C*HARLES ELSBERG was one of the American pioneers in neurosurgery. He belonged to the heroic age, which included Cushing and Frazier, when the foundation of neurosurgery was laid in America. All those pioneers were general surgeons first, who grew into neurosurgery as they literally created the discipline. While Elsberg did considerable work in the whole field of neurosurgery, his most important and lasting contributions were to surgery of the spinal cord.

Elsberg was born in New York City. Upon finishing his undergraduate studies at the College of the City of New York in 1890, he entered the College of Physicians and Surgeons of Columbia University and received his medical degree in 1893. Postgraduate studies were carried out with von Mikulicz-Radecki in Breslau. Upon returning from Europe he was appointed assistant pathologist to the Mount Sinai Hospital. He mothered his cultures of typhoid bacilli, often sleeping out the night next to the incubator, not without hazard, as on occasion the incubator exploded. His first paper (in 1895), on serum diagnosis of typhoid fever, followed Widal's by one year. Soon he became attached to the surgical staff, then (until 1929) served as attending surgeon. In 1909 he became neurosurgeon of the Neurological Institute of New York, which he helped found, and was associated with it until his retirement in 1937. It was during those years, both at Mount Sinai Hospital and at the Neurological Institute, that he made his chief contributions, starting with a paper on tumor in the cerebellopontine angle in 1904. The techniques he devised were always impeccable

Charles Albert Elsberg

As early as 1912 he reported on forty-three laminectomies.[1] In 1916 his imposing work on *Diagnosis and treatment of surgical diseases of the spinal cord and its membranes* (Philadelphia, Saunders) appeared, and in 1925 another on tumors of the spinal cord.[2] The latter was brought up-to-date and amplified in a volume on surgical diseases of the spinal cord,[3] which appeared in 1941. Elsberg was among many who published cases of spinal cord and posterior root involvement due to "extradural chondroma,"[4,5] but it remained for Mixter and Barr to demonstrate, in their classic paper,[6] that such "chrondromas" are, in actuality, prolapsed intervertebral discs. Elsberg did original investigation on vision, and

Portrait, courtesy of Dr. Israel S. Wechsler, New York City.

entered into a long series of studies on smell with Levy and Brewer in which new clinical tests of olfaction were devised; most of these papers appeared in the *Bulletin of the Neurological Institute of New York*. Localizing aspects of these tests were summarized in an article in 1937.[7] In all, Elsberg published about 150 papers dealing with refinements in diagnosis and treatment.

In addition to holding the position of chief of neurosurgery at the Mount Sinai Hospital and the Neurological Institute, he was professor of neurosurgery at the College of Physicians and Surgeons of Columbia University. Many honors came to him. He was vice-president of the New York Academy of Medicine from 1924 to 1928, and in 1947 was awarded an honorary degree by the College of the City of New York. In 1937 he was elected President of the American Neurological Association.

Elsberg was of a retiring disposition, shy, a "gentleman of the old school," possessing more than a touch of naiveté. He had few intimate friends. He plied his work with fierce intensity. He could habitually be seen leaving the Institute late in the afternoon, his briefcases crammed with things to do; being an early riser, he could do his thinking before the din of Manhattan started toward its daily crescendo. Drawings he made of operative procedures were superb, and he would invariably improve his artist's sketches. Somewhat late in life (1937) he married Jane Stewart, with whom he spent happily the years of retirement to his country home in Connecticut. It was here that he completed what his early morning hours in New York had failed to bring to fruition: his history of the Neurological Institute of New York.[8]

ISRAEL S. WECHSLER

References

[1]Ann. Surg., 1912, *55*:217–226.   [2]*Tumors of the spinal cord and the symptoms of irritation and compression of the spinal cord and nerve roots.* New York, Hoeber, 1925.   [3]*Surgical diseases of the spinal cord, membranes and nerve roots.* New York, Hoeber, 1941.   [4]Surg. Gyn. Obst., 1928, *46*:1–20.   [5]Bull. Neur. Inst. N.Y., 1931, *1*:350–388. [6]N. Engl. J. Med., 1934, *211*:210–214. *Neurosurgical classics.* New York, Johnson Reprint Corp., 1965, p. 495–503 (history of prolapsed disc, by Wilkins).   [7]Arch. Neur. Psychiat., Chic., 1937, *37*:223–236.   [8]*The*

story of a hospital; the Neurological Institute of New York. New York, Hoeber, 1944.

References to Biography and Works: 1) J. Mount Sinai Hosp., New York, 1948, *15*:266–269 (Cohen).   2) Walker, A. E. (ed.), *A history of neurological surgery.* Baltimore, Williams & Wilkins, 1951.

OTFRID FOERSTER (1873–1941)

FOERSTER, son of a professor of archeology, studied medicine at the Universities of Freiburg, Kiel and Breslau and received the M.D. in 1897 at Breslau. After two years' study under Dejerine in Paris and Frenkel in Switzerland, he returned to Breslau in 1899, where he remained the rest of his life, refusing calls to other universities. In 1922 he was made Ordinarius of neurology. He was head of the neurological department of a municipal hospital (Wenzel Hancke Krankenhaus), which in 1934 with the help of the Rockefeller Foundation was built into a neurological institute, and now bears his name. For nearly two years, with some interruptions, he was physician to Lenin at Moscow. A number of neurologists had been called to Moscow in consultation and ultimately Lenin became annoyed at seeing so many doctors around and ordered them all home. The Russian Government requested Foerster to stay on, and he remained for a year in an adjoining room, often having to watch Lenin through a keyhole. He was on hand at the autopsy in 1923.

Foerster, the clinical neurologist, began to practice neurosurgery at the age of forty. At heart he was a neurophysiological experimenter. He helped his patients, but they had to pay the price by being subjected to physiological experimentation. He wrote three hundred scientific works, all in longhand. Originality was their outstanding characteristic, with therapy their final goal. In the forty-four years of his scientific career, motility was his favorite subject, but he boldly attacked neurological problems on any level of the cerebrospinal axis. He was an enthusiastic therapist. His skeptical chief, Wernicke, once said of him: "I now have an assistant who makes lame walk and blind see."

Foerster wrote on tabes,[1] coordination,[2] associated movements,[3]

and spastic contractures.[4] Two operations bear his name: posterior rhizotomy in the treatment of spastic paralysis,[5] and posterior rhizotomy in the relief of gastric crises.[6,7] The idea that rhizotomy could be helpful in spastic paralysis (in children) came from his observation that patients with tabes dorsalis who develop hemiplegia do not become spastic. As to rhizotomy in treatment of pain, this had been successfully accomplished by Abbe[8] and by Bennett[9] (both in 1889); with respect to the lightning pains of tabes dor-

Portrait, courtesy of Yale Medical Library, New Haven, Connecticut. (Photographed in Breslau by R. U. Light, 1935.)

sales, Mingazzini[10] had suggested in 1899 that rhizotomy be done, but it remained for Küttner, in 1909[11] (at Foerster's request), to divide posterior roots Th 7–10 in eliminating gastric crises. In 1913 Foerster introduced anterolateral cordotomy[12] in Europe, some six months after the procedure had been carried out by Spiller and Martin in the U.S.A. In 1924, independently of Rosett, he reported on a hyperventilation test in epilepsy.[13] His work on extrapyramidal diseases[14] was a revealing masterpiece, as was his lecture on the dermatomes in man, delivered in 1933 in London.[15] The latter brought together his experience with posterior rhizotomy, in which he used Sherrington's method of "remaining sensibility" (of the single root left intact in the middle of a large number of divided contiguous roots). "All our present knowledge of the dermatomes in man," Foerster concluded, "has added little to the foundation . . . laid by Henry Head in 1892." In the *Handbuch der Neurologie* of Lewandowsky (1929), and that of Bumke and Foerster (1936),[16] Foerster brought out new concepts of motility and sensibility on the basis of his extensive experience in war neurosurgery. Decades will be needed to plumb the depths of this immense work. After Fedor Krause (1857–1937),[17] Foerster demonstrated what insights the systematic electrical investigation of the exposed, waking human brain will yield, and after Krause he was the first (with Altenburger) to produce an electrocorticogram in a case of brain tumor, with the use of Berger's new technique. Epilepsy, localization, muscle physiology, brain tumors, pain were his favorite subjects during his last years. All his life Foerster fought for the independence of neurology, and his resolution declaring that ". . . neurology represents an entirely independent specialty in medicine" was unanimously accepted by the First International Neurological Congress at Bern in 1931. To him fell the honor, during the meeting of the Second International Neurological Congress in London in 1935, of delivering the Lecture in commemoration of the 100th anniversary of the birth of Hughlings Jackson, and on this occasion he received the Hughlings Jackson Memorial Medal. His famous cytoarchitectonic map of the human cerebral cortex appeared in an article on *The motor cortex in man in the light of Hughlings Jackson's doctrines,* published in 1936.[18]

This was a man! At neurological meetings which he brilliantly addressed as chairman, everyone could feel his the strongest personality among them, the undisputed master, the most revered and most admired. In the twenties I had the opportunity of seeing the leading neurologists and neurosurgeons of Europe at work. In depth and breadth of knowledge, in the wide range of investigative work, in the happy blending of physiology with neurology and neurosurgery, of theory with practice, in his enthusiastic, stimulating drive, Foerster stood out as the foremost. On a visit to Boston he was invited by Harvey Cushing to act as surgeon-in-chief *pro tem*. The phrenetic tempo of his work was too much even for the staff of the Peter Bent Brigham Hospital.

He had one goal, one purpose: the search for helpful knowledge. This sacred fire burned within him and devoured him! Much of his experimentation was carried on at his own expense (though he was not wealthy), until aid came from the Rockefeller Foundation in 1930. He knew no holidays, no recreation, no regular vacations. He was a frail, sick man. He suffered from chronic gastrointestinal disturbances, from thromboangiitis obliterans, arteriosclerosis, tuberculosis, chronic nicotinism. But he was merciless to himself. His implacable spirit extracted the maximum from his delicate, fragile body. He completely disregarded physical pain. Once he said of himself that through year-long exercises he had learned " . . . to influence the intensity of bodily pain to complete disappearance." Few mortals have put as much enthusiasm, devotion and self-sacrifice into their research work as did Otfrid Foerster.

ROBERT WARTENBERG

References

[1]Deut. Aerzte Ztg., 1901, 7:101–102.   [2]*Die Physiologie und Pathologie der Coordination.* Jena, Fischer, 1902.   [3]*Die Mitbewegungen bei Gesunden,* etc. Jena, Fischer, 1904.   [4]*Die Kontrakturen bei den Erkrankungen der Pyramidenbahn.* Berlin, Karger, 1906.   [5]Zschr. orthop. Chir., 1908, 22:203–223.   [6]Beitr. klin. Chir., 1909, 63:245–256.   [7]Tr. Internat. Cong. Med. 1913. Sub-sect. VII (a) Orthopaedics, pt. 2. London, 1914, p. 7–16.   [8]Med. Rec., N.Y., 1889, 35:149–152.   [9]Med.-Chir. Tr., London, 1889, 72:329–348.   [10]Policlinico, Sez.

prat., 1899, 5:750–751. [11]Beitr. klin. Chir., 1909, 63:245–256 (with Foerster). [12]Berl. klin. Wschr., 1913, 50:1499–1502. [13]Deut. Zschr. Nervenh., 1924, 83:347–356. [14]Zschr. ges. Neur. Psychiat., 1921, 73:1–169. [15]Brain, London, 1933, 56:1–39. [16]*Die Leitungsbahnen des Schmerzgefühls und die chirurgische Behandlung der Schmerzzustände.* Berlin, Urban & Schwarzenberg, 1927. [17]*Chirurgie des Gehirns und Rückenmarkes nach eigenen Erfahrungen.* Vol. 2. Berlin, Urban & Schwarzenberg, 1908–1911, p. 185, *et seq.* (Engl. transl. by Haubold and Thorek, London, Lewis, 1910). [18]Brain, London, 1936, 59:135–159 (the Ninth Hughlings Jackson Lecture).

References to Biography: 1) J. Neurophysiol., 1942, 5:1–17 (contains bibliography). 2) Deut. Zschr. Nervenh., 1941, 153:1–23 (von Weizsäcker). 3) Arch. Psychiat., Berlin, 1941, 114:1–16 (contains bibliography; Gagel). 4) J. neurol. Sci., Amst., 1968, 6:384–385 (Zülch).

CHARLES HARRISON FRAZIER (1870–1936)

*F*RAZIER was one of the small group of pioneers who created neurosurgery as a new branch of surgery. As surgeon, he was an autodidact in the best tradition of his time.

After internships at the University of Pennsylvania Hospital and the Episcopal Hospital, he went to Europe for study in surgery, neurology and pathology (1895). He often said that the men to whom he owed the most were Ernst von Bergmann (1836–1907) and Rudolf Virchow (1821–1902). Young Frazier did well to seek out von Bergmann, who at that time dominated the surgical field in Berlin. As veteran of three wars including the Russo-Turkish War (in which he served on the Russian side), von Bergmann had mastered the scalpel and had instituted an aseptic operative ritual as modern as that of today. Through his association with this great surgeon, Frazier was well equipped when he returned to the University of Pennsylvania Hospital in his native Philadelphia.

Frazier's academic career began in 1896 as instructor in surgical pathology. In 1901 he was elected clinical professor of surgery, a position he held with distinction for some fifteen years. His decision in 1919 to devote himself almost exclusively to neurosurgery was influenced by his work during World War I on wounded sent

Charles Harrison Frazier

from France. A report on five hundred cases of peripheral nerve injury and reconstruction and two hundred cases of gunshot wounds of the head gives testimony of the direction his interests in surgery had taken. In 1922 he was appointed John Rhea Barton professor of surgery and head of the surgical department of the Hospital of the University of Pennsylvania. Here his interest in the surgical approach to intracranial and intraspinal tumors was stimulated by Charles K. Mills (1845–1931) and William G. Spiller (1863–1940), successive professors of neurology at the University of Pennsylvania.

Portrait, courtesy of Dr. F. H. Lewey, Philadelphia, Pennsylvania.

His close cooperation with Spiller had much to do with the latter's success. It was Frazier's merit to make workable Spiller's suggestions. Others had cured trigeminal neuralgia by operation before him: Victor Horsley in 1891, F. Hartley in 1892, and especially Fedor Krause (1856–1937), also in 1892.[1] Not until Frazier had introduced subtotal retrogasserian neurotomy in 1901[2] did the operation change from a serious procedure, endangering life and eye, to a safer intervention. In the seven hundred or more cases of tic douloureux operated on by Frazier, the mortality rate was less than 0.5 per cent, keratitis was minimal, and motor function undisturbed. Always ready to give credit where it was due, Frazier often referred to retrogasserian neurotomy as "Spiller's operation."

The second great success of the Spiller and Frazier collaboration was the development of Spiller's idea to cure pain by section of the anterolateral column of the spinal cord. At Spiller's suggestion, E. Martin had performed this operation in 1911,[3] after Schüller's *Chordotomie* in the monkey the previous year in Vienna.[4] Three years later, Frazier devised a more practicable operative technique, and thus placed cordotomy among the routine surgical procedures. Although Frazier's name is most closely linked with trigeminal neuralgia and cordotomy, his and his associates' fundamental contributions to the problems of pituitary and parasellar tumors and of neoplasms of the sphenoidal ridge should not be overlooked.

Frazier was sturdily built, had a ruddy complexion and piercing, keen, blue-grey eyes, topped by a head of hair which was always as orderly as he was precise. He had an intuitive, commanding temperament, made all the more impressive by his rich resounding voice. He began many an operation with a group of assisting residents and interns, only to finish with an operating nurse as his sole aid. The great demands which he made on his co-workers, as on himself, gave him a strictness which sometimes seemed to approach harshness, but this appearance was wholly superficial. Fundamentally, he was a gentleman, gracious, righteous, and helpful. He seldom talked to the gallery during an operation, but after operations, while he swept the floor of the operating room with a kitchen broom—to relax his shoulder muscles (this was in the early 1930's)—his discourses always captivated his audience. Six of his assistants came to occupy important positions in neurosurgery —Grant became his successor at the University of Pennsylvania,

Monroe went to Harvard, Gardner to Western Reserve, Watts to George Washington University, Kwan to Union Medical College in Peking, and Groff to the Graduate School of Medicine in Philadelphia. Others included Max Peet of the University of Michigan and Alfred W. Adson of the Mayo Clinic. It was natural that these and many other associates of Frazier should join in 1935—the sixty-fifth anniversary of his birth—to present him with a *Festschrift*.[5]

F. H. LEWEY

References

[1]In *A History of Neurological Surgery* (Walker). Baltimore, Williams & Wilkins, 1951, p. 314; 2d ed., 1967, p. 248–249 (biography of Krause, by Brown).   [2]U. of Pa. Med. Bull., 1901, *14*:341–352 (with Spiller). [3]J.A.M.A., 1912, *58*:1489–1490 (Spiller and Martin).   [4]Wien. med. Wschr., 1910, *60*:2292–2295.   [5]Ann. Surg., 1935, *1*:1–390.

References to Biography: 1) Ann. Surg., 1937, *105*:638–640 (Grant). 2) *Ibid.*, 1935, *1*:vii–viii (Stengel).   3) Lancet, London, 1936, 2:291–292 (Harris).

VICTOR HORSLEY (1857–1916)

V ICTOR ALEXANDER HADEN HORSLEY, an early pioneer in neurosurgery, was born in Kensington into a prominent family noted for its accomplishments in music, art and surgery. In childhood, Victor, as the result of his father's persistence, decided to be a surgeon. In preparation for this profession, he started very early to investigate the interior of birds and animals. His school life was not particularly noteworthy, but at the University of London, where he matriculated in medicine in 1873, his abilities were such that he received a gold medal in anatomy. In 1880 he passed his qualifying examination at the Royal College of Surgeons and a year later received the B.M. and B.S. Meanwhile he had become closely associated with Bastian, and with him published in 1880 his first work, which dealt with arrested develop-

ment of the left upper limb in the presence of a parietal lobe defect.

During his early postgraduate years, Horsley's interests were varied and included such subjects as myxedema and cretinism[1] and the preventive treatment of rabies. His interests became firmly fixed on the nervous system only after he joined Schäfer at University College and Beevor at the Brown Institution in research on the functions of the cerebral cortex. With a view to extending the

Portrait, courtesy of Dr. Foster Kennedy, New York City.

work of Fritsch and Hitzig and Ferrier, Horsley analyzed in minute detail by means of faradic stimulation the motor responses of the cerebral cortex, internal capsule and spinal cord of the higher primates.[2] His work in this field, carried out in association with Schäfer, Beevor, Semon, Spencer and Gotch over a period of seven years, is to be counted among the remarkable achievements of British neurophysiology. It culminated in his view,[3] now very modern, that not only the corticospinal system but also what recently has been called the "cortically originating extrapyramidal system (COEPS)" is indispensable for the performance of voluntary movement. Moreover, he had the distinction of being the first to achieve success in hypophysectomy, two dogs surviving five and six months after this operation,[4] but his data were exceedingly scant. Marinesco's work in this field in 1892[5] was more carefully documented, but his animals survived only as long as eighteen days. It was not until 1912 that Aschner,[6] by perfecting the operation so as to avoid damaging the hypothalamus, was able to keep hypophysectomized dogs alive indefinitely.

In 1886—he was then twenty-nine—Horsley was appointed surgeon to the National Hospital, Queen Square, London, a position for which his physiological studies had admirably prepared him. Until that time brain surgery had been confined to traumatic injuries, in which the site of the brain damage was known by the location of the scalp laceration or bruise. With the new knowledge of cerebral localization it was possible to make a topical diagnosis on the basis of clinical examination. Two years before Horsley's appointment, the first successful removal of a brain tumor had been accomplished by Godlee, although equal credit should be given Bennett, who localized the tumor and persuaded Godlee to operate. Much the same might be said of the first successful removal of an intraspinal tumor. As Critchley relates, Gowers had referred to Horsley an army officer of forty-five whose legs had become spastic. The diagnosis was spinal tumor. Horsley was invited by Gowers to operate, and on June 9, 1887, in the theatre at "Queen Square," the task was undertaken by Horsley with the assistance of Stedman and Ballance. The lesion was not found at the predicted level, and several higher laminae had to be removed before an encapsulated mass was exposed. The tumor proved to be a benign "fibromyxoma" of the fourth thoracic root.[7] A year later "the patient was working sixteen hours a day, which entailed much standing and walking."

In 1888 Horsley described decompressive procedures for the relief of inoperable brain tumors. In 1890, at the International Medical Congress in Berlin, he discussed the forty-four operations he had performed upon the brain. In this series there had been ten deaths, most of which were in cases of malignant glioma. At a time when brain operations were usually fatal and speed was a prime factor in surgery, this astonishing record is a tribute to Horsley's manual dexterity. In 1908 he aided R. H. Clarke, physiologist at St. George's Hospital in London, in building a stereotaxic instrument for the study of cerebral function.[8] A brief account of the historical aspects of the Horsley-Clarke instrument is to be found in a volume by Rasmussen.[9]

In the early 1900's Horsley's interests turned to medical politics, a field in which his enthusiastic and energetic spirit fared not too well. He became an ardent, almost fanatic crusader for medical, social, and educational reforms. His rigid views on the use of alcoholic beverages, propounded at both temperance and medical meetings, alienated some of his friends. For his leadership in medical administration and for his professional accomplishments, Horsley was knighted in 1902. Although he was fifty-seven years of age at the outbreak of World War I, he requested active duty and was given an assignment in charge of a surgical service of a General Hospital. Later he was made consultant to the Mediterranean Expeditionary Force. It was in the discharge of these duties that he met his death at Amara, in Mesopotamia, presumably of heat stroke.

BALTIMORE, MARYLAND   A. EARL WALKER

References

[1]Brit. Med. J., 1885, 1:111–115.   [2]Philos. Trans. Roy. Soc. London, 1888, ser. B., 179:1–45 (with Schäfer).   [3]Brit. Med. J., 1909, 2:125–132.   [4]Lancet, London, 1886, 1:3–5.   [5]C. rend. Soc. biol., Paris, 1892, 4:509–510.   [6]Virchows Arch., 1912, 146:1–146.   [7]Brit. Med. J., 1885, 1:988–989.   [8]Med-Chir. Trans., 1888, n.s., 71:377–430

(with Gowers).   [9]Brain, London, 1908, *31*:45–124.   [10]*Some trends in neuroanatomy*. Dubuque, Iowa, Brown, 1947 (Rasmussen).

References to Biography and Works: 1) *Sir Victor Horsley; a study of his life and work*. London, Constable, 1919 (Paget).   2) *The life of Sir William Osler*. Vol. 2. Oxford, Clarendon, 1925 (Cushing); p. 677. 3) Rev. Neur. Psychiat., Edinb., 1916, *14*:583–588 (Russell).   4) Penfield (ed.), *Neurological biographies and addresses*. London, Oxford U. P., 1936 (Evans), p. 65–70.   5) *Sir Williams Gowers 1845–1915. A biographical appreciation*. London, Heinemann, 1949, p. 46 (Critchley).   6) *The citizen surgeon. A biography of Sir Victor Horsley, F.R.S., F.R.C.S. 1857–1916*. London, Dawnay, 1966 (Lyons).

CLOVIS VINCENT (1879–1947)

*C*LOVIS VINCENT, who established modern neurological surgery in France, was born in Ingré (Loiret), the son and grandson of physicians. At the lycée he was something of a problem, but at examinations he sparkled; his grasp on every subject was a great surprise to his teachers. He studied medicine in Paris and found Souques his favorite clinical neurologist. Examined for an externeship (1900), he showed up in a thick woolen sweater and shorts—his bicycling outfit; no wonder they turned him away. A little later, however, he was externe des hôpitaux, under Babinski. As interne at the Salpêtrière (starting in 1905) he indicated to Widal his desire to spend a year with him, and got the reply: "Not until you receive the gold medal." He did (the medal is earned by the most outstanding interne in Paris), and again met Widal. "You want the position?" Vincent replied: "Oh, no. They say you are too much of a rabbit doctor. I want to get a job in which I can learn something of general medicine; the neurologists just talk and do nothing." And so he settled down with the internist, Chauffard, who time and again was startled by the massive Vincent, unpredictable in his sayings, clumsy in his doings. (His movements so relaxed as to suggest athetosis, his gait that of a sailor, his flushed face and tousled hair—they made some taxi drivers expect the worst.)

In 1913 he became Babinski's assistant at the Pitié, but the association was interrupted by World War I when Vincent joined the

Army. Vincent, trained along with the world champion Georges Carpentier, was skilled in "la boxe." It was essential for a neurosurgeon, he thought, and it served him well during the war. On one occasion he broke the jaw of a soldier, a Zuave. For simulating paraplegia a needle had been plunged into the man's buttock (*torpillage*—"torpedoing"—as the soldiers called it). Immediately cured, the Zuave struck Vincent a blow in the face. Vincent retaliated with an uppercut, *et voilà*. A friend of the victim, Private Deschamps, sued the Government, naming Vincent as co-defen-

Portrait, courtesy of Prof. Ludo van Bogaert, Antwerp, Belgium.

dant. In this *cause célèbre,* known as "le procès de Tours," famous medical authorities testified on Vincent's behalf: Huet, Babinski, Teissier. Vincent and *torpillage* were vindicated. But tired of the routine in the hospital at Tours, Vincent requested service as a commando at the front. As regimental doctor he received decorations of the highest order.

In the years with Babinski after the war, Vincent investigated paraplegia-in-flexion of cerebral origin,[1] hysteria, chronic syphilitic meningitis, epidemic encephalitis, and spinal compression. At Babinski's instigation, Vincent visited the United States for two months in 1927, with Puech and David, his assistants, to study the techniques of Harvey Cushing and Percival Bailey. Two years later, at the age of fifty, he performed his first operation, at the Pitié, extirpating a hydatid cyst from the fissure of Sylvius. He transformed the neurological wards at the Pitié into neurosurgical ones. Cushing watched Vincent operate in 1933, and later remarked: "You have in Paris someone who without doubt is the world's best neurosurgeon." Assistance in the operating room was excellent; not having been provided with the wherewithal to hire nurses (actually he had to dig into his own pocket to keep indigent patients in his private clinic), Vincent had pressed his wife and his housekeeper into service. Later, with the aid of the Rockefeller Foundation, a chair of neurosurgery was established for him at the Faculté de Médecine.

Vincent had to his credit about 150 publications. Of particular importance was his observation that temporal lobe herniation resulting from expanding cerebral tumor led to brain stem compression.[2] He developed the technique for totally extirpating encapsulated cerebral abscess and cerebellar tuberculoma.[3] One of his earliest contributions to neurosurgery (in collaboration with Lardennois) was the use of periarterial sympathectomy for the relief of post-amputation reflex disturbances and disorders of sensation.[4] He introduced intrathecal air therapy for the sequelae of head injury,[5] wrote on frontal lobe function[6] and on the diagnosis of tumors of the frontal lobes,[7] and provided a key paper on Hallervorden-Spatz's disease (in collaboration with van Bogaert).[8]

Vincent was usually on the wards by five in the morning. To warm up, he would box—often with de Martel before they became estranged. Some weekends Vincent would head for his lodge, where his forty hounds awaited him, but most Sunday mornings were devoted to ward rounds. Throughout the German occupation he worked harder than ever. He lived in the hospital, fought for his patients and for his work, struggling almost single-handed to keep his clinic open. Köbcke served secretly as a courier to bring him instruments from Sweden, donations from Olivecrona. He was worn out when the war ended.

Babinski, on his deathbed, was asked what would remain after his death. He replied: "I have shown the way to de Martel and Vincent."

SAN FRANCISCO, CALIFORNIA   WALTER F. SCHALLER
SAN FRANCISCO, CALIFORNIA   LEON J. WHITSELL

References

[1]Rev. neur., Paris, 1925, *1*:337–348 (with Krebs and Chavany). [2]*Ibid.*, 1936, *65*:536–545 (with David and Thiébaut). [3]Schweiz. med. Wschr., 1938, *68*:101–105. [4]Rev. neur., Paris, 1921, *1*:748–752. [5]*Ibid.*, 1931, *1*:651–655 (with Schiff, Puech and David). [6]Deut. med. Wschr., 1936, *62*:41–45. [7]Rev. neur., Paris, 1928, *1*:801–824. [8]*Ibid.*, 1936, *65*:921–959.

References to Biography: 1) J. Neurosurg., 1945, *2*:530–534 (Rabinovitch). 2) Arch. Neur. Psychiat., Chic., 1949, *61*:74–78 (Bailey). 3) Arq. neuropsiquiat., San Paulo, 1948, *6*:73–81 (contains bibliography; Gama). 4) Kolle (ed.), *Grosse Nervenärzte*, vol. 2, p. 208–214 (with partial bibliography; Köbcke). 5) Walker (ed.), *A history of neurological surgery*. Baltimore, Williams & Wilkins, 1951, p. 134–135 (Stern).

VIII
A NEUROHISTORIAN

JULES SOURY (1842–1915)

$\mathscr{A}$T THE TURN of the last century Carré and Naud, medical publishers in Paris, came out with a book the like of which had not been seen before. With its 1865 pages and weighing nearly nine pounds, it was entirely devoted to the history of a medical field which itself was still struggling for recognition as a specialty. (To this day people with an average education, such as members of a jury, have to be told what neurology is, what a neurologist does.) The book was so remarkable because it did not even claim to deal with more salable subjects such as diagnosis, prognosis, and treatment of nervous disease. No, it simply gave an extremely detailed up-to-date account of what from the beginning of recorded Western history learned men had thought and written about the nervous system. Together with that past, it represented the explosion of knowledge occurring since the second half of the nineteenth century; it also reflected the interest that professional people and the intelligensia as a whole were taking in the subject. That thrilling subject, of course, was the relationship between the mind and the brain. The marvels of cortical localization which the book extolled were still news. Its title in translation (never undertaken) was *The central nervous system. Structure and functions. A critical history of theories and doctrines.*[1] It was bought or borrowed by some of those whom the author's lectures at the Sorbonne had fascinated, or who had heard of that fascination.

Jules Soury was the talk of the literary salons. Anatole France and other prominent "students" wrote glowing descriptions of his magic touch, the way he had of drawing diagrams on the blackboard, or of dissecting the brain with that grace and skill of his tiny hands. One might think Soury was a dazzling but superficial society doctor, or some sort of charlatan. Like any inference drawn from any bit of information about him, this is likely to be wrong. For Jules Soury was paradox personified.

To start with, he was a doctor of letters, not medicine, but did take up the study of the nervous system at the age of twenty-three.

573

Originally a scholar in comparative religion, philosophy and anthropology, with many works in those fields to his credit, a friend also and collaborator of the renowned Ernest Renan, he had walked into the Salpêtrière and experienced a revelation when he saw the work in progress there. Paul Bert, the great physiologist, successor to Claude Bernard, and minister of education, had bestowed a professorship on Soury who just had lost out against some political bigwigs in a concours for a professorship in history of religion at the Collège de France.

The paradox began to show when Jules was a little boy. He was born almost in the shadow of Notre Dame and the old Hôtel-Dieu hospital, in the street symbolizing poverty in Paris, Rue Saint Julien le Pauvre. Sent to school at the age of six, he refused to learn anything whatsoever. His mother, whom he adored and from whom he was not separated for more than a few days at any time until she died at the age of eighty-six, on whom he lavished gifts as on a mistress, whom he used to entertain with a magic lantern and a barrel organ when he himself was grown up, was illiterate. His father and maternal grandfather were glassblowers. Given his total failure and his refusal to learn, he was sent, still a child, to another member of the glassblower trade. Again, instead of applying himself to what he was expected to do, he began to study voraciously on his own. Finally he managed to earn enough to put himself through school and to reach those heights of scholarship that made him the first and to this day the greatest and most voluminous writer on the history of neurology.

To us the whole volume has become history, including the two-thirds that dealt with the contemporary scene. The rest—the first 600 odd pages—traces the development of neurology from Alcmeon and the Ebers papyrus to Soury's day. Like every "bible," every encyclopedia, Soury has his blind spots. The period and the national background of the book precluded to some extent what neurologists today would be looking for with equal eagerness: motor mechanisms, their disorders, and their history. Despite all his admirable awareness of the shifting interests, the perpetual revolution in science, Soury was naturally not conditioned, as we primarily are, for seeing in the brain an organ of control for action. He does, for instance, devote considerable space to the origins of the reflex concept, yet experimental neurology, the basal ganglia, the spinal cord, and their history, left him rather cold: they were not obviously concerned with the mind. His bibliography and index also are not tailored after our efficient fashion.

While the elegance, solidity, and thoroughness of his work have made his fame among historians, the oddity of his person has marked him as a psychiatric case-history. His mother-fixation à la Flaubert, the compulsions of an outrageous original à la Toulouse-Lautrec and Eric Satie, stamp him as a cracked genius, the typical child of the fin de siècle. Soury would never sleep in a bed or eat at a table other than his own. This created some problems on speaking engagements involving conviviality, especially when he was out of town. On such occasions he was a mere spectator at a banquet, or in a hotel room where he would spend the night sitting on a chair. After his mother's death he would eat on a bench in the Jardin du Luxembourg. He was an Anti-Dreyfusard and member of the extreme right-wing Action Française—he hated the Jews; but then he also hated women, and life in general. He was tiny, totally bald, childfaced, mousy. His only photograph went into his mother's grave. Toward religion he was unpredictable. A fervent materialist, he loved the inside of churches for their quiet invitation to pray and meditate. Once when a sacristan asked him to leave, as the doors were about to be closed, he is supposed to have risen from his knees and growled: "God-damn your sh . . , man, don't you see I'm praying to the Holy Virgin?" "Love," he said on one occasion, "dazzles people into accomplishing its aim, which is permanence of species, in other words, eternity of pain." Notwithstanding his reflection that "Not to be is a great boon; not to have been would have been even better," he lived to be seventy-five. Whatever our feelings about his person, they will hardly exclude sympathy. As to the historian, directly or indirectly, all students of the neurological past are deeply indebted to him.

SAN FRANCISCO, CALIFORNIA   FRANCIS SCHILLER

Reference

[1] *Le système nerveux central, structure et fonctions: histoire critique des théories et des doctrines.* Paris, Carré et Naud, 1899.

Reference to Biography and Bibliography of Soury: Paris Méd., 1927, *66:* 30–35 (Mousson-Lanauze).

IX

OTHER SOURCES FOR THE HISTORY OF NEUROLOGY

$\mathcal{B}$EFORE Soury's time, and since, other histories have appeared, but by Soury's standard[1] they are only partial ones. In German Max Neuburger's account of neurological experimentation up to Flourens was published in 1897,[2] two years before Soury's.[1] Friedrich Burdach wrote, in 1819–26, the historical portion of his "Structure and life of the brain" as they were conceived before Flourens' day.[3] Kolle, in our time, has edited three volumes of short biographies of the "great doctors" of the nervous system.[4] In English we now have *Garrison's history of neurology* by McHenry[5] (a revision and enlargement of his hurried introduction to Dana's textbook of neurology[6]) and Wechsler's at the end of his textbook[7]; A. T. Rasmussen's work on trends in neuroanatomy[8]; Lewellys Barker's unequalled treatise on neuroanatomy up until 1909[9]; Walther Riese's pointed account of mechanistic versus vitalistic views[10]; John Fulton's work[11]; and Mary Brazier's two on physiology[12]; Owsei Temkin's on the "falling sickness"[13]; Fearing's[14] and Liddell's[15] on reflexes; Keele's on pain pathways[16]; Denny-Brown's on extrapyramidal disorders[17]; Earl Walker's on neurosurgery[18]; William Gibson's[19] in a wide survey of medical history; Robert Wilkins's in his *Neurosurgical classics*[20]; and finally, in 1968, Clarke and O'Malley's beautifully documented and annotated treatise on neuroanatomy.[21]

Recently, Brody and Wilkins have reproduced the contributions of some of the Founders, in translation where necessary, through current issues of the *Archives of Neurology,* and have provided succinct commentaries to a number of the masterpieces. Key articles dealt with thus far include those of Alzheimer, Argyll Robertson, Adie, Babinski, Brown-Séquard, Brudzinski, Charcot, Dejerine, Duchenne, von Economo, Erb, Horner, Guillain, Ramsay Hunt, Huntington, Kernig, Lasègue, Lhermitte, Little, Marie, Romberg, Sachs, and Wernicke.

References

[2]*Die historische Entwicklung der experimentellen Gehirn und Rückenmarksphysiologie vor Flourens.* Stuttgart, Enke, 1897. [3]*Vom Baue und Leben des Gehirns.* Leipzig, Dyk, 1819–26. [4]*Grosse Nervenärzte; Lebensbilder.* Stuttgart, Thieme, 1956–63. [5]*Garrison's history of neurology.* Springfield, Thomas, 1969 (McHenry). [6]*Dana's textbook of nervous diseases* etc. 10th ed. New York, Wood, 1925, p. XV–LVI. [7]*Clinical neurology.* 9th ed. Philadelphia, Saunders, 1963. [8]*Some trends in neuroanatomy.* Dubuque, Brown, 1947. [9]*The nervous system and its constituent neurones.* New York, Stechert, 1909. [10]*A history of neurology.* New York, M.D. Publ., 1959. [11]*Selected readings in the history of physiology.* Springfield, Thomas, 1966. [12]*Hdb. of physiology.* Washington, D.C., Am. Physiological Soc., 1959, sect. 1, vol. 1, p. 1–58. *A history of the electrical activity of the brain; the first half-century.* New York, Macmillan, 1961. [13]*The falling sickness.* Baltimore, Johns Hopkins Press, 1945. [14]*Reflex action, a study in the history of physiological psychology.* Baltimore, Williams & Wilkins, 1930. [15]*The discovery of reflexes.* Oxford, Clarendon, 1960. [16]*Anatomies of pain.* Springfield, Thomas, 1957. [17]*Oxford medicine.* New York, Oxford U. P., 1945, vol. 6, p. 261–302. [18]*A history of neurological surgery.* Baltimore, Williams & Wilkins, 1951. [19]*Young endeavour.* Springfield, Thomas, 1958. [20]*Neurosurgical classics.* New York, Johnson Reprint Corp., 1965. [21]*The human brain and spinal cord, a historical study,* etc. Berkeley, University California Press, 1968.

THE EDITORS

NAME INDEX

581

SUBJECT INDEX

A

Abducens nucleus, lesions of, and conjugate gaze, 533–534; *Also see* Cranial nerves

Abiogenesis, 407

Acacia, gum, effect on changes in blood volume in secondary traumatic shock, 192

Acalculia, 335

Accessory nerve, *See* Cranial nerves

Acetylcholine, in neurohumoral transmission, 284

Achondroplasia, 506

Acoustic nerve, pathways, 487
and sense of motion, 402
Also see Cranial nerves

Acromegaly, 345, 476

Action potentials, *See* Electrical current

Adiadokokinesis, 397

Adie's syndrome, 505

Adiposogenital dystrophy, 397

Adrenal cortex, over-functioning of, 546

Adrenaline, experiments with, 291

Adrenal marrow, chromaffin system, 273

Aging of brain, 387

Agnosia, 425
visual, 474

Agrammatism, 360

Agraphia, 335

Air therapy, intrathecal, for sequelae of head injury, 568

Alcoholic delirium, 474

Alcoholic insanity, 102

Alcoholic paralysis, 460

Alcoholic polyneuritis, 460

Alcohol, injections of, for painful conditions, 517–518

Alcoholism
brain in, 343–344
memory disturbances in, 461
and neuritis, 493

Allantoin, discovery of, 305

Allochiria, 356

Alpers' disease, 341

Alzheimer's disease, 317

Amaurotic family idiocy, 320, 347, 364, 365, 375, 515
term coined, 515

Amines, structure and sympathomimetic action, 282

Amnesia, in alcholic polyneuritis, 460

Amöboidose, 317

Amphetamines, introduction, 283

Amusia, 335

Amyostatic symptom-complex, 527

Amyotonia congenita, 425, 495

Amyotrophic lateral sclerosis, 422, 464, 511

Anaesthetic, action of, 273

Anaphylaxis, and histamine, 283

Aneurysm, 12; intracranial, 425
ruptured miliary, as cause of intracerebral hemorrhage, 422

Angina pectoris, 344

Angiogliona, 159

Angiography, cerebral, 489, 490

Animal electricity, 21

Animal spirit, 20, 202

Animism, 64

Ankle clonus, 422

Anorectal motility, cortical representation of, 170

Anosmia, in traumatic brain lesions, 501

Anoxia, and necrosis, 377

Anthropology, 13, 71, 162
criminal, 408
founding of, 12

Ants, study of, 28, 30

Aphasia, 39, 113, 122, 335, 359, 360, 366, 425, 476–478, 534, 538
brain lesion in, 13
causes of, 406–407
cerebral localization, 534
motor, 348